Natural disasters: protecting vulnerable communities

International Decade for Natural Disaster Reduction

Natural disasters: protecting vulnerable communities

Proceedings of the Conference held in London, 13-15 October 1993

Edited by P. A. Merriman and C. W. A. Browitt

Thomas Telford, London

Conference sponsored by the Royal Society, the Royal Academy of Engineering, the Society for Earthquake and Civil Engineering Dynamics, British Nuclear Fuels plc, British Geological Survey, the Institution of Civil Engineers and the Overseas Development Administration, and organized by Thomas Telford Services Ltd

Organizing Committee
Dr P. A. Merriman, British Nuclear Fuels plc, *Chairman*
Dr R. D. Adams, International Seismological Centre
Dr C. W. A. Browitt, British Geological Survey
Professor W. B. Wilkinson, Institute of Hydrology
Dr I. R. Davis, International Development and Emergency Relief Consultants Ltd
D. J. Oakley, Consultant, Disaster Preparedness

Published on behalf of the organizers by Thomas Telford Services Ltd, Thomas Telford House, 1 Heron Quay, London E14 4JD.

First published 1993.

Distributors for Thomas Telford Books are
USA: American Society of Civil Engineers, Publications Sales Department, 345 East 47th Street, New York, NY 10017-2398
Japan: Maruzen Co. Ltd, Book Department, 3-10 Nihonbashi 2 - chome, Chuo-ku, Tokyo 103
Australia: DA Books & Journals, 648 Whitehorse Road, Mitcham 3132, Victoria

A CIP catalogue record for this publication is available from the British Library.

Classification
Availability: Unrestricted
Content: Collected papers
Status: Refereed
User: Civil engineers, scientists and planners

ISBN 0 7277 1936 X

Printed in Great Britain by Redwood Books, Trowbridge, Wiltshire

Contents

Preparedness and protection

Lessons learned in recovery

Technology, knowledge transfer and future opportunities

NATURAL DISASTERS

Papers 8, 22, 23, 33 and 44 were not submitted for publication.

Keynote paper. Vulnerability assessment

Dr Y. F. AYSAN, International Federation of Red Cross and
Red Crescent Societies, Switzerland

INTRODUCTION

Assessment of hazards, especially the ones based in nature,
has been a concern for the scientific community for a long
time. Better instrumentation, global networks, collaboration
among the relevant institutions and agencies over the decades
have resulted in improved hazard assessment techniques and
data. There is still more to do in knowing the hazards,
especially in relation to slow-onset disasters such as drought
and environmental degradation. However, understanding the
phenomena better is only part of the picture. The Decade's
aim, that is, the reduction of natural disasters can not be
achieved unless there is as good an understanding of what or
who are vulnerable to the impact of hazards and why.

Assessment of vulnerability has been a key development in the
disaster field throughout the last decade. Much progress has
been achieved especially in measuring and mapping physical
vulnerability. This is partly due to the fact that physical
damage such as to buildings, infrastructure, land, agriculture
etc. are relatively easier to quantify than developing
indicators for social, political or household economic
vulnerabilities. Of course, another factor is that the
physical sciences have been specialised in the subject much
longer, hence, developed methods of assessment while the
interest of social sciences in the disaster field has been
relatively new. Similarly, most post-disaster mitigation
measures focus on strengthening the physical systems against
potential hazards because damage to them is tangible, while
the non-physical is not as visible and usually assumed to be
the responsibility of the affected communities.

It is true that most disasters are manifested in some physical
losses. Quite often, however, physical vulnerability to
hazards occur where people lack the resources, awareness,
knowledge,power, or, the choices to mobilise the defenses
against hazards.Reduction of disasters and its sustainability,
above all,necessitate making positive changes in these
conditions. Achieving some of these changes are long range

NATURAL DISASTERS

goals requiring social justice, equitable resource distribution and political empowerment. However, there are many short and medium-term measures that can be encouraged. This paper explores understanding how vulnerability arises and suggest approaches to take in the next decade to reduce them.

CHANGING TRENDS IN DISASTERS

According to statistics, the number of damaging events and their impact on property and people have been on the increase. This may be due to the fact that with improved communications and better data collection more disasters became known worldwide but this is not the key factor in the increase. Disasters occur when a hazard or a threat arises in vulnerable conditions and the trends reflect an increase in both.

Increase in threats:

The first step in identifying the increased disaster risks is knowing the historically known as well as newly emerging threats. These can basically be classified as:

> *Events Based in Nature; such as earthquakes, cyclones, volcanic eruptions, droughts, floods, pathogene (virus, bacteria, parasite) etc.

> *Events Based in Violence; such as war, conflict, intimidation, hostility etc.

> *Events Based in degradation and deprivation; such as environmental and technological degradation, political and economic deprivation, malnutrition, illiteracy etc

While some of the threats such as natural hazards and the patterns of their impact have been better understood others are relatively new, and furthermore very complex in nature often one triggering the other in a chain reaction. An evaluation of these reveal the following trends:

* The increase in nature based events have been random. Although there are some observed changes between the climatic changes and the number of floods, droughts and hurricanes, this is yet to be proven. The severity of the impact of these events seem to relate more to increased vulnerabilities and higher population exposure to the events rather than perhaps a significant increase in the number of hazard occurrences.

* Among the nature based events epidemics have been on the increase. The HIV/AIDS, as a new epidemic alone, has been accountable for 13 million affected people world-wide by 1993. The death of middle-aged adults and the selective loss of young will also radically alter the impact of other types of disasters in the future. For example, already the negative impact of this disease in coping with droughts in Africa has been noticible.

2

* Increase in the number of events based in violence has been significant during the last decade of this century. Since the Second World War at least 40 million people have been killed in 125 wars and conflicts. Today, in places like Somalia and former Yugoslavia, nine out of 10 people injured or killed are civilians. Wars and conflict situation in many parts of the world have also resulted in the rapid spread of epidemics due to damaged water and sanitary provisions and limited access to health facilities and food. Furthermore, natural disasters such as floods and droughts during conflict, for example, in Sudan and Mozambique had a far worst impact than usual on the communities.

*Similarly, events based in deprivation have been on the increase. Environmental and ecological conditions are weakened due to human activity resulting in more land slides, severe droughts or floods, contamination of air, water and land; political and economic deprivation progressively have increased vulnerability to other threats; rate of technological change and industrial developments and their misuse have introduced new risks, sometimes as a consequence of the impact of natural disasters such as floods or earthquakes.

The current hazard trends highlights the fact that the distinction between the events based in nature and others, in most situations, is not clearcut. Increasingly, the threats that we have to be prepared for are becoming complex and interrelated. The challenge throughout the decade is not only a better understanding of the known natural hazards but also the changing and newly emerging threats as well as their complex inter-relationship. The role for the scientific community in this respect is perhaps moving beyond the scope of their disciplines and better cooperation among various disciplines.

Increase in vulnerabilities:

Comparisons of impact between different types of disasters and between different countries suffer from weaknesses in statistics. While events, their physical characteristics, and to some extend damage to human life and property are better recorded, data on the human and economic impact of disasters is, as yet, far less satisfactory. Economic losses of a poor community can be small in dollars because they have very little material wealth to lose. But the impact of this loss is often devastating for the less well-off. Classification of 'people affected' can be equally problematic as there are no agreed scientific definitions for measuring human impact of disasters. Consequently, the indicators of non-physical vulnerability are equally weak.

In a recent collaboration between CRED in Belgium and the Federation of Red Cross and Red Crescent Societies on the World Disaster Report, CRED definition of 'affected population were used (fig.1). Out of this a comparison of top five

3

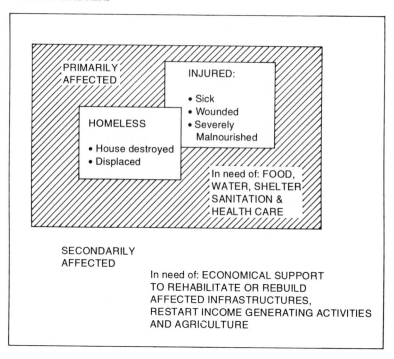

Fig. 1. Graphic representation of affected populations in
disaster situations

countries in relation to number of deaths and number of people
affected by disaster type were drawn (figs.2,3,4,5 6,7,8,9,10,
11,12,13,14).

The database for this kind of comparison is still weak as
information on complex disasters or the characteristics of the
affected population are seldom collected. Within the confines
of what is available, however, it is still possible to observe
some indicators of vulnerability. For example, China, India,
Bangladesh and Philippines appear among the top five countries
in terms of death toll and number of people affected from most
type of disasters. This is partly because these countries are
geographically located in hazard-prone areas but the
similarities go further than this. All of these countries have
very large populations who are also economically poor. Often,
these are the people who live on the most hazard-prone parts
of their countries with the least resources, awareness,
knowledge,power, or, the choices to mobilise the defenses
against these frequent hazards.

The question of who are the most vulnerable, however, can not
only be answered in economic or spacial terms. Not all poor
are affected by the disasters at the same level nor all people
living in the same area would face the same level of disaster

4

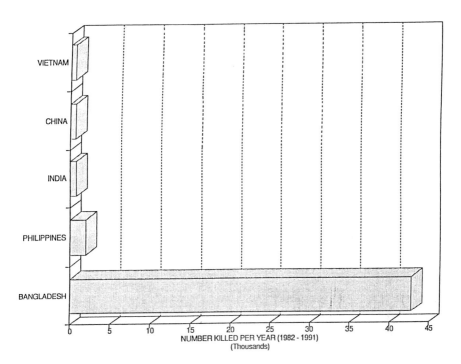

Fig. 2. Top five countries most affected by high winds (1982-1991 inclusive): 48,320 killed per year worldwide (1982-1991)

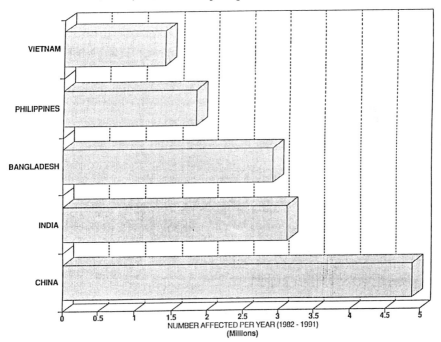

Fig. 3. Top five countries most affected by high winds (1982-1991 inclusive): 15,200,280 affected per year worldwide (1982-1991)

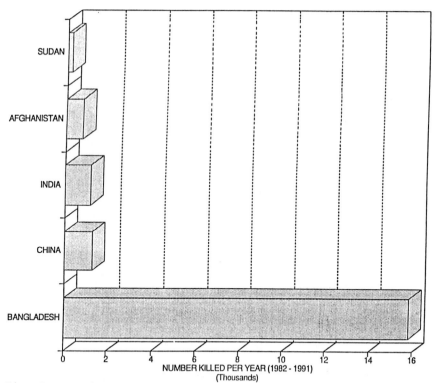

Fig. 4. Top five most flood affected countries (1982-1991
inclusive): 21,446 deaths per year worldwide (1982-1991)

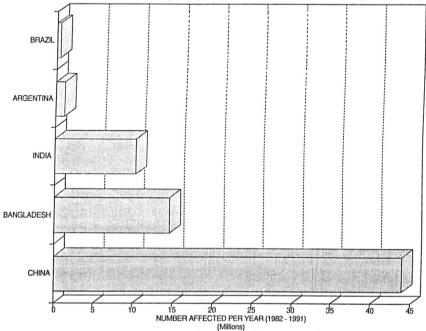

Fig. 5. Top five most flood affected countries (1982-1991
inclusive): 73,084,160 affected per year worldwide (1982-1991)

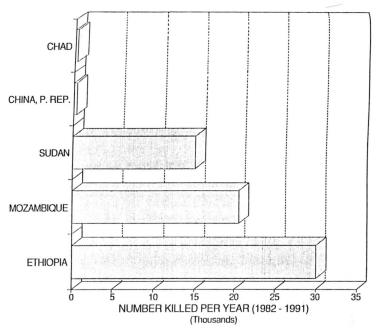

Fig. 6. Top five most famine affected countries (1982-1991
inclusive): 192,726 deaths per year worldwide (1982-1991)

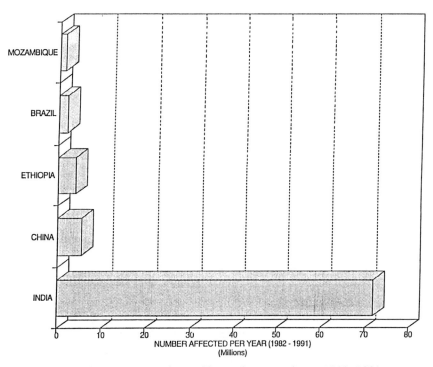

Fig. 7. Top five most famine affected countries (1982-1991
inclusive): 959,183,300 affected per year worldwide (1982-1991)

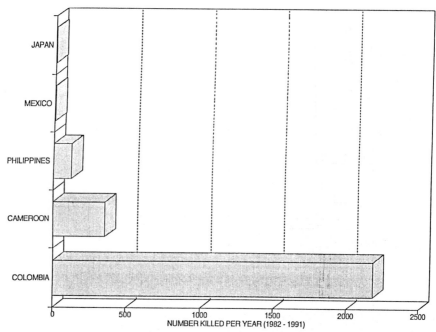

Fig. 8. Top five countries most affected by volcanic events
(1982-1991 inclusive): 2,687 killed per year worldwide (1982-
1991)

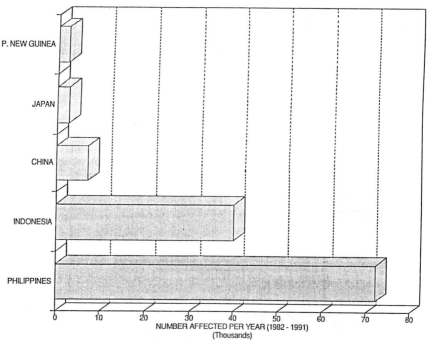

Fig. 9. Top five countries most affected by volcanic events
(1982-1991 inclusive): 130,368 affected per year worldwide
(1982-1991)

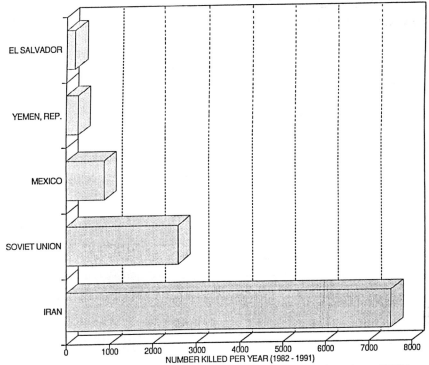

Fig. 10. Top five countries most affected by earthquakes (1982–1991 inclusive): 112,932 deaths per year worldwide (1982–1991)

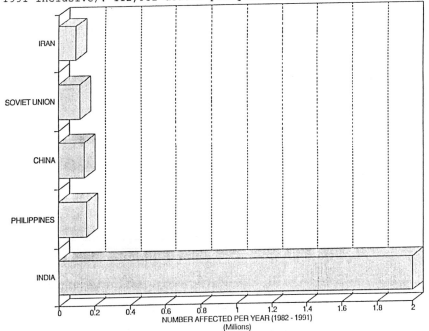

Fig. 11. Top five countries most affected by earthquakes (1982–1991 inclusive): 2,784,824 affected per year worldwide (1982–1991)

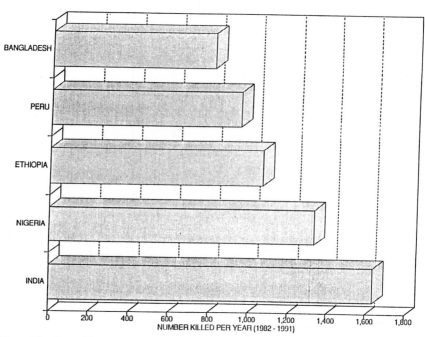

Fig. 12. Top five countries most affected by epidemic (1982-1991 inclusive): 9,201 deaths per year worldwide (1982-1991)

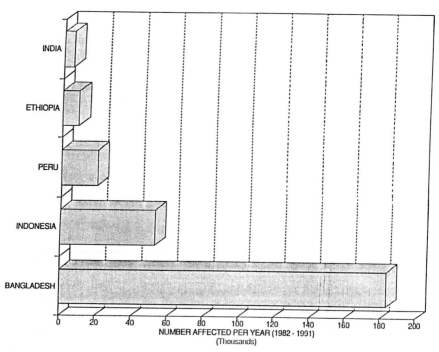

Fig. 13. Top five countries most affected by epidemic (1982-1991 inclusive): 310,608 affected per year worldwide (1982-1991)

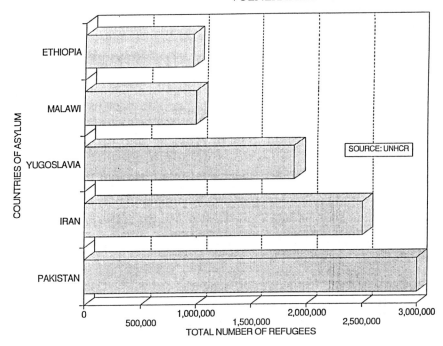

Fig. 14. Top five most affected countries of asylum (August 1992) total refugees worldwide 16,844,211

risk. Most communities are not homogeneous in their social make up. Although there is limited, and mostly epidemiological, data available on the subject there is enough evidence from case study surveys and field accounts to suggest that there is a strong causal relationship between vulnerability to disasters and such characteristics as socio-economic class, gender, ethnicity, age and disability. People who belong to the disadvantaged or marginalised groups in a number of these categories are often the hardest hit by disasters and the least able to recover from the impacts of it. Of course, the definition of disadvantaged or marginal varies from society to society and also changes in time. This is why vulnerability has to be understood as a dynamic phenomena and defined locally.

From the above analysis, only rough conclusions can be made in identifying the people who are most likely to be at risk from the impact of disasters:

* proximity/exposure: people who occupy or, for their livelihood, depend on areas of high hazard risk;

* capacities and resources: people who have limited means and capacity to mobilise them in order to increase and their defences against hazards;

11

* disadvantage/marginalisation: people who are peripheral or weak due to gender, age, ethnicity, class etc.

These characteristics are interrelated in most situations. The marginalised in most cases live in poor quality buildings, hazard prone areas. They often have the least resources and capacities to recover from the impact of disasters further pushed towards the edge after each event, becoming more and more vulnerable to many more threats.

From the impact point of view these simplified categories can help the aid worker, the donor, the authorities to target their inputs to support the most in need. As the 'humanitarian gap' between the needs and the resources are growing fast it is inevitable to look for ways of defining who are the most vulnerable for effective response. Protecting the most vulnerable also requires knowing why they are vulnerable so that the conditions that put them at high risk can be changed. This requires a focus on causation rather than simple or even complex correlation. Thus, one is interested not in vulnerable groups per se but in the conditions that bring about their vulnerability to disasters and their capacity to recover. Some of the critical causes in this process can be:

* lack of access to resources (material/economic vulnerability)
* disintegration of social patterns (social vulnerability),
* degradation of the environment and inability to protect it (ecological vulnerability),
* lack of strong national and local institutional structures (organisational vulnerability),
* lack of access to information and knowledge (educational vulnerability),
* lack of public awareness (attitudinal and motivational vulnerability)
* limited access to political power and representation (political vulnerability),
* certain beliefs and customs (cultural vulnerability).
* weak buildings or weak individuals (physical vulnerability)

The pursuit of causes, as one author puts it, can lead one back decades or even centuries.(1) The famine in Somalia can be traced back to the policies of its first independent government (2). The earthquake risk in Mexico City can be taken as far back to the urbanisation decisions of the Spanish conquerers. Though such pursuits can mostly be academic and not possible for all situations and for all involved in the disaster field, detailed vulnerability analysis and an understanding of its dynamics are useful if the aim is to mitigate disasters rather than to cure their symptoms.

DISASTER MITIGATION

There has been a growing interest, in the last three decades, in mitigation programmes but their impact has been limited. It is true that mitigation still is a low priority on most aid budgets, therefore, funding is tight; the number of vulnerable is growing fast, therefore, any level of mitigation will fall behind the needs. However, despite some advances made many mitigation programmes are also unsuccessful because they do not adress disaster vulnerability in its complexity. A recent review of some disaster mitigation programmes in Latin America highlighted some of the problems (3):

* Most programmes are related to strengthening one sector responding to a particular hazard type in a limited time period.

* Most programmes ignore the range and variety of local needs and priorities hence focus on a very limited part of the problem.

* Despite collection of data on people's conditions many programmes fail to take into account why people make certain choices such as living on a flood plain or a volcano.

* Most programmes rely on specialised technologies and professional skills, therefore, people can not easily be involved in decisions and implementation.

* Participation by people in most cases is reduced to providing labour.

* Some programmes are susceptible to political manipulation, therefore, maintain the status quo.

* Most programmes depend on external -both national and international- expertise, materials and funding, hence can not easily be maintained and duplicated at the local level.

The study shows that the failure of most mitigation programmes is not due to the lack of scientific or technological knowledge but rather of a methodological and attutudinal one. By definition, disaster vulnerability occurs at the local level and it needs to be understood and mitigated at the local level. However, very little work goes into understanding the frequent local threats and local conditions of vulnerability. Much of work still focusses on rare but big events resulting in specific mitigation programmes based on global analysis.

AGENDA FOR THE IDRDR

The Decade's focus is on disaster reduction. It is, therefore, essential that the conventional approaches are reviewed, lessons are learned and new alternatives are developed through out the Decade and beyond.

NATURAL DISASTERS

* The emphasis of the IDRDR is still on the hazards and physical aspects of vulnerability, more attention needs to be paid to human vulnerability.

* As the distinction between natural disaters and others are becoming more and more blurred, there is need for better understanding of comlex events and the relationship of various threats.

* Methods for human vulnerability assessment are still weak. Better indicators for social, economic, etx vulnerability needs to be developed.

* Better integration of hazard, vulnerability and risk studies should be sought through inter-disciplinary work.

* Integrated vulnerability assessment should be encouraged rather than one sector, one factor analysis.

* Although the Decade is International, the key levels for action in vulnerability reduction has to be national and local, and for networking regional.

* Funding should not be confined to global scientific and technical research but more resources need to be channelised to local level investigations and community based mitigation programmes.

* Disaster mitigation programmes have to become enabling activities, hence, the development aspect of mitigation is vital.

References:

1- Oliver-Smith, A., The Martyred City: Death and Rebirth in the Andes. University of Mexico Press, Albuquerque (1986).

2- Wisner, B., Disaster Vulnerability, Society for Applied Anthropology, Memphis, March 1992.

3- Maskrey, A., Defining the Community's Role in Disaster Mitigation, Appropriate Technology, v.19, n.3.

1. Relative impact on human life of various types of natural disaster: an interpretation of data for the period 1947-1991

A. M. WASSEF, University of Toronto

ABSTRACT

The paper sets out with a synthesis of data and information relating to the natural disasters that occurred in the period 1947-1991. The focus is on the destructive forms of wind, floods, earthquakes, and volcanic eruptions.

The relative impact of these disasters on human life is brought out by (i) the total death toll by country where more than 500 died as a direct result of natural disasters in the period under study; (ii) the number of lives lost by type of natural disaster, (iii) the extent of the suffering at the national level, in terms of lives lost per million of population, (iv) the number of persons made homeless, when the number exceeded 50,000, and (v) the geographical distribution of the hardest-hit countries.

Earthquakes come out a close second to wind-type disasters in terms of destructive power. The hardest-hit countries, judged by deaths per million population, are all developing countries, which calls for a concerted effort to involve developing countries' scientists in internationally coordinated long-term research in the field of prediction and early warning. And that, in turn, highlights the imperativeness of establishing and sustaining dedicated geoscience elements in the institutional fabric of each country.

A few thoughts are presented for consideration.

SOURCES OF INFORMATION

The data for this study were obtained from the Office of U.S. Foreign Disaster Assistance Agency for International Development, the Natural Hazards Research and Applications Information Centre of the University of Colorado, the New York Times Index, the Department of Geography, University of Toronto, and several books and papers. The synthesis of

these data and their interpretation are the author's
responsibility.

DEATH TOLL BY COUNTRY

Table 1 gives the death toll by country, where more than
500 died as a direct result of natural disaster in the
period 1947 – September 1991. Fifty-eight countries shared
a total of 1,715,660 deaths: Bangladesh lost more than
half a million, China close to four hundred thousand;   the
Soviet Union, India and Iran lost over one hundred thousand
lives each.

LIVES LOST BY TYPE OF NATURAL DISASTER

Figure 1 presents the number of lives lost by type of
natural disaster.   The death toll in wind-type and
earthquake disasters is 676,366 and 623,068, respectively.
Floods led to the loss of 229,000 lives, whereas volcanoes
caused the death of 31,469.

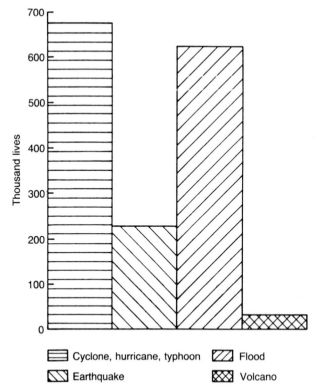

Fig. 1. Lives lost by type of natural disaster: 1947 to
September 1991

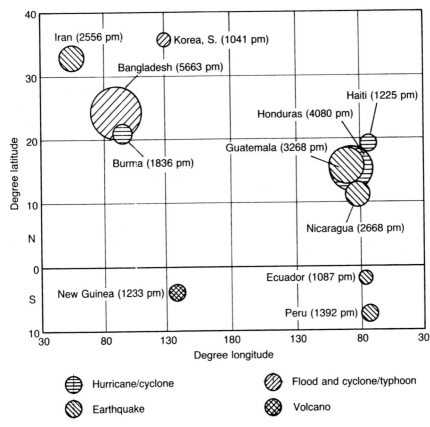

Fig. 2. More than 1000 deaths per million population: 1947 to
September 1991

EXTENT OF NATIONAL SUFFERING

Lives lost per million of population.

Table 2 conveys the extent of the suffering at the national
level in terms of lives lost per million of the population.
Only those countries which lost more than one per thousand
of the respective populations are shown. The hardest hit
is Bangladesh which lost 5,663 per million of its
inhabitants to floods and cyclones. Honduras follows with
4,080 lives per million because of hurricanes. Earthquakes
caused the death of 3,268 per million of the population of
Guatemala and 2,668 per million of the population of
Nicaragua and 2,556 per million of the population of Iran.
Volcanic eruptions killed 1,223 per million of the
population of New Guinea.

NATURAL DISASTERS

EXTENSIVE HOMELESSNESS

Table 3 gives the number of persons made homeless because of wind-type disasters, floods and earthquakes. Only those events which left 50,000 or more without a dwelling place are taken into account. Floods top the list of causes of homelessness, causing such suffering to more than 707,000 on average. Wind-type disasters are smaller in number but each deprived some 515,000 persons of shelter. Disastrous earthquakes follow cyclones and floods in terms of their destructive power. There is no record of volcanic activities causing such extensive homelessness in the period under review.

GEOGRAPHICAL DISTRIBUTION OF THE HARDEST-HIT COUNTRIES

Figure 2 shows the geographical distribution of the eleven hardest-hit countries that suffered more than 1,000 deaths per million population: with the exception of Iran, all the countries appear on the map of the Pacific Ocean. But the intensity of the impact of natural disasters in those countries should not overshadow the losses that befell many communities elsewhere.

INTERPRETATION OF THE DATA

Our analysis brought out two facts: (1) that earthquakes are a close second to wind-type disasters in terms of destructive power and (2) that the communities that suffered the most belong to developing countries.

Early warning is crucial. According to J.A.W. McCulloch (the Canadian Encyclopedia, 1985) the World Weather Watch, which is a programme of the World Meteorological Organization, attempts to provide the information analysis and exchange required by all national weather sources to create weather forecasts. The principal elements of WWW are the Global Observing System, which provides the weather observations required for forecasting; the Global Telecommunications System, which makes the observations available to all countries needing them for weather forecasting; and the Global Data Processing System, which analyses the observations and carries out the prognosis function on behalf of countries lacking these capabilities. The existence of GDPS invites speculation on the preparedness of the organization to be partner in the responsibility for the correctness of prediction and the timeliness of alerting the endangered communities everywhere.

Can earthquakes be forecast? A report entitled "Solid-Earth Sciences and Society", recently issued by the National Research Council, gives a lucid account of the current position: A first approximation of potential earthquake source location can be estimated reliably from

18

Table 1: Natural Disasters
More than 500 deaths in the period 1947 - September 1991

USA	11,680	Algeria	4,527
		Libya	580
Honduras	15,917	Madagascar	1,041
Cuba	1,441	Morocco	12,131
Dominican Republic	1,055	Mozambique	872
El Salvador	2,083	South Africa	516
Guatemala	24,507	Sudan	2,133
Haiti	7,348	Tunisia	784
Mexico	15,023	Zaire	2,023
Nicaragua	6,670	Cameroon	1,773
Argentina	797	Afghanistan	3,494
Brazil	9,462	Bangladesh	525,506
Chile	6,980	Burma	6,100
Columbia	24,735	China	396,935
Ecuador	8,910	Hong Kong	3,885
Peru	25,190	India	124,189
Venezuela	627	Indonesia	7,334
		Iran	101,751
France	1,066	Japan	33,411
Germany (W)	598	Korea, S.	40,519
Great Britain	4,982(*)	Nepal	3,323
Greece	2,406	Pakistan	37,585
Italy	8,015	Phillipines	21,510
Netherlands	1,876	Saudi Arabia	500
Portugal	636	Sri Lanka	2,772
Rumania	1,947	Taiwan	3,123
Spain	923	Thailand	2,595
Yugoslavia	1,126	Turkey	24,796
		Vietnam	19,469
Soviet Union	138,182	Yemen	2,068
		New Guinea	4,233

(*) mostly due to the "killer fog" which occurred in December 1952 in London

Table 2: Countries that suffered more than 1,000 deaths per million population
(1947 - September 1991)

Carribean and Central America		
Honduras	4,080 per million	Hurricanes
Guatemala	3,268	Earthquakes
Nicaragua	2,668	Earthquakes
Haiti	1,225	Hurricanes
South America		
Peru	1,392 per million	Earthquakes
Ecuador	1,087	Earthquakes
Asia		
Bangladesh	5,663 per million	Floods & Cyclones
Iran	2,556	Earthquakes
Burma	1,836	Cyclones
Korea, S.	1,041	Floods & Typhoons
Oceania		
New Guinea	1,233 per million	Volcanic Eruptions

Table 3: Natural Disasters
which made more than 50,000 persons homeless
in the period 1947 - September 1991

Country	Date	Number made homeless by type of disaster		
		HU/CY/TY/ST	FL	EQ
Afghanistan	76/04		80,000	
Algeria	73/04		61,000	
	80/10			443,000
Argentina	66/02		120,000	
	67/10		70,000	
	83/06		250,000	
	85/11		56,000	
	86/03		60,000	
Bangladesh	60/10	200,000		
	64/07		1,000,000	
	65/05	5,000,000		
	66/08		500,000	
	66/10	300,000		
	68/10		879,000	
	70/08		1,000,000	
	74/08		2,000,000	
	77/09		200,000	
	83/04		60,000	
	85/05	510,000		
	86/09	100,000		
	88/09		28,000,000	
	89/04	100,000		
	88/11	2,000,000		
Brazil	64/01		100,000	
	66/01		52,000	
	70/07		104,000	
	74/03		325,000	
	75/07		80,000	
	77/06		50,000	
	79		1,500,000	
	80/02		270,000	
	81/04		50,000	
	84/05		50,000	
	84/12		60,000	
	85/04		600,000	
	88/02		59,000	
	88/07		50,000	
	89/05		(LS) 78,000	
	80/07		52,000	
	89/12		200,000	
Burma	67/05	130,000		
	78/05	54,000		

Country	Date	Number made homeless by type of disaster		
		HU/CY/TY/ST	FL	EQ
Chile	60/05			2,000,000
	71/06	90,000		
	84/07	102,000		
	85/03			500,000
	86/06		54,000	
China	81/07		1,500,000	
	81/08		200,000	
	81/10		100,000	
	82/05		210,000	
	85/07	100,000		
	86/08		800,000	
	88/09		110,000	
	88/11			267,000
	90/06		125,000	
	89/10			50,000
	89/11			53,000
Columbia	70/11		105,000	
	88/08		130,000	
	88/10	100,000		
Cuba	82/06	75,000		
Djibouti	89/04		150,000	
Dominican Republic	79/09	350,000		
El Salvador	86/10			250,000
Ethiopia	90/09		350,000	
Guatemala	76/02			1,166,000
Haiti	66/10	67,000		
India	52/11	1,000,000		
	55/09	375,000		
	56/05	1,000,000		
	60/11	160,000		
	66/11	150,000		
	67/12			50,000
	67/09		1,000,000	
	70/07		350,000	
	71/10	2,000,000		
	75/07		7,000,000	
	77/11	5,432,000		
	79/10		1,000,000	
	80/07		50,000	
	82/06	300,000		
	85/11		400,000	
	86/08		245,000	
	86/09	200,000		
	91/06		100,000	
Indonesia	67/01		55,000	
	68/04		150,000	
	76/07			450,000

Country	Date	Number made homeless by type of disaster		
		HU/CY/TY/ST	FL	EQ
Iran	68/08			75,000
	80/07		150,000	
	90/06			500,000
Iraq	67/05		60,000	
	68/05		150,000	
Italy	68/01			55,000
	76/05			105,000
	80/11			400,000
Jamaica	79/06		50,000	
	88/09	810,000		
Japan	53/09	1,000,000		
	59/09	1,500,000		
Korea, R.	66/07		66,000	
	72/08		326,000	
	90/09		189,000	
Madagascar	84/04	100,000		
	86/03	84,000		
	90/01	55,000		
	91/03	125,000		
Malawi	89/03		80,000	
	91/03		50,000	
Mexico	72/05		100,000	
	76/10	100,000		
	80/11		100,000	
	85/09			100,000
	88/09	100,000		
Mozambique	67/02		50,000	
	78/03		200,000	
Nicaragua	72/12			300,000
	82/05		52,000	
	88/10	60,000		
Niger	88/08		80,000	
Pakistan	64/06	400,000		
	67/07		150,000	
	73/08		4,800,000	
	77/06		245,000	
Paraguay	79/05		70,000	
Peru	72/03		75,000	

Country	Date	Number made homeless by type of disaster		
		HU/CY/TY/ST	FL	EQ
Phillipines	60/06	50,000		
	60/10	375,000		
	64/06	927,000		
	64/11	300,000		
	66/12	90,000		
	67/11	137,000		
	70/08	67,000		
	70/10	1,214,000		
	70/11	430,000		
	72/06	385,000		
	72/07		371,000	
	74/10	300,000		
	78/10	50,000		
	80/07	300,000		
	80/11	229,000		
	81/12	180,000		
	82/03	304,000		
	84/08	328,000		
	84/11	766,000		
	87/08	298,000		
	88/11	660,000		
	90/07			135,000
	89/10	84,000		
	90/11	640,000		
Romania	77/03			175,000
Solomon Is.	86/05	60,000		
South Africa	87/09		50,000	
Soviet Union	66/04			100,000
	88/12			530,000
	91/04			160,000
Sri Lanka	57/12	250,000		
	64/12	100,000		
	66/09		100,000	
	67/10		470,000	
	82/05		100,000	
	83/12		250,000	
	84/05		70,000	
	89/05		200,000	
Sudan	88/08		1,000,000	
Syria	74/03		75,000	
Tanzania	68/03		57,000	
Turkey	66/08			108,000
	67/07			87,000
	70/03			81,000
	75/09			50,000
	76/11			51,000
Venezuela	67/07			80,000

Country	Date	Number made homeless by type of disaster		
		HU/CY/TY/ST	FL	EQ
Vietnam	64/11	700,000		
	66/09		70,000	
	78/08		79,000	
	80/07	165,000		
	80/09	250,000		
	83/09	265,000		
	85/10	225,000		
	87/11	352,000		
	89/05	336,000		
Yemen, Republic of	82/03		50,000	
	82/12			400,000
	89/03		80,000	
Yugoslavia	69/10			85,000
	79/04			100,000

the regional tectonic setting. The total seismic energy released in plate boundary regions is more than 99 percent of the total worldwide seismic energy release. The problem is that most plate boundary regions have earthquakes quite frequently, which relieves stress incrementally, while the 1 percent of seismic energy released in intraplate events occurs very occasionally. Those singular events may therefore be extremely violent spasms. Nevertheless, it is hoped that through the development of a framework encompassing all that is known about a particular region seismologists can work toward making useful predictions.

The NRC report expounds the opportunities which the instantaneous communication capabilities offer to mitigate damage from earthquakes centred some distance away, given the relatively slow speed of seismic waves. Of particular relevance to the theme of this paper is the effort to set up a tsunamic warning system which will alert areas around the Pacific when any large submarine earthquake occurs in the Pacific ocean.

The prospects of life-saving forecasting are in no small measure determined by the amount and quality of observations systematically collected on the ground. This task may be entrusted to local government officials and members of the educational institutions, but the coordination and control should be assigned to a geoscience group fully involved in the international effort.

2. Communicating risks to reduce vulnerability

T. HORLICK-JONES, EPICENTRE, London, and Open
University, Milton Keynes, and D. K. C. JONES, London School
of Economics and Political Science

ABSTRACT

Social science research has revealed the essential importance
played by beliefs, attitudes and subjective judgements in shaping
human behaviour and action in response to hazards. This paper
seeks to apply these insights in the context of the communication
of information about hazard and risk to reduce vulnerability in
developing countries.

Effective disaster reduction programmes need to recognise the
social and cultural aspects of risk communication processes.
Omission of such considerations largely account for the apparent
difficulty of many public education programmes in generating
awareness and mitigating action in some communities at risk from
major natural hazards.

The emerging media in developing countries offer a number of
important possibilities as risk communication conduits. These
developments present both opportunities and dangers.

INTRODUCTION

The communication of information about hazard and risk to the
public has a key role in the prevention and mitigation of
disasters. To date great emphasis has been placed on the
scientific assessment of hazard over space (prediction for hazard
zoning) and through time (forecasts of specific events), with
stress placed on the technological needs of data gathering, data
analysis and information transmission required for warning
systems.

Such emphasis on "accuracy" and "efficiency" of warnings is
understandable but has to be balanced against the "effectiveness"
of warnings as measured by public behaviour and response.
Recognition of this consideration has led to the establishment of
increasingly varied public education programmes, designed to
improve awareness and receptiveness to information.

Whilst such programmes are to be welcomed, many tend to treat the
populations at risk as homogeneous, and neglect the social and
cultural aspects of the process. These omissions largely account
for the apparent difficulty in generating awareness and
mitigating action in some communities at risk from major natural
hazards.

NATURAL DISASTERS

The risks posed by so-called "natural" hazards can only be understood in terms of their human and socio-economic dimensions. They arise from the interaction between physical phenomena and the vulnerability of human systems.

Indeed, the continued use of the outdated term "natural" hazard fails to note the two-way interaction between the physical environment and human systems which has resulted in various hazardous phenomena changing in terms of their spacial extent and magnitude-frequency characteristics (eg flooding, landslides, desertification). As there are few truly natural disasters which continued to occur irrespective of human agencies (eg earthquakes, volcanic eruptions, tropical storms), the term environmental hazard is considered preferable (Smith, 1992), for it not only draws attention to the essentially ecological character of hazard, but also emphasises the role of humans in contributing to the hazardous nature of place.

This paper focuses on medium to rapid-onset geophysical or meteorological hazards, although a number of the themes addressed apply equally to slow-onset disasters such as famine or disease.

Vulnerability derives from the complex interplay of a range of socio-economic and cultural factors. The relative importance of these factors, and the way in which the resulting vulnerability depends upon them, are matters of continuing debate. In this paper, however, special attention is focused on the vulnerability associated with a lack of public information, and ways in which communication processes can contribute to the reduction of vulnerability; in particular, the possible existence of cultural barriers to effective risk communication.

Social science research in technologically advanced countries has revealed the essential importance played by beliefs, attitudes and subjective judgements in shaping human behaviour and action in response to hazards. This paper seeks to apply some of the insights gained by this work in the context of efforts to achieve disaster reduction in developing countries.

The emerging media in developing countries offer a number of possibilities as risk communication conduits, in encouraging the implementation of mitigation measures, and in the transmission of early warning. New technologies now make possible increasingly interconnected global media with potentially profound cultural and political implications. These developments bring both opportunities and dangers.

THE PROBLEM OF CHOICE IN THE FACE OF ADVERSITY

Communities in areas prone to natural hazards may adopt a range of measures designed to reduce the level of risk. This process of adjustment to hazard has been extensively studied for many decades, and is synthesised by Burton, Kates and White (1978) and Smith (1992). It has been recognised that the process can be very unsatisfactory, in the sense that people often appear ignorant of the potential for serious consequences or seem prepared to take unnecessary risks.

This phenomenon led Burton, Kates and White (1978) to consider the associated decision-making processes, and subsequently to recognise the difficulty in modelling them. Individuals are, of course, not completely free when it comes to making choices.

Their behaviour is constrained by socio-economic and cultural factors, and everyday problems, and people therefore act according to the logic of their circumstances. Burton et al (1978) arrived at the conclusion that individual decision-making rules are associated with at least four factors. These are:

* Prior experience with the hazard

* Material wealth of the individuals

* Personality traits

* The perceived role of the individual in a social group

They also identified four distinct behaviour patterns observed in the response of people in hazardous places, namely:

* Risk denial, with outcome dependent upon the resilience of their livelihoods

* Passive acceptance of risk

* Action to reduce future losses

* Drastic change in land use or livelihood considered (choose change)

These can be paraphrased as:

* "It will never happen" ie a rejection of risk combined with an exposure to absorbing possible effects

* "It doesn't matter what I do" ie an acceptance or risk combined with an exposure to absorb possible effects

* "I must be ready" ie an acceptance of risk combined with action to deflect, or mitigate, its possible effects

* "I will not let it happen" ie a rejection of risk combined with measures to deflect, or avoid, its possible effects

It should be noted that these observations focus on decision processes associated with individuals and small groups. They therefore tend to reflect a process of local decision-making without state intervention, an increasingly rare phenomena which led to the serious criticisms contained in Hewitt (1983).

Whilst state controls may constrain actions with respect to location, land use and housing style, individual awareness and choice is still paramount in determining response to warnings about specific events and is, therefore, of continuing relevance to disaster reduction strategies.

The patterns of response identified by Burton et al (1978) display no apparent correlation with the material wealth of the community. They do, however, show close similarities with the risk-handling styles associated with some anthropological models of the relationship between social structures and perception of risk.

NATURAL DISASTERS

The "Grid-Group" cultural theory, developed by Douglas (1970, 1992) and others (reviewed by Rayner, 1992), identifies four distinct cultural forms arising from high (+) or low (-) combinations of "group", or strength of group identity, and "grid", or constraints by social norms. Hence, for example, high group and high grid produces "hierarchical", caste-like, social organisation.

Each of the four possible combinations displays stability and each demonstrates its own characteristic "bias", or adherence to certain beliefs and attitudes. These beliefs serve to reinforce dominant social structures, and, so the theory goes, result in the selection of certain risks for special attention.

In this theory, each cultural form is associated with a risk-handling style. These are set out in Table 1. The correspondence between these styles and the four modes of response identified by Burton et al (1978) suggests that the roots of decision-making in the face of potential hazard may be deeply embedded in cultural formations. There is certainly a need for more research to investigate and clarify this observation. The conclusion is supported by comparative studies of response to hazards in ethnically plural regions (Mejer, 1991).

TABLE 1   CULTURAL FORMS AND RISK HANDLING STYLES (After Schwarz and Thompson, 1990)

Cultural form	Group	Grid	Risk-handing style
Hierarchical	+	+	Reject and absorb
Egalitarian	+	-	Reject and deflect
Individualist	-	-	Accept and deflect
Fatalist	-	+	Accept and absorb

Sociologists have for many years recognised the importance of such cultural factors in generating barriers inhibiting some development initiatives. Bailey (1971) observed that in many peasant communities "external" things are regarded as evil and dangerous, and apparent gifts or suggestions by "outsiders" are seen as hidden traps. In some cases, of course, such caution arises from bitter experience. Nevertheless, effective communication of risk information requires the establishment of a relationship of trust, so that such barriers can be overcome.

Bailey (1971) examined the categorical frameworks, or "cognitive maps", of peasant societies, and observed that some omit the idea that human agency can overcome impersonal forces, and so may present profound difficulties in accepting the conception of planning for natural hazard mitigation. Alternatively such attempts to modify the future may be regarded as seeking to change the natural order, and so make little sense according to some conceptualisations of events in the world.

Such difficulties probably lie at one end of a spectrum of culturally-based barriers to communication. Resistance to, or suspicion of, ideas, advice or warnings from "outside" is not restricted to peasant societies, but also occurs in technologically advanced nations were "outsiders" can be interpreted as "from elsewhere" (eg the capital, another region) or scientific experts. Wynne's (1992) study of the interaction between Cumbrian sheep farming communities and government scientists concerning advice about Chernobyl radioactive fallout demonstrates that such barriers can exist even when the actors share many cultural artefacts. Wynne (1992) recognises the general process as one of "informal resistance by people in solitary sub-cultures to meanings, identities or rationalities imposed on them from 'outside'".

VULNERABILITY AND MITIGATION

A wealth of empirical evidence demonstrates the key role played by socio-economic factors in creating a community's weakness, or vulnerability, in responding to, and recovering from, the physical effects of a hazard (Cuny, 1983; Smith, 1992; Horlick-Jones, 1992; Horlick-Jones; 1993). Vulnerability can be simply conceptualised as the potential to suffer harm. As such, it provides a unifying concept, allowing "natural" and "technological" disasters to be treated within the same theoretical framework (De Marchi, 1991; Horlick-Jones, 1993; Horlick-Jones, Fortune and Peters; 1993).

Horlick-Jones (1993) has identified a number of themes that have emerged from research into vulnerability:

* Location - the geographical proximity to the hazard in question

* Livelihood/circumstances - the position and status in society, which in turn is related to wealth, class, gender, ethnicity, health and other factors

* Self-protection - the capacity of the population to protect itself from harm, including access to materials knowledge and information

* Social protection - the extent to which the society in which the population is embedded can provide mitigation measures, including resources and technical knowledge

Cuny (1993) has observed that measures to reduce, or mitigate, the harmful effects of natural hazards requires three categories of action:

* Reduction of physical vulnerability (eg housing, industry, infrastructure)

* Reduction of economic vulnerability

* Strengthening the social structure of the community, so that coping mechanisms can help to absorb the shock of a disaster and promote rapid recovery (increased resilience)

NATURAL DISASTERS

All of these may involve changes in human attitudes and behaviour towards hazards. It is these social processes on which we wish to concentrate. As Smith (1992) notes, this area has received much less attention that the technocentric engineering-based approaches to mitigation which emphasise protection, defence, constraint and control.

In particular we wish to address processes of risk communication that seek to encourage and foster community awareness and preparation, so as to reduce vulnerability and make more efficient local responses to early warning messages of impending threats, both in the sense of relative danger of location and with reference to specific events.

Researchers in the United States have addressed such preparations, especially with regard to earthquake hazards (Perry and Nigg, 1985; Mileti, Fitzpatrick and Farhar, 1992). Such work recognises the need to understand the complexity of communication processes, a point emphasized and elaborated in Europe by De Marchi (1991). All of these writers stress the dynamic nature of the communication process, and the importance of contextual aspects of the process.

Critiques of traditional "top-down" mitigation programmes stress the need for local participation and sensitivity to local needs (Cuny, 1983; Maskrey, 1989). A position underlined by Winchester's (1990) case study of storm warning failure for the poor inhabitants of the Krishna delta in India. There is, however still a widespread belief in the need for the dissemination of authoritative information from centralised sources (Smith, 1992).

RISK PERCEPTION AND COMMUNICATION

As noted above, much research into risk perception conducted in technologically advanced countries has recognised the importance of a range of subjective factors in determining how people view the threats posed by different hazards. Pidgeon, Hood, Jones, Turner and Gibson (1992), in a recent comprehensive review of the literature, observe that attempts to explain the mismatch between objective and "scientific" assessments of risks, and the subjective interpretation of those at risk fall into two broad categories, the first concentrating on psychological processes, and the second on social and cultural ones.

The earlier psychometric approach adopted by risk perception research is well grounded empirically. It recognises the importance of certain factors, including voluntariness, lack of personal control, and experience of the hazard that influence risk perception and acceptance. On the other hand, such research offers a relatively undeveloped theoretical framework.

The more recent social and cultural approaches have been subject to far less empirical testing, but offer more wide-ranging theoretical insights.

Over the last decade the new discipline of risk communication has emerged. This development is associated with legislative changes that require the public to be informed about specific risks, in Europe the Seveso Directive (Gow and Otway, 1990) and, in the United States, the Community Right to Know Act (Hadden, 1989).

Arguably still more important has been the occurrence of well-publicised and costly conflicts over the risks associated with certain technological developments, in particular hazardous waste treatment facilities (Portney, 1991).

Pidgeon et al (1992) identify in the literature four different conceptual approaches to risk communication, ranging from simple one-way "top-down" transmission of information to a process that is embedded in the politics of choice and decision-making:

* "Scientific communications" - "top-down" or one-way transmission of some message about a hazard from a particular "expert" source to a target "non-expert" audience

* Two-way exchange - an interactive process that recognises the important role that feedback plays in any complex communication

* Wider institutional and cultural contexts stressed - communicator takes account of the actions of risk management institutions, possible conflicting messages and the history of the hazard in question

* Risk communication as part of a wider political process - the process as a prerequisite to the enabling and empowerment of risk-bearing groups

The first approach tends to derive from propaganda and persuasive communication techniques, and sees the process as involving the provision of information to "non-experts" by "experts". The second approach recognises the need for feedback and interaction, forming a two-way exchange, for effective communication. The third approach goes one step further in stressing the institutional and cultural contexts in which the communication process takes place, and leads to the full complexity of the final approach.

Research in this area has recognised the potential practical difficulties created by the complexity of these processes. In this regard, the work of Otway and Wynne (1989) is especially noteworthy. They identify a number of "paradoxes" associated with risk communication processes. These include the "information cultures paradox" which arises from the meaning of communications being shaped by existing and past relationships between the organisation disseminating the information and the targeted recipients.

Also pertinent in this context are the "body language paradox" and the "credibility-authenticity paradox" which focus on tacit communication processes that affect the credibility of the communicating organisation and the authenticity and trustworthyness of the associated messages. Pidgeon et al (1992) identify trust in risk management institutions as being the current point of contact between the various schools or research.

We suggest that there is potentially much value in seeking to apply the insights gained by this research in the context of designing communication processes that seek to reduce vulnerability in developing countries.

NATURAL DISASTERS

THE ROLE OF THE MEDIA

The risk communication literature referred to above includes some consideration of the possible role of the media as conduits for such information. Peltu (1985) observes that journalists are often keen to set new agendas, to investigate the failure of compliance with regulations, and to act as "whistle blowers". However Mazur (1989) expresses concern about the volume of simple, and routinely negative messages carried by the media about risk issues.

The changes in media coverage that have occurred over recent decades, most especially the widespread use of colour TV and improvements in telecommunications, have had profound influences on perceptions of hazard and risk.

The rapidity with which views of mayhem can be transmitted into homes has undoubtedly contributed to the widely held misconception that the Earth is becoming increasingly dangerous due to riding levels of natural violence, and quite possibly instrumental in causing the United Nations to declare the 1990s as the International Decade for Natural Disaster Reduction (Jones, 1993). It is also possible that the increased frequency and impact of reports of disasters may have contributed to some overall increased awareness of hazards and risks amongst viewing audiences (Blomkvist and Sjoberg, 1987).

Hadden (1989), whilst recognising the importance of the media as a source of information, is cautious about any deliberately enhanced role because of the media's tendency to distort information by simplification and dramatisation of the issues. On the other hand, De Marchi (1991) and Kelly, Gibson and Horlick-Jones (1992) point to the need for emergency management authorities to understand media agendas in order to effectively target information and so maximize helpful and positive coverage.

The construction of such "media strategies" requires a detailed analysis of the media coverage of hazards and risks. Such an analysis is offered by Wilkins and Paterson (1990) who claim that the media interpret complex social, scientific and political problems associated with risks in terms of culturally understood "scripts", or stereotypical stories about dangers and disasters. They propose the utilisation of findings from psychological research that suggests people use "schemas", or primitive cognitive maps, to understand media news coverage. This would allow the presentation of risk information in terms of these fundamental "building blocks". In practical terms, they claim this approach suggests public understanding is best achieved by portraying risk information as a conflict between competing costs and benefits.

Peltu's (1988) review covered a number of important avenues of research. He reported on work that suggests the media covers harms rather than risks, and is more interested in outrages than hazards. These ideas seem to constitute criteria of newsworthyness, together with the identification of "victims" and associated "guilty" officials who can be blamed. It has also been noted that the media is particularly interested in "new" risks (Blomkvist and Sjoberg, 1987) or new aspects, or "angles", of risk management, such as fund-raising extravaganzas or "fashion compassion". However such attention soon wanes.

Overcoming media "interest decay" is one of the main problems in achieving the effective use of the media in reducing levels of risk.

Peltu (1988) also addressed the question of deregulation of western media and a concern of wider applicability, the effects of commercial pressures on the coverage of risk. He concluded that these developments, whilst offering some new possibilities, present major difficulties for risk communication because of the probable elimination of detail and complexity in news coverage.

Similarly, new technologies, allowing more television, cable and radio channels, together with cheaper publishing, could make risk communication to mass audiences more difficult, whilst enabling more effective communication to some well-targetted audiences.

The fundamental difficulty lies in structuring risk communication messages concerning prevention and avoidance in such a way as to appear attractive to media criteria of newsworthyness, and the potential of the media to act as a distorting-lens for the information it conveys. Free-market electronic media present more difficult problems than the state-subsidized "public service" tradition in some countries. Media forms other than news and current affairs, such as drama, may offer new possibilities, however the existence of covert messages raise complex ethical issues (Morgan and Lave, 1990).

Despite these problems, the power of the media to convey messages and images continues to present an enticing challenge to risk communicators.

THE MEDIA IN DEVELOPING COUNTRIES

In many ways, the "global village" predicted by McLuhan (1964) has arrived. The very rapid growth in electronic communications and the spectacular proliferation of television has significantly contributed to a process of "globalisation" linking events in geographically distant localities (Sreberny-Mohammadi, 1991). Increasingly, powerful economic and social forces are being released (Giddens, 1990) that will change the very meaning of "local" and "global".

Within these momentous developments are important opportunities for the communication of risk information to reduce vulnerability to environmental hazards. Whilst radio may offer greater flexibility for conveying early warnings of impending danger, television, with its powerful ability to overcome local cultural barriers (Sreberny-Mohammadi, 1991), presents perhaps the greatest potential for public education and awareness.

Television is already used to convey social messages. In India, for example, popular "soap operas" are deliberately constructed to encourage viewer identification, and to cover issues such as the status of women, family harmony and family planning (McIntosh, 1992). Clearly the dividing line between persuasive communications of public interest and propaganda is a narrow one.

The ethical problems associated with covert messages have already been mentioned. Many of these concerns turn on questions of democracy - a difficult and complex matter in many developing countries.

NATURAL DISASTERS

Use of the media also provides an opportunity to overcome the resistance of people to impersonal advice from "experts" or "outsiders" as described earlier. It is well known that personal communications are more effective that mass communications (Cronholm and Sandell, 1987). Much anecdotal evidence exists that recipients of warnings discuss the possibilities with friends, neighbours and trusted "local experts" before deciding on action. In this context, the role of media personalities becomes of great importance, for these people are familiar (not outsiders) and tend to be believed. Thus the use of personalities to convey warnings and advice is likely to greatly improve receptiveness.

The insights of risk communication research, together with media developments, may present more effective ways for governments and relief agencies to encourage the implementation of local risk mitigation measures. However other possibilities, such as the enabling and empowerment of risk-bearing groups, possibly leading to the media-generated arena for public debate envisaged by some social theorists (Habermas, 1989), would be politically unacceptable in many countries. In addition the widespread existence of censorship currently precludes activities such as investigative journalism about certain risks (Article 19, 1991).

On the other hand, the very interconnectiveness and immediacy of the emerging global media may make certain changes inevitable. For example, the media restrictions claimed to be responsible for the prevention of aid supplies and ensuing major famine in Ethiopia (1983-1985) and China (1959-1961) (Article 19, 1990) may become increasingly difficult for unscrupulous governments.

CONCLUSIONS

Disaster reduction programmes that are over-dependent on a technocentric approach are unbalanced and are likely to prove ineffective. A balanced approach should including an emphasis on reducing vulnerability, and a recognition of the role of social and cultural factors in risk communication processes.

Recent social science research into the perception and communication of risk may offer important insights in seeking to address such social and cultural issues. This is an area in need of further investigation.

The emerging media in developing countries have potentially very important, and powerful roles as conduits for risk information.

REFERENCES

Article 19 (1990) Starving in Silence, Article 19, London

Article 19 (1991) Information Freedom and Censorship, Library Association Publishing, London

F. Bailey (1971) "The peasant view of the bad life" in T. Shanin (ed) Peasants and Peasant Societies, Penguin, Harmondsworth

A. Blomkvist and L. Sjoberg (1987) "Risk and accident reports in the mass media" in L. Sjoberg (ed) Risk and Society, Allen and Unwin, London

I. Burton, R. Kates and G. White (1978) The Environment as Hazard, Oxford University Press, New York

M. Cronholm and R. Sandell (1987) "Scientific information - a review of research" in L. Sjoberg (ed) Risk and Society, Allen and Unwin, London

F. Cuny (1983) Disasters and Development, Oxford University Press, New York

B. De Marchi (1991) "Effective communication between the scientific community and the media" Disasters 15 3 237-243

M. Douglas (1970) Natural Symbols: Explorations in Cosmology, Barrie and Rockliff/The Cresset Press, London

M. Douglas (1992) Risk and Blame: Essays in Cultural Theory, Routledge, London

H. Gow and H. Otway (eds) (1990) Communication with the Public about Major Accident Hazards, Elsevier, London

A. Giddens (1990) The Consequences of Modernity, Polity, Cambridge

J. Habermas (1989) The Structural Transformation of the Public Sphere, Polity, Cambridge

S. Hadden (1989) A Citizen's Right to Know: Risk Communication and Public Policy, Westview, Boulder

K. Hewitt (ed) (1983) Interpretations of Calamity, Allen & Unwin, London

T. Horlick-Jones (1992) "Natural disasters, human failures" New Scientist 135 1830 18th July 44-45

T. Horlick-Jones (1993) "Patterns of risk and patterns of vulnerability" in A. Amendola and B. De Marchi (Eds) Workshop on Emergency Management, European Commission Joint Research Centre, Ispra

T. Horlick-Jones, J. Fortune and G. Peters (1993) "Vulnerable systems, failure and disaster" in F. Stowell, D. West and J. Howell (Eds) Systems Science Addressing Global Problems, Plenum, New York

D.K.C. Jones (1993) "Environmental hazards in the 1990s: problems, paradigms and prospects" Geography 78 2 161-165

A. Kelly, R. Gibson and T. Horlick-Jones (1992) Local Authorities, the Media and Disasters: Developing a Peacetime Media Strategy, EPICENTRE, London

C. McIntosh (1992) "Television as a catalyst for social change" Cooperation South (United Nations Development Programme) December 14-16

M. McLuhan (1964) Understanding Media, Routledge Kegan Paul, London

NATURAL DISASTERS

A. Maskrey (1989) Disaster Mitigation: A Community Based Approach, Oxfam, Oxford

A. Mazur (1989) "Communicating risk in the mass media" in D. Peck (ed) Psychosocial Effects of Hazardous Toxic Waste Disposal on Communities, Charles C. Thomas, Springfield

J. Mejer (1991) "Cultural issues in the mitigation of hazard: recent events in Puna, Hawaii" Paper presented to the Emergency Planning '91 conference, Lancaster University, September

D. Mileti, C. Fitzpatrick and B. Farhar (1992) "Fostering public preparations for natural hazards" Environment 34 3 16-39

M. Morgan and L. Lave (1990) "Ethical considerations in risk communication practice and research" Risk Analysis 10 3 355-358

H. Otway and B. Wynne (1989) "Risk communication: paradigm and paradox" Risk Analysis 9 2 141-145

M. Peltu (1985) "The role of the communications media" in H. Otway and M. Peltu (Eds) Regulating Industrial Risk, Butterworth, London

M. Peltu (1988) "Media reporting of risk information: uncertainties and the future" in H. Jungermann, R. Kasperson and P. Wiedemann (eds) Risk Communication, Kernforschungsanlage, Julich

R. Perry and J. Nigg (1985) "Emergency management strategies for communicating hazard information" Public Administration Review 45 January 72-77

K. Portney (1991) Siting Hazardous Waste Treatment Facilities - The NIMBY Syndrome, Auburn House, New York

N. Pidgeon, C. Hood, D. Jones, B. Turner and R. Gibson (1992) "Risk perception" in Royal Society Study Group Risk: Analysis, Perception and Management, Royal Society, London

S. Rayner (1992) "Cultural theory and risk analysis" in S. Krimsky and D. Golding (eds) Social Theories of Risk, Praeger, Westport

M. Schwarz and M. Thompson (1990) Divided We Stand: Redefining Politics, Technology and Social Choice, Harvester Wheatsheaf, Hemel Hempstead

A. Sreberny-Mohammadi (1991) "The global and the local in international communications" in J. Curran and M. Gurevitch (eds) Mass Media and Society, Edward Arnold, London 118-138

K. Smith (1992) Environmental Hazards, Routledge, London

L. Wilkins and P. Paterson (1990) "The political amplification of risk; media coverage of disasters and hazards" in J. Handmer and E. Penning-Rowsell (eds) Hazards and the Communication of Risk, Gower Technical, Aldershot

P. Winchester (1990) "Economic power and response to risk: a case study from India" in J. Handmer and E. Penning-Rowsell (eds) Hazards and the Communication of Risk, Gower Technical, Aldershot

B. Wynne (1992) "Misunderstood misunderstanding: social identities and public uptake of science" Public Understanding of Science 1 281-304

3. The development of a combined regional strategy for power generation and natural hazard risk assessment in a high-altitude glacial environment: an example from the Cordillera Blanca, Peru

J. M. REYNOLDS, Applied Geology Ltd, UK

ABSTRACT

In glacierized mountainous regions, the risk of natural hazards is high, especially in areas also prone to significant seismic activity. In regions such as these, natural hazards can be divided into two types: (a) those which are likely to occur over a time period of hours to days following a seismic triggering event, and (b) those which are gradual and are significant over much longer time scales (decades).

The potential risk of seismic activity is obvious. What is less clear is how instabilities in zones affected by seismic activity are likely to respond to disturbances caused by earthquakes. For example, in the Himalayas and Andes, earthquakes have frequently triggered major landslides and avalanches, some of which have had catastrophic consequences in human terms.

Earthquakes can also directly affect the engineering integrity of natural moraine dams associated with high-altitude glacial lakes. The failure of such dams can release millions of cubic metres of water which combine with superficial sediments and surface detritus to form an aluvión, a catastrophic flood of liquid mud.

It is possible to identify which high-altitude glacial lakes are prone to collapse by ground inspection and/or by using remote sensing (aerial photographs/satellite imagery). Furthermore, the potential run-out paths of such features can be estimated and a local hazard map produced. While this in itself can be of use, it becomes all the more beneficial when such information is integrated into a regional hazard assessment.

As regional climates change and glaciers recede, more glacially-derived water may become stored in neo-glacial lakes. Where these are vulnerable to seismic risk, the potential threat of catastrophic discharge is increased.

It is necessary, therefore, that the requirements of water storage for hydro-electric power generation are balanced against increased risks of catastrophic drainage from high-altitude neo-glacial lakes. This combined approach provides for a more comprehensive and effective strategy which facilitates the provision of electricity while protecting the local population. While the principal behind the development of an integrated strategy is universal, an example of how such a strategy might be formulated is given for the Cordillera Blanca, Peru.

Natural disasters. Thomas Telford, London, 1993

INTRODUCTION

High-altitude mountain ranges, such as the Himalayas, the Andes, and the Southern Alps of New Zealand, for example, are affected by earthquakes. These in turn have been known to trigger ice and rock avalanches ranging in size from small sloughs causing no significant damage, to major catastrophic sturzstroms with major loss of life. An example of the latter is the devastating earthquake and massive rock avalanche ('sturzstrom') of 31st May 1970 in the Cordillera Blanca, Peru (Figure 1), which resulted in the deaths of some 80,000 people (refs. 1 and 2). Details of hazard assessment work being undertaken in Nepal have been given by Damen (ref. 3), for example, and by Reynolds (ref. 4) for the Cordillera Blanca, Peru.

In glacierized mountainous regions, the presence of snow and ice provides much needed water to drink, for washing and for irrigation of small hill farms. Adjacent to the steep glaciers, lakes containing melt-water drain through moraine dams to feed the rivers below. Increasingly, as populations grow, there is a greater requirement for potable water and for electric power for heating, lighting, cooking and for industry. With improved power supplies local populations can develop their economic base and so improve their overall living standards.

The very nature of mountainous terrain means that space for urban expansion is limited and often people are forced into building houses is areas which are prone to natural hazards, such as flooding by rivers, or mudslides, for example (Figure 2). Furthermore, the pressure of greater population density on the local economy requires some form of co-ordinated plan for such growth not to become chaotic and result in shanty towns built in high-risk areas and with little or no prospect for employment for the inhabitants.

Consideration also has to be given to social and ethnic pressures too. People who have a tradition of being hill farmers, for instance, do not take readily to having to live in towns or to work in environments which are totally alien to them. After the Huascarán disaster in 1970, many local farmers decided to stay put rather than move to the safer areas in local towns. They prefer to continue farming the hills they know even though there is an increased risk of further devastating mudslides.

The regions most affected by these pressures are usually to be found in the developing countries. There tends to be little money available or encouragement given to developing strategies for improvement which provide a co-ordinated approach to the physical, social and economic welfare of the local population over time scales relevant to the ambient environmental conditions. Today's short-term expediencies may lead to tomorrow's catastrophes!

This paper presents a brief overview of how consideration of natural hazards and their potential risks can be integrated into a regional strategy for development which also takes account of social and economic considerations. In order to illustrate how this may be done, examples are given from ongoing hazard assessment work in the Cordillera Blanca, Peru. There are, however, two principal components which also have to be present if a strategy is to stand any chance of being put into practice, namely, the political will and the resources. There needs to be co-ordination between the public and private sectors as each can benefit the other. Often the two working in partnership can achieve far more than the two acting independently. The upshot of there being no strategy for the future is that a significant natural hazard may occur and the local populous is unprepared. The result is likely to be a high casualty figure at the outset and long periods of serious disruption to the local community. The length of such disruption can, in places, be of the order of at least one or more generations. Careful planning can minimise the potential loss of life and disruption arising from a major hazard event.

THE NATURE OF THE NATURAL HAZARDS

In glacierized mountainous regions affected by active seismicity, the likely natural hazards can be divided into two types: (a) those which are likely to occur over a time period of hours to days following a seismic triggering event, and (b) those which are gradual but which are significant over much longer time scales (e.g. decades).

Hazards which are likely to occur over the short time scale are:

- Earthquakes.

- Landslides;
- Rock and ice avalanches;
- Catastrophic failure of moraine-dammed lakes;
- Flooding.

A general description of glacial hazards has been given by Reynolds (ref. 4). While earthquake prediction is still something yet to be achieved, the assessment of probability of there being an earthquake in a region can be determined. Methods by which this can be accomplished are discussed later. The main danger of the earthquake-related series of hazards is that large areas are affected simultaneously. Many hundreds of avalanches may be started following an earthquake combining with the failure of natural dams to lakes full of glacial melt-water leading to widespread flooding. The risks due to the other hazards listed are easier to identify as they are more physically evident. Methods of assessing these potential hazards are discussed later. While the last four hazards may occur in response to an earthquake, as happened in May 1970 in the Cordillera Blanca, they may also happen individually. A single moraine-dam may fail for reasons quite unrelated to any external stimulus; a flood may occur due to a sudden influx of water following an unusually heavy period of rain, for instance. In these cases, the areas affected by each incident are usually quite restricted. While locally significant, they only represent a small event on a larger scale and, in most instances, should have little impact on regional development.

Hazards which are likely to develop over a long time scale:

- Failure of an ice-cored moraine dam;

- Changes in water levels in lakes and rivers, and significant recession of local glaciers due to climatic change.

Both of the above hazards are related in part or totally to climatic change. The formation of ice-cored moraines and the subsequent damming of proglacial lakes is generally a consequence of a general warming of climate. Such an increase in mean annual air temperature may be related purely to natural decadal climatic fluctuations rather than being a direct consequence of the 'enhanced greenhouse effect' induced by pollution generated by Mankind.

It is the presence of high-altitude lakes fed by glacial melt-water that has attracted hydroelectric power generation. In order to maintain a more regular throughput to power stations, it has been considered necessary to maintain a water storage capacity in these lakes. As the lakes are at high altitude, typically in excess of 4,500 m above sea level, there is a good head of water for gravity feed to the power stations.

In Peru, Corporación Peruana del Santa (CPS) was established in order to evaluate the safety of these mountain lakes and to use the naturally-stored water in the generation of hydro-electric power. In the mid-1940s, what is now the second largest power station in Peru was constructed at Huallanca with its water intake 9 km upstream at Cañon del Pato (Figure 1). This intake had to be rebuilt after it was very badly damaged by an aluvión on 20th October 1950.

CPS later became known as ElectroPeru, of which Hidrandina S.A. is a subsidiary based in Huaraz, in the Ancash Department. Hidrandina S.A. has conflicting interests; on one hand it has to provide more water storage in order to maintain and, if possible, increase the water flow through the Cañon del Pato intake to raise the power still further from 150 MW. On the other hand, it is responsible for maintaining the safety of the high-altitude lakes in case of failures of moraine dams, or impact from ice and rock avalanches, potentially resulting in catastrophic flooding. Remediation has included the construction of tunnels or siphons either to maintain lower water levels within the lakes or to drain the lakes completely. However, the practicalities of undertaking such remediation are difficult and may induce premature failure, as has happened elsewhere in Peru (ref. 5). A further example from Hualcán will be described later.

NATURAL HAZARD ASSESSMENT

In mountainous regions where access is difficult it is important not to miss possible sources of major risk. Furthermore, it is essential to determine appropriate criteria by which to identify both regionally important risk and those potential hazards which have a high probability of happening. These criteria are unlikely to be exactly the same for different geographical regions, and care must be taken for this process not to become prescriptive. It also a salient factor that scientists in Europe, for example, tend not to be familiar with the scale of terrain in such places as the Andes or the scale of the devastation that can occur in very short periods of time (of the order of a few minutes to hours). An example of the effect of an aluvión near Laguna Paron is shown in Figure 2; the width of the lake at its widest was about 380 m, a similar distance from the breached moraine to the rock cliff. In 1951 the moraine breached discharging 1.13 million m^3 in a matter of hours and, three months later, a further breach occurred with an extra 3.52 million m^3 disgorged over a similar time period into another lake downstream. The glacier above the lake is also a source of ice avalanches. As long as the current breach in the moraine remains, there is little risk from this lake. However, the moraine cliffs at the breach are almost vertical and are highly unstable. Should they collapse in on themselves, the moraine could again act as a dam and a new build-up of water take place. Routine monitoring would easily identify this risk.

The objective of hazard assessment is to map locations which may be the sources of hazards, such as areas likely to be affected by rock or ice avalanches, unstable cliffs, fault zones, etc., and to determine the likely effects away from the sources. For example, if a potential aluvión is identified, its run-out down stream should be identified in order to highlight areas of population (however small), bridges and roads, power cables, communications systems, etc., which may be affected by any subsequent aluvión. One such map produced for a glacial lake at Hualcán, north of Huaraz, is shown in Figure 3. This lake was dammed by an ice-cored moraine which was melting and lowering the freeboard of the natural dam. It was identified in 1988 by the author and colleagues from Hidrandina S.A. as being in imminent danger of failing. Within a very short period afterwards, remediation was put into effect to lower the water level using siphons, paid for in part by the British Government. Further details of how this was done are given in refs. 2 and 4. The upshot of this was that the water level was reduced sufficiently so that a channel could be cut through the moraine down to rockhead thus ensuring that there could be no failure of the lake dam. Unfortunately, by lowering the water level, the glacier within the former lake was no longer supported by the water, and large masses of ice collapsed in 1991 into the lake setting up a displacement wave which overtopped the remaining dam. This produced an aluvión which destroyed several farms and a bridge downstream; there were no reports of casualties. The risk to Hualcán and Carhuaz, a total population of circa 25,000 persons, remains unless the lake can be drained completely. Hidrandina S.A. is currently appealing for funds (of the order of $160,000) to construct a drainage tunnel.

The methods by which potential hazards can be identified are multivarious and range from the use of satellite imagery over 120 by 120 km areas with resolutions of 80 m (Landsat) to SPOT imagery over areas with a resolution smaller than 20 x 20 m. Basic hazard maps can be produced extremely quickly by using such tools. Further details can be provided by using aerial photography. Such facilities permit the compilation of hazard maps remote from the areas affected. Indeed, much of the mapping in Peru could be undertaken by staff in the UK, for example, without the immediate need to go into the remote areas of the regions affected.

For regional-scale hazard maps to be effective, however, adequate ground truth needs to be gained. For example, while it was easy to identify the presence of the lake at Hualcán and its proximity to its source glacier, it was only possible to determine the immediacy of the risk by visiting the site first hand. Furthermore, evidence of past aluviones can be identified and mapped by field observations and other examples of such hazard maps are given in ref. 4.

While spatial mapping of potential hazards can be undertaken quite readily, the determination of the potential of hazards may need more specialized input. In some cases, geotechnical assessment is required in order to calculate potential slope stability. Ground geophysical investigations may be needed to complement drilling in order to investigate structures within the ground which may pose a threat. For instance, it may be necessary to investigate the deeper structure of a major moraine resting on a slope in case there are potential planes of weakness along which the moraine could fail. Considering that moraines in parts of the Cordillera Blanca are in excess of 400 m thick, this is not a trivial exercise.

In order to gauge the temporal risk of certain hazards, particularly those related to earthquakes, two approaches can be taken. The first is an historical search of records, maps, etc., in order to identify how frequently certain types of hazard have occurred in a given area. In the Cordillera Blanca, for example, the chronicles of a Catholic Priest, Father Bertrano, indicate the first recorded aluvión as being on the 4th March 1702. The second approach is to measure the active seismicity of an area either by using existing seismological networks or, if financially possible, by establishing a specific seismometer network. Deverchère and others (ref. 6) have reported that the Cordillera Blanca fault, which lies parallel to the Rio Santa river on its northern side, is very active seismically. They recorded over 150 tremors with magnitudes up to Richter 3.2 over a 34-day period in 1987.

GENERATION OF ELECTRICITY

In a developing economy, the provision of an industrial base is essential but is dependent upon adequate generation of energy. The Callejón de Huaylas is a fertile valley corridor through which the Rio Santa flows northwards and ultimately westwards to the Pacific Ocean. The area is known locally as the 'Little Switzerland' of the Peruvian Andes because of its rich agriculture. Indeed, parts of the flat valley floor are given over to extensive plantations for carnations which are sold for export particularly to California. These farms use large amounts of artificial light and are thus dependent upon the provision of reasonably-priced electricity. The supply for this area is derived from the hydro-electric power plant at Huallanca. Consequently, the region is at serious risk economically should this power plant be put out of operation for any significant period. It was put out of operation for about a year as a result of an aluvión on 20th October 1950. There was further damage arising from the major earthquake on May 31st 1970. The existing environment around the Cañon del Pato intake (Figure 4) is known to be unstable, as described later, and consequently, this water intake is extremely vulnerable.

A further complication is that the supply of water derived from the local glaciers is decreasing with time due to the general recession of the glaciers which has been recorded over 5 decades (ref. 7). There is also a distinct variation in discharge from the glaciers according to season. During the dry season (May to October), loss of mass is largely caused by solar radiation and sublimation rather than melt. During the wet season (November to April), ablation is up to 50% higher than during the dry season, but is accompanied by increased melt-water run-off. Consequently, power generation needs to take account of this significant seasonal variation. Furthermore, the risk of moraine-dam failures is likely to be greater during the wet season, due to increased capacity within the dammed lakes, and this too needs to be considered.

Cañon del Pato water intake

The course of the Rio Santa at Cañon del Pato is along a major north-south fault which separates Plio-Pleistocene volcanic rocks and, slightly to the north, Mesozoic sediments from the Pliocene grano-dioritic batholith to the east (ref. 9). With the uplift of the Andes, the volcanics now dip steeply to the west. Those which occur on the east of the Rio Santa thus dip steeply towards the river. It is these rocks which are now causing severe problems of instability at this location.

The 1970 earthquake mentioned previously left an area of about 315,000 m² of mountainside to the east of the power station water intake in a highly unstable state. The zone in immediate proximity to the water intake is shown in Figure 4.

There are several types of instability within a distance of 400 m from the power station intake: reactivated normal faults, rock slides, detached slabs creeping under gravity, and perched alluvium on steep rock slabs. The distribution of these is shown in Figure 4. The main plant at Cañon del Pato is threatened by general slippage of a zone 900 m long, from an altitude of 2320 m, and about 360 m wide, part of which is shown at the top of Figure 4. The volume of potentially mobile material is estimated to be about 10^7 m³. From about 100 m south of the plant, there are three detached blocks which are slipping as discrete units, each topped by a prominent platform. These three blocks constitute a mobile volume of about 600,000 m³ and could fail completely given another moderate earthquake.

Any significant failure of the rocks at this location could be a major setback not only for the local area but could have far more serious consequences. Firstly, the power plant intake could be totally destroyed thereby crippling the power station at Huallanca. Secondly, should the Rio Santa become blocked by a major rock slide to a depth of some 50 m, which is quite feasible given the magnitude of the unstable zones within immediate proximity of the river, then a lake totalling some 10-50 million m³ of water could form upstream. This would have two immediate effects: submerging farm land adjacent to the river for a distance of about 3 km upstream and destroying the road tunnel alongside the Rio Santa thereby cutting road communications between Huaraz and the coastal towns of Santa and Chimbote. If the road tunnel is not destroyed but the river is blocked, the tunnel could act as a pipe to drain away the excess water downstream. If the river was totally dammed, the areas downstream would be adversely affected by the loss of water as well as increased flooding upstream. Even more worrying would be the stability of the resulting rock dam across the Rio Santa. Given the potential volume of stored water, a sudden breach of the dam would be catastrophic all along the river course to the coast. It is likely that the consequences of this would be substantially greater than those caused when a similar but smaller event occurred after the 1970 earthquake and mudflow.

DEVELOPMENT OF A REGIONAL STRATEGY

It is clear from the foregoing discussions that the Callejón de Huaylas remains extremely prone to (a) earthquakes, (b) aluviones and (c) rock slides. All of these could combine to cause both local damage and widespread disruption. The possible destruction of the Cañon del Pato water intake and the probable resulting blockage of the Rio Santa at this location have far reaching consequences. The effects would be extreme in the immediate vicinity of the river, but the loss of electricity across the region would be a major loss for the social and economic survival of the area. Since 1988, ElectroPeru, through its agent Hidrandina S.A., is attempting to implement recommendations for hazard resource mapping. However, the speed and scale of any remediation is dependent upon obtaining adequate funding. This is the prime limiting factor in Peru at present.

Having identified such hazards and estimated their probability, albeit qualitatively at this stage, there is obviously a great and urgent need to develop alternative forms of power generation if the area is to develop economically.

It is a relatively simple matter to map out the obvious tangible hazards using methods described earlier. It is also feasible to determine seismic risk and probability of occurrence using historic information and active seismic monitoring. Consequently, hazard potential maps can be produced for the Callejón de Huaylas relatively easily. Using these, it should be possible for the relevant authorities to compile maps of where building and industrial development can take place with minimal risk. Buildings can be constructed using appropriate construction codes for materials and designs to minimise damage caused by earthquakes.

What is more difficult to achieve, because of the likely cost implications, is an alternative strategy for the generation of electricity. If the region is going to continue to grow, and for local industry to develop, then there should be an urgent review of alternative energy supplies.

45

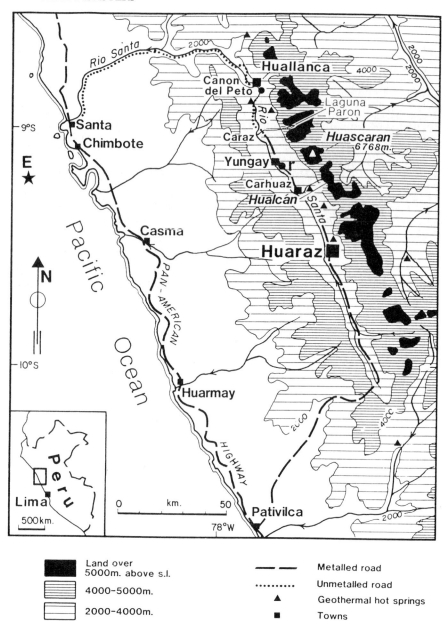

Figure 1. Map of western central Peru. The Callejón de Huaylas is in the part of the Rio Santa valley between Huaraz and Huallanca. The letter 'E' indicates the epicentre of the main shock of the earthquake on 31st May 1970 which caused the deaths of up to 80,000 people within 5 minutes of the earthquake happening. The letter 'r' indicates the location of Ranrahirca.

Figure 2. A residual debris fan is evidence of two previous aluviones from this lake at Artesancocha totalling some 4.6 million m³ of discharge in 1951. The ice cliff of the glacier Artesanraju (arrowed) is a source of ice avalanches.

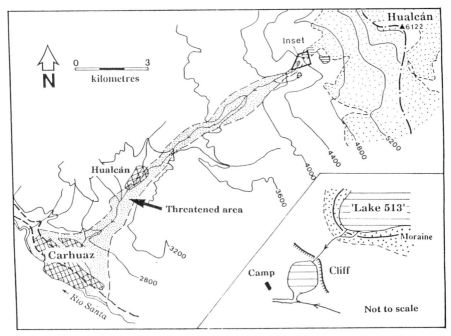

Figure 3. A hazard map of the Hualcán-Carhuaz area showing the location of the problematical 'Lake 513' which is the potential source of aluviones and which is undergoing remediation (from ref. 4).

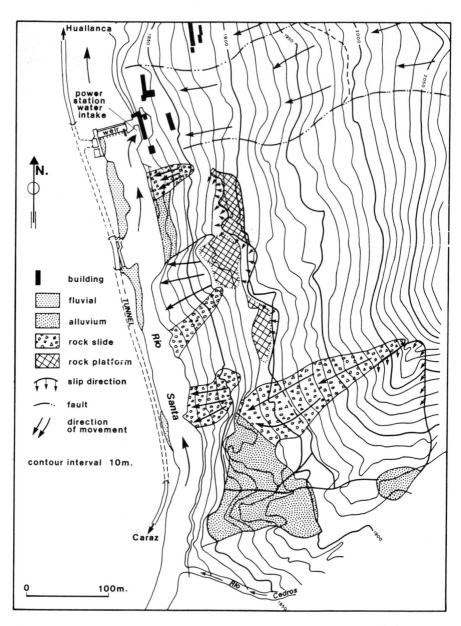

Figure 4. Map of the Cañon del Pato water intake facility for the Huallanca hydro-electric power plant. Areas of instability are clearly shown. Based on a larger map produced by Zapata (ref. 8).

48

It is noted that along the Rio Santa valley there are a significant number of geothermal springs. The locations of these are indicated by solid triangles on Figure 1. Should ElectroPeru be considering the use of a number of small but discrete geothermal power plants along the Rio Santa valley? In the event that the Rio Santa becomes blocked at Cañon del Pato and the power plant at Huallanca is put out of operation, then at least there are alternative sources of power. It is far less likely that all of these locations would be destroyed by a single event and consequently the overall risk of critical loss of power is thereby reduced. The Peruvian authorities have recognized the scale of the problems present and are endeavouring to put into effect recommendations made.

RECOMMENDATIONS

It has been demonstrated that the development of an integrated regional development strategy, combining hazard mapping with a provision for the generation of electricity, can be achieved without the need for vast expenditure on resources. The prospective benefits to a particular region, whether in the Andes, Karakoram, Himalayas, etc., far outweigh the costs.

In the Cordillera Blanca, in Peru, for example, the vulnerability of the region to the potentially devastating effects of another major earthquake and associated hazards has been highlighted. It is recommended that hazard maps are compiled along with regional development strategies. Arising from these there should be contingency plans to develop alternative energy sources to compensate for the likely loss of the Huallanca power station. Furthermore, damage limitation studies should be put into effect to consider the possible effects of a blockage of the Rio Santa caused by rockslides at Cañon del Pato. It is hoped that the ongoing attempts to raise finance to assist with the various remediation projects, particularly at Hualcán, will be successful.

While the above discussion has centred on the Callejón de Huaylas in the Cordillera Blanca in Peru, the development of regional hazard and development strategies can be undertaken for any similar region, such as parts of the Himalayas, for example.

ACKNOWLEDGEMENTS

The author is very grateful to the Royal Society for funding an initial study visit to Peru in 1988. Collaboration with colleagues at Hidrandina S.A. in Huaraz has been a vital part of this work and is ongoing. Thanks are also due to the British Embassy staff in Lima for facilitating the funding of the initial remediation work at Hualcán.

REFERENCES

1. PLAFKER G. and ERICKSON G.E. Nevados Huascarán avalanches, Peru. In: VOIGHT B. (Ed.), Rockslides and avalanches. 1: Natural Phenomena, Elsevier, Amsterdam. p. 277-314, 1978.

2. REYNOLDS J.M. Geological hazards in the Cordillera Blanca, Peru. AGID News, 1990, No. 61/62, 31-33.

3. DAMEN M. Study on the potential outburst flooding of Tsho Rolpa Glacier Lake, Rolwaling Valley, East Nepal. International Institute for Aerospace Survey and Earth Sciences, ITC, Enschede, The Netherlands, pp.77, 1992.

4. REYNOLDS J.M. The identification and mitigation of glacier-related hazards: examples from the Cordillera Blanca, Peru. In: McCALL G.J.H. and others (eds), Geohazards natural and man-made, pp 143-157, Chapman and Hall, London, 1992.

5. LLIBOUTRY L., MORALES B., PAUTRE A., and SCHNEIDER B. Glaciological problems set by the control of dangerous lakes in Cordillera Blanca, Peru. I: Historical failures of morainic dams, their causes and prevention. Journal of Glaciology, 1977, vol. 18, no. 79, 239-254.

6. DEVERCHERE J., DORBATH C. and DORBATH L. Extension related to high topography: results from a microearthquake survey in the Andes of Peru and tectonic implications. Geophysical Journal International, 1989, vol. 98, No. 2, 281-292.

7. KASER G., AMES A. and ZAMORA, M. Glacier fluctuations and climate in the Cordillera Blanca, Peru. Annals of Glaciology, 1990, vol. 14, 136-140.

8. ZAPATA M. Estudio geologica definito sobre deslizamientos y derumbes de roca en la zona de bogatoma de la central hidroelectrica Cañon del Pato. Internal Report (unpublished), Hidrandina S.A., Huaraz, 31 pp. 1987.

9. DALMAYRAC B. Un example de tectonique vivante: les failles subactuelles du pied de la Cordillère Blanche (Pérou). Cahier ORSTOM, sér. Géologique, 1974, vol. 7, no. 1, 19-27.

4. Alleviation of natural disasters in the southwestern area of Bangladesh

R. J. MADDRELL, BSc, PhD, DiplDelft, FICE, FGS, MBAE,
Sir William Halcrow & Partners Ltd, UK

SUMMARY

Bangladesh is geologically young, being created by its three main rivers the Ganges, Brahmaputra and Meghna. Recently its surface area has been static as, even though its rivers carry 1 billion m³ of sediment annually, most is discharged to the Bay of Bengal, with the remainder balancing subsidence. The Southwest Area (SWA) is made up of the moribund western delta and an active eastern one, reflecting varying rates of subsidence and the morphology of the three main rivers which form its boundary.

Morphological changes have major, though gradual, impacts on the SWA and, while almost impossible to control, their influence must be recognised if disasters are to be avoided. The area is also beset by many more immediate types of disaster such as floods, droughts, earthquakes (and tsunami), cyclones and the longer term impact of increasing sea levels. Their occurrence is frequent; e.g. droughts can be expected 1 in 5 years and major cyclones, 1 in 2 years. Man too has played his part, with coastal embankments increasing inundation and the Farakka Barrage, changing river morphology.

The resilient population has learned to cope with disasters and a major Government effort is underway to reduce their impact. However, more drastic measures may be required in the medium to long term if the area is to develop and prosper.

1   INTRODUCTION

Bangladesh is situated at the northern end of the Gulf of Bengal on the tropic of Cancer (see Figure 1) in an area of active crustal movement, is young geologically, very flat and dissected by the three major rivers that formed it, ie the Ganges, Brahmaputra (Jamuna) and Meghna. Their combined flow is the third largest in the world and their ocean delta fan is the largest (ref 1). Some 90% of its river flows are generated outside the country.

Rainfall is seasonal with the monsoon months being May to October while the winter is dry. Cyclones are also seasonal, occurring of the beginning and the end of the monsoons. The river flows

Natural disasters. Thomas Telford, London, 1993

reflect the rainfall but, fortunately, their peaks do not normally coincided although they did in 1988 with disastrous consequences. Droughts also occur and for three years in the 1980's, rainfall failed to achieve 80% of its median value.

Following the disastrous floods of 1987 and 1988, the Government of Bangladesh formulated a systematic long term Flood Action Plan (FAP) to implement a countrywide flood control strategy, consistent with the country's development. Phase 1 of the 1989 FAP for the period 1990/95 contained fourteen main components and fifteen supporting ones. The Southwest Regional Study or FAP-4, on which this paper is based, is one of the main components.

The SWA, containing both the moribund western and an active eastern deltas, was formed by its three Boundary rivers, firstly the Ganges, then the Padma (a combination of the Ganges and Brahmaputra) and then the Lower Meghna, which was joined by the Padma. Land elevations are low, the highest point being about 17m above mean sea level with flat gradients. The area's morphology is dominated by the Boundary rivers, even though the coastal zone is tidal with ranges of up to 3m (ref 14). There are seasonal variations in mean sea level, ie of 0.6m, due to the onset of the monsoon wind field. The discharge of the three rivers is on average about 14,000 cumecs; they transport in excess of 1 billion m^3 of sediment annually (ref 8), most of which passes through to the Bengal Fan, but some remains to balance the significant subsidence.

The population of Bangladesh in the 1991 census was 110 million and that of the SWA, 26.4 million. The SWA covers an area of about 37,000km^2; has a population density of 786 people/km^2, which falls to 710 if the coastal Sundarban forest is included; 89% of its population is rural; has a literacy rate of about 26%; and, like the rest of Bangladesh, some 70% if its people live in absolute poverty. At 1.89%, the rate of population increase is slightly less than elsewhere and is falling faster, while nearly 50% of its population is under 14 years of age. Data for the country as a whole indicates that both food intake and nutritional values have been reducing, e.g. protein from 57.9gm in 1962/64 to 48.2gm per person per day in 1981/82. Fish are the major source of protein.

The SWA is subjected to different disasters such as floods, droughts, cyclones and earthquakes, but man too has had an impact. For this paper, a disaster is defined as an event - natural or man-made, sudden or progressive - that seriously disrupts the functioning of society causing human, material or environmental losses of such severity that exceptional measures are required to cope. The disruption is of such a scale that the affected society cannot cope using its own resources. Disaster management includes all aspects of planning for and responding to disasters, from prevention and preparedness measures to response and rehabilitation.

Over the last 20 years there have been on average one natural disaster annually (see Table 1). The people are, however, naturally resilient born out of centuries of having to cope with such events, which enables then to return to normal life relatively quickly. The institutional arrangement and procedures for dealing with disasters has evolved over many years and has coped remarkably well. While the impact of such disasters can be reduced, there is also a need for improvement, but changes must be introduced gradually.

The impact of most disasters can, with foresight, be reduced. However, the SWA is young geologically and there have been three geotectonic avulsions of its Boundary rivers in the last 200 years, which have had large impacts. Thus, before deriving alleviation strategies for disasters, it is essential to first understand the processes involved.

2 GEOLOGICAL AND PHYSIOGRAPHIC SETTING

The Bengal Basin is a flat Cretaceous - Eocene depositional centre, covering some 60,000 km^2 and, as a deep geosynclinal area, is marked by a gravity high and magnetic anomalies. It was formed by the deltas of the Ganges, Brahmaputra and Meghna rivers and its Fan complex is the largest in the world.

The Basin is part of the Indo-Australian Plate, which is moving NE beneath the Eurasian Plate and its main boundary thrusts move at 10mm/year, based on geomorphic evidence (ref 2). While such movements do not occur in the SW Region, they are important as sediment from these upland areas has resulted in the development of the delta. Stripping of forests may also increase sediment loads.

In the Meghna estuary the sequence is over 12,000m thick, while in the Sundarbans it is 5,000m and at Khulna and Kushtia it is 8,500m and 6,500m, respectively. Subsidence has been considerable although sedimentation appears to have kept pace with the recent world sea level rise of about 150mm/century. However, in recent years this rise appears to be accelerating (ref 3), affecting flooding, sedimentation and drainage.

The SWA exposures are generally a variety of fine grained Quaternary and Recent deposits, the most significant, geomorphologically, is the Chandina Alluvium, which occurs below the Tippera surface (ref 4). The active river corridors are, however, sandy. The whole area is below elevation 17m, 75% below 5m and slopes vary from 1 in 6,000 in the north to 1 in 10,000 overall, reflecting the recent depositional history.

The Madhupur High to the north (see Figure 2) is thought to be rising at a rate of between 0.1 and 0.6mm annually, while the adjacent Sylhet basin is subsiding at up to 21mm annually (ref 4). Within the SWA the presence of the peat and wood at depth, indicates subsidence at Khulna of between 1mm and 5mm annually, with rates of between 0.75mm and 1.4mm annually in the Sundarbans. From recent work (ref 5) accretion at Barisal is twice that at Khulna and thus, compared with Barisal, Khulna and Faridpur appear moribund. Apart from a regression around 12,000 BP, the rise in sea level has been regular though increasing (ref 6). The borehole data confirms that, while the west is relatively stable, the east is an active sedimentary area and is subsiding more rapidly.

NATURAL DISASTERS

3   MORPHOLOGY

The Ganges was probably the first river to break through the Indian Shield (ref 7), building deltas to the east as its course gradually migrated eastward. Sometime in the 15th or 16th century, the Ganges probably followed a course close to the present Gorai River and the Bagirathi - Hoogly system became a right bank distributary. The Ganges continued to migrate eastwards and by the mid-eighteenth century it entered the sea close to the present Arial Khan, but had no connection with either the Brahmaputra or Meghna Rivers. However, the major earthquakes in 1762 and 1782 were possibly accompanied by crustal movement and, following a particularly large flood in 1787, the Teesta, a major Ganges tributary, was diverted to the east and confluenced with the Brahmaputra. A few years later the Brahmaputra itself avulsed westwards to join the Ganges near Goalanda to form the Padma. This change seems to have taken place over decades rather than years, but was essentially complete in 1830 (ref 8). The last major change followed about 40 years later when the Padma broke through a strip of resistant Chandina Alluvium confluencing with the Meghna to form the Lower Meghna. For the first time, the three great Boundary rivers of the SWA entered the Bay of Bengal together; a situation which prevails today.

The Boundary rivers can be categorised by their age with the older Ganges being the easiest to predict and control. The Padma, formed about 200 years ago, has already had one major avulsion, is far less stable and is subject to bankline changes of up to 1km in a season. The Lower Meghna was only formed about 150 years ago, lies in a zone of significant subsidence, is tidal throughout and is the least stable. The contribution of their Regional rivers, in terms of fresh water supply, is inversely proportional to the stability of the Boundary River. The Gorai/ Madhumati, which is the one remaining distributary of the Ganges, appears to be dying in a similar way to the older ones, while the Arial Khan on the Padma is a dynamic river in its own right, with a wide river corridor and a number of tributaries at its head. The Lower Meghna contains a number of major spill rivers such as the Tentulia, Jayanti and Ilisha, whose spill flows are always fresh and are tidally driven.

The Inland rivers eg Chandana and Kumar (see Figure 1) are the channels of moribund Regional rivers and simply transport run-off and, occasionally, flood spill. At the coast, the Inland and Regional rivers become tidal rivers or estuaries whose influence extends over 60% of the SWA. In the west, because the freshwater discharges are low, they are mainly saline, especially in the dry season. In the east, though tidal, they remain mainly freshwater, being fed by spill from the Lower Meghna.

4   DISASTERS

4.1 Floods

Flooding in the SWA results from overbank flow of the Boundary rivers and their distributaries (see Figure 1). In general there is little flooding resulting from flows in the inland rivers because, as they are moribund distributaries, their channels are oversized. Their flooding tends to be where there is drainage congestion or where beels (low marshy areas) overflow. Flooding is perhaps not as widespread as might be expected from a simple analysis of the monsoon rainfall. This is because, while the Ganges flows are monsoon driven and usually peak in August, the Brahmaputra responds primarily to snowmelt and peaks a little earlier, in July. Occasionally their peaks coincide with disastrous consequences, as in 1988.

Statistical extrapolation of the extreme water levels should be treated with caution because of the significant interaction flows and of the loss of embankments and flooding. Thus, design events can only be based on flows and not water levels. The return periods of the 1988 peak flows were 1:20, 1:50 and > 50 in the Ganges, Brahmaputra and Padma, respectively. As a 10% difference in maximum discharge changes a 1:40 year to 1:100 year event, the choice of design return period has little effect on design level, especially because relatively large freeboards are chosen (0.45m for a 100 year event) due to significant standard errors. However, this will change when all the rivers are embanked. It is not possible to establish a statistical relationship between the peak flows in the two main rivers, because of the different origins.

The mechanisms of flooding (over bank spill) and inundation (standing water) are inter-related, with the latter caused primarily by local run-off and impeded drainage. Thus, inundation dictates land use patterns, whereas flooding is more a measure of occasional damage and loss.

In the SWA, the South Central Region and the eastern part of the Southwest Region are mostly subjected to overbank flooding. The FAP-4 mathematical model results for the 1988 flood gave a total flooded area of some 6,500km^2, about 52%, being caused by the Arial Khan and the lower half of the Padma, 33% by the Ganges and Gorai/Madhumati and 15% by the Lower Meghna (see Figure 1). In addition, there was local flooding with the Bishkhali, Swarupkati, Nabaganga, etc, overtopping their banks. Field information indicates that some low lying areas were flooded to depths exceeding 3.0m, e.g. at Gopalganj. It is estimated that an average flood event, such as in 1982, would affect about 3,000km^2 and water levels in the inland rivers would be up to 2.5m higher than the surrounding land for 2-3 months causing inundation (drainage congestion) in some 86% of the area.

Similar analyses and field information for Coastal Embankment Project (CEP) and the coastal river network, indicate that about 40% of the CEP area of about 8000km^2, would suffer drainage congestion. The ongoing morphological changes in these coastal rivers and tidal flow into some of the polders due to overtopping, breaches or public cutting, have aggravated the drainage congestion.

4.2 Droughts

Droughts, like floods, are climatic extremes and Table 1 indicates 7 significant events since 1644. Droughts were more frequent than floods, which may reflect lower population densities and that flooding, while disruptive, was 'normal'.

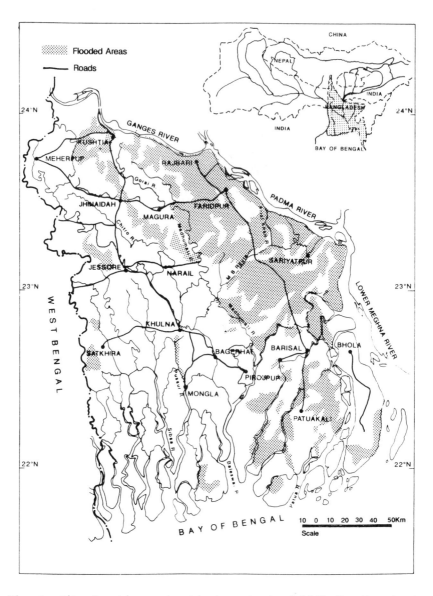

Fig. 1. Site location and estimate extent of 1988 flooding in SW area

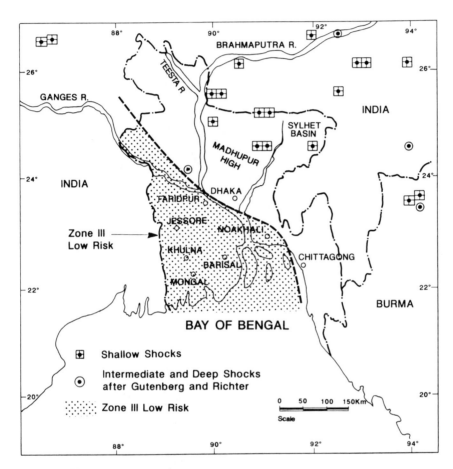

Fig. 2. 20th century epicentres

57

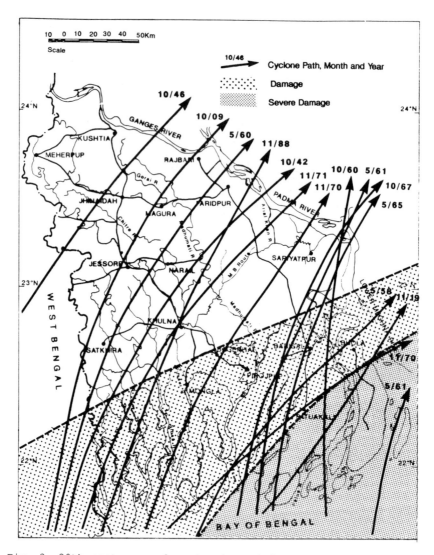

Fig. 3. 20th century cyclone tracks and damage zones

Droughts appear to have become more prevalent, again reflecting their greater impact with increasing population densities. While the SWA might be expected to be immune from droughts, in that its Boundary rivers flow throughout the year, water cannot be distributed. This is especially so with the Southwestern Region, whose only distributary, the Gorai/Madhumati, is now dry for seven months of the year. However, analysis of the rainfall recorded at Khulna since 1902 indicates a trend of increased precipitation. The average annual rainfall is about 1900mm, with November to February being the driest months. In the 25 years of full records (1955-1991), there were 5 drought or near drought occurrences, i.e. for 20% of the time and during the 1980's three years (1982, 1985 and 1989) rainfall failed to meet the long-term 80% value of 1375mm. Two years, 1982 and 1989 were officially described as droughts.

During droughts, the saline front moves landward. On average, salinity of 1ppt or greater (which adversely affects agriculture) is experienced in 10% ($4000km^2$) and 40% ($16,200km^2$) of the SWA in the wet and dry seasons respectively, i.e. 1ppt isohaline is 75km and 150km inland. During droughts, saline penetration will be much greater with unknown effects in the Sundarbans.

4.3 Cyclones

Major cyclones have been reported for centuries as causing loss of human life and livestock and devastating crops, property and flood embankments. During the last 125 years, more than 24 cyclones have crossed the coastal belt, of which fifteen occurred during the last 25 years. The most severe recent ones were in November 1970, May 1985, November 1988 and April 1991 (see Table 1 and Figure 3). The latter was the worst, killing some 140,000 people, but only a relatively small number in SWA. However, the November 1988 cyclone on the Khulna coast, had wind speeds of 160 km/hour; produced a 4.4m surge at Mongla Point; killed about 6,000 people, 150,000 deer, 9 tigers and 65,000 cattle; and damaged over Tk 9 billion (£160 million) of crops. The return period of the surge is not known as frequency analyses only exist for the Chittagong area.

Cyclone occurrences have averaged 1 every 5' years in the SWA since 1882, although there is a gap in the records from 1926 to 1941. However, their frequency appears to be increasing as, this century, their occurrence was 1 in 3 and, since 1950, has been less than 1 in 2 years. This increase in frequency may be due to changes in climate or, with increased population, an increase in impact. The frequency of severe cyclones has been the same for the two periods, pre and post monsoon. The predicted 1 in 20 year deepwater significant wave is 8.8m with a period of 12.5 seconds.

Since the start in 1966 of the coastal zone afforestation programme; over 120,000 ha of mangrove have been planted (ref 12). This zone provides a very effective protection to embankments and the hinterland i.e. 100 to 200m of dense mangrove can reduce wave energies by 20 to 25%. The Sundarbans have been very effective in this regard.

There are 134 cyclone shelters in the SWA, built in the 1970's, accommodating up to 2,000 people each, but their distribution is very uneven. Killas have proved effective for protecting livestock and there are some 160 of them in the country.

4.4 Seismic events

There appear to be two distinct populations of seismic event, very large disastrous ones, such as in 1897, 1934 and 1950, and the smaller, more frequent events. The latter occur mainly in the Himalayas, while the former are to the south (ref 13). Catastrophic earthquakes in 1762 and 1782 are believed, in part, to have been responsible for river avulsions. At the time of the 'Brahmaputra diversion the Ganges was fordable (ref 9) and there may have been some surface movement in the SWA.

Recent seismic activity is almost coincident with that of the Quaternary faults and folds and thus lies to the north of the Ganges and Padma rivers. Figure 2 shows the main epicentres this century of the 1082 events, most of which have been relatively shallow. Since 1860 there have been over 20 shallow and intermediate earthquakes in Bangladesh. Most occurred during the Monsoon season at time of a relatively high water table and their joint probability is significant in terms of disasters.

The most obvious effect of seismic events is the impact of the energy being released and damaged to structures, etc. However, the July 1897 earthquake in the Rangpur area had, in addition, major surface fissuring up to 3m wide and 1km in length. Stream beds were changed and the Teesta and Ghoghat rivers became fordable. High areas, difficult to irrigate, were also created as well as low marshy zones. In the Chittagong earthquake in April 1762 large areas were submerged while other areas were raised. It also generated a tidal wave (tsunami) which caused deaths as far inland as Dhaka.

The SWA can be considered a Zone III - Low Risk Class Area (see Figure 2) with a relatively low risk of seismic activity and rapid crustal movement. However, seismic events can have a catastrophic impact on the SWA by significantly influencing its Boundary rivers, causing tsunami etc.

4.5 Relative sea level rise

The SWA lies in an area of active crustal subsidence and is underlain by over 12,000m of relatively unconsolidated Quaternary deposits. Rates vary but are greatest in the youngest and morphologically the most active area of the delta; the two are undoubtedly linked. In the past, the rivers were attracted to the low areas, building them up before being diverted again (ref 10) and this can be seen today on the Gorai/Madhumati.

Subsidence in the more moribund delta areas appears lower than elsewhere and the capacity of its river and the supply of sediment is even less. This deficiency is compensated for by marine sediment ingress but, with coastal embanking, accretion is limited to the channels (see Section 4.6.1).

Global warming is thought to be responsible for the recent rise in sea level, which appears to be increasing (ref 6) and could reasonably attain about 600mm in 100 years. In the recent geological past, the rivers would have reacted by changing their courses and that of their distributaries and increasing sedimentation rates in the flooded areas. This is not possible now without costly and extensive changes in land use.

For the SWA, it is estimated that the relative rise in sea level will be about 700mm for the year 2050. If it were greater, say 1m, approximately 40% of the SWA would come under direct threat, as well as being exposed to more severe tidal and cyclone conditions.

4.6   Man-made influences

4.6.1   Coastal embankments

In the 1960's and 1970's about 1 million ha were empoldered in the SW of the SWA under the Coastal Embankment Project (CEP). Embankments upgraded the low overtopping bunds used by the Zaminders since the 17th century to prevent tidal flooding. It was an immense undertaking involving over 3700km of embankment and 114 million m^3 of material. Gravity drainage removed the excess rainfall into the surrounding tidal rivers. Initially, agriculture improved, but poldering halved the tidal cubature and the rivers silted. Since the early 1980's outlets became obstructed and siltation has been progressive, resulting in tidal level increases and large areas being inundated.

The problems associated with coastal embankments are not new, i.e. in the last century (ref 10) extensive poldering and reclamation created widespread channel siltation with consequent drainage and navigation problems and an increase in high and low water levels. It was recognised that by removing some of the embankments and polders and increasing tidal volumes, tidal scouring would improve. The results of the planned progressive opening improved ground levels and drainage. Within 12 months the results were dramatic; where accretion had been occurring at 150mm/yr, erosion took place at up to 900mm/yr. It was estimated that these operations would sustain the river for another 100 years.

Before the embankments were removed, they found that land, which prior to reclamation may have been only 300-600mm below high water, soon become 1-2m below as tide levels in the adjacent channels were forced to rise. What at first appeared easy land to reclaim, soon became impossible to drain.

4.6.2   Farakka Barrage

Farakka Barrage is located on the Ganges a few kilometres upstream of the border with Bangladesh. Completed in 1975, it augments flows in the Bhagirathi-Hoogly system during the dry season and supports irrigation. Its success is reported to have been limited (ref 11). Under the India-Bangladesh Agreement of 1977, dry season abstraction was limited to 20,500 cusecs (580 cumecs), with Bangladesh receiving the remainder and a guaranteed minimum of 80% of the average flow, even if the actual flow fell short in any year. The impact of Farakka was initially limited, but in 1988 the Agreement expired and it has not yet been renewed or replaced and dry season flows have decreased markedly since 1989.

NATURAL DISASTERS

Early signs are that the flow changes may have induced measurable impacts on river morphology of the Southwest Region. Many of these impacts are difficult to distinguish from natural changes, but it is apparent that the operation of Farakka has reduced dry season flows in the Ganges to record low levels; closed the Ganges-Kobadak Irrigation Scheme; accelerated flow recession; produced morphological changes and the early abandonment of the Gorai/Ganges link; reduced flows in the Gorai/Madhumati system during seven months, i.e. from October to April; accelerated the possible permanent abandonment of the Gorai as a distributary; and increased salinity levels in the dry season in the coastal zone.

5   ALLEVIATION STRATEGIES

5.1 Floods

Floods can be prevented by the construction of embankments along the Boundary and distributary rivers and it is the policy of the GB that they should be completed early next century. They do, however, have an adverse environmental impact in that they can isolate the flood plain beels, which affects fisheries. Thus, regulators are required which also allow controlled flooding. Whether or not the sediment carried is sufficient to balance subsidence remains to the seen and the impact of the embankments will have to be closely monitored.

Embankment construction has only been recommended for the Ganges and Padma, as the Lower Meghna's right bank is too young and morphologically unstable. Here, the security of polders cannot be guaranteed and require regular retirement.

Embankments must be carefully maintained as once completed, the consequences of their failure are even more disastrous. The need to involve local people as well as Government in their maintenance has been recognised. The variation in construction methods, e.g. a section completed with minimum supervision under the Food for Work programme, must form part of any long-term maintenance plan. An alternative to embankments is the raising of ground levels in populated areas. This is difficult, however, with such high population densities.

The need for flood forecasting has been recognised, although it is difficult to enforce as 90% of the flow originates from outside Bangladesh. There is a real need for International co-operation in this area as, at present, data is supplied from only one external station. While there does not appear to be an obvious increase in flood frequency in relation to climatic change, this will have to be monitored.

5.2 Droughts

The situation in the moribund Southwestern Region has become more serious with the elimination of spill flows from the Ganges, with even the Gorai/Madhumati showing signs of dying. Groundwater development is limited both by soil types and the rise in salinity in the most vulnerable areas. It is, therefore, essential both to recognise the need to supply clean drinking water and to limit its exploitation in critical areas. It is also

62

essential to re-invigorate the Gorai/Madhumati so that, even with the present severe limitations of freshwater flows due to Farakka, there is a minimum of 150 cumecs during the dry season and a guaranteed supply to major centres such as Khulna.

In the coastal areas, fresh water conservation will become increasingly important and the balance between saline shrimp farming and fresh water paddy may have to change, reflecting the increasing levels of salinity. In the South Central Region, it should be possible to augment the supply of freshwater from distributaries with groundwater. Again, water conservation will be required in the coastal zone.

The same comments on forecasting given in 5.1 also apply to droughts.

5.3 Cyclones

The requirement for two-storey cyclone relief shelters in each village or population centre, which have other uses such as schools, mosques etc, has been recognised as has the need for other protective measures such alternative types of shelter, suitable roads for evacuation, etc. These measures, together with means for evacuation, emergency plans etc, form part of the Integrated Master Plan and, in the coastal region, there is a real need to co-ordinate transport, including the use of emergency boats. Where dredging is the preferred option for improving drainage, spoil should be used to raise land levels to provide protection and as an embankment construction material.

Recommendations are being formulated to improve forecasting and early warning systems and the short time period available is a real constraint. In addition, there is a need to assess design level risks for embankments in the SWA, including surge/tide joint probability analyses.

If the plans are implemented, they will have a beneficial environmental impact overall, but some negative sociological impacts can be expected in the coastal margins. The development of coastal mangroves to provide some degree of embankment protection is essential.

5.4 Earthquakes

The risk of earthquake damage to buildings appears low (see Figure 2), but it is important that all new buildings, especially cyclone shelters, have adequate factors of safety.

In the past, earthquakes have produced large tsunami and their associated crustal movement have probably caused river avulsions. Little can be done to prevent such disasters, but their impact can be reduced by the alleviation strategies adopted for the cyclones, floods etc. As with all major disasters, considerable external assistance will be required.

5.5 Relative sea level rise

Subsidence and the rise in sea level is estimated at about 10mm annually and will increasingly put the SWA under threat. The rate is variable, increasing in an easterly direction from the moribund west to the morphologically active eastern delta. In the past, nature has redressed the balance by depositing sediment. The problem is less serious in those areas protected by the main embankments, but the coastal zone will increasingly come under threat. It will be essential to closely monitor the changes and be prepared to raise polder levels and change agricultural methods. It may also be essential to selectively flood areas in order to raise ground levels. This is one area where working against nature will become increasingly risky and expensive.

5.6 Man-made influences

5.6.1   Coastal embankments

The adverse impact of the CEP has been gradual but, with the relative rise in sea level described above, will become more serious and more rapid. The present strategy of dredging, closing off inadequate channels while utilising the still vigorous ones, can only be regarded as a short-term strategy. In the medium to long-term, embankments may have to be made larger and ways devised of selectively and gradually raising land levels. Even if successful, they will have little impact on the overall increase in salinity which will accompany a rise in sea level.

5.6.2   Farakka Barrage

The Farakka Barrage has assisted in the demise of the Gorai. It is important, therefore, that winter flows are retained to the levels agreed between Governments at the opening of the Barrage. If they are not the Gorai will require expensive control works and, say, an additional barrage on the Ganges.

5.7 Other works

A barrage on the Ganges, some 12km upstream of its confluence with the Brahmaputra, would allow the full development potential of the SWA to be realised, protecting most of it from droughts and floods. It would reduce salinities in the coastal zone, but could do little to combat the relative changes in level between land and sea.

Larger coastal embankments or polders should reduce drainage congestion and help protect the vulnerable communities from cyclones. They may require pumping and could become increasingly isolated as the difference between land and sea levels increases. The logical extension of these large polders would be a series of coastal barriers and barrages which would release freshwater in the flood season, but restrict tidal exchange and saline intrusion in the dry season. Care would have to be taken in the Sunderbans to maintain the ecological balance.

Some 1 billion m^3 of sediment is discharged annually through the delta. While some is required to combat subsidence, net accretion in the area has been small and most material passes to the Bay of Bengal. A barrage built across the Bay, say on the 5m contour from the Sundarbans to the south of Chittagong, would, in time, provide large land areas, reduce drought impacts, control floods and protect the whole area from cyclones and the impact of sea

Table 1   Chronology of Major Disasters in the SWA

Date	Affected Area	Nature of phenomena	Approximate Deaths/Damage
1644-45	SWA	Floods	+
1648	SWA	Floods	+
1769-70	SWA	Drought	+
1783-84	SWA	Drought	+
1822 May	Barisal	Severe Cyclone	40,000 people 100,000 cattle
1831 Oct	Barisal	Storm Wave	+
1865-66	SWA	Drought	135,000 people
1873-74	SWA	Drought	+
1876 Oct	West Meghna	Severe Cyclone	100,000 people enormous property
1869 Oct	Sundarbans	Cyclone	+
1896-97	SWA	Drought	+
1901 Nov	Sundarbans	Cyclone	+
1906-07	SWA	Floods	+
1909 Oct	Khulna	Cyclone	+
1917 May	Sundarbans	Cyclone	+
1919 Sep	Barisal	Cyclone	+
1942 Oct	Sundarbans	Severe Cyclone	+
1943-44	SWA	Drought and War	+
1950 Nov	Patuakhali	Cyclone	+
1955	SWA	Floods	+
1958 May	Barisal	Cyclone	+
Oct	West Meghna	Cyclone	+
1960 May	Sundarbans	Cyclone	+
1961 May	West Meghna	Severe cyclone	People and Damage
1963 Jun	Jessore	Cyclone	+
1965 May	Barisal	Severe Cyclone	19,270 people
1967 Oct	Khulna and Sundarbans	Cyclone	+
1970 Oct	Khulna, Patuakhali	Severe Cyclone and surge	+
1970 Nov	West Meghna	Severe Cyclone, surge 11m	300,000 people, livestock widespread damage.
1971 May	West Meghna	Cyclone	+
1971 Nov	Sundarbans	Surge 0.6m	+
1972	SWA	Drought	+
1973 Dec	Sundarbans	Severe Cyclone	+
1974	SWA	Floods, Famine	+
1974 Aug	Khulna coast	Severe Cyclone	+
1975 May	Bhola/Khulna	Severe Cyclone	41 people
1975	SWA	Floods	+
1976 Oct	West Meghna	Cyclone	+
1977 May	Khulna/Barisal	Cyclone, 110kph	+
1978 Sep	Khulna	Cyclone winds	+
1978-79	SWA	Drought	+
1982	SWA	Drought	+
1984	SWA	Floods	+
1986 Nov	Patuakhali	Cyclone	People and damage
1987	SWA	Floods	+
1988	SWA	Floods	+
1988 Nov	Khulna coast	Severe cyclone, surge 4.42m 160kph	5708 people, 15000 deer, 9 tigers, 65000 cattle, £170 million damage
1989	SWA	Drought	+
1991 Apr	Barisal	Severe Cyclone 120mph	150,000 people
1991 Jun	Barisal	Tidal bore	+

Source: Bangladesh Government Records and Refs 9 and 10

+ = No data

level rise. It would be a mammoth undertaking whose environmental impacts would have to be carefully assessed. It might be considered in the medium to long-term and its costs and benefits compared with the alternatives.

6   ACKNOWLEDGEMENTS

Sincere thanks are given to the Government of Bangladesh for their permission to publish the paper and the assistance of their Ministries and Local Bodies and to all those who have contributed to the FAP-4 study.

REFERENCES

1.   Curray J R and Moore D G, Sedimentary and tectonic processes in the Bengal Deep Sea Fan and geosyncline, The Geology of Continental Margins, 1974, New York, 617-627
2.   Evans P, The tectonic framework of Assam, J. Geol. Soc. Ind., 1964, Vol 5
3.   Paw J N and Thia-Eng C, Climatic changes and sea level rise, Ocean and Shoreline Management, 15, 1991, 205-232
4.   Morgan J P and Mc Intire W G, Quaternary geology of the Bengal Basin, Bull. Geol. Soc. Am, Vol 70, 1959, 319-341
5.   Umitsu M, Late Quaternary sedimentary environment and landform evolution in the Bengai Lowland, Geo. Rev. of Japan. Ser. B, Vol 60, No 2, 1991, 164-177
6.   Maddrell R J and Burren K, Predicted sea level changes and their impact on coastal works Worldwide, 3rd Australian Port and Harbour Eng Conf, 1990
7.   Khan F H, Geology of Bangladesh, 1990, The University Press Ltd
8.   Coleman J M, Brahmaputra river; channel processes and sedimentation, Sedimentary Geol. Vol 3, 1969, 129-239
9.   Fergusson J, Recent changes in the delta of the Ganges, QJGS, 1863, 321-354
10.   Addams Williams C, History of the rivers in the Gangetic Delta, 1750-1918, Bengal Secretariat Press, 1919, reprinted 1966
11.   Basu, Environment of the Ganges Delta, University Press Ltd, 1992
12.   Saenger P and Siddiqi N A, Land from the sea: The mangrove afforestation program of Bangladesh, Ocean & Coastal Man. 20, 1993, 23-39
13.   Seeber L and Ambruster J B, Great detachment earthquakes along the Himalayan Front and long-term forecasting, earthquake predictions, International Review, 1981, Maurice Ewing
14.   Bangladesh Tide Tables - 1992, Department of Hydrography

5. Combatting the vulnerability of communities

E. E. ALLEY, OBE, SBStJ, FRSA, FICD(Dip)GM, Consultant,
UN Department of Humanitarian Affairs, Geneva, and President,
Institute of Civil Defence and Disaster Studies

During the past thirty years the international community has become increasingly alarmed by disasters which have tended to be more destructive as they affect even larger concentrations of population. The Department of Humanitarian Affairs (DHA) Geneva have recently published statistics for 1992 which graphically illustrate this trend (Figure 1).

In addition, there has been some concern that too much response has been focussed primarily on relief actions, whereas the actual and potential consequences of disasters are becoming so severe that greater emphasis must be given to planning, prevention and management at local level, where the suffering and distress is the greatest.

The effects of disasters must be analysed not only in technical and scientific terms but also in humanitarian, social and economic terms. Particularly, natural disasters are a formidable obstacle to development. Thus there has been a growing awareness , on the part of governments, for the need to focus more attention on disaster preparedness and prevention and a recognition of the fact that pre-disaster planning and organisation must be focussed on the most vulnerable section of society - the community.

But, what is a community ? There have been many attempts to define it, but community is a complex term to define acceptably because it is used in so many different ways: for example, to describe an area where all the inhabitants have face to face contacts, or an area the size of a large town or city. The word has been used to describe groups of people, physicians, lawyers and others who are in similar occupations or professions. For some the boundaries of their area may reflect merely administrative convenience; for others they may represent feelings of common interest and attachment. Community tends to be a 'God' word. In the international field we talk of the 'international community' - 'the community of nations' - 'the European community' and so on. In many circumstances when it is mentioned we are expected to abase ourselves before it rather than attempting to determine what it is. Nevertheless, for the purposes of disaster preparedness it contains some or all of the following: a territorial area. a complex of organisations within an area, and above all, a sense of 'belonging'. However, without doubt, the most logical definition of a community has been produced by the World Health Organisation (WHO) in which a community has been defined as ' a group in face-to-face contact having a harmony of interest and aspirations, and bound by common values and objectives.'

In considering the vulnerability of communities, therefore, it is necessary to consider the general framework for analysis and evaluation of the social content of the disaster problem.

* How do communities at large react to the threat of disaster or to disasters themselves ?

* Is individual behaviour different to collective behaviour in times of emergency ?

* Can communities be educated and trained so as to respond predictably to disaster ?

* Is it always necessary to evacuate people after disaster ?

* Are disaster victims necessarily passive bystanders during emergencies, or indeed need they be ?

* How can reconstruction and rehabilitation be accelerated through social planning and programming ?

* What further research is necessary to strengthen social response to disaster

These and many other questions must be addressed at this seminar, which should be seen as an initiative to set out basic principles of social analysis and planning to combat the vulnerability of communities in disasters.

Whilst preparedness must be carried out at each administrative level, without doubt the most important is the household and community level. The success or failure of disaster preparedness is always measured at community level. National and regional levels are of little value if household and community measures at not implemented effectively.

Just as every individual, family, organization, business and public service within a community will be affected by a disaster, each has a role to play in preparedness. To be blunt, on a practical basis the multitude of actions that must be taken to implement an effective disaster preparedness programme requires the participation of the entire community. Such a programme must :

- be bi-participatory in design.

- be community-specific.

- be based on an assessment of the information required.

- be integrated with existing disaster warning and response systems.

Fig. 1. Natural disaster summary for 1992 (Department of Humanitarian Affairs, Geneva Office)

Date Started in 1992	Affected Country/Region	Disaster	Number of persons affected				Amount of damage as reported to DHA-GENEVA	Total** Contributions reported to DHA-GVA	Contributions through DHA-GVA***	DHA-GVA Emerg-Grant	No. of Sit/Inf Reps issued
			Dead	Injured	Missing	Homeless					
06JAN	Argentina	Floods	34	n/a*	11	2,000	250,000,000	59,868	0	N	Inf 2
07JAN	Yemen-Socotra Islands	Floods	0	0	0	30,000	n/a	0	0	N	Inf 1
09JAN	Vanuatu	Cyclone 'Betsy'	n/a	10	n/a	n/a	n/a	46,992	0	N	Inf 5
21JAN	Algeria	Heavy Rains/Earthquake	18	n/a	3	n/a	n/a	0	0	N	Inf 1
01FEB	Lebanon	Snowstorms	25	75	n/a	3,000	n/a	1,160,196	37,690	Y	Sit 4
01FEB	Turkey	Avalanches	261	69	n/a	n/a	n/a	0	0	N	Inf 2
06FEB	Cuba	Floods	n/a	n/a	n/a	9,127	n/a	2,589,900	241,000	Y	Sit 3
10FEB	Brazil	Floods	41	n/a	n/a	1,578	n/a	0	0	N	Inf 1
20FEB	Philippines	Volcano Alert 'Taal'	0	0	n/a	0	0	0	0	N	Inf 2
07MAR	Costa Rica	Earthquake	0	0	0	0	0	0	0	N	Inf 1
09MAR	Vanuatu	Cyclone 'Fran'	0	0	0	0	n/a	0	0	N	Inf 1
12MAR	Bolivia	Floods	n/a	50	n/a	5,125	n/a	609,815	0	Y	Sit 2
13MAR	Turkey	Earthquake-Erzincan	547	2,000	0	90,000	n/a	11,212,593	1,450,700	Y	Sit 9
24MAR	Ecuador	Floods 'El Nino'	22	n/a	4	10,000	n/a	2,108,783	119,463	Y	Sit 3
09APR	Nicaragua	Volcanic Eruption	2	75	0	10,000	n/a	1,397,678	40,147	Y	Sit 6
18APR	China	Hailstorms	109	n/a	n/a	n/a	96,000,000	0	0	N	Inf 1
06MAY	Papua New Guinea	Floods/Volcanic Activity	n/a	n/a	n/a	n/a	n/a	1,118,000	0	N	Inf 1
11MAY	Paraguay	Floods	n/a	n/a	n/a	75,000	n/a	2,162,290	0	Y	Sit 6
15MAY	Kyrgyzstan	Torrential Rain/E-quake	4	n/a	n/a	20,000	31,000,000	200,000	100,000	N	Sit 3

- continued

69

Fig. 1 - continued

Date Started in 1992	Affected Country/Region	Disaster	Number of persons affected				Amount of damage as reported to DHA-GENEVA	Total** Contributions reported to DHA-GVA	Contributions through DHA-GVA***	DHA-GVA Emerg. Grant	Inf/Sit Reps issued
			Dead	Injured	Missing	Homeless					
20MAY	Iran	Floods	n/a	n/a	n/a	n/a	59,121,622	0	0	N	Inf 2
20MAY	Pakistan	Earthquake	n/a	115	n/a	n/a	n/a	0	0	N	Inf 2
25MAY	Cuba	Earthquake	0	50	0	5,829	n/a	0	0	Y	Sit 1
09JUN	Brazil	Floods	29	270	0	125,223	n/a	12,346	0	N	Inf 1
09JUN	Argentina	Floods	n/a	n/a	n/a	110,000	260,000,000	2,018,903	0	Y	Sit 4
12JUN	Uruguay	Floods	n/a	n/a	n/a	4,700	n/a	365,897	0	N	Inf 3
02JUL	Vietnam	Typhoon 'Chuck'	4	4	10	0	n/a	0	0	N	Inf 1
06JUL	Panama	Tornado	12	50	0	0	n/a	0	0	N	Inf 1
09JUL	Iran	Torrential Rain	n/a	n/a	n/a	n/a	n/a	0	0	N	Inf 1
10AUG	Pakistan	Monsoon Rains	94	n/a	n/a	60,000	n/a	0	0	N	Inf 2
19AUG	Kyrgystan	Earhquake	50	100	50	n/a	130,000,000	720,811	376,067	Y	Sit 3
20AUG	Philippines	Volcano/Landslide/Floods	50	13	10	n/a	74,000,000	7,519,736	90,583	Y	Sit 8
23AUG	Bahamas, USA	Hurricane 'Andrew'	4	n/a	0	1,700	n/a	253,306	0	Y	Inf 3
28AUG	Pakistan	Earthquake	4	n/a	n/a	n/a	n/a	0	0	N	Inf 1
01SEP	Nicaragua	Earthquake/Tsunami	116	489	63	n/a	25,000,000	10,055,531	389,352	Y	Sit 7
03SEP	Afghanistan	Flash Floods	85	0	38	n/a	n/a	180,000	100,000	Y	Inf 3
07SEP	Pakistan	Floods in Azad Kashmir	1,334	n/a	n/a	875,000	1,000,000,000	11,161,893	139,605	Y	Sit 8
11SEP	Zaire	Earthquake	9	61	n/a	n/a	n/a	**	0	N	Inf 1
21SEP	India	Floods	500	n/a	n/a	n/a	n/a	0	0	N	Inf 1

- continued

Fig. 1 - continued

Date Started in 1992	Affected Country/ Region	Disaster	Number of persons affected				Amount of damage as reported to DHA-GENEVA	Total ** Contributions reported to DHA-GVA	Contributions through DHA-GVA***	DHA-GVA Emerg. Grant	Inf/ Sit Reps issued
			Dead	Injured	Missing	Homeless					
28SEP	El Salvador	Floods in South E.Reg.	2	n/a	n/a	n/a	n/a	0	0	N	Inf 1
05OCT	Viet Nam	Floods/Typhoon 'Angela'	93	0	0	n/a	18,000,000	688,203	115,556	Y	Sit 5
07OCT	Montenegro	Floods	1	0	0	6,000	n/a	377,231	201,206	Y	Sit 3
08OCT	Indonesia	Landslides	77	n/a	0	n/a	5,400,000	0	0	N	Inf 2
08OCT	India	Flash Floods	51	n/a	n/a	n/a	n/a	0	0	N	Inf 1
10OCT	Papua N. Guinea	Volcanic Activity Alert	0	0	0	0	0	0	0	N	Inf 1
12OCT	Egypt	Earthquake	561	9,929	0	n/a	n/a	193,703,931	12,000	Y	Sit 9
17OCT	Colombia	Earthquake	6	60	n/a	2,500	n/a	150,000	0	N	Inf 5
24OCT	Georgia	Earthquake	1	n/a	0	n/a	n/a	0	0	N	Inf 1
12NOV	Sri Lanka	Cyclone	3	n/a	n/a	n/a	n/a	0	0	N	Inf 2
16NOV	India	Flash Floods	263	0	0	0	n/a	0	0	N	Inf 2
20NOV	Albania	Floods	7	n/a	n/a	n/a	7,000,000	2,203,890	83,115	Y	Sit 4
29NOV	St. Vincent&Grenadines	Floods	3	n/a	n/a	n/a	n/a	0	0	N	Inf 1
08DEC	Armenia/Azerbaijan	Emergency Appeal	n/a	n/a	n/a	500,000	n/a	306,748	0	N	Inf 1
08DEC	Bolivia	Mudslides	49	n/a	n/a	850	n/a	158,440	0	Y	Inf 4
11DEC	Fiji	Cyclone	n/a	n/a	n/a	500	n/a	0	0	N	Inf 1
12DEC	Indonesia	Earthquake/Tsunami	2,500	2,103	69	90,000	100,000,000	5,208,628	229,683	Y	Sit 9

This table covers natural disasters occured in 1992. It has been compiled by the Relief Co-ordination Branch of DHA-GENEVA. Issued on 10 March 1993.

* n/a - data not available or not reported to DHA-GENEVA

** This does not include in-kind contributions not costed.

*** Several contributions pledged for 1992 disasters, have not, so far, been received at DHA-GENEVA. The total amounts can therefore be expected to change slightly, depending on the rates of exchange prevailing at the time of receipt of contribution.

The figures reflecting the populations affected and damages may also be revised in the future, based on additional available information.

- be established as an ongoing process.

- include as a priority the most vulnerable people,

- include information on prevention, mitigation and long term recovery.

There are several common problems to be faced in developing this programme, not least of which is that of an administration writing and preparing plans as though it is the only organisation likely to, or capable of, responding. Whereas the disaster plans will be most effective if they have a major contribution from those involved - namely the communities.

Another problem is encountered in public education which is often limited to immediate emergency assistance, first aid and relief measures. Whilst these concerns are critically important the lack of attention to preparedness and prevention issues continues to be a major shortcoming. The implementation of more effective ways to protect people and property would eliminate, or at least reduce,the need for some relief, and would certainly substantially reduce losses and suffering.

Currently, the weakness arises from the fact that public information campaigns are carried out on a regional or national, rather than a community, basis. This results in disaster information that is very general and of little practical value in assisting people to know what specific actions must be carried out.

The need for disaster preparedness is assessed by the determination of three basic questions:

(i)   Do people know they live in a potential disaster area ?

(ii)   Do people know the risks ?

(iii) Do people know effective ways to reduce such risks ?

It follows therefore that training, awareness and education programmes are essential if communities are to have a more realistic understanding of the disaster risks, and to take more practical measures to protect life and property, and thus reduce their vulnerability.

Nevertheless, public information campaigns can be negated in those countries which are afflicted by a sense of fatalism about natural disasters, and therefore acts as a brake to the development of effective disaster preparedness as a whole, particularly at community level. We know that in the past many people believed that natural disasters were sent by the Gods to punish them for their sins and consequently they believed that there was little they could do. Although those beliefs have, by and large, been overcome, the psychological problem remains deep down in the human psyche.

Very often the population which sees floods and droughts, earthquakes and storms, periodically spreading death and destruction of property, draws no conclusion from them. They remain ill-informed , do not know what initiatives to undertake in order to arm themselves against disaster, and often have no idea of the most elementary preventive measures. This state of mind reinforces that state of fatalistic resignation.

It can be appreciated that this sense of fatalism arises because of the enormity of the problem and the accumulated burden of successive disasters, probably compounded by the lack of resources to plan for timely assistance in emergency situations. Nevertheless to counteract this mentality. it is governments which bear the basic responsibility for action with respect to disasters. They should initiate appropriate measures and promote a national consciousness of, and active interest in, disaster preparedness. These measures should be based on educational programmes and introduced with priority in zones where disasters are frequent, or those areas subject to frequent risks, and where human, material and financial resources allow for a steady follow-up of programme conceptions.

The bases of such programmes can be outlined by emphasising the long-term rather than the short term education, and by incorporating the programmes into the pedological infrastructure from elementary school to university. The media, press, radio and television, which have an important function to fulfil regarding information and education concerning disaster preparedness can also be profitably utilized to sensitize the adult population. It should be noted that they have played a not unimportant role in social and economic development, especially in developing countries. One of the new ideas introduced in the early seventies was the utilization of radio, followed by television, for teaching and development instead of concentrating on leisure and culture. The necessity for people's participation in development programmes on the subjects of family planning, nutrition, agricultural information and land reform opened a new path for the media. These results can be use to answer the needs of public education oriented to fight against disasters.

The task is not easy. Research on reactions unleashed by disaster , shows that short term efforts in public education, though intensive and treating of urgent matters, have no lasting effect, mainly because in many areas, disasters do not fortunately re-occur, or at least recur at infrequent intervals.

Public education measures must be considerably improved in order that its reactions to events, to warning signals be changed - reactions which generally tend to remain passive. Such improvement must start with Governments, both host governments and donor governments.

Governments must give priority to public education by information and training in the field of disaster preparedness and in order to better educate the public the collaboration of people in responsible positions, professionals in housing, industry, in construction, public health, medical services, scientists and engineers in the fields of vulcanology, and chemical hazards, should be sought and used to establish links with the inhabitants of the areas concerned, not only the

73

community leaders but also the population as a whole. They must understand the feelings and reactions of the public, its behaviour in its trials, and they must try to lessen the emotion while encouraging confidence. It is the unknown and misunderstood dangers that terrify. As T.S.Eliot says in 'The Wastelands' "I will show you fear in a handful of dust".The explanations of experts and specialists can combat that fear, rekindle confidence and encourage faith in the future.

Much effort and money has been spent in the past by donor countries in some pro-active elements of disaster mitigation and prevention, such as building research, planning and engineering, however the most basic problems in the field of disaster prevention are those related to education, training and information. Little thought has been given to the subject of disaster education, to transferring knowledge, skills and expertise to the disaster prone countries. Knowledge that could be passed on to the populations who are particularly vulnerable. Education is one of the most cost effective forms of disaster relief available, and yet it is the most neglected.

There is a need for teams of expert trainers from the donor states to establish courses of public education for civil protection officials and technicians in disaster prone regions, to enable them to organize programmes of self-sufficiency and self- protection extended to the entire population of the countries concerned. It is essential that such courses should be undertaken either in-country or at least to an entire group of countries in the same geographical region.

Concurrently use should be made of modern techniques of mass education through the preparation and publication of suitable video films, audio tapes and publications aimed at the mass audience. These can be undertaken by the various departments of the United Nations concerned. WHO has already made a start in this direction by preparing a manual of community guidance in case of disaster. There are too few publications at present available which are understandable by, or useful, to the communities and this needs rectifying. The overall task could be very effectively coordinated by DHA Geneva as they have already demonstrated their ability to undertake such work in the extremely efficient and highly successful DMTP programme, .

Up to now no one has really thought about public education in more than abstract terms. Much lip service has been paid to the concept, but little has been done. Disaster education is an abstract term that means different things to different people. To some it is a matter of public relations aimed at publicizing the activities of Civil Protection departments and winning public good will. Some consider it synonymous with propaganda, i.e. spreading particular synthesized doctrines about disaster effects. Many equate it with the transmission of information about disasters and their effects from the expert professional to the lay client. For others there is no difference between disaster education and mass campaigns. These differing perceptions are attributable to the historical development of disaster management education and the learning process. Whatever these perceptions maybe it is necessary to produce a definite attitude and develop understandings of the meaning of the term 'disaster education'.

It has knowledge, attitude and behaviour components, it must aim at the individual, family and the community behaviour and their interaction patterns. Disaster education must be a process involving a series of steps and efforts by people and not a single procedure, and it must provide situations in which people educate themselves. By this I mean that learning takes place through the efforts of learners and that the disaster educator provides the circumstances in which the learning takes place.

The success of disaster preparedness training programmes, whether for the provision of basic lifeline services, or for the development of life saving services depends on the active and voluntary cooperation of people to bring about desired changes in their existing attitudes. Many existing attitudes are the result of contacts and socialization within the family or community environment during the lifetime of the individual. Experience shows how hard to is to induce people to accept new practices. It requires systematic efforts and simultaneous attention to a number of variables - social, psychological, economic, technological, administrative and political.

In their day to day work emergency planning professionals come across many individuals, families, groups and communities and some educational work is done during these contacts, deliberately or otherwise. These educational contacts have to be spread over a much wider section of the community to make maximum impact. How can we then strengthen and systematize educational activities so that greater self generating results can reduce the vulnerability of communities?

Much experience has accumulated from programmes aimed at inducing people to accept new practices in the fields of health, agriculture, and home economics etc. While the purpose here is not to catalogue the lessons learned, the following are a few of the most important principles which could be considered for use in disaster preparedness programmes:

* Perceptions should be studied and opportunities created for people to modify their perceptions where necessary.

* Create opportunities through which the curiosity of the individual is aroused, and create a desire for change.

* Individuals and communities should be helped to compare existing ways with proposed innovations, to relate innovations to the basic needs and overcome barriers to acceptance.

* Adopt educational methods that have a heavy emphasis on community involvement and participation.

* Learning by doing. and develop participation in various activities connected with the identification of disaster preparedness needs.

NATURAL DISASTERS

* Group approval influences the adoption of new behaviour
  patterns. In traditional societies most of the decisions
  regarding new practices are multipersonal decisions, and the
  role of the family and other social groups are the
  determining factor.

* Behaviour is motivated. Motivation is the inner drive with
  human beings that helps them move forward to attain a
  desired goal.

* Disaster preparedness behaviour is concerned with changes
  in knowledge, attitude and behaviour, and the ultimate goal
  is sustained disaster preparedness behaviour.

* Since different agencies work simultaneously at community
  level, it is necessary for them to come to an understanding
  in order to avoid the dissemination of conflicting advice.

* Pyschological factors are not the only determinants in
  behaviour. They combine and interact with physical, social
  and other factors.

The most effective programmes are likely to be those carried
out "with" people rather than "for" people. Working "with"
people requires two way communication which is essential in
preparedness, warning and assessment, and the establishment of
assistance programmes. An ill-informed public will hinder any
effective relief operations. We have a recent example in one
developing country, after a cyclone, calls of requests for
information blocked the telephone lines and seriously hampered
the information dissemination process. After disaster local
officials are frequently besieged with information requests
from the public.

In spite of the significant resources available from the
international community, we have seldom quantitatively or
qualitatively assessed the resources made available by the
clan, tribe, kin and community which represents the initial
response or first aid administered well before external
assistance ever arrives. In other words, with few exceptions,
our first order of business in mitigation and reducing
vulnerability is to learn from traditional practice and
response, and to strengthen local capacity.

Like any other policy for civil protection or emergency
planning, disaster preparedness and mitigation requires
research to support it. Yet the information which is available
in the public education field is scarce, especially when
referring to developing countries. If education is to yield
predictable results this acute lack of basic information must
be addressed.

The conclusion is clear. Vulnerability to disaster is the
product of interaction between the eco-system, of which people
are part, and the socio-economic arrangements which they use to
flourish and even win prosperity, from that environment
therefore:

- it is necessary to redress the imbalance between the
overwhelming amount of input into disaster relief and that of

disaster preparedness. Indeed, of the funds which are currently devoted to disaster mitigation on a world-wide basis, by far the largest portion goes on disaster relief in the understandable search for life saving and first aid. The pro-active disaster preparedness factors such as education and training have been largely ignored. For developing countries, with sizable human resources and relatively restricted capital, this imbalance is a particular handicap.

- it is important how people make their choices in the face of the uncertainty of nature, and also how they respond when steps are taken to reduce that uncertainty. There is currently a serious lack of usable knowledge in this key area. Without this kind of knowledge it is impossible to be sure that national policies intended to reduce vulnerability do indeed have that effect, and do not in fact make matters worse by inducing people to lower their own defences.

- we need a better understanding, not only of the way in which people perceive their environment and the risk in it, but of the way different influences affect their actions.

- in parallel to the need for greater understanding of why people do or do not take action to protect themselves from disaster on a long term basis, there is a need for more information on the factors which influence the effectiveness of emergency warnings, especially in developing countries. In particular, systematic investigation is needed of the variables which influence public response when warning is given.

- it is not readily apparent that many of the techniques which could be employed in an attempt to reduce vulnerability and improve preparedness are very similar to those employed to promote community development. Nevertheless, given a very new orientation in disaster preparedness this type of community level work requires both capable promoters and sensitive rapporteurs, It should, indeed it must, be given priority in future programmes of community preparedness.

"The community is like a ship - everybody should be prepared to take the helm".

Henrik Ibsen.

6. Designing for failure

C. H. GREEN, D. J. PARKER and
E. C. PENNING-ROWSELL, Flood Hazard Research Centre,
Middlesex University

Introduction

The objective of intervention in the use of hazard prone land is
not to minimise losses, but to maximise the economic efficiency
of use of that land within the constraints of sustainable
development. A rise in the annual losses from a hazard is not
then necessarily a sign of economic inefficiency. Formally, an
economic efficiency improvement has occurred as a result of an
intervention if:

$$O_a - I_a > O_b - I_b$$

where:

  O_a is the output from the land after the intervention
  I_a is the inputs required after the intervention to achieve
  that output
  O_b is the output from the land before the intervention

  I_b is the inputs required before the intervention to achieve
  that output

For example, Figure 1 illustrates an intervention in a flood
prone area is economically efficient even though annual flood
losses are greater after the intervention than they were before.
Whilst annual flood losses increase from 4 units to 6 units after
the intervention, the ratio of outputs to inputs increases from
1.54 to 1.86 (Green 1992). The kind of shift illustrated might
result from flood protection enabling more intensive use of the
land. Equally, technological innovation and increases in real
income are themselves likely to increase flood, and other, losses
in areas both where interventions have been undertaken and also
in other areas.

Maximising the economic efficiency of the use of hazard prone
land is not a sufficient objective. Most countries have now
formally ascribed to the principles of sustainable development
as these were set out by the Brundtland Commission (World
Commission on Environment and Development 1987). These
principles set constraints on the options that may be considered
in managing hazard prone land. Similarly, neo-classical economic
analysis is simply one of a multiplicity of possible 'ethical

Natural disasters. Thomas Telford, London, 1993

calculi of choice' (Newsome and Green 1992) which might be adopted as aids to decision making. As such it embodies ethical and moral assumptions both as to the appropriate objectives to be maximised in choices and as to the distribution of resources and consumption over individuals and time. Consequently, these ethical assumptions need not be considered to be either appropriate or sufficient to guide some particular decision.

Thus, it may be judged necessary to consider some other objectives, such as the distribution of resources across the population, as well as the total availability of resources.

Intervention strategies

It is usual to make a distinction between 'structural' and 'non-structural' interventions. In the case of flooding, structural measures are usually defined as such engineering works as channel improvements, embankments or levees, or retention reservoirs. Nonstructural measures are then taken to include hazard zone mapping, flood warning systems, flood insurance and the flood proofing of individual properties.

We argue that this distinction is superficial because almost all adjustments involve some physical change or action; the primary difference is who takes that action. Thus, for example, flood warnings may lead to individuals undertaking flood proofing of their property. More importantly, there has come to be a view that non-structural interventions are good and structural interventions are bad. Such an assumption is as potentially damaging to effective hazard management as a sole reliance on structural measures.

However, the distinction between structural and non-structural does contain an implicit and valuable recognition that the issue is one of enabling effective hazard management by the public rather than hazard management by and through government. Thus, nonstructural measures are those which recognise that governments cannot successfully treat hazard management as an activity which can be reserved to government. The success of nonstructural methods, on the other hand, rests on the capacity of the public to adapt to the threat which adaptation such methods aim to enhance.

The real distinction between structural and nonstructural approaches in then as to whom is assumed to have chief responsibility for hazard management. 'Structural' measures have traditionally been associated with an implicit belief that governments should manage hazards in the broader public interest. This assumption has often been associated with a rather paternalistic belief that the public would not be able to cope with the recognition of the existence of hazards. Indeed, an associated belief is often that the public should not be informed as to the existence of a potential hazard. Were they aware of the existence of the hazard, then it is assumed that they would panic, or be very alarmed about the affects of the public availability of that information on the value of their land.

Conversely, 'nonstructural' approaches have tended to be associated with a belief that government management will be

```
Figure 1: Economic efficiency of intervention strategies

original situation
                                                            units

        Gross annual output                                   22
        Annual loss of output from flooding                    2
                                net output                     20

        Gross annual inputs                                   10
        Annual loss of inputs through flood damage             2
        Annual costs of adaptations to reduce flood
        losses                                                 1

                                total inputs                  13

            ratio of outputs to inputs                       1.54
            net output                                          7

after intervention

        Gross annual output                                   34
        Annual loss of output from flooding                    4
                                net output                     30

        Gross annual inputs                                   12
        Annual loss of inputs through flood damage             2
        Annual costs of adaptations to reduce
            flood losses                                       3

                                total inputs                  17

            ratio of outputs to inputs                       1.86
            net output                                         13
```

ineffective and/or inefficient, and that the locus of management must lie with those at risk. The role of government in this model is an enabling role to empower the public to manage more effectively the hazards to which they are exposed. However, an enabling role for governments does not mean that only nonstructural approaches should be adopted.

At each level of decision making, from central government down to the individual, there are three generic decision options which can be adopted:

- encourage or enable others to do something,
- do something,
- do nothing

At government level, the three strategies available to encourage others to act:

- economic instruments (subsidies, charges);
- legal instruments (prohibitions or requirements);

- provision of information.

In turn, governments may intervene in the process of hazard management by the public at various points (Green 1990). The public may currently be unable to manage the hazard in the most effective manner because they either:

- lack the resources; and/or
- lack sufficient information or knowledge to identify the most effective strategy to adopt.

Thus, land which is highly exposed to hazards may be developed because those so developing it may lack resources to develop any other land. Or, because they are unaware of the magnitude of the risk. A government may, therefore, intervene by banning or controlling the development of the land if an effective land use zoning system is in operation. This is often not the case. Conversely, the government might seek to develop attractors in other areas so that development is pulled to these other areas away from the zones of high hazard. This might, for instance, involve the selective provision of infrastructure. Equally, the government may provide the resources to mitigate the challenge posed by the hazard by, for instance, stabilising slopes. Again, the government may provide hazard maps or advice on disaster mitigation to those at risk.

These measures vary in effectiveness from country to country; in many countries hazard mapping and zoning controls are irrelevancies either because of the pressure of development or because of absence of any effective planning control mechanism.

Overall, the weakness of the nonstructural approach has been the overestimation of the effectiveness of such methods. For example, early estimates of the potential benefits of flood warning systems in reducing the losses from flooding (Bussell, Cole and Collier 1978; Day 1978; Penning-Rowsell, Chatterton and Parker 1978; Working Group 1983) now appear to have overestimated the benefits of flood warnings to a significant degree (Herschy, Newsome and Green 1991; Parker 1991). This overestimation has occurred both because the reliability of warning systems has been overestimated and because assumptions were made as the response the public would adopt if they received a warning. The provision of flood warnings has been treated as largely as problem of flood forecasting, a technical question, whereas in practice it is usually a social science problem of dissemination. Resources have consequently often been invested in technical improvements in forecasting whilst the reliability of dissemination methods has largely been neglected.

Figure 2 is a simple reliability model of some of the main components in a flood warning system where a forecast of an event must be turned into a warning to those at risk. Once realistic allowance is made for the proportion of the population who will not be home to receive a warning, or who are asleep; those who are physically unable to respond through infirmity or disability; and for failures in the dissemination system, then it has been estimated (Herschy, Newsome and Green 1991) that a flood warning

Figure 2   The reliability of flood warnings: turning flood forecasts into flood warnings

$$reliability = P_f * P_d * P_i * P_a * P_e$$

where:

P_f	probability that an accurate forecast is made
P_d	probability that the forecasts are disseminated
P_i	probability that the individual household will be available to be warned
P_a	probability that the individual household is physically able to respond to the warning
P_e	probability that the individual knows how to respond effectively

will, at best, result in a saving of 61% of the theoretically possible savings in flood losses. Performance levels in practice are typically much lower; in Britain and France, a flood warning system may be considered to have performed better than average if warnings are disseminated to 50-60% of the population before the onset of flooding (Parker 1991; Torterotot, Kauark-Leite and Roche 1992).

Parker (1991) provided some estimates of the probabilities respectively that a household will be available to respond (0.55); that the household will be capable of responding (0.75) and will respond effectively (0.70). Taken together these limit the upper bound of actual to potential savings to 29%, assuming absolute reliability for the remainder of the system. However, these probabilities depend upon response projected and are likely to be specific to raising and moving the contents of the home.

In addition, the effectiveness of flood warnings has often been overestimated because of assumptions as to what the recipient would then do once the warning was received. It is usually assumed that the householder will move property to a safe place. In practice, their first action is often to try to keep water out of the property but to fail in this objective; only when this action has failed do people often seek to move goods (Green, Parker and Penning-Rowsell 1990; Torterotot, Kauark-Leite and Roche 1992). To improve the effectiveness of flood warnings it is then necessary to understand the public's expectations of the appropriate response and then either to enable them to carry out that response more effectively or to seek to change their expectations.

Although the 'nonstructural' paradigm does locate the locus of hazard management with the public, it is too often assumed that the public will behave in those ways which the 'expert' deems most appropriate, or will only act when told what to do. Any realistic emergency planning must then start with an understanding of the public's beliefs and expectations about hazards and, consequently, how they would intend to act in specific circumstances (Green 1990). For example, studies in the

United States and the United Kingdom have found that a significant proportion of the population would self-evacuate if warned of a radioactive release (Johnson 1984; Lindell and Barnes 1986; Pheby and Robinson 1990). Other studies (Stern 1989) have found, not surprisingly, that parents would seek to collect their children from school before evacuating in the face of a threat.

A final distinction between the 'structural' and 'nonstructural' paradigms is that structural measures typically result in reductions in the risks of a hazardous event occurring. Conversely, nonstructural approaches typically target the vulnerability of those at risk.

Vulnerability

Vulnerability is necessarily a relative concept and expresses the relationship between the challenge to be confronted and the resources available to meet that challenge. For instance, a knight in armour is invulnerable to someone armed with a club but highly vulnerable to someone armed with a heavy calibre machine gun. Conceptually, therefore, vulnerability is equivalent to Lazarus's (1966) concept of stress.

We, therefore, will distinguish vulnerability from risk, where the latter is defined as the probability of experiencing a challenge of a given magnitude. In practice, a hazard presents a range of possible events and associated outcomes: earthquakes of different severities and associated probabilities; floods of different heights and predicted return periods. Since vulnerability is a relative concept, then it follows that whereas a community may be invulnerable to some relative minor event it may, nevertheless, be highly vulnerable to more extreme events. Vulnerability can then be defined at the level of the individual or household, company, community or country. An event to which a household is highly vulnerable may leave the country untouched.

In turn, action may be taken by government or by the individual which reduces the vulnerability of the individual, community, organisation or country. These actions may either seek to reduce the challenge or demand which must be confronted from a given event, or to increase the degree or effectiveness of the resources which can be mobilised to meet that challenge. Alternatively, the effect of the intervention may simply be to reduce the risk that such a challenge will occur. These reduce the frequency with which the vulnerability of the individual or community will be exposed.

We argue that it is important to distinguish between interventions which reduce vulnerability and those which reduce risk. Further, that interventions which reduce the risk of an event can have the effect of increasing an individual or community's vulnerability to that event.

Elsewhere (Penning-Rowsell et al 1993), the vulnerability of households to flooding has been defined in functional form. In slightly modified form this equation is shown in Figure 3. In this equation, the characteristics of the household and community support specify the coping resources available to the individual household which can be mobilised to cope with the specific event.

The availability and features of any flood warning affect the time available to mobilise resources before the flood occurs and to take action to reduce the effects of the flood. The flood characteristics define the challenge to be confronted, which is mediated by the characteristics of the property.

Whilst the characteristics of the household and of the property are unlikely to be affected by any actions previously taken to reduce the risk of flooding, all of the other components may be so affected. 'Floodplain' incursion, any tendency for additional development on the floodplain by forms of development which had previously not taken place, is arguably an exception to this generalisation. But, at the individual level, it is an exception only in so far as the form of development differs in type after the intervention has been undertaken and not just simply in the extent of that development. A change in type would occur if, for instance, prior to the intervention zoning laws required properties to be built with a floor level above the height of the highest known flood and this zoning control was abandoned after the intervention. However, at the community level, flood plain incursion may increase vulnerability by reducing the resources unaffected by flooding which can then be mobilised to support those affected by flooding.

On the other hand, the evidence is, for example, that the reliability of flood warning systems is highest when the frequency of flooding is greatest (Smith 1986). When flooding is frequent, both the disseminators and recipients of the warnings have the greatest experience. Reducing the risk of flooding, and hence the experience of flooding, will, all other things being equal, reduce the reliability of any flood warning system.

Experience of flooding also can affect expectations about flooding in the future as well as providing knowledge about what are the most effective adaptations to adopt (Green, Parker and Penning-Rowsell 1990). Where people have been flooded, adaptations to reduce the consequences of any future flooding and to identify times of high risk are almost invariably adopted (Correia, Saraiva and Soczka 1992; Green, Tunstall and Fordham 1990; Halcrow Fox 1988; Ives and Furuseth 1983; Paul 1984). Indeed, it may argued that the purpose of hazard information campaigns is provide the lessons of experience without the pain of the experience itself.

Organisations as well as individuals have expectations; in the case of organisations, these reflect beliefs about their role as well as the challenges which they can expect to confront. Organisations, not surprisingly, tend to do best what is routine. Reducing the experience an organisation has with a particular hazard then tends to reduce its capacity to respond effectively to a challenge if and when it does occur. When the challenge is seen as unlikely, then neither the public nor the organisations responsible for providing warnings and responding in other ways is likely to respond in the most effective way.

Intervention strategies may, and often do, change the characteristics of the flood as well as well as the risk of flooding. This is, after all, the intent of the intervention.

But taken across the spectrum of possible events, the challenge-probability distribution function, the intervention may only affect vulnerability to the events in one part of that distribution function. Or, it may decrease vulnerability in one sector of the function whilst increasing it over another sector.

However, the effects of the intervention are normally considered only up until the point on the challenge-probability curve where the intervention fails, and all interventions are designed to fail at some level of risk. The discussion then usually focuses upon what is the 'acceptable' or 'tolerable' level of risk and how it should be set. The discussion then focuses upon the change that the proposed intervention will cause in the event characteristics up to the design risk of failure. In analyses of flood alleviation, the challenge-probability curve is termed the 'stage-probability' curve. The event up to which the intervention is designed to eliminate flooding is then termed the 'design standard of protection'. Such a concern is to arbitrarily truncate the examination of these effects, since most interventions will also have effects on the characteristics of flood events occurring beyond the design standard of protection.

In particular, the intervention may result in a discontinuity in the challenge presented as the risk decreases: the characteristics of low probability floods may be markedly different to those from high frequency floods. This 'change in state' may mean that an adaptation which is effective for high frequency floods is not only inefficient but positively dangerous for the low frequency floods. For high frequency flood events, sheltering and raising the contents of the property may be the most effective coping response; for more extreme events, the only safe response may instead be precautionary evacuation.

For example, the construction of a dam may essentially eliminate the possibility of flooding from frequent floods. However, if the dam fails then the resulting flooding will be much more extreme than if the dam did not exist. Of course, such marked shifts in the challenge presented at points in the challenge-probability curve may occur naturally without any intervention having taken place.

Shifts in event characteristics as the extremity of the event increases, particularly when minor events are frequent, so as to change the nature of the most appropriate response, are always likely to cause problems. In South Africa, for example, in at least one flood, residents took shelter from the flood in their own homes. However, the flood continued to rise so that the depth and velocity of the floodwater then trapped residents in their homes and they were unable to escape. Eventually the force of the flood waters became such that the houses were destroyed and many of the residents drowned as a result. Both individuals and organisations are liable to be trapped in their responses by their expectations which are derived from the frequent events. It might be suggested that the distinguishing feature of 'extreme' events is not that they are unlikely but that they are different: they present an entirely different challenge.

NATURAL DISASTERS

The effectiveness of intervention strategies

Intervention strategies can be broadly split into those which reduce the challenge and those which improve the effectiveness with which resources can be mobilised to cope with the challenge. Those intervention strategies which reduce the challenge take place before the event which causes the challenge; those which enhance the response may be taken before the event, like flood warning, or after the event such as disaster relief.

The ideal intervention strategy, we have argued, is one which decreases the vulnerability of the at risk community across the entire spectrum of possible events from that hazard.

For example, in flood alleviation benefit-cost analyses, the economic benefits of the alleviation strategy are calculated as the reduction in the average annual reduction in flood losses compared to the present situation (Penning-Rowsell and Chatterton 1977). Although conventionally these benefits are calculated only over that range of events up until the point where the project fails (for example, embankment walls are overtopped), the changes in the expected value of flood losses should be calculated over the entire range of floods, across all return period events. The change in the expected value of losses from events greater than the design standard of protection has been termed 'over-design standard' benefits (Penning-Rowsell et al 1992). In broad terms, flood alleviation schemes which increase channel capacity will reduce the extent of flooding for flood events of all magnitudes. Even though in an extreme event flood flow exceeds the enlarged channel capacity, less water will come out of bank than would have been the case before the improvement was undertaken. In this case, the project will decrease the vulnerability of the community across the entire spectrum of possible events. These 'over design standard' benefits should be added to those conventionally included in the benefit-cost analysis.

Conversely, with an embankment scheme, an extreme event will result in the embankment being overtopped or a breach occurring. In this case, the flood that occurs is likely to be worse than if there was no embankment. The speed of onset is likely to be greater and the duration of flooding may well longer than would be the case without the scheme. Thus, over design standard benefits are likely to be zero to negative, although they should again be included in the benefit-cost analysis.

More generally, this illustrates the difference between an intervention option which degrades gracefully on failure and one where failure is potentially catastrophic. In principle, options which fail gracefully are to be preferred to those whose failure mode is of rapid and which involves a catastrophic change of state. For example, the recent emphasis in nuclear reactor design has been on 'intrinsically' safe reactor designs as opposed to the risk reduction strategies, using redundancy of systems, which previously predominated. The use of crumple zones in cars is another example of a system designed to fail gracefully.

Usually graceful failures involve both a slow mode of failure and ample precursor signs: mobilising any response typically takes a considerable amount of time. In particular, issuing warnings and undertaking evacuations are both slow processes (Sorensen 1988; Sorensen and Rogers 1989).

After a disaster has occurred, both spontaneous and planned social support is often given to the disaster victims. Remarkably little research has been undertaken on the effectiveness of social support in mediating the impacts of disasters. The evidence is that victims find it important (Green and Herring 1993) but there is little evidence as to how effective it is, and which forms of social support are most effective.

Moreover, the tendency in the developed world has been to professionalise this support: instead of enabling neighbours, voluntary groups and extended kinship groups to provide more effective support, increasing reliance is placed upon the use, for example, of trained counsellors (National Institute of Mental Health 1979). This is likely to be a negative development in that it will not be possible to mobilise a sufficient number of counsellors in large scale disasters even in the United Kingdom. Moreover, it is a strategy that the countries of the South could never emulate. Of necessity, those countries can only look to means of improving the effectiveness of community self-help. Equally, there may well be lessons for the countries of the north from existing community self-help strategies in the disaster areas of the South.

Conclusions

Reducing the risk of hazardous events occurring is not the same as reducing the community's vulnerability to those events. Indeed, reducing the risk of some event occurring can increase the community's vulnerability should that event occur by decreasing the community's preparedness and coping capacity. In some cases, the effect of reducing the risk of some events is to increase the challenge which will be presented by more extreme events. The emphasis in developing hazard management strategies should, therefore, be upon reducing vulnerability rather than upon risk reduction. Indeed, the weakness of assessing interventions in terms of reducing risks is that a risk only matters if the community is highly vulnerable to the consequences. The risk of some event can be very high but this does not matter provide that the community can cope with the consequences. The vulnerability of a household, community or country can be reduced either by reducing the challenge posed by an event or by enhancing the effectiveness of the response which can be mounted to cope with that challenge.

In assessing the relative effectiveness of different intervention strategies, it is necessary to compare these across the whole spectrum of possible events. The danger of the concept of 'acceptable' or 'tolerable' risk is that it will induce myopia: a concern only for events whose probabilities of occurrence are estimated to be greater than what is assessed to be the acceptable level of risk. This may mean that events beyond the design standard of failure would pose more severe challenges than

Figure 3 The vulnerability of a household to flooding

$$vulnerability = f([\frac{A}{H,S,I,C,E,I_n}], [\frac{S_c,S_b,I_t}{S_t,R_o}], [T_f,D_e,D_t,S_d,S_t,W,V,P_l,R], [\frac{1}{W_o,W_t,W_a}], [T_r,R_a,R_q])$$

where:

Socio-economic characteristics of the household

A   Age profile of the household
H   Health status of the household
S   Household savings
I   Household income
C   Cohesiveness of the local community
E   Expectations about flooding
I_n Prior information

Property and infrastructure characteristics

S_t Number of storeys
R_o Robustness of building fabric
S_c Susceptibility of building contents to damage
I_t Time taken to restore infrastructure (especially sewerage, electricity and telecommunications)

Flood characteristics

T_f Timing of flood
D_e Depth of flooding
D_t Duration of flooding
S_d Sediment concentration

S_t Sediment size
W   Wave/wind action
V   Velocity of flood water
R   Rate of water rise during flooding onset
P_l Pollution load of flood waters

Warning characteristics

W_o Whether or not a warning is received
W_t Warning time provided
W_a Advice content of the warning

Community support

T   Time taken for assistance to arrive during or after the event
R_a Extent of the assistance offered
R_q Quality of the assistance offered

they would in the absence of the intervention. Engineering should thus be more interested in the consequences of failure than of success, and a goal of design is therefore to ensure that the consequences of failure are manageable. Engineering and other interventions should, consequently, be designed for failure.

Although a strong emphasis has been given to enabling more effective hazard management by the public, effective hazard management is likely to involve a range of measures executed by a variety of different decision makers. A mixture of 'structural' and 'nonstructural' approaches is often likely to be appropriate. The distinction between 'structural' and 'nonstructural' works has been argued to be rather unhelpful, the key distinction being between direct action by government and the government taking an enabling role, using a range of legal, economic and informational strategies to enhance hazard management by the public. Structural measures can often reduce the challenge to be confronted and public works will often also be more efficient than private works. Equally it has been noted that the effectiveness of 'nonstructural' methods has often been overestimated.

References

Bussell R B, Cole J A and Collier C G 1978 The Potential Benefit from a National Network of Precipitation Radars and Short Period Forecasting, Reading: Central Water Planning Unit

Correia F N, Saraiva M de G and Soczka L 1992 "Coping with floods in Setubal: a few steps towards an integrated approach", paper given at the NATO ASI Coping with Floods, Erice, Italy

Day H J 1978 Benefit and Cost Analysis of Hydrological Forecasts: A state-of-the-art report, Operational Hydrology Report No. 3, Geneva: World Meteorological Organisation

Green C H 1990 "Perceived Risk: Past, Present and Future Conditional" in Handmer J W and Penning-Rowsell E C (eds) Risk Communication and Response, Aldershot: Gower

Green C H 1991 "Enabling effective hazard management by the public" in Parker D J and Handmer J W (eds) Hazard Management and Emergency Planning: Perspectives on Britain, London: James and James

Green C H 1992 "The Human Aspects of Flooding", paper given at the Natural Hazards Forum, Institution of Civil Engineers, London

Green C H and Herring A 1993 "Flood Impacts" in EUROFLOOD: First Annual Report, report to the European Commission, Enfield: Flood Hazard Research Centre

Green C H and Newsome D W 1992 "Ethics and the Calculi of Choice", paper given at the Stockholm Water Symposium

Green C H, Parker D J and Penning-Rowsell E C 1990 "Lessons for hazard management for United Kingdom floods", Disaster Management 3(2), 63-73

Green C H, Tunstall S M and Fordham M 1991 "The risks from flooding: which risk and whose perception?", Disasters 15(3), 227-236

Halcrow Fox 1988 Taiz Upgrading Project: Conceptual Design and Planning Report, London: Halcrow Fox

Herschy R, Newsome D W and Green C H 1991 The Benefit-Cost of Hydrometric Data - River Flow Gauging, Marlow: Foundation for Water Research

Ives S M and Furuseth O J 1983 "Immediate response to headwater flooding in Charlotte, North Carolina", Environment and Behaviour 15(4), 512-525

Johnson H J 1984 "Planning for Spontaneous Evacuation During a Radiological Emergency", Nuclear Safety 25, 186-195

Lazarus R S 1966 Psychological Stress and the Coping Process, New York: Academic Press

Lindell M K and Barnes V E 1986 "Protective Response to Technological Emergency: Risk Perception and Behavioral Intention", Nuclear Safety 27(4), 457-467

National Institute of Mental Health 1979 Crisis Intervention Programs for Disaster Victims in Smaller Communities, Washington DC: US Department of Health and Human Services

Parker D J 1991 The damage-reducing effects of flood warnings, Enfield: Flood Hazard Research Centre

Paul B M 1984 "Perception of and agricultural adjustment to floods in Jamuna Floodplain, Bangladesh", Human Ecology 12(1), 3-19

Penning-Rowsell E C and Chatterton J B 1977 The benefits of flood alleviation: a manual of assessment techniques, Aldershot: Gower

Penning-Rowsell E C, Chatterton J B and Parker D J 1978 The Effect of Flood Warning on Flood Damage Reduction, Enfield: Flood Hazard Research Centre

Penning-Rowsell E C, Green C H, Thompson P M, Coker A M, Tunstall S M, Richards C and Parker D J 1992 The Economics of Coastal Management: A Manual of Benefit Assessment Techniques, London: Belhaven

Penning-Rowsell E C, Peerbolte B, Correia F N, Fordham M, Green C H, Pflugner W, Rocha J, Saraiva M da G, Schmidtke R, Torterotot J-P, Van der Veen A and Wind H 1992 "Flood vulnerability analysis and decision making for flood alleviation: The core concepts of the EUROFLOOD project", paper given at the Third International Conference on Floods and Flood Management, Florence

Pheby D and Robinson P 1990 "Nuclear Accidents: How People React", Health Visitor 63(4), 119-121

Smith D I 1986 "Cost-effectiveness of flood warnings" in Smith D I and Handmer J W (eds) Flood warning in Australia, Canberra: Centre for Resource and Environmental Studies, Australian National University

Sorensen J H 1988 Evaluation of Warning and Protective Action Implementation Times for Chemical Weapons Accidents, ORNL/TM-10437, Oak Ridge: Oak Ridge National Laboratory

Sorensen J H and Rogers G O 1989 Protective Actions for Extremely Toxic Chemical Accidents, Oak Ridge: Oak Ridge National Laboratory

Stern E 1989 "Evacuation Intentions of Parents in an Urban Radiological Emergency", Urban Studies 26, 191-198

Torterotot J-P, Kauark-Leite L A and Roche P-A 1992 "Analysis of individual real-time responses to flooding and influence on damage to households", paper given at the Third International Conference on Floods and Flood Management, Florence

Working Group on National Weather Radar Coverage 1983 Report of the Working Group on National Weather Radar Coverage, London: National Water Council/Meteorological Office

World Commission on Environment and Development 1987 Our Common Future, London: Oxford University Press

7. A hazard need not a disaster make: vulnerability and the causes of 'natural' disasters

T. CANNON, University of Greenwich

INTRODUCTION

Not very many years ago, most people assumed that the disasters associated with earthquakes, hurricanes, floods and other natural hazards were themselves 'natural' disasters.[2] It was accepted that their impact could be reduced (through attempts at preparedness, mitigation and post-event humanitarian action), but the emphasis (including in much academic and policy work) was on the naturalness of disaster events. There has long been an awareness that some disasters, which may resemble those usually blamed on nature, are inherently caused by human action (as with famines triggered by war). But this perception was limited, and it seemed difficult for people to extend such explanations to other types of disaster (especially those linked with sudden-onset hazards like earthquakes) which might have less obvious, more complex, but just as significant links with human causes.[3] Much disaster policy still puts emphasis on the impact of nature, and this has led to the dominance of technical interventions focused on predicting the hazard or modifying its impact.

This paper intends to clarify those less obvious human connections between natural hazards and disastrous outcomes. It argues that hazards are natural, but that in general disasters are not, and that they should not be seen as the inevitable outcome of a hazard's impact. The stress here is on the condition of the people which make it possible for a hazard to become a disaster. This includes the extent and types of their vulnerability, in combination with the technical issue of how society deals (or does not deal) with the hazard in terms of mitigation and preparedness. To concentrate on preparedness and mitigation of hazards without considering the social and economic systems that both generate vulnerability and determine the type of technical interventions leads to inadequate and potentially dangerous situations. One pioneer of hazards research expressed this well nearly twenty years ago:

> [M]odern societies cannot expect to cope effectively with hazards in the environment by relying solely upon technical solutions. A crucial aspect ... is the skilful, sensitive use of a wide range of adjustments, including engineering devices, land management and social regulation. To depend on only one sort of public action is to court social disaster,

Natural disasters. Thomas Telford, London, 1993

environmental deterioration, and enlarged public obligations.
(White, 1974: 13)

The technical interventions themselves which are supposed to
reduce hazard intensity or prepare people for them are not
socially-neutral, must not be taken in isolation from the factors
that create vulnerability, and should only be implemented with
full awareness of their impact on different sections of the
people. The paper argues for the use of vulnerability analysis
as a framework for understanding disasters and the development
of better policy interventions.[4]

NATURAL HAZARDS AND THE ENVIRONMENT

Nature presents Humankind with a set of opportunities and risks
which vary greatly in their spatial distribution. Opportunities
include the many different ways in which people utilise nature
for production (raw materials, energy sources) and to service
their livelihoods (absorbing or recycling waste products). The
risks inherent in nature consist of a wide range of hazards that
put constraints on production (e.g. frosts affecting agriculture)
and on other aspects of livelihoods and safety (earthquakes,
floods, droughts etc.).

Conventional analysis of the relationship between Humankind and
the environment has tended to emphasise nature as a set of
determinants, without adequately integrating nature with social
and economic systems. I argue that in effect the environment is
itself a social construction. Opportunities and risks are
fashioned by the varying characteristics of different types of
social system, and the differing demands each society puts on
Nature, combined with the varying impacts that nature may have
on varying types of social system.[5] This means that there are no
really generalised opportunities and risks in Nature, but instead
there are sets of unequal access to opportunities and unequal
exposures to risks which are a consequence of the socio-economic
system.

Much conventional analysis of disasters considers a direction of
causality that proceeds from hazard through spatial variability
to the impact on society. The argument of this paper is that
explanation of disaster causality is only possible by
understanding the ways in which social systems themselves
generate unequal exposure to risk by making some groups of
people, some individuals, and particular societies more prone to
hazards than others. In other words, disasters are not 'natural'
(not even sudden ones) because hazards affect people differently
within societies, and may have very different impacts on
different societies (e.g. earthquakes of equal energy may cause
devastation in one country, but not in another).

Inequalities in risk (and opportunity) are largely a function of
the principle systems of power operating in all societies, which
are normally analysed in terms of class, gender and ethnicity.
These in turn may be seen as social structures rooted in (and
mutually influencing) the patterns of national and international
economic and political systems. In other words, in order to
understand the relationship between humans and nature, it is more
important to discern how human systems themselves place people

in relation to each other and to the environment than it is to interpret natural systems. Concern here is not with the opportunities provided by the environment, but its risks. This paper attempts to interpret how social and economic systems place people at different levels of risk from nature's hazards. The main concept by which this 'social causation' is explained is vulnerability, being a measure of the degree and type of exposure to risk generated by different societies in relation to hazards. This approach can be termed vulnerability analysis.

DISASTERS ARE NOT NATURAL

Many people now accept that human activity itself has created the conditions for disaster events. This is partly because of growing awareness that through negligence or inappropriate response, the workings of social systems have made a disaster out of a situation which otherwise might not have been so serious. There has also been a growth in understanding that it is hazards that are natural, but that for a hazard to become a disaster it has to affect vulnerable people. The last decade has seen increasing use of various concepts of vulnerability by academics and development practitioners. These are also indicative of how disasters can be analysed as the product of economic and political factors. This shift in opinion is a vital step in the creation of a new international framework of thought and action for avoiding disasters.

Another reason for the shift is the growth in awareness of development problems and the difficulties of improving peoples living standards in Third World countries. Many now realise that the impact of disasters in the Third World often produce only a more acute, more extreme form of the general chronic daily suffering of many of the people. There is a realisation that explanation of the entire set of problems is required, rather than understanding of the 'natural' disaster in isolation. Another reason for the new awareness is the more widespread recognition of human destruction of the environment, and that natural hazards themselves can be precipitated (or exacerbated) by the pursuit of economic and social goals which hitherto were seen as the normal objectives of economic growth.

But there are two other reasons why attitudes have changed, especially among people in Western countries. First has been the growing critique of international inequalities, including the awareness of the surplus of food in the West contrasted with the dearth in Africa. Although the general public may not be aware that a transfer of this surplus will not solve the problems, its existence (and the international system which gives rise to it) at least showed them that something was wrong with 'nature' as an explanation. Secondly, and linked with the first, the widespread civil unrest and wars in areas affected by famine (in Mozambique, Ethiopia and Sudan especially) showed, even if in a rather crude manner, that the famines were at least partly man-made. The result is that more people than perhaps ever before are conscious that economic and political factors are causes of disasters, and that (in those instances at least) famines are not simply a result of the lack of rain.

Yet there are gaps in this new awareness, or rather it is patchy and disconnected. Much of it is a product of reactions to single events (e.g. the Ethiopian famines) or particular processes (e.g. deforestation and desertification), and fails to connect a wider range of phenomena. While the new awareness is to be welcomed, it is still incomplete and not yet universally accepted. Even the focus of the 1990s United Nations 'International Decade for Natural Disaster Reduction' (my emphasis) betrays the strength of the old outlook. Not only does the approach of the UN Decade fail to distinguish the naturalness of hazards from the human causation of disasters; it also (by focusing on the behaviour of nature) encourages technical solutions to the supposed excesses of that natural, yet untamed side of nature.

This paper instead develops a framework of factors and processes which explain how it is vulnerable people who are the victims of disasters. This is no mere tautology: it is not like saying that the victims of disasters were vulnerable to that hazard, as is demonstrated by their being its victims. The purpose is to demonstrate that there are particular characteristics of different groups of people (derived from economic, social and political processes) which mean that with the impact of a particular type of hazard of a given intensity, some avoid disaster and others do not.[6] The processes which make people more or less vulnerable are largely (but not exactly) the same as those which generate differences in wealth, control over resources, and power, both nationally and internationally. The vulnerability concept is a means of 'translating' known everyday processes of the economic and political separation of people into a more specific identification of those who may be at risk in hazardous environments.[7]

The emphasis which many of those involved in 'disasters work' have placed on economic and political factors as the 'causes' of disasters seems to be percolating through to the public, to aid workers, and even to some governments.[8] Something which has been obvious to many victims of disaster - that their suffering is not simply the result of an act of God - is being understood. It is easy to identify war and civil disturbance as relevant economic and political factors. What is more difficult but essential is to identify the processes and conflicts which generate and maintain vulnerability to disaster in the more general sense. This is more difficult to substantiate, because it usually involves analysis of the means by which some people live (and survive hazards better) at the expense of others. While many will condemn wars, and be critical of desertification, famine and pestilence, or population growth, there is more reluctance (especially amongst those who have power) to accept that the conditions which create vulnerability in some people have as their counterpart a more comfortable life for others.

This conflict of economic interests is one of the most intractable barriers to the mitigation of disasters. It is evident in widely different circumstances. These include the enforced marginalizing of people onto less productive land, or the need for those who earn low wages, have few resources, or are discriminated against, to live in particular places where hazards strike more harshly.

In the first type of case, the move is often so that superior land can be used for commercial agriculture or ranching, and the losers are made more vulnerable to drought and other hazards. In the second, examples include the need for those dispossessed of land or other income opportunities in Bangladesh to live in extremely flood-prone areas of the delta, the unemployed and those on low wages having to live in insubstantial housing located on unstable slopes in many cities (e.g. Rio de Janeiro), and the poor living in buildings which landlords and governments fail to proof against earthquakes.

To see disasters as being natural is about as useful as a doctor signing a death certificate with the explanation of 'natural causes'. It gives no indication as to whether the person's life might have been extended by a different social system which allocated resources differently (leading for instance to provision of a better diet, which would increase physical and mental ability, longevity and resistance to disease), or provided a health care system which makes early diagnosis and treatment possible (including appropriate technological interventions) of many 'natural' causes of death, and regulated risks in a different way (for instance by the removal or reduction of health hazards from the workplace, and discouraging self-damaging behaviour such as drug taking, including tobacco and excessive alcohol), and enabling access to scientific knowledge of factors such as diet and toxins.

Of course the analogy with disasters is not perfect, but the parallels are there in terms of resource allocations, risk management and the type of science and education. In disasters associated with natural hazards, it is much more useful to understand how the political and economic processes in a society act in various ways to generate varying levels of exposure to risk among different people. The economic system and class structure allocates income and access to resources, and this has an impact in terms of peoples' ability to cope with hazards (in nutritional level and health resilience, and subsequent access to resources, all affecting their potential for recovery). These also affect the degree of preparedness and mitigation through the level of scientific concern, resource allocation, and type and extent of technical preparation allocated within society. The manner in which social systems assign resources for the reduction of the impact of hazards is particularly important. It often fails to take account of peoples' needs, just as in medical care preventive work is often neglected and resources spent on expensive curative facilities. The level of scientific knowledge of both hazards themselves and their impact, and the allocation of the resulting technologies as means for intervening to reduce their intensity or impact, are normally determined by the power of private companies and government agencies. These are driven by their own criteria for success, which need not correspond with the needs of people.

Obviously in the death certificate illustration, the people would not die were it not for the factors which are inadequately labelled 'natural causes'. But such information on the death certificate is hardly informative about the underlying reasons for the many medical conditions which can hasten death. Equally in an earthquake, were it not for the ground shaking there would not be the potential for deaths, injuries and disruption. But this is far from being the same thing as saying that the earthquake caused an associated disaster.

The analogy can be extended. For various reasons 'natural causes' can be recorded on death certificates because the medical profession, other interest groups, or even the state, wishes to suppress knowledge of the underlying cause of death. The reasons may be personal (to protect the feelings of family), social, or political (to guard the reputation of the state). Similarly, it has served some political interests to maintain the notion that disasters are natural rather than 'caused' by political and economic processes.

Someone who dies in their nineties might be said without much controversy to have died from natural causes, since there is little likelihood that any modification of lifestyle or medical intervention could have delayed it further. In disasters there are also cases which reach the limits of the analysis presented here, and which are similarly – at least partially – natural. For instance, there may be completely unforseen or unknown hazards, or a hazard with a return period so long that people are unable to anticipate it at all. With the impact of such hazards, it is difficult to blame human action (or inaction) for any disastrous outcome (although there is an argument that human inaction should be blamed where there is a body of scientific knowledge that could have been used to warn of such occurrences). But in general disasters are not natural: they happen to people who are put at risk as a result of their vulnerability.[9]

DEFINING VULNERABILITY

The vulnerability we are concerned with here is that associated with natural hazards. Vulnerability is a characteristic of individuals and groups of people who inhabit a given natural, social and economic space, within which they are differentiated according to their varying position in society into more or less vulnerable individuals and groups. It is a complex characteristic produced by a combination of factors derived especially (but not entirely) from class, gender, or ethnicity.[10] Differences in these socio-economic factors result in hazards having a different degree of impact. Secondary factors may be important, such as age; older people may be generally less robust in recovery from illness or injury (and less able of escape from some hazards), though the elderly from poorer classes or ethnic groups may be more vulnerable than others.

Vulnerability itself may be divided into three aspects: the first is the degree of resilience of the particular livelihood system of an individual or group, and their capacity for resisting the impact of a hazard. This reflects economic resilience, including the capacity for recoverability (another measure of economic strength and responsiveness to hazards). This can be called 'livelihood resilience', and has some affinity with Sen's concept of entitlement (Sen, 1981). The second is the 'health' component (medical), which includes both the robustness of individuals (itself largely a function of livelihood strength), and the operation of various social measures (especially preventive medicine). The third component is the degree of preparedness of an individual or group. This is determined by the protection available for a given hazard, something which depends on people acting on their own behalf, and on social factors.

Preparedness is the area which is most recognisable in disaster planning, because it relates to the various technical interventions that are commonly seen as necessary for disaster avoidance (especially warning systems, land zoning, preparedness planning). But it is also clear that peoples' ability to protect themselves depends on their livelihood strength, and on their relationship to the state or other social and political structures. For instance if living in an earthquake zone, self-protection affects the nature and strength of the building, and is closely related to income and savings capacity; in a flood-prone area livelihood governs the price that can be paid for building plots in different places in relation to expected flood water levels. This 'self-protection' element of vulnerability, is in some respects linked to the economic advantages and disadvantages of high or low levels of livelihood (though it is not determined only by income or wealth). The level of protection granted by the activities of the state or other social institutions (such as unions, co-operatives and non-governmental organisations (NGOs) can be termed 'social protection'. These may intervene in determining the level of protection of particular people or groups from a hazard. This The two 'protection' elements depend on a range of factors which are clearly also linked to the major inequality factors in a society (class, gender and ethnicity), but also relate to the level of scientific and technical knowledge (and the manner in which it is used).

These three components are summarized in Table 1. A hazard may be seen to have a greater or lesser impact on a person or group according to their bundle of these characteristics, by virtue of which they possess a higher or lower level of vulnerability. Whether a disaster happens or not is conventionally related to an emphasis on the hazard itself, and on the need for physical protection measures. With this alternative vulnerability approach, the intensity of the hazard (and of protection against it) is not nearly so relevant to explaining disaster as are the social and economic factors that affect overall vulnerability, including technical issues of protection.

A highly vulnerable group may be badly affected by a relatively weak earthquake, and a low vulnerability group little affected by a strong one. It is the degree of vulnerability of people in the area of the hazard-strike which counts, and the different components of their vulnerability in relation to different types of hazard. The number of people at a level of vulnerability to a hazard of a given intensity will be a measure of the disastrous or non-disastrous impact of that hazard. It is therefore also possible for two earthquakes of the same intensity and characteristics to strike areas with similar population densities, and for one to be a disaster (in terms of mortality, injury, and disruption to livelihoods and future well-being) and the other to be a (relatively minor) disruption with few deaths and injuries and with easy recoverability. The hazard is natural; a disastrous outcome is not, and is in many senses largely caused by the vulnerability conditions generated by human systems.

Table 1 The Components of Vulnerability

TYPE OF VULNERABILITY	COMPONENTS	DETERMINANTS
Livelihood vulnerability	income opportunities livelihood type entry qualifications assets and savings health status	class position; gender; ethnicity; age; action of state;
Self-protection	building quality hazard protection location of home/work	Socio-economic: as above, plus technical ability or availability; Hazard-specific: return period; intensity; magnitude;
Social protection	as above plus: building regulations technical interventions	as above, plus: level of scientific knowledge; level (and characteristics) of technical practice; type of science and engineering used by state and dominant groups;

In areas where people face multiple hazards, the impact of one may be less serious than another. The 'protection' element of vulnerability is therefore usually specific to each type of hazard, in its interaction with the particular characteristics of people. For instance, some people may be more vulnerable to an earthquake than to a flood striking the same location. This variability in regard to the type of hazard might result from the places where a person lives or works being better protected against flooding than earthquakes.

VULNERABILITY AND THE CAUSES OF DISASTER

What is it about the condition of the people (rather than the natural hazard) which make it possible for a hazard to become a disaster? Disasters happen when a natural hazard strikes vulnerable people, as illustrated in Figure 1. Thus they involve both the extent and types of vulnerability generated by peoples' situations within political and economic systems, and the manner in which society deals with the hazard in terms of mitigation and preparedness. If people can be made less vulnerable or non-vulnerable, then a hazard may still occur, but need not produce a disaster.

From this analysis, it is apparent that reducing disasters is possible not only by modifying the hazard, but also by reducing vulnerability. However, most of the efforts of those concerned

Figure 1: Model illustrating the relationship between hazard and vulnerability (and its root causes) in the causation of disasters

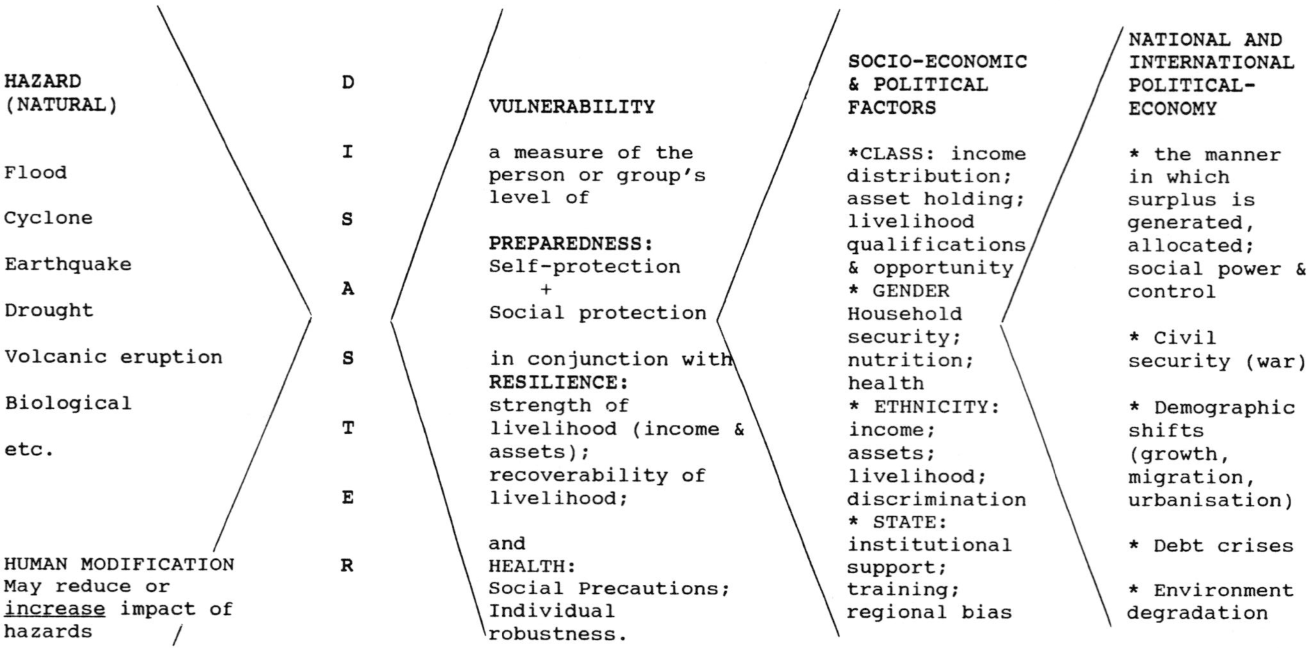

HAZARD (NATURAL)

Flood

Cyclone

Earthquake

Drought

Volcanic eruption

Biological

etc.

HUMAN MODIFICATION
May reduce or increase impact of hazards

D I S A S T E R

VULNERABILITY

a measure of the person or group's level of

PREPAREDNESS:
Self-protection
+
Social protection

in conjunction with
RESILIENCE:
strength of livelihood (income & assets); recoverability of livelihood;

and
HEALTH:
Social Precautions; Individual robustness.

SOCIO-ECONOMIC & POLITICAL FACTORS

*CLASS: income distribution; asset holding; livelihood qualifications & opportunity

* GENDER Household security; nutrition; health

* ETHNICITY: income; assets; livelihood; discrimination

* STATE: institutional support; training; regional bias

NATIONAL AND INTERNATIONAL POLITICAL-ECONOMY

* the manner in which surplus is generated, allocated; social power & control

* Civil security (war)

* Demographic shifts (growth, migration, urbanisation)

* Debt crises

* Environment degradation

with disasters is focused either on reducing the impact of the hazard itself (sometimes in expensive and inappropriate ways), or on reducing one rather narrow aspect of vulnerability - social protection through certain forms of technological preparedness.[11] The major determinants which make people vulnerable (i.e. the social, economic and political factors which determine the level of resilience of peoples' livelihoods, and their ability to withstand and prepare for hazards) are rarely tackled.

Mitigation of hazards is normally associated with attempts to reduce the intensity of a hazard, or to make some other modification which is supposed to lessen its impact. It is often hazard-centred rather than a people-centred approach. As a result it may deal with the hazard threat without taking account of peoples' needs, as with the major plans for taming floods in Bangladesh. By contrast, preparedness should aim at reducing the impact of a hazard by improving the protection of people in ways that centre on people and reducing their vulnerability. This may be done by people themselves, for instance in the type of building and its resilience in earthquakes (self-protection). It may be organised at a higher level (social protection) by the state (e.g. through building regulations) or through local groups or NGO activities. However, the State is often unreliable. It may recognise the need to offer social protection to reduce vulnerability, but it is normally a party to the economic and social processes that lead people to be unable to protect themselves in the first place.

The vulnerability of a group can be improved by changes in the different components of their vulnerability bundle, and improvements in preparedness and mitigation measures are only one aspect. It is dangerous to rely on the development of scientific knowledge and technical means of hazard reduction, because they may have little or no effect, depending how other components of the vulnerability profile are altered. For instance, expensive satellite warning systems for hurricanes (tropical cyclones) may have no impact on people who cannot afford radios, or live in places where the state is unwilling or unable to provide warnings. At present the Government of Bangladesh and major industrialised countries are planning major engineering works to counter river floods (like those that covered much of the country in 1987 and 1988). There is grave uncertainty about the efficacy of these enormously expensive measures, or indeed whether they are even the best way of dealing with the vulnerability of the people affected (Boyce, 1990; Rogers et al, 1989).

In general, many people in most Third World countries are vulnerable in both the lack (or inappropriateness) of preparedness measures (the level of protection), and in the livelihood level and resilience. It is often the case that they are unable to provide themselves with self-protection, and the state is unable or unwilling to offer much relevant social protection. In developed industrialised countries, the preparedness levels may be high, and in general livelihoods are more secure and insurance makes them more resilient. This has given rise to a perception of disasters as having little impact in terms of deaths in industrialised countries but much material damage (in physical and value terms), while in the Third World the situation is seen as the opposite. This is based on a crude and ill-informed understanding of the value of a great deal of property in Third World countries for the actual users. While the homes, goods, tools and animals which might be lost by Third World disaster victims may have low values when converted into Western currency and culture, they are often of great value and their loss may be devastating for the people concerned.

But vulnerability analysis is not only valid in Third World situations. There are sizeable groups of people in the industrialised countries who are economically vulnerable to various hazards. For instance in the United States not everybody enjoys social protection (preparedness and mitigation measures) against hurricanes or earthquakes, and although the state may alleviate their livelihood damage through Federal aid, not all are eligible and many poorer people cannot improve their recoverability through insurance.

CONCLUSION

Better awareness about what causes natural hazards is insufficient for reducing their impact unless it is also translated into an understanding of the way economic systems affect people differentially. This is a major difficulty: if one of the obstacles to disaster reduction is self-interest of some groups in maintaining their position within economic systems, then how useful is it to develop this knowledge? The vulnerability approach to disasters is immediately concerned with political and economic power. It is focused on peoples' access to resources, their livelihoods, and on external pressures which may act detrimentally on these. It is concerned with the type of (and absence of) social protection affecting different groups of people, and is therefore concerned with the role of the state, the type of technical interventions used in hazard preparedness, and whether or not self-organisation of vulnerable people to improve their own protection is permitted by powerful groups. Does the vulnerability approach involve irreconcilable conflicts, since we have to live with governments and systems (national and international) that maintain the economic inequity which causes vulnerability?

That vulnerability analysis is inherently about power and politics is no argument for abandoning it as a superior way of understanding disasters. A combined effort by academics, civil servants, political activists, NGOs, aid workers and others to promote some new thinking about disasters is part of the way in which dominant interest groups can be changed (see Maskrey, 1989 for related ideas). There is usually scope for something to be done within existing situations to reduce vulnerability and promote disaster mitigation. It is rare for governments to explicitly support the processes by which some people become more vulnerable than others; there are 'spaces' in most societies where the political shift which accompanies this type of disaster analysis can be inserted. In particular I would argue for the need to support and promote organisations of civil society which can provide the monitoring of hazards, and the measurement and analysis of vulnerability, outside of the control of the state. The struggle to make vulnerability analysis available (which includes the formation of such institutions) - both to potential victims and their allies - would itself become part of the process by which society is changed to avoid and reduce vulnerability being generated.

BIBLIOGRAPHY

Blaikie, Piers, Cannon, T., Davis, I., and Wisner, B., 1994, At Risk: natural hazards, peoples' vulnerability and disasters, Routledge, London.

Bohle, Hans, Cannon, T., Hugo, G., and Ibrahim, F. N., Famine and Food Security in Africa and Asia: indigenous response and external interventions to avoid hunger, University of Bayreuth.

Boyce, James, K., Birth of a mega-project: political economy of flood control in Bangladesh, Environmental Management, vol.14,4 419-28

Burton, I., Kates, R., & White, G., 1978, The environment as hazard, Oxford University Press, New York.

Cannon, T., 1990, Hunger and famine: using a food systems model to analyse vulnerability, in: Bohle et al (eds) (1990): 291-312.

Clarke, John I., Curson, P., Kayastha, S.L., & Nag, P., (eds), 1989, Population and disaster, Blackwell, Oxford.

Crow, Ben, 1984, Warnings of Famine in Bangladesh, Economic and Political Weekly vol.19,40, 1754-1758.

Cuny, Frederick C., 1983, Disasters and development New York, Oxford University Press.

Curson, Peter, 1989, Introduction, in: Clarke et al (1989): 1-23

Franke, Richard W. & Chasin, Barbara H., 1981, Seeds of Famine: ecological destruction and the development dilemma in the West African Sahel, Allanheld, Osmun & Co., Montclair, New Jersey.

Hewitt, K. (ed), 1983, Interpretations of Calamity from the viewpoint of human ecology, Allen & Unwin, London.

Maskrey, Andrew, 1989, Disaster mitigation: a community-based approach, Oxfam, Oxford.

Rogers, Peter, Lydon, P., & Seckler, D., 1989 Eastern Waters Study: Strategies to Manage Flood and Drought in the Ganges-Brahmaputra Basin, U.S. Agency for International Development, Washington.

Sen, Amartya, 1981, Poverty and Famines: an essay on entitlements and deprivation, Clarendon Press, Oxford.

Torry, W.I., 1986, Economic development, drought and famine: some limitations of dependency explanations, Geojournal, vol.12,1, 5-18.

United Nations Disaster Relief Organisation (UNDRO), 1978, Disaster Prevention and Mitigation: a compendium of current knowledge, Various volumes, United Nations, New York.

United Nations Disaster Relief Organisation (UNDRO), 1988, International Decade on Natural Disaster Reduction, UNDRO News Jan-Feb, vol.2, 24-25.

White, Gilbert F., 1974, Natural Hazards: local, national, global, Oxford University Press, New York.

NATURAL DISASTERS

Whittow, John, 1980, Disasters: the anatomy of environmental hazards, Penguin, Harmondsworth.

Wijkman, A. and Timberlake, L., Natural disasters: Acts of God or acts of Man, Earthscan, London.

NOTES

1. This paper is a shortened version of a chapter to appear in A. Varley (ed.) 1994 'Disasters, Development and Environment' London: Belhaven. It incorporates ideas from the book Blaikie et al., 1994, and I acknowledge my co-authors' in the development of the ideas.

2. This situation is reflected in examples of books specifically on disasters that treat them as natural, with very little attention given to the socio-economic system. See for instance Whittow, 1980.

3. A disaster is defined here as an event associated with the impact of a natural hazard, which leads to increased mortality, illness and/or injury, and destroyed or disrupted livelihoods which affects people of an area such that they (and/or outsiders) perceive it as being exceptional and requiring external assistance for recovery.

4. This framework has been used to analyse a range of specific hazards in Blaikie, Cannon, Davis & Wisner (1993); there is no space here to provide detailed cases.

5. There is a partial exploration of these ideas in relation to food production systems in Cannon (1990).

6. This is not to say that a study which happened to precede a hazard impact would permit a perfect match between those who are actual victims and the predicted categories. There is great difficulty in determining accurately different levels of vulnerability, given for instance that earthquakes vary in power and floods vary in intensity. In theory though this is a data problem rather than an inadequacy of the framework; it is inherently possible to identify the different levels of vulnerability of a population to the impact of earthquakes or floods of varying intensities.

7. It is important that recognition is given to the difference between vulnerability and poverty. This is elaborated later. While most poor people may be vulnerable to drought, flood, earthquake etc, not all vulnerable people are necessarily poor. In addition, some people (poor or not) may be vulnerable to one type of hazard more than another: a poor group in a flood plain may suffer a flood but be exempt from the effects of an earthquake (at least in terms of mortality and injury) by virtue of their type of housing, while a middle-class group in nearby apartments may be victims in large numbers to the earthquake but not the flood.

8. It is recognised implicitly in the shift in the early 1980s by Non-Government Organisations (NGOs) like Oxfam to the emphasis on development work rather than emergency disaster relief.

9. Differentiated levels of vulnerability may be enhanced by hazard strikes. In other words, the society may already be structured economically according to the manner in which its people have experienced past hazards: those who are relatively

less successful in the recovery process are likely to be more vulnerable to the next hazard strike.

10. There may not be much surprise at seeing class and ethnicity mentioned here (although unfortunately there is no space to be more specific about their impact: that is attempted in Blaikie et al, 1994). The argument that gender is a significant factor in generating differential vulnerability is more difficult to support, simply because there are virtually no studies of it. Most disasters work avoids and ignores gender relations, although there is much primae facie evidence for their significance (for instance the imbalances in the vulnerability of women and men to some hazards, especially drought and related hunger). Earlier 'radical' analyses of disaster tended to regard class as the major factor. Yet gender operates from the level of household politics and economics (as in the allocation of food) right through to the level of the state and the international political economy (as in the overwhelming dominance of the economic growth model as the means of achieving development, a model which allows little space for any redefinition of the objectives of development by women).

11. The Resolution that established the UN Decade for Natural Disaster Reduction makes no mention of vulnerability or indeed even of the possible role of social science in preparing for disasters. It is overwhelmingly oriented to scientific and engineering approaches. (see UNDRO, 1988)

9. Progress in assessing famine vulnerability and drought risk

T. E. DOWNING, Environmental Change Unit, University of Oxford

CONCEPTS OF VULNERABILITY AND RISK

Nearly two decades ago, natural hazards were portrayed as the product of a natural system and a set of human activities and responses (ref 1). The probability of a disruptive event (such as a flash flood) and the sensitivity of human social and economic systems were differentiated. This approach characterized societal sensitivity to sudden disasters, with a focus on the immediate effects and individual responses. A larger view of hazards research, particularly focused on drought in developing countries, generated integrative concepts of vulnerability that sought to portray the space of disasters: why they occur in specific regions; why specific groups are more affected than others (ref 2, 3). The African droughts of 1980s and 1990s spawned parallel efforts and intense research on methods to monitor famine, incorporating geophysical assessment of drought, models of vulnerability to famine and understanding of drought coping strategies (refs 4-8).

This paper draws together the implications of advances in vulnerability assessment for research and policy on natural disasters. In the context of this paper, key concepts are defined as:

Risk is the probability of occurrence of a hazardous event of a specified magnitude and duration. For example, the 100 year flood plain is be mapped based on assessments of meteorological, hydrological and geomorphological conditions.

Sensitivity is a measure of the extent of impacts, given a specific hazardous event. A depth-damage curve, for example, charts the relationship between flood depth and expected economic losses for housing, commercial buildings and municipal facilities. Resilience implies attenuation of a hazard, in contrast to fragile or sensitive sectors that magnify the potential consequences of hazardous events.

A hazard is the potential loss associated with the risk of natural events and the sensitivity of human natural resource use. For example, the flood hazard can be portrayed as annual

Natural disasters. Thomas Telford, London, 1993

expected losses based on the expected distribution of flood events, given the exposed populations and facilities in the flood plain.

A disaster is a specific event with adverse impacts (e.g. the 1991 tropical cyclone that flooded coastal Bangladesh and killed over 130,000 people).

Vulnerability is a measure, for a given population or region, of the underlying factors that influence exposure to the hazardous event and predisposition to adverse consequences. In this lexicon, vulnerability refers explicitly to an adverse consequence (e.g. loss of life, disease or economic costs) rather than the hazardous event itself (e.g. a trigger such as flood). It is related to sensitivity and resilience, but is an aggregate measure that reflects a social objective rather than the coefficient for a damage assessment. To assign vulnerability to a trigger (flood) implies an adverse but unspecified consequence--in fact, floods may benefit some populations and sectors. Vulnerability encompasses a wider social, economic and political analysis of the temporal and spatial patterns that determine who suffers most from hazardous events (ref 9).

Vulnerability varies over time. The most pressing concern is current vulnerability: the present status. A temporal integration of current vulnerability, perhaps for the past five years, yields a baseline of chronic vulnerability. The temporal dimension of vulnerability includes the daily cycle of, for instance, home, school and work, seasonal variations in activities (such as outdoor activities in warmer weather) and trends in conditions over the course of years (e.g. preferred vacation resorts). These changes greatly determine who is exposed to various hazards.

To illustrate these terms: The flood hazard, for example in Bangladesh, is well-established, portrayed in various maps and assessments (ref 10). Damaging floods may have a 1 in 25% chance of occurrence--a 0.04% risk--in any given year. Local structures, farms and people are sensitive to floods: relationships between the depth of flooding and extent of damage or loss of life have been established, based on the experience of specific disasters. In contrast, coastal smallholder agriculturalists in Bangladesh are vulnerable (to the loss of their livelihood and life), due to the flood hazard among a range of resource, social, economic and political conditions.

WHY ASSESS VULNERABILITY?

Experience in famine vulnerability and drought hazard assessment over the past few years suggests that vulnerability assessments have four functions:

First, information on current vulnerability helps interpret the potential consequences of future risk. For example, if current vulnerability is low, following a good year, with healthy rural labour markets and adequate on-farm storage, a below-average season probably is not a significant threat to smallholder food security. On the other hand, even a moderate drought (or for some an average season) could lead to famine if it follows several years of inadequate production, poor economic performance and lack of food relief.

Second, an assessment of vulnerability at the start of the most hazardous period (i.e. the growing season for drought) enables analysts to foreshadow the possible outcome of the next season. With increased accuracy of weather forecasts (ref 11), the current status of vulnerable groups can be projected into the coming months.

Third, targeting appropriate adaptive responses depends on knowing who is most vulnerable. And, planning the most effective responses requires sensitivity to the pathways by which a hazardous event is translated into a disaster.

Fourth, recurrent vulnerability assessments build up an institutional experience in maintaining data bases, interpreting signals from monitoring systems, and gauging the need for various levels of response. Broadly cast, such experience is useful for development objectives to mitigate vulnerability. Formal vulnerability assessments integrate the sensitivity to and risk of multiple natural and technological hazards, a considerable aid to disaster management.

AN EXAMPLE FROM RESEARCH ON VULNERABLE FOOD SYSTEMS

Food security (or famine, as the acute failure of food security) is not a random experience. It is related to a variety of environmental, social, and economic factors. An appraisal of vulnerability to food insecurity must begin with a conceptual framework of these factors. Three components of vulnerability, emphasizing the scale of geographical and social organization, appear useful, based on contributions from a diverse research literature (ref 12).

Regional food shortage comprises estimates of the regional food balance, the ability of national production, storage, and net imports to meet aggregate food consumption requirements of the resident population. Geographical factors may be important, or related to a number of influences that affect vulnerability. Institutional development--the adequacy of infrastructure to support agricultural production, distribute food to markets, provide health services, and promote income and food entitlement--may reflect the ability of isolated communities and markets and marginalized ethnic groups to command commercial food or food aid.

Household food poverty is directly related to household income (or food entitlement) from agricultural production on-farm and from communal lands, market exchanges, barter/labour exchanges, transfers, and assets to meet consumption requirements. The choice of crops, agricultural practices, diet, income-generating activities, and the utilization of other resources are influenced by cultural patterns that affect household income, expenditure, and consumption. The composition of the household (e.g., age-sex distribution, size, lifecycle stage) influences consumption requirements, availability of labour, and the intra-household distribution of food.

Ultimately, food deprivation (and vulnerability) is individual. Data on malnutrition gauge individual ability to withstand deprivation of food once it occurs. The distribution of malnourishment is often correlated with the risk of exposure to food shortage or famine. The incidence of diseases, such as cholera, diarrhoea, malaria, and vitamin A deficiency, reflects both individual ability to withstand further food deprivation and the effects of malnutrition and food stress. Although difficult to gauge, the social status of individuals within households affects who suffers first from food poverty and who experiences the greatest deprivation. For instance, women and the elderly may have a lower status than male labourers and sons and therefore receive less food in times of crisis.

National differences in vulnerability to hunger are portrayed by indicators of the three components of food security described above: national food shortage (food availability in kcal/day per capita for 1986); household food poverty (Gross National Product per capita in 1987); and individual food deprivation (childhood (under 5) mortality per 1000 in 1987). More systematic data, e.g. on food availability relative to consumption requirements, distribution of wealth (such as the Gini coefficient) and nutritional status (such as the prevalence of malnutrition), were not available for a sufficient number of countries.

Data for the three indicators were drawn from World Bank sources (refs 13-14) for 172 countries. The nominal values of each indicator were normalized, and a composite food security index based on the three indicators was constructed.

Five classes of vulnerability, based on the distribution of the food security index, are shown in Figure 1. The index illustrates the diversity of countries vulnerable to hunger. The famine-prone countries of Africa, with a food security index of less than −1.00, comprise 37 countries with a total population of over 800 million in 1988.

At a more detailed level, an initial step in a vulnerability assessment is to define the socioeconomic groups that have different patterns of food production and procurement, and possibly different rates of food poverty. In most circumstances, vulnerable groups can be defined by their principal means of livelihood, with additional discrimination according to wealth (e.g., size of holding, levels of skill), reliability of income (related to tenure for instance), and geographical location (related to natural resources, but also the political economy that commands development assistance).

In Kenya, seven vulnerable socioeconomic groups establish the range of livelihoods that might be affected by drought: pastoralists, landless poor, rural landholders (squatters, smallholders) and urban poor (ref 16). For each group, the rate of food poverty—the proportion of people in each class with incomes insufficient to procure the recommended minimum

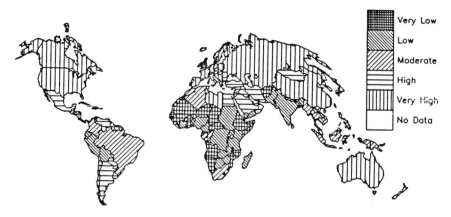

Figure 1. World food security, based on national indicators of food availability per capita, Gross National Product per capita, and childhood mortality (ref 15).

level of food—has been estimated. Almost 7 million people were estimated to live in food-poor households in 1990. The largest vulnerable group (over half of the food-poor population) encompasses smallholder agriculturalists. Pastoralists have a higher rate of food poverty, but with a lower population, total just over 1.5 million food-poor people in 1990. Urban poverty comprises only 3 per cent of the total, but may rapidly escalate in the future as rural-urban migration increases (ref 17).

Building upon the definition of two vulnerable groups (smallholders and pastoralists), a spatial analysis illustrates methods in vulnerability assessment. Data, at a 5 km resolution from the Food and Agriculture Organization (FAO) (ref 18) included: district boundaries; population density in 1979 census; land class; location of national parks, forests, and game reserves; location of towns; and agroclimatic zones. The population data were projected to 1984, using published estimates of district population growth (ref 19).

Smallholder agriculturalists, comprising over half the population of Kenya, reside in the highlands of western, central, and eastern Kenya, and along the coast. These agricultural lands were mapped based on the suitable agroclimatic zones (I through V, in the Kenya Soil Survey typology) in districts known to be settled predominately by agricultural groups. Pastoralists occupy the remainder of Kenya not devoted to agriculture or major towns. Vulnerability assessment in pastoral areas is compounded by the high degree of variability in resources and mobility of pastoral groups.

The selection of indicators follows the above typology of vulnerability to hunger. Regional food shortage is assessed by agroclimatic resources and distance from market towns, with areas excluded from settlement (parks, forests and game reserves) omitted from the analysis. Food poverty is modelled by the balance between production and consumption (an indicator of self-sufficiency) and an indicator of off-farm income relative to food prices. The distance to market towns is also an indicator of access to government, private and commercial institutions, particularly food markets and food aid. Individual food deprivation encompasses indicators of nutritional status and summaries of the population in each class of vulnerability, including those with special nutritional needs.

The index of aggregate vulnerability to hunger is the sum of the individual indicators, converted to a standard score and grouped into classes: low vulnerability, scores less than - 0.5; average vulnerability, scores within 0.5 standard units of the area-mean; and high vulnerability, with scores more than 0.5 units above the mean (Figure 2 and Table 1).

The areas of highest vulnerability for smallholder agriculturalists are the densely populated Lake Victoria environs, the semi-arid fringe of the highlands (Kitui and parts of the Rift Valley), and the dry hinterland of the coastal strip. The population most vulnerable to food insecurity comprises 17 percent of the smallholder agriculturalists, over half of whom are children and pregnant or lactating women.

Table 1. Population by Class of Vulnerability for Smallholder Agriculturalists and Pastoralists in Kenya

Vulnerability:	Low	Average	Moderate-High	Total Vulnerable Groups
Agricultural areas Population	4,015,675	3,086,300	1,458,775	8,560,750
Special needs	295,642	1,683,660	869,676	2,848,978
Pastoral areas Population	595,425	330,975	313,675	1,240,075
Special needs	313,310	168,976	98,334	580,620

The results for pastoralists encourage less confidence since only two indicators were used and data on the balance of population and livestock production are not available. Indices such as the number of livestock units per person, proportion of nutritional requirements met from livestock products, or value of livestock holdings in cereal equivalents, would greatly expand the analysis and could be developed. The composite index shows pockets of high vulnerability between major towns and in northwestern Kenya. Over one fourth of the pastoralists are moderately-highly vulnerable, of which a third may be children and women with special nutritional needs.

Additional layers of analysis can incorporate individual and household dynamics. For example, a hierarchy of household vulnerability in six districts of central and eastern Kenya was compiled based on survey data for 565 households (ref 20-

21). Food short households produce less than two-thirds of their food requirements (based on estimated crop yields). Market-sensitive households lack reliable off-farm incomes. Individuals with special nutritional needs include children under 5 and lactating and pregnant women.

The food-short households comprise 27 percent of the population in an average year (chronic vulnerability), but 82 percent in a severe drought (a potential trigger for a disaster). Households vulnerable to food poverty are those that are both food-short and market-sensitive, 10 and 30 percent of the population in average and drought years. The most vulnerable individuals are 2 to 8 percent of the population.

RESEARCH AND POLICY ISSUES

Models of vulnerability and hazard processes abound, reflecting hundreds of definitions of risk and resilience, vulnerability and sensitivity, hazard and disaster. The choice of the best vulnerability model might reflect three approaches:

Conceptual: A priori, what dominates vulnerability? What typology provides insight and leads to effective responses?

Model-derived: What influences vulnerability, based on statistical (correlation, discriminant), spatial (catchment, potential, and flow), and dynamic (water balance, food balance) models?

Empirical: What model provides the best predictions of the adverse consequences of disaster? Or, prompts the most appropriate, timely responses?

A set of generalized equations illustrates the range of assumptions that might go into a compiling an integrated measure of vulnerability (Figure 3). The simplest approach is to compile a set of indicators in an indiscriminate aggregation. If the indicators are chosen carefully to capture specific dimensions of famine risk, this approach may be warranted: it assumes each indicator is equally weighted (i.e., they all contribute equally to vulnerability, or the weights shown in (4b) are 0). The major issues, common to any quantitative model, are:

Definition of vulnerability: If diverse indicators are used, what is meant by vulnerability? A clear concept of vulnerability leads the analyst to compile a structured set of indicators rather than an indiscriminate aggregation. While the equation may be similar to (4a), it reflects a conscious model of vulnerability.

Choice of indicators: How many are required? How should missing data be handled? What is the effect of correlations between indicators (i.e. childhood mortality rates and malnutrition)?

112

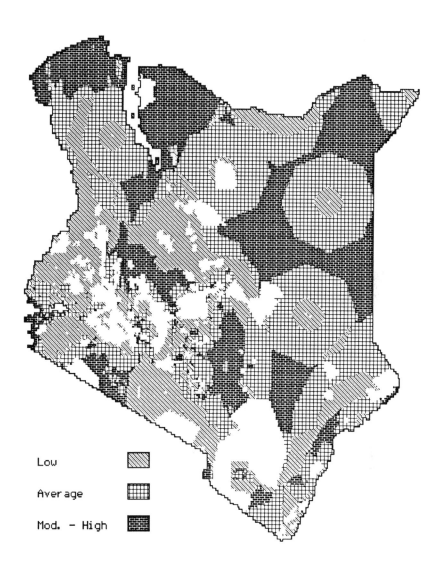

Figure 2. Composite index of vulnerability for smallholders and pastoralists in Kenya (ref 6).

NATURAL DISASTERS

(a) Indiscriminate Aggregation:
$$V=\sum (I_i)$$

(b) Weighted Indicators:
$$V=\sum (I_i*W_i)$$

(c) Targeted Indicators:
$$V_g=\sum (I_{i,g}*W_{i,g})$$

(d) Contingent Indicators:
$$V=\sum (I_i*W_i) \quad where: \ W_i=\int (I_j)$$

(e) Dynamic Indicators:
$$V=\sum (I_i*W_i) \quad where: \ W_i=\int (I_{i-t}, I_{i+s}, I_g)$$

(f) Hierarchical Vulnerability Indices:
$$V_k=\sum_K \sum_1 (I_i*W_i)$$

Where:
V= composite vulnerability index
V_k *= vulnerability index for domain k*
$\sum$ *= method of aggregation, e.g. summation, averaging, or rank ord*
I_i *= indicator (i)*
W_i *= weight for indicator (i)*
I_g *= indicator (i) for group g*
I_{i-t} *= indicator (i) at time t*
I_{i+s} *= indicator (i) at space s*

Figure 3. Indicators of famine vulnerability.

As shown in the Kenya example, a refinement is to target
indicators according to vulnerable socioeconomic groups (4c),
perhaps based on livelihood or production systems, for famine
assessments, or health and age for rapid disasters. Targeted
indicators recognize that processes, vulnerability and
critical thresholds differ between each group. However, major
issues revolve around the definition of vulnerable groups and
coherent regions for analysis:

Single variable: Is the group defined according to the
assumed dominant determinant of vulnerability, such as
production (food supply), economic access (off-farm or
permanent wage employment), or physical access (distance to
markets)?

Integrated variables: Alternatively, is vulnerability
differentiated by an integrating factor, such as natural
resources (agroecological potential), income (poverty lines or
diversity of sources), ethnicity (discrimination, political
access), or consumption (malnutrition)? This is conceptually
appealing, but difficult to implement: membership in a
category may change quite quickly.

Multiple variables: A hierarchy of variables could be used, such as production system, natural resources, and individual nutrition, e.g., resource-poor smallholders with chronic malnourishment.

Correlation and distributions: The average household is not the most vulnerable: defining the tails of a distribution is more difficult than broadly categorizing the average conditions. Single variables are usually reported in survey data, but may be cross-correlated with each other. Determining the distribution, for example, of smallholder agriculturalists without permanent employment and with malnourished children requires access to original survey data.

Response-driven: Definitions of vulnerable groups according to their responses to crises are worth considering. Such a typology might include those dependent on food aid (refugee camps), communities with effective political representation, remote areas, and those with "effective coping strategies".

Data requirements: Ultimately, the definition of vulnerable groups depends on the availability of data and needs of decision makers in monitoring and responding to specific hazards.

Vulnerability often depends on networks that mobilize physical, economic, and social access to resources. Vulnerability for one group or household or individual may be contingent on vulnerability for other groups, regions, or sectors of the economy (4d). The issues of spatial scale and sectoral or social linkages are difficult in hazards research:

Space as a location: Geographic Information Systems register variables by their Cartesian location, an x,y coordinate on a map. By imposing rigorous standards for data, many disparate types of data can be portrayed in a common format. The layers of a GIS may reveal patterns of vulnerability, or simply plot relative vulnerability according to a common unit of analysis (e.g., the arrondissement).

Space as a variable: Space may also be considered a variable, such as distance from markets; transport costs for providing food aid or relocating surplus production; distance and access to wage employment or income from mining; and information flows between rural and urban areas or remote, vulnerable groups and decision makers. There is a danger that spatial variables will be mapped using limited data that do not reflect micro-topological features, current road conditions, social and cultural networks, and the political economy that determine vulnerability.

Definition of spatial regions: GIS methods enable distinct spatial regions to be defined, whether by isopleths of rainfall, overlays of temperature and rainfall, or correlation models that cluster pixels according to their similarity on one or more variables.

Similar issues are raised with the use of dynamic indicators (4e). The premis of a vulnerability analysis is that future risk is compared to current vulnerability. For example, a seasonal drought is only a significant risk to most smallholder or pastoral systems if it has followed at least two previous seasons of drought (or production failures) that depleted food reserves, reduced disposable assets, impoverished local labour markets, and resulted in deteriorating nutritional status. Specific issues include:

Current or chronic vulnerability: The emphasis in monitoring vulnerability is the current status--the product of the recent past and current resources. Long-term development planning, in contrast, focuses on chronic vulnerability--the integration of current vulnerability over time, perhaps the past decade with an assessment of prospects for the next decade as well.

Temporal variability: Are households residing in environments that vary over time (e.g., with highly variable food production) better able to cope with perturbations than those accustomed to more stable production? This is a recurrent issue that may be difficult to resolve in a generic sense. It probably depends as much on economic integration and access as it does on resource variability and traditional coping strategies.

Monitoring temporal changes: How reliable are data that may be out of date? Some factors, such as soil fertility, may vary little over the course of several years. Some data from previous months or seasons can be estimated. Variables that are themselves a response to crisis, such as remittances, may be the most difficult to gauge.

Finally, vulnerability may be composed as a hierarchy of indices that reflect specific domains (4f), are targeted by socioeconomic group, contingent upon spatial and temporal process, and weighted by a process of expert opinion and empirical analysis. This "full vulnerability model" is probably not yet operational for any specific country. At this stage, suitable time series of vulnerability and crisis should be compiled and various vulnerability models tested and compared.

The ultimate goals of vulnerability assessments are to reduce the threat of hazards and respond effectively to emerging crises. To some extent, improvements to famine early warning systems in the late 1980s and early 1990s have been successful. Famine is rarely hidden or sudden: the media bring attention to dire destitution that has already been foreshadowed by monitoring agencies. The failure, in most cases, of adequate responses can be attributed to the political economy of famine, rather than the failure of information systems per se. At the same time, the structural causes of chronic vulnerability--widespread food poverty that seldom emerges as famine--has impeded efforts to provide for sustainable livelihoods in much of Africa and South Asia. While famine remains a serious risk for many peoples, vulnerability assessment requires widespread collaboration, new experimentation in methods, and evaluation by concerned decision makers.

REFERENCES

1. BURTON I., Kates R.W. and White, G.F., Environment as Hazard, Oxford University Press, Oxford, 1978.

2. HEWITT K., ed., Interpretations of Calamity, Allen and Unwin, Syndey, 1983.

3. PALM, R.I., Natural Hazards: An Integrative Framework for Research and Planning, Johns Hopkins University Press, Baltimore, 1990.

4. DREZE J. and Sen A., Hunger and Public Action, Clarendon Press, Oxford, 1989.

5. DAVIES S., Buchanan-Smith M. and Lambert R., Early Warning in the Sahel and Horn of Africa: The State of the Art, Institute of Development Studies, University of Sussex, Brighton, 1991.

6. DOWNING T.E., Assessing Socioeconomic Vulnerability to Famine: Frameworks, Concepts, and Applications, World Hunger Program, Brown University, Providence, RI, 1991.

7. BORTON J. and Shoham J., Guidelines for WFP Country Offices Preparing Baseline Vulnerability Maps: The Sudan Case Study, Relief and Development Institute, London, 1991.

8. ANDERSON M. B. and Woodrow P.J., Rising from the Ashes: Development Strategies in Times of Disasters, Westview, Boulder, 1989.

9. WATTS M.J. and Bohle H.G., The space of vulnerability: the causal structure of hunger and famine, Progress in Human Geography, 1993, vol. 17, no. 1, 43-67.

10. CURREY, B. Mapping Areas Liable to Famine in Bangladesh, PhD. Dissertation, University of Hawaii, Manoa, 1979.

11. HULME M. Biot Y., Borton J., Buchanan-Smith M., Davies S., Folland C., Nicholds N., Seddon D., and Ward, N., Seasonal rainfall forecasting for Africa. Part I: Current status and future developments, International Journal of Environmental Studies, Section A: Environmental Studies, 1992, vol. 39, no. 4, 245-256.

12. MILLMAN S. and Kates R.W., Toward understanding hunger, In Hunger in History: Food Shortage, Poverty, and Deprivation, L.F. Newman, W. Crossgrove, R.W. Kates, R. Matthews and S. Millman, eds., Basil Blackwell, New York, 1990.

13. WORLD BANK, Social Indicators of Development 1989, World Bank, Washington, 1989.

14. WORLD BANK, World Development Report 1990, World Bank, Washington, 1990.

15. DOWNING T.E., Climate Change and Vulnerable Places: Global Food Security and Country Studies in Zimbabwe, Kenya, Senegal and Chile, Environmental Change Unit, Oxford, 1992.

16. HUNT D.M., The Impending Crisis in Kenya: The Case for Land Reform, Gower, Brookfield, VT, 1984.

17. DOWNING T.E., Lezberg S., Williams C. and Berry L., Population change and environment in central and eastern Kenya, Environmental Conservation, 1990, vol. 17, no. 2, 123-133.

18. KASSAM A.H., van Velthuizen H.T., Fischer G.W., and Shah M.M., Agroecological Land Resources Assessment for Agricultural Development Planning: A Case Study of Kenya; Resources Database and Land Productivity, Food and Agriculture Organization, Rome, 1991.

19. CENTRAL BUREAU OF STATISTICS, Population Projections for Kenya, 1980-2000, Central Bureau of Statistics, Nairobi, 1983.

20. DOWNING T.E., Climatic Variability, Food Security and Smallholder Agriculturalists in Six Districts of Central and Eastern Kenya, PhD Dissertation, Clark University, Worcester, MA, 1988.

21. DOWNING T.E., Gitu K. and Kamau C., eds., Coping with Drought in Kenya: National and Local Strategies, Lynne Rienner, Boulder, 1989.

10. Vulnerability and warnings

J. SALTER, Australian Emergency Management Institute, and
J. BALLY, J. ELLIOTT and D. PACKHAM, Australian Bureau
of Meteorology

INTRODUCTION

In this paper we consider severe weather related warning
systems in Australia and propose some vulnerability related
lessons that may have appropriate transfer potential to merit
consideration in relation to other hazards and locations.

Given vulnerability is in part a function of " ... the degree
of social- and self-protection available to potential victims"
(ref.1), then clearly, improved warning reduces vulnerability.
What then is the essence of warning? We suggest information.
Information is that which reduces uncertainty. Warning
information involves both warning messages in times of
emergency, and education about the general character of risk.
'Warning' incorporates the communication of risk in times of
impending emergencies, with the purpose of eliciting public
protective actions (ref.2). If appropriate protective action
is not elicited, then effective warning has not occurred.

The meaning of 'DUCK!', is different for hunter and hunted.
Meaning is what warning is about and meaning is contextual,
culture bound. If the warning message is not entirely in the
lexicon of the target audience then the warning must be
'decoded' by a process that relies on 'intrinsic' information,
ie that already possessed by the recipient. Then the coupling
of education and warning message is essential.

The severe weather and flood warning systems in Australia are
generally well served at the data collection, analysis and
prognosis 'hard end' of the systems. However, effective
warning requires the complete system to be functional. The
areas of the systems currently offering significant
opportunities for improvement and 'return for investment' are
related to communicating with the public(s) at risk. These
include the format of warning messages, techniques for
dissemination and the methods of public education. The 'soft
end' of the systems.

NATURAL DISASTERS

ISSUES

There are many issues surrounding warning messages and their
effectiveness. The following issue set has been developed
from the framework proposed by Mileti and Fitzpatrick (ref.2).
We have found it a useful set of prompts and considerations,
and have used it as the framework for workshops run to study
warning systems in Australia.

1. Elements of message construction

*   relates to 'what is said', the (warning) message itself.

    1.1   What are the 'necessary' key elements for inclusion
          in warning messages which contribute to 'sufficient'
          warning?
          Examples of elements might be:
          ►   a brief description of the danger
              (what is happening),
          ►   location specificity
              (where 'it' is and where 'it' is likely to
              go/impact),
          ►   likely severity of impact
              (what is likely to happen and what the
              consequences are likely to be),
          ►   guidance specificity
              (what protective action should be taken),
          ►   further advice
              (when and how the next warning message,
              and other information will be available).

    1.2   Is the most important information (for public
          safety) included at the start of messages?
          Should it be?
    1.3   Who is competent to provide action statements in
          warnings?
    1.4   Do warnings currently place too much emphasis on
          technical (scientific) details?
          How much is 'too much'?
    1.5   How much information about potential dangers should
          be included in warning messages (when realisation of
          the threat is in doubt)?
    1.6   The influence of the speed of onset of the event.
          (For example, what do you do differently for flash
          floods compared to other forms of flooding?)
              How do you convey a sense of urgency for one
              more than another? Do you need to?
    1.7   To what extent should risk communication involve
          graphic and visual material?
    1.8   If a set of guidelines on the style and content of
          warnings is desirable, who should develop it?

2. Clarity, understandableness

*   relates to 'how it is said', the simplicity of the
    message.

    2.1   To what extent do we use plain language and avoid
          traps (e.g. jargon)?

120

2.2 To what degree is it appropriate to use 'category systems' which aim to indicate the severity of any hazard agent?

2.3 Is it acceptable to mix units (e.g. Knots v km/hr)?

3. Consistency, accuracy, certainty and frequency

* relates to 'how well it is received'.
* consistency relates to ambiguities and discrepancies.

3.1 Is there consistency within the message itself, between the message and other communications / other agencies, and across time?

3.2 Are discrepancies between messages noted and explained in subsequent messages?

* accuracy relates to the extent to which the message is perceived by the public to be factual, accurate, timely and complete.

3.3 Does detail enhance credibility?

3.4 How much detail is 'enough'/'too much'?

* perceived certainty relates to the degree to which the message portrays confidence in what is being said.

3.5 How does the 'tone' of messages enhance perceived certainty?

3.6 What other issues are important in relation to 'how to deal with uncertainty' in extreme event problems?

* frequency relates 'to how often', and whether the message is reinforced.

3.7 How often is 'as often as necessary'?

4. Dissemination channel(s) and credibility

* dissemination channels relates to 'how it is delivered', the mechanisms through which risk information is disseminated.

4.1 To what extent are messages disseminated using a range of possible channels instead of a single channel to communicate to a public?

4.2 What does 'the media' need to be aware of in order to contribute to effective risk communication? How can this awareness be achieved?

* source credibility relates to 'who says so', the extent to which the source of risk information seems credible.

4.3 Is credibility of the information source maximised when it comes from one authority or a set of sources?

5. Personalisation and public participation

* personalisation relates to how characteristics of a

121

          community such as ethnicity, age, and gender shape risk
communication.

  5.1 To what extent are these factors considered when
       implementing risk communication programs?
  5.2 Should we have different messages for different
       clients?

*   public participation relates to how the community is
actively incorporated into risk communication programs
and feedback mechanisms indicating warning effectiveness.

  5.3 Is the community actively encouraged to participate
       in risk communication? If so, how?
  5.4 Are education and awareness programs structured to
       incorporate dialogue? If so, how?
  5.5 How can 'informal systems' be incorporated into the
       total warning (risk communication) system?

6. Boundaries, roles and responsibilities

*   relates to who makes decisions involving the above
issues, who participates in the decision processes.

  6.1 What if any (legal) liabilities are attached (e.g.
       action statements)?
  6.2 Are roles/responsibilities clearly delineated and
       understood?
  6.3 Who is responsible for 'workable plans' (e.g.
       evacuation) if the workability of a plan is also
       influenced by the effectiveness of the warning
       system?

MESSAGE STRUCTURE

These prompts were used during workshops involving a wide
range of clients of the Bureau of Meteorology's warning
service. These workshops examined the effectiveness of
selected warning systems in Australia. From the output of
these workshops, we submit the following considerations as a
model for structuring warning messages.

Not all information is of significance to all receivers of
warning messages. Public(s) at risk do not generally require
long messages of technical detail. However, some target
audiences may derive benefit from such detail. As a general
guide, aim for the least amount of detail necessary to
communicate. This model advocates a hierarchical message
structure to replace the dominant paradigm of single level
warning messages that emphasise technical detail.

Hierarchical messages should consist of two main areas. The
first, and essential segment should contain crucial
information for public safety expressed clearly and simply.
This essential area should be highlighted by an attention
grabbing header or title. As most agencies that originate
warnings do not have a comprehensive public dissemination
system it is likely that control of the message will be handed

over to a broadcaster. Therefore there is a chance that on occasion the title may be called upon to stand alone.

The second, and discretionary segment of the warning message could contain technical information for that segment of the audience who could use it, or advise how more information can be obtained.

Within the above segments of the warning message, there should be three components; information, forecast and warning. Each of these parts would have different prominence at different stages of an event. Variables which influence the specific nature of the above components relate to time, space, nature of the event and target audience(s). This relatively open-ended structure allows movement through different levels of advice as certainty and confidence increase. The primary advantage of such a structure is its accommodation of uncertainty and an associated retention of the issuing authority's credibility during the development or onset of an extreme event.

MESSAGE ELEMENTS

The question of which elements should be included in a warning message is widely recognised as a fundamental and crucial issue. This recognition extends to the assertion that there are key elements that need to be incorporated into warning messages.

Guidelines

A set of guidelines on the style and content of warnings should be developed. The development process needs to be 'user driven' using an extensive joint agency/stakeholder approach that includes public consultation wherever possible.

The identification of key elements should be negotiated by stakeholders. Ongoing and iterative processes are an appropriate way to integrate key elements into the structure of warning messages. These processes occur both 'pre-season' and during events.

Necessary elements to be incorporated by negotiation into the message to facilitate sufficient warning, include:

1) Sequencing of messages, by serial numbers
2) Date/time of issue
3) Issuing source/authority
4) Validity period
5) Target audience
6) Header or Title - threat descriptor
7) Synopsis
8) Prognosis
9) Location of phenomena and likely impact areas
10) Staging for action e.g., 'ready, set, go'.
11) Recommended public protective action
12) Availability of next warning

NATURAL DISASTERS

Action Statements

For warnings related to severe weather, the Bureau of
Meteorology is not the appropriate authority to determine
recommended action. It should, however, include within
warning messages recommendations for public protective action
agreed by the competent credible authorities. This would
generally be the 'lead combat authority' with expertise in its
particular hazard. Under this concept, the input of
appropriate individual agencies such as the Bureau of
Meteorology, Rural Fire Authority, and the State Emergency
Service would be clearly identified. Due to the short lead
times associated with many severe weather warnings, the Bureau
of Meteorology should have the delegation to choose and
assemble 'canned action statements' given certain weather
thresholds are reached. This demands the preparation of
action statements well before they are used.

Action statements should:

1)   refer to the most common/threatening dangers
     (e.g. 'flying roofing iron')
2)   concentrate on protective actions that can be
     undertaken in the time available
3)   employ (prearranged) graphics wherever appropriate
4)   be credited to the appropriate response agency
     (e.g. " ... and the police suggest... ")

CLARITY

Impact information needs to be understood by the receiver of
the message. Understanding is enhanced by presenting
information within a known context. For example, the standard
hydrological forecast of "gauge height" will be less effective
than an impact description specifying the probable depth of
flooding in the town (e.g. "to the top of the hotel door").

CATEGORY SYSTEMS

The description of phenomenon severity using predefined
categories, such as the tropical cyclone category system and
the McArthur fire danger rating scale, can cause some
misunderstanding or confusion when used in public warnings.
With numeric systems, a significant proportion of the public
are unclear over whether higher numbers signify a greater or
lesser threat.

Category systems that use technical classes such as "Minor",
"Moderate" or "Major" (flooding) are more easily interpreted
in that the class names alone carry some useful information
about severity. However even these can be misleading to a non
expert audience. For example, a message about "High" forest
fire danger may cause alarm. This is, in fact, a common
summer occurrence in southeast Australia and in some areas
"Very High" is also common and only "Extreme" fire danger need
elicit protective action. The jargon categories "High" and
"Extreme" carry very different technical meanings yet are all
but indistinguishable to many members of the public.

Category systems should not stand alone. The category should be supported by a self explanatory plain language phrase such as "category four cyclone with very destructive winds." Any category systems used for public warning should be consistent across the country.

THE USE OF MIXED UNITS FOR MEASURING PHENOMENA

The international marine and aviation industries use knots as their unit of speed. Wave heights are described in metres, cloud heights are in feet and visibility is in metres or kilometres. In contrast, public weather and warning services in almost all countries, including Australia, use the metric system. This sometimes results in two sets of forecasts / warnings for the same phenomena and area using different units. This clearly has the potential to cause confusion and is undesirable. However, a range of imposed conventions require it (e.g. international maritime conventions to use nautical miles) and this is problematic.

FREQUENCY

The frequency warning messages are issued depends on the nature of the event and the resources available to the warning agency. There should be preparedness and provision to receive and accept feedback to allow warning frequency to be modified to an appropriate level suited to each situation.

DISSEMINATION CHANNELS

The general strategy recommended is to use multiple channels. This maximises coverage and provides confirmation, especially when communicating with diverse communities. It becomes even more crucial when confronted with a fast onset event.

A range of technological opportunities are available to enhance dissemination, but high technologies are not always appropriate fixes. There is a need to overcome the overconfidence in the reliance by some groups on certain channels of communication. This problem of over-reliance is both technical and cultural.

Other constraints and limitations imposed on the choice of dissemination channels include:

1)   available lead time
2)   limits on the availability of distribution networks (e.g. the trend in the mass media to move from local broadcasters to regional networks)
3)   available technology

PUBLIC PARTICIPATION

Community participation is encouraged by warning authorities but presently this is only on an ad-hoc basis, is resource dependant and is currently not widely valued by the warners. Public participation needs to be systematically structured and provided for before the actual warnings are issued.

NATURAL DISASTERS

PUBLIC EDUCATION

The connections between education and effective warnings are
not simple. Education must be done well to have any real
effect. A realistic premise for emergency managers is 'when
developing warning systems and constructing warning messages,
one cannot assume any positive influence from public
education'.

With respect to public education, a multitude of channels and
methods is identifiable. The appropriate channels should be
linked to the nature and needs of the vulnerable populations.
Because lead time is not a constraint in public education, the
opportunity of exploring as many channels as possible exists.
Emphasis should be placed on the need to be innovative in a
world that is information rich and attention poor. Schools
should be targeted for incorporation of themes across the
curriculum, not merely within specific subject areas.
Opportunities exist for inclusion in sections of the main
stream mass media through story lines in serial dramas (soap
operas).

Progress in the way public education campaigns are conducted
in Australia has been quite marked over the last ten years.
Techniques have improved from the 'lots of text pamphlet,
occasionally shoved in the letterbox' to a range of 'slick,
sophisticated, and glossy, multi media' methods.
Nevertheless, these campaigns often treat risk as if it were
an objective phenomenon for the public at large to be informed
about, and this approach may well be fundamentally flawed.

Community analysis has advised some useful considerations in
the arena of public education and participation. Methods of
identifying community characteristics and vulnerabilities are
not new. Where vulnerability depends on proximity to hazard,
the severity of the physical impact at each location can be
easily identified. However, we are not all equally
vulnerable to the same hazard agent. Varley (ref.1) drew
attention to " ... the possibility of producing
socio-economic and spatial maps of vulnerability, rather than
mapping physical risk alone."

The identification and mapping of differential vulnerability
have been recognised for several years (ref.3) and been
applied within Australian emergency management using census
data available on Compact Disk Read Only Memory (CD ROM)
technology (ref.4). An example of such an application that
was used in 1988, is shown in Figure 1 "Inundation areas for
a dam failure above Canberra," and Table 1 "Selected community
characteristics by Collector's Districts (CD's)" (ref.4). This
data is useful for informing a range of considerations, from
logistics through to matters of culture.

Due to differences in characteristics such as ethnicity and
age, people derive different messages from the same
information. The implications of this for the management of
education campaigns are generally poorly understood by
warners.

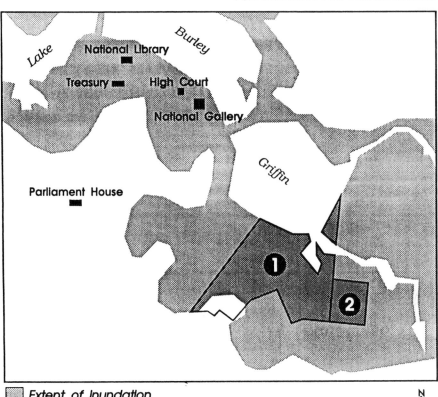

Fig. 1. Inundation areas for a dam failure above Canberra

CD (1986)	1	2
1) Total population	407	132
2) % same residence (1985)	46	91
3) %households income less than $15,000	4	11
4) % households income greater than $32,000	25	0

Table 1. Selected community characteristics by Collector's Districts (CD's)

NATURAL DISASTERS

In the delivery of warning messages, one may reasonably premise occasions when it will not be possible to provide separate warnings to embrace community diversity, therefore words should be simple enough to be accurately translated into other languages (by ethnic radio).

One of the most productive uses of public education may be in the encouragement of local self-help. This approaches risk as a social construct, to be negotiated. It requires developing an appreciation within the community of the high levels of uncertainty associated with severe weather phenomena coupled with a realistic understanding of other limitations of emergency service capability. This policy requires political will and is currently being trialled for some hazards in some parts of Australia (e.g. bushfire in Victoria, cyclones in Queensland). The net effect of such a strategy is to increase community resilience.

BOUNDARIES, ROLES AND RESPONSIBILITIES

Some difficulties (do and probably will) exist regarding overlapping interests and responsibilities. Varying perceptions exist regarding different responsibilities. However it is generally accepted that many groups and authorities share responsibility for and / or have an interest and influence in the 'complete' warning system. Therefore, an integrated planning process is needed. Any conflicts should be identified, clarified and if possible, resolved 'pre-season'.

The threshold of phenomena intensity at which it is appropriate to issue public warnings should be negotiated by all of the stakeholders in the warning system. Recent examples in Australia are the raising of the threshold for tropical cyclone warning in Queensland and the reduction of the threshold for fire weather warning in Tasmania. Risk affirms itself as a social construct rather than an 'objective/scientific' phenomenon.

CLOSING REFLECTIONS

Australia's providers of social-protection have shown a strong will to ask the right questions about warning and vulnerability; to ask difficult questions of their own role in the risk imposition equation. Asking the right questions progresses one along the path to appropriate solutions. There are several significant parts of Australian warning systems where progress has been quite marked and these are currently pioneering the way for the more cautious.

The most heartening progress is not in the realm of information formatting techniques. The linguistics and psychology of marketing and public relations have a role, but not a pivotal one. Their role is mainly in the 'wording of warnings'. The 'meaning of warning' and the methods of public education must be central. This is fundamentally a cultural and political question. The key is the provision of appropriate enabling processes. Processes founded on dialogue, which arm a community with an understanding of how and why they are vulnerable. Processes that provide appropriate resources and strengthened political structures. Processes that facilitate the development of resilience.

REFERENCES

1. VARLEY A. Diasters: Vulnerability and Response. Disasters, 1991, Vol. 15, No. 3, 285-287.

2. MILETI D.S.; FITZPATRICK C. Communication of Public Risk: Its Theory and its Application. Sociological Practice Review 1991, 2, 1, Jan, 20-28.

3. NORRIS D.A.: Disaster Demographics - Mapping high-risk populations can save lives during a catastrophe. American Demographics, 1987, Vol. 9, No. 8.

4. SALTER J.; TARRANT M. Computer manipulated census data and disaster management. The Macedon Digest, 1988, Vol. 3, No. 4, 4-5.

5. SALTER J. Public Education and Disaster Preparedness. Australian National Committee On Large Dams (ANCOLD) Bulletin, 1989, No. 83, 17-19.

Keynote paper. Countering natural disasters— a global view

A. J. ASKEW, J. B. MILLER and J. C. RODDA, World
Meteorological Organisation, Switzerland

ABSTRACT

Countering natural disasters continues to absorb the efforts
of a number of branches of science and engineering and a wide
range of institutions, both national and international. Amongst
the bodies of the UN system, the World Meteorological
Organization has global responsibilities for countering the
extremes of weather and water, through the upgrading of forecasts
and warnings, the improvement of predictions and in various other
ways.

Hurricanes, droughts, floods, storm surges and locust
plagues have occupied the attention of a number of WMO programmes
and this paper will present an overview of these activities.
Then it will focus on initiatives in the field of floods and
droughts and consider the progress and potential of the projects
launched by WMO in response to the IDNDR. It will conclude with
a look into the future at what needs to be done during the
remainder of the Decade and how this might relate to progress in
implementing the UNCED Agenda 21.

1. BACKGROUND

Natural disasters have threatened mankind since history
started. Now the news media report all too frequently the
occurrence of typhoons in the Philippines, droughts in the Sahel,
earthquakes in Guatemala and like phenomena. Horrifying pictures
of damage, destruction and loss of life appear on our television
screens, but there are many more smaller scale events which go
unnoticed by the press. These can be just as devastating for the
communities and groups of people concerned and often they do not
feature in the global statistics of disasters. Indeed, knowledge
on a world scale of natural disasters, particularly their
severity and impact, are not easy to collect and data bases on
disasters are generally incomplete. However, disasters of the
fluid earth, particularly floods and droughts, along with
typhoons, hurricanes and cyclones seem to be especially virulent
and they are not as restricted in a spatial and a temporal sense
as those of the solid earth.

Natural disasters. Thomas Telford, London, 1993

With the rapidly rising global population, which is estimated to reach 10 billion by the middle of the next century, the likelihood is that the impact of natural disasters will become even larger, by simple reason of the increase in the size of the target. There is also the potential of climate change which, coupled with sea level rise, may result in alterations in the magnitude and frequency of floods, cyclones, etc., as well as in making communities more vulnerable to them.

Since the International Decade for Natural Disaster Reduction (IDNDR) commenced on 1 January 1990 there has been a global focus for attracting attention to disasters; UN attention, government attention and NGO attention. Of course, the IDNDR has a number of different aims, but probably the most important is to seek to divert the present predilection for post-disaster relief to one concentrating on pre-disaster preparedness. Large amounts of money are usually given by donors to assist victims after a disaster has struck, for example, to Bangladesh, the Philippines or Ethiopia. These same donors could save themselves many millions by investing a little in "preparedness" in order to provide the warning systems that the poor countries lack. Such systems would provide the needed forecasts and warnings of the onset of disasters, and at the same time, they would produce data for the design of structures to resist these events better. The donor countries themselves have, of course, equipped themselves with such systems, systems which they employ with great effectiveness to save lives and reduce damage to property.

The IDNDR received attention during the preparations for the United Nations Conference on Environment and Development (UNCED) and its aims feature in the relevant parts of AGENDA 21, often as a result of the pressures that mounted in preparatory meetings, such as in the International Conference on Water and the Environment (Dublin, January 1992). In the follow up to UNCED, which is being discussed and planned in various fora, such as within the programmes of the World Meteorological Organization, attention is also being given to improved means for countering natural disasters.

2. ROLE OF WMO

The World Meteorological Organization (WMO) is a specialized agency of the United Nations system -- standing alongside FAO, UNESCO and WHO and about a dozen similar bodies. WMO celebrated its 40th anniversary in 1990, but international collaboration in meteorology started much earlier, in fact in 1877 with the founding of the International Meteorological Organization, the international body which existed until WMO was established. This collaboration is based on the essential need to exchange weather data for weather forecasting purposes, especially to warn of storms, droughts and related events. Now WMO, through its 169 Member countries and their national Meteorological and Hydrological Services, facilitates the exchange of these data. Through the World Weather Watch and its three components, the Global Data-processing System, the Global Observing System and the Global Telecommunication System, data are collected, transmitted and processed to produce forecasts and other products, which are then disseminated to users. Weather data become climate data with the passage of time and both weather and climate data are strongly linked to water data and to the data and products in other areas, such as agriculture. These connections have resulted over the years in WMO becoming concerned in a number of these allied areas, including not only hydrology but also oceanography and seismology and related areas of geophysics.

WMO consists of its 169 Members and the Secretariat in Geneva. The Organization does not fund research, but it encourages and facilitates the planning and organization of research and the establishment of the operational activities and standards that its constituent Meteorological and Hydrological Services need. The mechanisms used include meetings of various types, publications, support to education and training, technology transfer and capacity building undertaken on a world-wide basis, together with technical assistance projects.

The work of WMO is carried out through seven major programmes shared between the Secretariat and its Members. Four of these programmes are significant to the IDNDR. The most important of these is the World Weather Watch Programme (referred to above), which through its three components, coordinates the world-wide collection, processing and exchange of meteorological and related data for forecasting and other purposes (Table 1). It also includes a very effective programmme specifically geared to the forecasting of tropical cyclones and the upgrading of associated warning systems and preparedness measures. The Atmospheric Research and Environment Programme fosters and coordinates research on the structure and composition of the atmosphere, on the physics of weather processes and on weather forecasting. One area of this research is aimed at understanding the mechanisms that induce tropical cyclones in order to improve forecasting methods.

The World Climate Programme is involved with the subjects of climate variability and climate change including the assessment of drought and its impact (The component concerned with research into these phenomena, the World Climate Research Programme, also plays a vital role in this respect). The Hydrology and Water Resources Programme (HWRP) is the fourth programme of relevance to the IDNDR. A major area of its work is directed to the mitigation of water-related hazards, through support to the world's Hydrological Services aimed at improving their forecasting capabilities.

3. The IDNDR and WMO's Hydrological Initiatives

Since the early days of WMO, the Organization has been involved in hydrology. The HWRP now addresses three broad areas of concern for Hydrological Services, namely water resources assessment, mitigation of natural hazards and the impact of human activities on the aquatic environment. A capability for producing hydrological forecasts is the essential technology for countering floods and droughts, as well as for estimating water levels in navigable rivers, inflows into lakes and reservoirs and a large number of other variables of concern to the water sector. There are of course various types of floods, while droughts too can be classified in different ways, and there is also a range of hydrological forecasts (Table 2).

GLOBAL OBSERVING SYSTEM	GLOBAL TELECOMMUNICATION SYSTEM	GLOBAL DATA-PROCESSING SYSTEM
About 10 000 observation stations, 900 of which monitor the upper atmosphere	Links world, regional and national weather centres	3 World Meteorological Centres (Washington, Moscow and Melbourne)
Information from 7 000 ships, 3 000 aircraft, more than 600 radar stations and some 220 fixed and drifting buoys	Collects observed data and distributes globally	29 Regional Specialized Meteorological Centres
A space-based observing system comprising geostationary and polar-orbiting satellites	Distributes analyses and forecasts from data-processing centres	149 National Meteorological Centres

Table 1. The World Weather Watch and its three components

The following are definitions of standard terms used to identify the range of hydrological forecasts:

Term	Definition
Short-term hydrological forecast	Forecast of the future value of a hydrological element for a period no greater than two days from the issue of the forecast.
Medium-term (extended) hydrological forecast	Forecast of the future value of a hydrological element for a period ending between two and ten days from the issue of the forecast.
Long-term hydrological forecast	Forecast of the future value of a hydrological element for a period extending beyond ten days from the issue of the forecast.
Seasonal hydrological forecast	Forecast of the future value of a hydrological element for a season (usually covering a period of several months or more).
Hydrological warning	Emergency information on an expected hydrological phenomenon that is considered to be dangerous.

Table 2.   Types of hydrological forecast

Timely hydrological forecasts and the warnings issued as a result of the forecasts, can save lives, prevent damage and avoid disruption.   They are also important to the operation of hydraulic structures and the same data provide the basis for the design of these works.   Economic studies of flood forecasting systems demonstrate that their benefits are high and their costs are, in general, low by comparison.

The patterns of organization of hydrological forecasts vary widely from country to country (ref. 1) but normally they consist of the following components:

1.   a network of hydrological and meteorological stations
2.   a communications system for collecting the data
3.   a data processing system including a forecast model
4.   a communications system for disseminating the forecast.

The HWRP gives attention to the design of hydrological networks and to the operation of data collection systems.   To this end studies have been conducted of instrument performance, of different methods of network design and of the effectiveness of   different   communications   systems.   However,   particular

134

attention has been given to comparing the effectiveness of the hydrological models that make up the heart of most forecasting systems.

3.1 Intercomparison of Hydrological Forecasting Models

In 1974 WMO successfully completed a comparison of conceptual models used in operational hydrological forecasting (ref. 2). For the models considered, their basic structure, the data needs and the computational requirements were examined along with the accuracy with which they simulate flood hydrographs. A second intercomparison was conducted between 1977 and 1983 devoted to the study of models for forecasting snowmelt (ref. 3) terminating in a technical conference that evaluated the results.

A third intercomparison project commenced in 1985. In this case it took the form of a simulated real time intercomparison of hydrological models. The focus of the project was the workshop held at the University of British Columbia in Vancouver in early August 1987 where 14 models from 11 countries were compared on six flood events from each of the four data sets available to the project. The results of the workshop (ref. 4) were presented in a number of different ways, but the commonly used Root Mean Square Error (RMSE) statistic was selected as one of the most appropriate measures of model performance (ref. 5). Figure 1 shows one set of results for six of the different models on one set of test data. The models exhibited a wide range of accuracies. Although the small sample size made it was difficult to draw definitive conclusions about the overall performance of the models, the comparative statistics contain a wealth of useful information for those working in this field.

3.2 A Technology Transfer System in Hydrology

Many of the techniques required to prevent or mitigate disasters are well known, and computer programs, technical manuals, and instruments have been developed in a number of countries to implement these techniques. A means of making these more widely available is thus needed to enable all countries to benefit from their disaster reduction potential. A similar situation exists in a number of other technical fields. Some years ago WMO developed a system for transferring the technology used by operational hydrologists. This system, called HOMS[1], provides the technology required for hydrological data collection, processing and storage as well as for hydrological forecasting and analysis. The technology in HOMS is offered by the Hydrological Services of WMO Member Countries from amongst the techniques they use themselves in their normal operations. This ensures that the technology in HOMS is relevant to the purpose, and is fully operational. The technology is provided in the form of discrete components, for example a computer program to apply a flood forecasting model, a manual on river gauging, or a description of a recording raingauge with engineering drawings. Most are available free, or at only nominal cost. Since it started operations in 1981, some 2800 components have been transferred through HOMS. Currently 114 countries are participating in HOMS, and over 420 different components are available for transfer.

---

[1]Hydrological Operational Multipurpose System

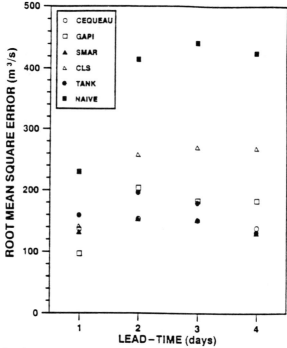

Fig 1.   Root mean square error for six models and different lead times using daily Bird Creek data

Many of the components in HOMS are of relevance to disaster prevention. These include components related to data bases which hold information required for risk analysis (or more strictly hazard analysis), methods of statistical analysis, models for hydrological forecasting and warning, monitoring instruments and data transmission components. As well, there are components for the many analyses which are required for pre-disaster planning purposes. A recent study showed that 143 components would be useful in disaster prevention, that is to say, about one third of all HOMS components. A sequence of 3 components in river flood forecasting gives a flavour of what is available:

C30.3.01   ALERT rain gauge
C71.3.01   ALERT river level station
F00.3.05   ALERT data collection substation

The first two of these report rain and river level by radio to the data collection substation, a suitably equipped PC which maintains a data base of the recorded data. A rainfall-runoff model, also running on the PC, provides a forecasting capability. This system is widely used in the USA for community based flood warning and it has been transferred through HOMS to a number of other countries.

3.3 Floods and Tropical Cyclones

The major sources of deaths from tropical cyclones are coastal storm surges and the floods caused by intense rainfall accompanying the cyclone. Consequently the programmes that WMO manages for combating the effects of tropical cyclones in each of the affected areas in the world have an important hydrological element based on predicting the storm surge and the flood and issuing flood warnings. An effective forecasting system depends on a large number of elements, each of which must work to enable a successful warning to be given. These include instrumentation to measure sea level, river level and rainfall (perhaps weather radar), data transmission, processing and storage systems, hydrological and meteorological analysis and modelling systems, and data displays, as well as methods to issue the warnings to the civil defence authorities, and through them to the media and the public. In any given system the relative importance of each element will differ, and if the overall system is to be assessed, a flexible method is needed. WMO has recently been using a system called MOFFS[2] developed in the UK for use in these assessments and based on experience gained in rating sewage works in Wales on their relative need for investment. The method gives a maximum score to each element of the forecasting and warning system depending on the importance of this element in the overall system. This maximum score for an element can be different in different systems, just as the different elements differ in their relative importance from one system to another. For example, in a river with a short time of concentration, precipitation measurements and the speed of data transmission would rate higher than in a large river where river level may be considered more important. The performance of each element is then rated against the maximum desired score. The total score obtained is a measure of the overall performance of the system, but the scores for major subsystems are probably more useful and give the system operator a valuable insight into where improvements are most needed. MOFFS is being used in all tropical cyclone areas as an aid to upgrading the hydrological component of each country's system.

3.4 Comprehensive Risk Assessment

Under the IDNDR, WMO is undertaking a number of projects aimed at improving disaster prevention capabilities. One of these is the Comprehensive Risk Assessment project which has been given the acronym CRASH. This project aims to demonstrate the use of modern technology, such as remote sensing, GIS, etc. in assessing the risks from a number of different types of disasters within a particular area. The project will assemble a number of experts in different types of disasters such as floods, earthquakes and volcanoes, to apply their risk assessment methods jointly to a particular region in a developing country. The project has had an initial meeting, and is planning to prepare a risk assessment manual to describe the techniques available. In a second phase these methods will be applied in the field. Switzerland has provided support to the project for the preparation of the manual and discussions are proceeding with different institutions who could undertake the field studies in

---

[2] Management Overview of Flood Forecasting Systems

the second phase.   At the same time, a field site is being selected with Guatemala, Kenya and the Philippines expressing interest.

3.5 Technology Exchange for Natural Disasters

The second IDNDR project described here is an extension of HOMS, described above.   This aims to develop a similar system for technology transfer, but in this case providing technology for disaster reduction purposes.   The hydrological component of this system will come from HOMS, which the discussion above shows to be a rich source of disaster related technology in hydrology. Links will be established with relevant institutions which have technology available for transfer.   As an example of what might be provided, consider the field of structural engineering, and the building of structures to withstand earthquakes and high winds.   Suitable components might include model building codes or methods, computer programs and manuals of structural analysis for earthquake and wind loads, and these might be provided at several levels, from the most simple to the most sophisticated.

3.6 Technical Co-operation activities

With funds provided by UNDP and through the WMO Voluntary Co-operation Programme, WMO has executed a large number of technical assistance projects in many different parts of the World.   These projects are undertaken with the meteorological and hydrological services of the countries concerned to meet pressing national or regional problems. A number of different fields have been covered but protection against natural disasters is the most important.

Of these projects, the one with the greatest potential for saving lives and reducing damage is concerned with Bangladesh. Following the disastrous cyclone which hit Bangladesh in 1987, a number of governments and bodies of the UN launched the Flood Action Plan (FAP).   One part of the FAP has been directed to improving the forecasting of the floods on the Ganges, Brahmaputra and Meghna in a project implemented by WMO in co-operation with the Government of Bangladesh.   The project involved the improvement of the data collection system, installation of an improved data base, the development and proving of a detailed forecast model and the issuing of warnings based on these forecasts.   The next stage of the project will involve the improvement of the channels for communicating these warnings so that they can reach the community level and the women's groups who represent the bulk of the vulnerable population.

4. Future Prospects

Mankind is currently facing a growing number of challenges. The application of science and engineering offers the prospect of surmounting the challenge concerned with natural disasters by providing systems for protection against them.

While the developed world has deployed extensive systems and methods for forecasting and warning which have demonstrated their value for combating the hazards of hurricanes, floods, droughts etc, the developing world, in general, lacks such systems.

Redressing this disparity is a fitting task for the IDNDR and for WMO, in co-operation with other bodies of the UN system, and with national agencies. It endeavours to extend the application of forecasting and warning systems to previously unprotected areas. It would be a very fine end to the Decade, if the population of the entire world could be protected from these disasters by the year 2000.

REFERENCES

1.   WMO 1993.   Guide to Hydrological Practices Fifth Edition. World Meteorological Organization (in press).

2.   WMO 1975.   Intercomparison of hydrological models used inoperational hydrological forecasting.   WMO Operational Hydrology Report No. 7 - World Meteorological Organization, 172p.

3.   WMO 1986.   Intercomparison of models of snowmelt runoff. WMO Operational Hydrology Report No. 23 - World Meteorological Organization, 36p.

4.   WMO 1987. Real-time intercomparison of hydrological models. Technical Reports to the Commission for Hydrology No. 23, 78p.

5.   WMO 1992.   Simulated real-time intercomparison of hydrological models. Operational Hydrology Report No. 38, 241p.

11. Geological investigations of tsunami generation and long-term tsunami frequency

A. G. DAWSON, S. SHI and D. E. SMITH, Coventry University, and D. LONG, British Geological Survey

INTRODUCTION

The word tsunami is derived from the Japanese word meaning harbour wave. Tsunamis are large ocean waves with very long wavelengths and very high velocities. They are frequently described as tidal waves but this view is incorrect since they have nothing to do with tides. Most tsunamis are generated by fault displacement on the seabed caused by earthquakes. However, many tsunamis are generated by submarine landslides and are therefore unrelated to seismic activity. In ocean floor areas where sediment or rock has been displaced, water rushes in from the surrounding sea to restore the water level. When this happens, there is a rapid lowering of sea level at the coast, usually below the level of the lowest tides. Thereafter, large kinematic waves travel outwards as a tsunami from the area located above the zone of seabed displacement. The velocity of the waves is mostly a function of the depth of the water over the area of seafloor at which the displacement or landslide has taken place. Areas of very deep water generate the fastest waves that may often exceed 480km/hr. The height of the waves in the open ocean is usually quite small (often no more than 1-2 m). so that sailors on ships often do not notice the passage of a tsunami. At the coast, the flood levels (runup) associated with a tsunami is partly a function of the dimensions of the propagated waves but it is also greatly influenced by the topography and bathymetry of the coastal zone where frequently the effects of wave resonance may result in the amplification of the advancing waves.

Tsunamis occur relatively infrequently and are most common in the Pacific region. For example, over 40 tsunamis have struck the Hawaiian islands since 1819 with five of these having caused severe damage and loss of life. Recently, during 1992, two exceptionally large tsunamis have attracted considerable media attention as a result of the considerable loss of life and widespread destruction that they caused. On 2nd September 1992, an offshore earthquake of magnitude 5.3 occurred west of the Pacific coastline of Nicaragua. The earthquake magnitude was remarkably low in proportion to the size of tsunami that was generated. Indeed, in some areas devastated by the tsunami, the earthquake was not even felt (Ref.1). However, the tsunami caused immense destruction along most of the Pacific coastline of Nicaragua and neighbouring Costa Rica. More recently, on 12th December 1992, a large tsunami followed an earthquake that occurred north of the island of Flores in Indonesia and led to the loss of life of approximately 2,000 people. In eastern Flores, several villages were completely destroyed by waves associated with runup levels up to a maximum height of 26m.

The relative infrequency of tsunamis and the complex processes of tsunami generation make it extremely difficult to predict the likely recurrence

Natural disasters. Thomas Telford, London, 1993

interval of tsunamis for any given coastal region. The greatest problem in estimating recurrence frequency is the limited timescale over which tsunamis have been documented. Usually this time interval corresponds to the length of time for which there is historical and archaeological evidence. Thus, whereas the list of known tsunamis in Hawaii extends no farther back than 270 years, our knowledge of historically documented tsunamis in the Aegean Sea region extends as far back as circa 1600 BC to the well-known Thera eruption on Santorini that is alleged to have led to the destruction of the Minioan civilisation.

RECENT DEVELOPMENTS IN GEOLOGICAL STUDIES OF PAST TSUNAMIS

During the last five years, tsunami research has been influenced by two developments in geology that have profoundly affected the perception of tsunamis as a coastal flood hazard. The first is the realisation that many tsunamis can be generated by submarine landslides as well as by earthquake -related fault activity. The most important consequence of this discovery has been that in the geological past, certain tsunamis have struck coastal areas that are typically aseismic and which have never conventionally been associated with such floods. A well-known example of this is the tsunami associated with the second Storegga submarine landslide that took place circa 7,000 years ago on the continental slope west of Norway (Refs. 2-4). The second development is that tsunamis cause sediment deposition as well as erosion in the coastal zone (Refs.2,5,6,7 and 8). Implicit in this apparently simple statement is the realisation that sedimentary evidence of many ancient tsunamis should be preserved in the geological record. This, in turn, means that long-term records of past tsunami activity along particular coastlines may be investigated by detailed geological studies of coastal sediment sequences.

The Storegga Slides

At present, relatively little information is available regarding the ages of the complex of three submarine landslides that occur on the continental slope west of Norway. The second Storegga slide, which was associated with the downslope movement of circa $1700km^3$ of material, is considered to have taken place between 5,000 and 8,000 yrs BP (Ref.9). However, a more accurate date of circa 7000 yrs BP has been obtained as a result of radiocarbon dating of coastal sediment believed to have been deposited by the tsunami generated by the landslide (Ref.2). Numerical models of the tsunami generated by this landslide give good agreement with the values of tsunami runup determined as a result of field observations (Refs.3,4).The most extreme water level fluctuations predicted by Harbitz are for western Norway where sea level may have fallen by as much as 10m during the period of tsunami drawdown. This was shortly followed by tsunami runup to an altitude of circa +10m with the entire 20m oscillation of sea level likely to have taken place within an hour. According to both the numerical models and field observations, the tsunami that struck the coastline of mainland Scotland a few hours later was associated with an average runup of 3-5m. The passage of the tsunami along the length of the British North Sea coastline is likely to have taken well in excess of 6 hours (Ref.10). Thus whereas in the Shetland Isles the tsunami may have struck the coast during high tide, in southeastern Scotland and northern England the flood may have reached the coast during mid-tide or possibly low tide. Surprisingly, no detailed investigation has yet been undertaken to examine the associated tsunami flood levels in the southern North Sea. Geological research is presently in progress to investigate the dimensions of runup of this tsunami along the western Norwegian coast, eastern Iceland,

Svalbard and the Shetland Isles

Relatively little information is available regarding the age of the first and third Storegga landslides. Oxygen isotope analysis of sediments resting upon

141

the first Storegga Slide, involving a movement of circa 3,900 km[3] of sediment
and rock, suggest a provisional age of circa 28,000 yrs BP (Jensen, personal
communication). If this age is approximately correct, then the landslide took
place shortly before the last major period of glaciation in NW Europe at a
time when regional sea level may have been considerably lower than present.
Thus, there is little likelihood that tsunami deposits associated with this
slide will ever be found except possibly within isolated offshore sediment
cores. The third Storegga slide is believed to have taken place shortly after
the second slide and a possible date of circa 6,000 yrs BP has tentatively
been suggested (Ref.11). At present, there is no convincing evidence of
tsunami deposits on land associated with this slide. The research of Harbitz
(Refs.3,4) appears to indicate that the tsunami runup levels are approximately
proportional to the average velocity of the submarine slide. Thus, whereas a
Storegga landslide moving at circa 15ms^{-1} is likely to have resulted in an
average runup of circa +1m, runup levels in the order of +10m are likely to
have been produced had the landslide moved at an average velocity of circa
50ms^{-1}. Harbitz (Refs.3,4) concluded that the modelled runup elevations of
circa 3-5m are consistent with a second Storegga landslide that moved
downslope at circa 35ms^{-1}.

Other slide-induced tsunamis

As many as 17 large submarine landslides/slumps and debris avalanches have
been described from the slopes of the Hawaiian island chain (Ref.12). One of
these features, the Alika phase 2 submarine slide/ debris avalanche, is
believed to have been responsible for one of the world's largest tsunamis that
took place circa 105,000 years ago and was associated with flood run-up levels
to an astonishing elevation of 326m above sea level along the southern
coastline of the island of Lanai (Ref.12). This tsunami is also believed to
have caused 20m high tsunami waves to strike the coastline of News South
Wales, Australia (Ref.13). The astonishing 326m tsunami runup elevation is
based on very detailed geological studies in which evidence purporting to
indicate former raised beach sedimentation on Lanai was reinterpreted as
indicative of a tsunami (Refs.13,14). A future test of the hypothesis that the
Alika phase 2 debris avalanche caused a giant tsunami throughout the Pacific
basin at circa 105,000 yrs BP will be to undertake a numerical simulation of
the debris avalanche using a modified Harbitz landslide model.

The fact that submarine landslides do not have to be extremely large to
generate tsunamis is illustrated by studies of the 1989 Loma Prieta earthquake
in California where tsunamis were generated by relatively small underwater
slumps triggered by earth tremors (Ref.1). Similarly, during the Flores
tsunami in Indonesia on December 12th 1992, submarine landslides are believed
to have caused exceptionally high tsunami runup (circa 20m) in the eastern
part of the island. By contrast, those parts of the coastline unaffected by
offshore landsliding were associated with tsunami runup elevations of circa 5m
(Ref.16).

TSUNAMI SEDIMENTATION AND RUNUP

Recent investigations in Scotland of coastal sediments deposited by the
tsunami associated with the second Storegga submarine slide have shown that
tsunami sediment deposition was associated with the development of sheets of
sediment that rise in altitude inland as tapering sediment wedges (Ref.2).
Tsunami deposits generally consist of massive accumulations of sands and
coarse silts although in rarer, extremely high-magnitude events, coarse
gravels and boulder-sized materials may be deposited (Refs.14,17). Generally,
patterns of tsunami sedimentation are determined by offshore sediment supply
and rock lithology. For example, in Flores, where the December 1992 tsunami
travelled over nearshore coral reefs, wave erosion resulted in the widespread
deposition of eroded coral boulders up to 1m in diamter (Ref.8). In other

areas, the Flores tsunami was observed to have been associated with the deposition of extensive sheets of sediment, up to 1m thick, that are continued landward by discontinuous sediment accumulations (Ref.8).

In most cases, it has been concluded that the landward limit of continuous sheets of tsunami-deposited sediment is represented by a tapering sediment wedge, the limit of which has been considered to represent a minimum estimate of former tsunami run-up since flooding may have extended farther inland without having resulted in sediment deposition (Refs.2,18). Recent studies of tsunami sedimentation associated with the Flores tsunami has shown that this view is only partly correct since continuous sheets of tsunami sediment are frequently continued landward by discontinuous and sporadic accumulations of tsunami sediment (Ref.8). These studies have shown that the identification and measurement of sediment accumulations deposited by individual tsunamis enables very detailed information to be provided on spatial variations in run-up. This information is particularly valauble since it enables numerical models of former tsunamis, where no documentary evidence of former runup exists, to be tested and calibrated against empirical data based on field observation (Refs.3,4 and 10). Furthermore, since it is often possible to trace and correlate individual sheets of tsunami-deposited sediment over wide areas, extremely detailed information on the spatial distribution of former tsunami runup levels can be obtained, thus enhancing the accuracy of the numerical model.

ACCURACY OF TSUNAMI NUMERICAL MODELS

Prior to the recognition that some tsunamis are produced as a result of submarine landslides, most numerical models of tsunamis sought to explain observed patterns of tsunami run-up in terms of earthquake-induced faulting of the seabed. If the runup predicted by a numerical model did not correspond with the pattern of runup observed at the coast, attempts were made to alter the parameters of the numerical model (usually the dimensions of the seabed fault plane), so that a greater degree of correspondence was obtained. The recognition of submarine landslide activity as an additional tsunami-generating mechanism, poses considerable problems since it is very difficult to determine if an individual tsunami has resulted from:-

(a) earthquake-induced fault activity
(b) a submarine landslide
(c) the combined action of earthquake-induced fault activity and submarine sliding

The Flores tsunami illustrates these problems very clearly. Here, the field observations of tsunami runup indicated that most of the northern coastline was associated with tsunami runup levels of no higher than 5m. By contrast, a small area of eastern Flores, near Riangkrok, was overwhelmed by waves that reached a maximum evelation of 26m above sea level. By contrast, the numerical model of the tsunami predicted that the maximum runup should have been no higher than 1.4m (Shuto and Imamura, unpublished information). The presence of submarine slumps close to the coast in eastern Flores led to the suggestion that the exceptionally high values of runup observed in this area are the product of nearshore submarine sliding rather than fault-plane induced tsunami waves (Ref.16). The Flores example therefore, represents a complex example of (c) above where spatial variations in tsunami runup appear to have been principally influenced by the spatial distribution of a series of small earthquake-induced submarine slides rather than by a single large submarine slide that took place at the same time as a seabed fault and an earthquake. Similar complex explanations can be used to account for the patterns of runup associated with other former tsunamis. For example, it has been argued that the 1946 Aleutian tsunami, which destroyed the city of Hilo in Hawaii, resulted from large-scale submarine sliding that took place during or after an episode of seabed faulting (Ref.1).

NATURAL DISASTERS

PROTECTION OF PEOPLE AT RISK

As a result of loss of life and damage to property caused by Pacific tsunamis, attempts have been made to develop tsunami warning systems the purpose of which is to alert the public in advance of the arrival of individual tsunamis. Tsunami warning systems did not exist for the Pacific prior to the Aleutian Trench earthquake of April 1st, 1946. Eventually, a tsunami warning system network was established by the United States Coast and Geodetic Survey with its headquarters on the Island of Oahu, Hawaii. The centre, known as the Pacific Tsunami Warning Centre (PTWC), became operational in 1948 and is now linked to over 30 seismographic stations throughout the Pacific Basin. These provide data on Pacific earthquakes whose magnitude and epicentres make them tsunamigenic (capable of producing tsunamis). Once an earthquake has taken place, the PTWC issues a tsunami watch to all receiving stations. In addition, the initial registration of a tsunami on tide gauges, is relayed to the PTWC and once the estimated times of tsunami arrival are computed for different coastal areas, a tsunami warning is issued by PTWC.

The accuracy of PTWC tsunami warnings is exemplified by the well-known Chilean earthquake and tsunami of May 21st, 1960. Once the earthquake epicentre had been determined and tide gauge data analysed, it was predicted that the tsunami would reach the Hawaian islands 14 hours and 56 minutes after its generation off the Chilean coast. The prediction was that the first wave would strike Hilo, Hawaii at 9.57 p.m. - it arrived one minute late.

The presence of a tsunami warning system is essential for the Pacific region due to the large number of tsunamis that are known to have taken place. However, large tsunamis are also known to have taken place in other parts of the world, albeit less frequently. Some of these tsunamis have been very destructive - for example the tsunami that accompanied the Lisbon earthquake of November 1st, 1755; the tsunami that followed the earthquakes in Sicily and Calabria on February 5th 1783 and December 8th 1908. Similarly, the Flores disaster demonstrates clearly that destructive tsunamis are not confined to the Pacific basin.

Since tsunamis are less frequent outside the Pacific region, it might be argued that the cost effectiveness of separate tsunami warning systems for other areas is very low. Until recently, this was the case in Portugal where on 1st November, 1755 AD, one of the highest magnitude earthquakes documented for Europe led to the complete destruction of the city of Lisbon. The earthquake, that was associated with the movement of a fault on the seabed on the Gorringe Bank west of Portugal, produced an extremely large tsunami that caused widespread damage and loss of life across a coastal zone stretching from northern Portugal to southern Morocco. In Lisbon alone, approximately 50,000 people were killed with most being drowned by the tsunami which reached 17-20m in height in many areas.During recent decades, two other tsunamis have struck the Portugal coast, one on 25th November 1941 and the other on 28th February 1969. Both tsunamis were generated as a result of crustal movements along the Gorringe Bank and fortunately both were of a relatively small magnitude. The Portuguese authorities, aware of the risk to coastlines posed by tsunamis, are presently planning the positioning of seismometers and wave recorders west of Portugal with the aim of providing advance warning of any future tsunmai similar to that which struck Lisbon in 1755. In many areas of the world, however, coastal populations have no protection from tsunamis and rely on chance that no tsunamis will ever strike the particular coastline on which they live. Unfortunately for the people of Flores and Nicaragua, chance was not on their side.

Geological studies of former tsunamis can contribute greatly to our knowledge of the susceptibility of particular coastal areas to tsunami flooding. In particular, such studies offer the potential of being able to provide information on the long-term frequency of tsunamis for particular coastal areas. Thus, for example, we now know that a major tsunami, generated by a large submarine landslide, struck many coastal areas of NW Europe circa 7,000 years ago. We also know as a result of geological investigations that two other submarine slides in the Storegga area, at circa 28,000 and 6,000 years ago are both likely to have generated tsunamis. All three landslides took place as a result of slope failure along a 100-150km stretch of continental slope. The potential danger of tsunami flooding of the coastline of NW Europe is largely a function, therefore, of the stability or otherwise, of this area and its susceptibility to future slide generation. Remarkably, no such studies have been undertaken or are planned.

ACKNOWLEDGEMENT

D. Long publishes with permission of the Director of the British Geological Survey, NERC.

REFERENCES

1. OKAL, E A Predicting large tsunamis. Nature, 1993, vol.361, 686-687.

2. DAWSON, A G, LONG, D and D E SMITH The Storegga Slides: evidence for a possible tsunami from eastern Scotland. Marine Geology, 1988, vol.82, 271-276.

3. HARBITZ, C B Model simulations of tsunami generated by the Storegga slide. Institute of Mathematics, University of Oslo, 1991, Series No. 5, 30pp.

4. HARBITZ, C B Model simulations of tsunamis generated by the Storegga Slides. Marine Geology, 1992, vol.105, 1-21.

5. ATWATER, B A and YAMAGUCHI, D K Sudden, probably coseismic submergence of Holocene trees and grass in coastal Washington State. Geology, 1991, vol.19, 706-709.

6. MINOURA, K and NAKAYA, S Traces of tsunami preserved in inter-tidal lacustrine and marsh deposits: some examples from Northeast Japan. Journal of Geology, 1991, vol.99, 265-287.

7. DARIENZO, M E and PETERSON, C D 1990 Episodic tectonic subsidence of Late Holocene salt marshes, northern Oregon and central Cascadia margin. Tectonics, 1990, vol.9, 1-22.

8. SHI, S, DAWSON, A G and D E SMITH (in press) Geomorphological impact of the Flores tsunami of 12th December, 1992. 1993, Natural Hazards.

9. BUGGE, T Submarine slides on the Norwegian continental margin, with special emphasis on the Storegga area. Continental Shelf and Petroleum technology Research Institute A/S publ. 1983, no.110, 152pp.

10. HENRY, F and MURTY, T (in press) Model Studies of the effects of the Storegga slide tsunami. 1992, Science of Tsunami Hazards.

11. JENSEN, E, BEFRING, S, BUGGE, T, EIDVIN, T, HOLTEDAHL, H and H.-P. SEJRUP Large submarine slides on the Norwegian continental margin: sediments, transport and timing. Marine Geology, 1987, vol.78, 77-107.

12. MOORE, J G, CLAGUE, D A, HOLCOM, R T, LIPMAN, P W, NORMARK, W R and M E TORRESAN Prodigious subamrine landslides on the Hawaiian Ridge. Journal of Geophysical Research, 1989, vol.94, 17,465-17,484.

13. STEARNS, H T Geology and groundwater resources of the islands of Lanai and Kahoolawe, Hawaii. Hawaii Division of Hydrography Bulletin 1940, vol.6, 177pp.

NATURAL DISASTERS

14. YOUNG, R W and BRYANT, E A Catastrophic wave erosion on the southeastern coast of Australia: impact of the Lanai tsunamis ca. 105ka? Geology, 1992, vol.20, 199-202.

15. MOORE, J G and MOORE, G W Deposit from a giant wave on the Island of Lanai, Hawaii. Science, 1984, vol.226, 1312-1315.

16. KANAMORI, H and KIKUCHI, M The 1992 Nicaragua earthquake: a slow tsunami earthquake associated with subducted sediments. Nature, 1993, vol.361, 714-716.

17. YEH, H and IMAMURA, F Tsunamis of the Flores Island Earthquake. 1993, Unpublished report.

18. MOORE, G W and MOORE, J G Large-scale bedforms in boulder gravel produced by giant waves in Hawaii. Geological Society of America, Special Paper 1988, vol.229, 101-110.

19. DAWSON, A G, FOSTER, I D L, SHI, S, SMITH, D E and D LONG The identification of tsunami deposits in coastal sediment sequences. Science of Tsunnami Hazards, 1991, vol.9, 73-82.

12. The project GITEC: a European effort to address tsunami risk

S. TINTI, University di Bologna

INTRODUCTION

GITEC is an acronym standing for ''Genesis and Impact of Tsunamis on the European Coasts'' and is the name of an international scientific project with the ultimate goal of contributing to reduce hazards and risks associated with tsunamis affecting the European countries. Tsunamis are long sea waves produced by a large and abrupt deformation and/or displacement of the sea floor. One frequent generation mechanism is a submarine earthquake causing substantial vertical movements of the sea bottom in the epicentral region. Other important causes of tsunamis are submarine landslides and slumps on slopes with unstable and thick sedimentary cover as well as explosive eruptions of submarine or coastal volcanoes. Tsunami waves travel very fast in the open sea and tend to slow down as they approach the coasts, since their propagation velocity is proportional to the square root of the ocean depth to a first approximation. A large tsunami can cause vast destruction all along the invested coasts in the proximity of its source region; but unfortunately, since long water waves travel with no substantial loss of energy, it can produce severe damage even several hundreds or some thousands of kilometers away from the generation region.

Most tsunamis occur in the Pacific ocean. Europe however is neither immune from tsunami attacks nor safe. The existing catalogs of tsunamis report some three hundreds events which occurred in the European seas in historical times, the first one being that traditionally attributed to the Santorini explosion (circa 1400 BC) in the Aegean Sea. The most affected countries are Greece and Italy in the Mediterranean and Portugal in the Atlantic ocean. But tsunamis have been reported even in the Black Sea and in the Marmara Sea, and coastal areas in Northern Europe as well are exposed to tsunami threat. Norwegian fjords are periodically affected by tsunamis produced by rockfalls from the coastal cliffs. Recent geological studies have identified coastal deposits of paleotsunamis which took place in Holocene times and were caused by a series of huge slides that occurred in the Storegga area in the Northern Sea: very likely the whole basin was affected by the ensuing sea waves.

Some of the European tsunamis are classed amongst the largest or the most disastrous ever observed in the world. For example the November 1, 1755 tsunami, following an earthquake occurred in the Gorringe Bank area, about 250 km offshore of Cape St.Vincent (southern Portugal), struck with disastrous waves Portugal and the Atlantic coasts of Spain and was observed thousands of miles far from the source in Ireland, West

NATURAL DISASTERS

Indies and northern Africa. From tsunami data Abe (ref.1) was able to estimate the magnitude of the generating earthquake to be about 8.5-9.0, that is in the range of the major tsunamigenic earthquakes affecting Japan.

The disaster that can be caused by a violent tsunami was impressively shown by two recent events that occurred in September and in December of 1992. On 2 September 1992 a large thrust earthquake (the moment magnitude estimated from long-period surface waves is Mw=7.6, ref.2) with epicenter about 100 km offshore Managua set in motion a tsunami that struck the neihgbouring coasts of Nicaragua causing severe damage and loss of lifes. And even more devastating was the tsunami that took place on 12 December 1992 as a consequence of a Ms=7.5 (NEIC estimate) earthquake with epicenter in the Bay of Maumere. The waves invested the northern coast of the island of Flores causing vast destruction, substantial environmental changes, such as erosion of long strips of the coastline, and a lot of victims: more than 2,000 people lost their lives because of this disaster and approximately 50% are ascribed to the tsunami. The observed tsunami runup was on average about 4-5m, but locally at the eastern promontory of the bay wave heights larger than 25m were measured, probably as a result of submarine landslides (refs 3-4 and personal communications from the international tsunami survey team).

Tsunamis constitute a serious source of natural hazard and of risk for environment and populations over very extended coastal areas of Europe. The 2-year project GITEC, that is financed by the European Community within the framework of the programme Environment, addresses this problem in a global way, being based on a systematic approach which involves international and interdisciplinary cooperation among European partners: it engages seismologists, oceanologists, marine geologists, sedimentologists, numerical modellers, hydraulic engineers, experts in urban planning originally from six European countries, namely France, Greece, Italy, Norway, Portugal and United Kingdom, with the recent addition of Bulgaria.

TSUNAMI RESEARCH IN EUROPE

The development of the modern research on tsunamis in Europe started 35 years ago and was impelled by the occurrence of a large tsunami that from the source region close to the islands of Amorgos and Astipalaia involved the whole Aegean Sea (ref.5). This was a key-event because to a scientific community which until then had not shown too much concern on this problem, it was reminded with strong and crude evidence that tsunamis do have a large potential of destruction. A second support to the European research came in those years by the parallel growth of interest on tsunamis in the main countries of the Pacific ocean, i.e. USA, USSR and Japan, as a result of two extremely large tsunamis: the 1960 Chilean and 1964 Alaskan earthquakes, both with fault ruptures as long as some hundreds of kilomenters (Mw=9.5, Mt=9.4 and Mw=9.2, Mt=9.4 respectively, refs 1 and 6) produced sea waves that hit the nearby coastlines with great violence and that were able to cause severe damage even hundreds of miles away from their source across the Pacific. The International Tsunami Commission (ITC), that was created in 1960 as a body of the International Union of Geodesy and Geophysics (IUGG), and the ITSU group (International Coordinating Group for the Tsunami Warning System in the Pacific within the Intergovernmental Oceanographic Commission - UNESCO), that came to light a few years later, are two examples of an internationally integrated reaction to the worldwide growing awareness and perception of the tsunami menace.

The first European investigations were mainly focussed on compilations
of tsunamis (see e.g. Galanopoulos, 1960, ref.7) and created a
potentially fruitful basis for further studies. Strangely enough,
however, European research rapidly and blamably declined, disappearing
almost completely from the international scene until the end of the
'80s, when the International Working Group on tsunamis was formed by the
European scientists within the European Geophysical Society (EGS). Since
then this group, which nowadays is included in the Interdisciplinary
Working Group on Natural Hazards (EGS), has been extremely active
in promoting studies on tsunamis in Europe and has been a steadily
important reference point for all European specialists (ref.8).

Greece and Italy

Greece and Italy are the European countries most exposed to tsunami
threat. Recent tsunami catalogs (refs 9-10) showed that tsunami
events have been observed on all the Greek coastlines, and allowed to
delineate, at least broadly, the most tsunami-prone regions. The island
of Crete, the Cyclades islands, including Santorini, and the Corinthian
Gulf are among the most active tsunamigenic sources (refs 11-12). The
greatest tsunami of seismic origin which took place in the Mediterranean
in historical times, was initiated near Crete on 21 July 365 AD and
invested the entire eastern basin according to the coeval sources, but
it was also observed along the Ionian Sicilian coasts and possibly in
the Adriatic sea (ref.13). It is still under discussion if this tsunami
source was north or south of Crete, though recent seismotectonic studies
support the latter hypothesis by identify the generation area in the
outer compression zone of the Hellenic Arc (refs 11 and 14).

The occurrence of tsunamis in the Italian seas is very well documented.
The Italian catalogs were produced mainly by extracting relevant
information from the existing catalogs of earthquakes and volcanic
eruptions (ref.15), whereas the present research points to i) a
critical revision of the historical records in order to obtain a better
reconstruction at least of the major events and a more valuable base of
data to support hazard and risk evaluations (see e.g. refs 16-18) as
well as to ii) a general reconsideration of the catalog skeleton and
basic criteria in order to provide a prizable and serviceable tool for
tsunami research (ref.19). Tsunami potential evaluations have been
repeatedly attempted by means of ever more refined methods and checked
toward the known tsunami records: these investigations show that the
highest expected activity in Italy is attributed to the Messina Straits
and the surrounding seas, i.e. the Tyrrhenian to the north and the
Ionian sea to the south, the coastlines most threatened being eastern
Sicily and western Calabria (ref.20). Other source regions deserving
careful investigations are the Gargano promontory in southern Adriatic
where historical sources report of a potentially devastating tsunami
that took place in 1627 (ref.21) and the Ligurian sea, where submarine
landsliding and slumping is believed to be a credible mechanism of
tsunami generation in addition to earthquakes. Tsunamis of volcanic
origin are in Italy not negligible and are mainly associated with the
activity of Vesuvius in the Gulf of Naples, and of Stromboli and Vulcano
in the Aeolian Islands (ref.22)

France and Portugal

Tsunamis in France are not frequent, but there are examples of events
affecting the Côte d'Azur where submarine landslides can be mobilized
either by intrinsic instability or by earthquake triggering producing
water waves locally dangerous, likewise in the nearby Riviera di Ponente

(western Ligurian sea): the last known relevant case occurred in 1979 offshore the Nice airport resulting in a sequence of waves travelling along the coasts and reaching their maximum amplitude at Antibes on the opposite side of the bay. Research is therefore mainly focussed on problems of waves generation by underwater mass·displacements: particular emphasis is posed on numerical simulations and on hydraulic experiments in tanks in order to improve the understanding of the energy tranfer from the sliding material to the water and the role of nonlinearities in waves propagation (refs 23-24). But France is the European country which, due to its overseas provinces located in the Pacific ocean, has the most direct experience of the great Pacific tsunamis. As a result, a quite important chapter of the French research regards methods for tsunami fast detection and warning as well as tsunami protection. The concept of mantle magnitude Mm, that is of an earthquake magnitude evaluated on the basis of the long period mantle waves recorded by a single seismic station, was developed to allow a quick estimate of the tsunami potential of an earthquake and the efficiency of the method has been tested satisfactorily in the French Polinesia (refs 25-27) and showed to be reliable even for the December 1992 Flores tsunami (ref.3).

Research in Portugal is predominantly concentrated on the tsunamis generated in the Gorringe Bank, some 250 km offshore Portugal, which is the most dangerous tsunamigenic source for the Atlantic coasts of the Iberian peninsula (ref.28). The largest tsunami known to have struck the Portuguese coasts was generated here in 1755: it caused extensive damage in several coastal towns as well as deep geomorphological littoral changes (ref.29). Also here it was produced a small event in 1969, while some 300 km to the west another small event took place in 1975. These tsunamis were recorded by a number of tide-gauges located in Portugal, in Spain and in Morocco and it is worthwhile pointing out that these mareograms are one of the few examples of instrumental records of tsunamis in Europe (ref.30). The Gorringe Bank area is one of the European tsunamigenic regions that are most distant from the coastline: this means that, if a tsunamigenic earthquake takes place in the open ocean, the ensuing tsunami takes some time before reaching dangerously the coasts. Recognizing the tsunami potential of such earthquake is then essential to issue a beneficial warning to the population. Studies to device and develop a proper tsunami warning system based on ocean bottom seismic sensors and satellite broadcasting have been undertaken. The warning system called DETWS is still in an experimental phase (ref.31)

Northern Europe

Tsunamis in northern Europe seas are much more unfrequent than in the south of Europe. Seismicity is at a level too low to be responsible for major events. Local tsunamis are known to be occasionally generated in fjords in Norway by slides sinking into the sea water, such in the 1934 tsunami in the Tafjord fjord (ref.32). Large tsunamis in the Atlantic can also penetrate the northern seas and be observed in northern Europe (this was the case of the 1755 Lisbon tsunami). Recent investigations have revealed that the Northern Sea was involved in Holocene times by a series of giant tsunamis caused by huge submarine landslides, known as Storegga slides, their volume being in the range of 3-4 10^3 km^3 of sediments. This research has been primarily undertaken by geologists studying tsunami deposits along Scotland coastlines and supported by evidences found in the Norwegian coastal lakes, and has stimulated numerical modeling of the wave generation and propagation across the Northern Sea (refs.33-36).

GITEC PARTICIPANTS

GITEC is an international project that is based on a multinational collaboration and a multidisciplinary approach. The organizations taking part in the project are: University of Bologna (DFGEO, project coordinator) and University of Genoa (DISTER), Italy, Coventry University (CU), United Kingdom, Laboratoire de Géophysique (LDG), France, University of Lisbon (CGI), Portugal, Hellenic Air Force Academy (HAFA), and Institute of Geology and Mineral Exploration (IGME), Greece, University of Bergen (UIB) and University of Oslo (UIO), Norway. An additional partner joining the project after its beginning is the Geophysical Institute of the Bulgarian Academy of Sciences, Sofia, Bulgaria.

GITEC GOALS

GITEC represents a basic integrated approach to the investigation of tsunamis in the European area, which means that it intentionally embraces a broad spectrum of activities on various scientific fronts and in different geographical regions. As regards the scientific topics, they may be simply classed into four categories: 1- tsunami generation, 2- tsunami potential, 3- tsunami propagation and end effects, 4- tsunami warning and tsunami risk mitigation.

The generation mechanism of a tsunami is only partially understood, though in principle it is a simple process of water waves excited by a sudden ocean floor displacement or by a mass collapsing into the sea. What is still not perfectly known, however, is the mechanism and efficiency of the earth-to-ocean energy transfer in the initial nucleation phase, which can only be modelled in a gross way due to the unexplored role of turbulence and dissipation. One of the GITEC objectives is to investigate the generation mechanism of tsunamis produced by earthquakes and by submarine or subaerial landslides. As regards tsunamis of seismic origin, particular emphasis will be posed on near-coast generation mechanism since most of the European tsunamis have a source region very close to the shoreline (mainly DFGEO). Landslide-induced tsunamis will be also studied. Hydraulic experiments in tanks with controlled sliding blocks will be performed to investigate the water waves excitation process (LDG). Special seismic and bathymetric ship campaigns will be carried out in order to evaluate sediment cover thickness in areas of the Ligurian Sea (DISTER) and the Aegean Sea (IGME) characterized by high-slope morphology and to possibly identify regions in conditions of critical instability.

Assessment of tsunami potential in the European seas will be based on a primary revision of the existing regional tsunami catalogs and on their integration by using unifying criteria, with the aim of producing a preliminary data bank in digital form (mainly DFGEO, CGI and HAFA in cooperation with ING, i.e. the Istituto Nazionale di Geofisica, Rome). This should be made available to the scientific community, to the decision-makers and in general to the public administrators. Further investigations based on statistical methods will help identify the most important tsunamigenic sources in Greece, in Italy and in the Atlantic ocean (DFGEO, CGI and HAFA). To this end also geological methods, where possible, will be used to estimate event return times from tsunami signatures preserved in coastal cored and dated deposits (CU and UIB).

151

NATURAL DISASTERS

Tsunami wave propagation in the open ocean, wave modification in shallow waters and tsunami effect on the coasts are of special interest primarily to identify coastline segments particularly exposed to wave attacks. Numerical models will be employed to simulate wave radiation of great events (at least one for Greece, for Italy and for Portugal in addition to the last Storegga case involving the Northern Sea, (DFGEO, LDG, HAFA and UIO)) as well as wave runup in selected areas, known to have been invested by large tsunamis, such as for example the 1755 Lisbon case (LDG and UIO). This event seems to be exceptionally suitable because the recent rather well documented 1969 tsunami that was generated in the same area can provide good data for model calibration (CGI). Wave impact on the coast can also be inferred by studying sand deposits along shallow coasts and coastal lagoons and lakes for prehistorical or poorly documented historical events (CU and UIB).

Tsunami risk reduction is a goal of primarily importance from a socio-economic point of view. The problem is very complex and is addressed in a preliminary way in the GITEC framework. Warning systems for tsunamis can be effective only where the generation region is somewhat offshore and the time elapsing between the tsunami onset and the tsunami impact against the coast is sufficiently long to allow launching alert or alarm signals. This condition is frequently matched in the Pacific, and is also fulfilled for the Gorring Bank tsunamigenic region offshore Portugal. This region will be monitored by two independent systems, namely DETWS developed by CGI and TREMORS developed by LDG. The former is based on a set of sensors installed in a buoy placed in the source region and transmitting to a central station via a satellite link. The core of the latter consists of a single seismometer station capable of recording long mantle waves and to timely infer source coordinates and origin time. It is one of the GITEC objectives to compare the performance and efficiency of the two systems preparing the basis for a future possible integration. A second facet of risk reduction regards tsunami mitigation strategies that can be developed by means of proper long- and medium-term policies: in a pilot approach a few sites will be considered in Crete (Heraclion and surrounding) to study plans of urban and territorial develpoments specifically appropriate for minimizing the effects of a tsunami attack (HAFA).

CONCLUSIONS

GITEC has been conceived mainly to fill a dangerous gap in the field of tsunami hazard assessment, since this problem has been substantially overlooked for many years in Europe. Consider that, at the present time, should a large tsunami unfortunately occurr somewhere in Europe, we would be essentially unprepared and we will have no defense. In the course of its two-year lifetime, GITEC will pose the basis for future detailed research. At the end of GITEC we will have a clearer knowledge of the most important tsunami sources, improved numerical models to investigate tsunami excitation and radiation, a better know-how on tsunami warning systems and some basic guidelines for tsunami mitigation.

ACKNOWLEDGMENTS

The author acknowledges that this work describes the activities performed in the project GITEC, involving many organizations and researchers. He is therefore thankful to all participants in the project. GITEC is financed by the European Community in the framework of the programme ENVIRONMENT under the contract EV5V-0175 and with an additional contribution from the programme ''Cooperation in Science and

Technology with Central and eastern European Countries'' to cover the Bulgarian group participation.

REFERENCES

1. ABE K. Size of great earthquakes of 1837-1974 inferred from tsunami data, J.Geophys.Res., vol.84, 1561-1568.

2. KANAMORI H. and KIKUCHI M. The Nicaragua earthquake: a slow tsunami earthquake associated with subducted sediments, Nature, 1993, vol.361, 714-716.

3. OKAL E. Predicting large tsunamis, Nature, 1993, vol.361, 686-687.

4. YEH H. Disaster on Flores island, Nature, 1993, vol.361, 686.

5. PAPAZACHOS B.C., KOUTITAS C., HATZIDIMITRIOU P.M., KARAKOSTAS B.G. and PAPAIOANNOU C.A. Source and short-distance propagation of the July 9, 1956 southern Aegean tsunami, Marine Geology, 1985, vol.65, 343-351.

6. ABE K. and KANAMORI H. Magnitudes of great shallow earthquakes from 1953 to 1977, Tectonophysics, 1980, vol.62, 191-203.

7. GALANOPOULOS A.G. Tsunamis observed on the coasts of Greece from antiquity to present time, Annali di Geofisica, 1960, vol.13, 369-386.

8. TINTI S. Tsunami research in Europe, Terra Nova, 1990, vol.2, 19-22.

9. PAPADOPOULOS G.A. and CHALKIS B.J. Tsunamis observed in Greece and the surrounding area from antiquity up to the present times, Marine Geology, 1984, vol.56, 309-317.

10. SOLOVIEV S.L. Tsunamigenic zones in the Mediterranean Sea, Natural Hazards, vol.3, 183-202.

11. PAPAZACHOS B.C. and DIMITRIU P.P. Tsunamis in and near Greece and their relation to the earthquake focal mechanism, Natural Hazards, 1991, vol.4, 161-170.

12. PAPADOPOULOS G.A. and SKAFIDA H. Tsunami hazard probability in the Gulf of Corinth, Greece, Annales Geophysicae, Special Issue on XV EGS General Assembly, 1990, 336.

13. JACQUES F. and BOUSQUET B. Le raz de marée du 21 juillet 365. Du cataclysme local à la catastrophe cosmique, Mélanges de l'Ecole Française de Rome, Antiquité, vol.46, 423-461.

14. TINTI S. Contributions expected from marine geodesy to the study of tsunamis in the Mediterranean Sea, Marine Geodesy, 1990, vol.14, 243-254.

15. CAPUTO M. and FAITA G. Primo catalogo dei maremoti delle coste italiane (in Italian), Atti dell'Accademia Nazionale dei Lincei, Memorie, Classe Scienze Fisiche, Matematiche e Naturali, Serie VIII, 1984, vol.XVII, 213-356.

16. TINTI S. and GIULIANI D. The Messina Straits tsunami of the 28th of December 1908: a critical review of experimental data and observations, Il Nuovo Cimento, 1983, vol.6C, 424-442.

17. TINTI S. and GUIDOBONI E. Revision of tsunamis occurred in Calabria and Sicily (Italy), Science of Tsunami Hazards, 1988, vol.6, 17-22.

18. GUIDOBONI E. and TINTI S. The largest historical tsunamis in the Northern Adriatic, Science of Tsunami Hazards, 1989, vol.7, 45-54.

19. MARAMAI A. and GASPARINI C. A proposal for a new catalog on tsunamis in the Mediterranean area, Science of Tsunami Hazards, 1991, vol.9, 39-46.

20. TINTI S. Assessment of tsunami hazard in the Italian Seas, Natural Hazards, 1991, vol.4, 267-283.

21. GUIDOBONI E. and TINTI S. A review of the historical 1627 tsunami in the Southern Adriatic, Science of Tsunami Hazards, 1988, vol.6, 11-16.

22. TINTI S. and SARACENO A. Tsunamis related to volcanic activity in Italy, in ''Tsunamis in the World'', S.Tinti (Ed.), Kluwer Academic Publishers, Dordrecht, The Netherlands (in print).

23. Heinrich P. Etude numérique et expérimental des vagues générées par des effondrements de terrain, Thèse de Doctorat, Ecole Central de Paris, France, 1991.

24. Heinrich P. Nonlinear numerical model of landslide-generated water waves, Int.J.Engineering Fluid Mech., 1991, vol.4, 403-416.

25. OKAL E.A. and TALANDIER J. Mm: a variable-period mantle magnitude, J.Geophys.Res., 1989, vol. 94, 4169-4193.

26. REYMOND D., HYVERNAUD O. and TALANDIER J. Automatic detection, location and quantification of earthquakes: application to tsunami warning, Pure and Applied Geophysics, 1991, vol.135, 361-382.

27. REYMOND D., HYVERNAUD O. and TALANDIER J. An integrated system for real time estimation of seismic source parameters and its application to tsunami warning, in ''Tsunamis in the World'', S.Tinti (Ed.), Kluwer Academic Publishers, Dordrecht, The Netherlands (in print).

28. CAMPOS M.L. Tsunami hazard on the Spanish coasts of the Iberian peninsula, Science of Tsunami Hazard, 1991, vol.9, 83-90.

29. ANDRADE C. Tsunami generated forms in the Algarve barrier islands (south Portugal), Science of Tsunami hazard, 1992, vol.10, 21-33.

30. BAPTISTA M.A., MIRANDA P. and MENDES-VICTOR L. Maximum entropy analysis of Portuguese tsunami data. The tsunamis of 28.02.1969 and 26.05.1975, Science of Tsunami Hazard, 1992, vol.10, 9-20.

31. SIMÕES J.Z., AFILHADO A. and MENDES-VICTOR L. Complementary land-based tsunami warning system in SW Portugal, in ''Tsunamis in the World'', S.Tinti (Ed.), Kluwer Academic Publishers, Dordrecht, The Netherlands (in print).

32. HARBITZ C. Numerical simulation of slide generated water waves, Science of Tsunami Hazards, 1991, vol. 9, 15-22.

33. DAWSON A.G., LONG D. and SMITH D.E. The Storegga slides: evidence for a possible tsunami from eastern Scotland, Marine Geology, 1988, vol. 82, 271-276.

34. DAWSON A.G., LONG D., SMITH D.E., SHI S. and FOSTER I.D.L. Tsunamis in the Norwegian Sea and North Sea caused by Storegga submarine landslides, in ''Tsunamis in the World'', S.Tinti (Ed.), Kluwer Academic Publishers, Dordrecht, The Netherlands (in print).

35. SVENDSEN J.I. and MANGERUD J. Sea-level changes and pollen stratigraphy on the outer coast of Sunmøre, western Norway, Norsk Geologisk Tidsskrift, 1990, vol.70, 111-134.

36. HARBITZ C. Model simulations of tsunamis generated by the Storegga slides, Marine Geology, 1991, 105, 1-21.

13. Research needs for wind hazard mitigation

B. E. LEE, University of Portsmouth

1. INTRODUCTION

Wind storms are estimated to cause worldwide an average of 30,000 deaths and over $2.3 billion in damage each year. Disasters associated with a single severe storm can cover hundreds of square kilometres, lead to hundreds of thousands of casulaties and cause billions of dollars in economic loss. Complete structural collapse or severe damage is experienced by 93% of the buildings damaged by torandoes and by 51% of those damaged by hurricanes. Loss of life correlates directly with such extreme damage. The worldwide losses and deaths obseved are expected to increase substantially in the coming years due likely to increases in population, concentration of people and properties in cities, settlement in exposed coastal areas, higher construction and repair costs and more hazardous technologies.

Wind storms can be classified into three categories based on severity and physical origin. Storm types include tornadoes (winds to 500 km/hr), hurricanes, cyclones or typhoons (winds from 115 to 250 km/hr) and severe winds, thunderstorms, downbursts, downslope winds, strong depressions, etc (winds from 80 to 300 km/hr). Due to the variety of such wind-storm drivers, virtually no community in the world is immune from a wind-related natural disaster.

Over the past several decades, various international programmes have been carried out to help co-operating countries understand and mitigate the effects of wind related natural hazards. In addition to the 4 year cycle of International Wind Engineering Conferences, a number of specific meetings have been held to focus on the alleviation of wind-related disasters. These include the Indo-US Workshop on Wind Disaster Mitigation (1985) the US-Asia Conferences on Engineering for Mitigating Natural Hazards Damage, Thailand (1987), Indonesia (1991), and most recently, the WFEO Symposium on Alleviation of Natural Disasters held in Tanzania in 1991.

This present paper builds on the findings of these earlier meetings and proposes an identification and prioritisation of research needs for wind hazard mitigation. As noted above the origins of wind storms result in various destructive wind fields

Natural disasters. Thomas Telford, London, 1993

to which different characteristics can be assigned. These combine with the principles of mechanics to result in different types of structural response. Engineers and scientists use various physical and numerical models to predict such response and subsequently design structures to protect people and property. The engineering knowledge is implemented into various design procedures and codes which must be disseminated to the engineering design, regulatory and administrative communities. This process is indicated in the flow chart shown in Figure 1.

The public has an increasing desire for mitigation as opposed to post-disaster relief and reconstruction. In general, mitigation which results in reduced loss of human lives and property might be applied to all three driving factors in wind hazards: the hazard, the exposure and the vulnerability. These concepts are considered in the paper and proposed projects are arranged in priorities.

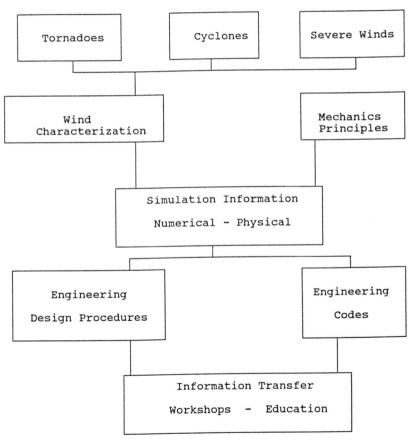

Figure 1. Extreme Wind Hazards

NATURAL DISASTERS

2. RESEARCH PRIORITIES

Research projects covering the following areas,

    wind characteristics,
    numerical and physical modelling,
    codes and design information,
    pre- and post-disaster risk analysis, and
    education and workshops,

have been arranged in priority categories A and B. Category A projects are described in full in the following section. Additionally a list of the titles of Category B projects are given at the end of the paper for consideration by future conferences.

3. CATEGORY A PROJECTS

The recommended Category A projects are:

1. Characterization of extreme winds in tropical cyclones.

2. Simulation of extreme winds and their influence on buildings and structures.

3. Development of construction design and code information related to extreme-wind hazards.

4. Preparation of wind engineering training and workshop materials.

These projects are detailed in the following sections.

3.1 Project 1
Characterization of Extreme Winds in Tropical Cyclones, Typhoons and Hurricanes

3.1.1 Project Goals

The overall project goal is to maximize the cooperative use of meteorological resources. The goals of the subprograms are to develop a consensus in a regional area on the most effective instrumentation, data recording and dissemination procedures to be used with extreme-wind response and warning systems that can result in wind hazard mitigation. It is hoped that the associated improvement in data quality and quantity will lead to better understanding of wind phenomena and to improved predictive models.

The subprograms and their goals are:

(a) Development of instrumentation for severe wind measurements

The standardization of instruments for cyclone wind measurements and their calibration are required. This will provide correlatable data taken at stations in as many parts of a region as possible. The standards should be reviewed every five years so that new developments in instrumentation can be incorporated. Additional instruments may be installed as necessary to enhance the quality and scope of cyclone meterological information.

(b) Specification of uniform data recording, tabulation and dissemination procedures

The goal of this subtask is to establish standards for measurement, storage and retrieval of wind data. An extension of this subtask would define standard methods to convert between the different wind intensity definitions currently used.

(c) Development of extreme-wind response and warning systems based on an expert-system approach

The goals are to create a regional extreme-wind data base for decision making in specified applications, to offer knowledge-based advice for specified applications and to establish warning systems pertaining to various levels of risks anticipated.

3.1.2 Background and Strategy

(a) Instrumentation for severe-wind measurements

Today, even within a single country, different agencies such as national meteorological departments and research institutes are working without strong coordination. In addition, among research institutes there is very little exchange of instrumentation experience. A survey of instrumentation practice and pitfalls is expected to increase the coordination and cooperation between various agencies. Increased communication and coordination of meteorological researchers can also contribute to standard instrument specifications and calibration procedures. Such pooling of information will help the other tasks arrive at some commonality between national codes, and the improvement in data reliability should lead to designing safer and more economical structures.

(b) Uniform recording, tabulation and dissemination procedures

Different countries use different definitions and statistics for extreme winds. This causes difficulties and inconvenience when data from different areas of the region are used to evaluate the character and impact of a given tropical storm. Such differences in nomenclature are common and tend to limit and confuse engineers whey they work on projects outside of their own geographical areas. Teams of researchers would meet to normalize the methods of measurement and presentation of wind data.

(c) Expert-system approaches for extreme winds and warning systems

Rarely does a meteorologist or engineer have available the resource of expert opinion when interpreting cyclonic winds or other wind storms. Yet lives and property often depend upon making the "best" decisions related to warning, protection or evacuation. A knowledge-based expert system for extreme-wind warning systems constructed from an internationally based collection of area experts could put "expert advice" at the fingertips of meteorologists and engineers. A cooperative program would draw upon regional experience to produce an application-oriented programme which could be disseminated among regional nations.

3.1.3 Potential Benefits

The standardization of instrumentation, recording and dissemination procedures will lead to:

o Pooling of data across national boundaries;

o The linking of data sets across large regional areas for a better understanding of tropical storms which encompass or intercept more than one country; and

o The potential standardization of engineering practice and codes.

Expert systems based wind response and warning systems will permit effective use of personnel and knowledge otherwise separated by national boundaries and language barriers. It was felt that substantial accomplishments could be made on the projects listed above in a three-year programme.

3.2 Project 2
Simulation of Extreme Winds and Their Influence on Buildings and Structures

3.2.1 Project Goals

The goals of this project are: (1) to obtain improved specifications of wind loads acting on components of a building envelope for tall buildings as well as shorter buildings such as warehouses, apartment complexes and private domiciles; and (2) to provide a source of full-scale data which can be used by wind tunnel operators and numerical modellers to evaluate the reliability and accuracy of their modelling techniques and to monitor the various comparison exercises.

3.2.2 Background and Strategy

Engineers work with analytic, physical or numerical models to design engineered structures such as buildings, towers, bridges, and industrial facilities. These models are only as reliable as the phenomenological understanding of wind, upon which they are based. In order to improve engineering practice and national design codes, there is an urgent need for improved validated models. This need suggests a two-part research programme consisting of a laboratory - and full-scale measurement programme, viz.,

    (a)   Characterization of cladding loads on small, medium and tall structures; and

    (b)   Concurrent instrumentation of full-scale structures for physical and numerical model validation.

Lack of design information about the behaviour of cladding and external building components to wind often results in under-design and failure under extreme wind conditions. Information of this type can be used in code preparation, post-disaster failure analysis and wind zoning of land for commercial or private use. There does not seem to exist any conceptual limitation to research programmes of the types suggested below; however, a commitment of resources is necessary. Research periods of three to five years are anticipated to provide substantial information.

(a)   Characteristics of cladding loads

Research into building-component failure can be subdivided into studies related to the:

    o   Evaluation of cladding response to static versus dynamic effects, load duration, material properties and internal pressures;

    o   Evaluation of the effects of loads and failure associated with wind-borne missiles and debris; and

    o   Response of roofing systems and roof materials to strong winds.

Research tasks would include post-failure analysis of damaged structures, wind tunnel measurements and full-scale testing of components or modules of buildings.

(b)   Instrumentation and measurements on full-scale buildings

The derivation of a full-scale data set, eg. the B.R.E. Aylesbury house experiment, is very expensive and time consuming. The Arts Tower monitoring programme at Sheffield, UK, took place over an eight-year period from 1975 to 1983. Thus, few new full-scale data sets are likely to become available in the next decade. For this reason, international support of full-scale measurement programmes is essential, as is international comparison of laboratory and numerical modelling observations.

An international research team needs to identify a limited set of buildings with various heights, which represent particularly popular but wind-vulnerable structures. These buildings should be instrumented and data gathered over a duration of at least three annual storm periods. Subsequently, the data should be analyzed in a uniform manner and comparable laboratory and numerical experiments must be performed to evaluate simulation techniques.

3.2.3 Potential Benefits

Characterization of cladding and structural loads is a subject of high interest in coastal areas where increased population density has resulted in rapid urbanization. Failure of buildings and other structures can often result in massive loss of employment, death, homelessness and economic losses equal to a sizeable fraction of a nation's gross national product. Design codes are recognizing increasingly the need to specify the use of wind-tunnel and other modelling techniques to provide design data for cases not covered by the codes. Such specifications are already included in the United States, Japanese and Australian codes, and are likely to appear more widely as other national codes are revised. Thus, as the design profession moves away from uniform, if conservative, code-derived data to individual specifications based on ad hoc modelling tests, the degree of variability within a design system is likely to increase. In order to control an inevitable increase in the degree of uncertainty associated with any particular test, the modelling technique must be calibrated against a number of reliable and accurate data sets derived from full-scale observations.

3.3 Project 3
Development of Construction Design and Code Information Related to Extreme-wind Hazards

3.3.1 Project Goals

Improving the understanding of the action of wind on actual structures is desirable with an emphasis on a more precise definition of the wind forces for structural design. Yet, to be cost effective this understanding must be integrated with actual economic and risk assessments to produce a rational engineering design approach specified by consistent and clear codes.

The overall goal of this project is to develop better guidelines for design and construction against wind effects. Three tasks are proposed in this total project with their respective goals as follows:

(a) To develop design and construction methods for mass housing in extreme-wind zones;

(b) To apply risk and cost/benefit analysis to the use of extreme-wind construction techniques; and

(c) To develop specifications for a regional uniform building code.

3.3.2 Background and Strategy

(a) Mass Housing in extreme-wind zones

There is an acute shortage of housing in most of the countries in Asia and Africa. Every year in the coastal belts of cyclone-prone countries a large number of houses are damaged due to the high winds of cyclones. Large sums of money are spent every year to repair and renovate damaged structures. Some of the non-engineered structures are non-repairable, further aggravating the shortage of housing. Thus a large effort should be devoted to developing construction techniques for wind-resistant mass housing in cyclone-prone regions.

Much work needs to be done to understand the flow patterns of cyclonic winds, particularly in the vicinity of clusters of residential buildings. The effect of interference between groups of buildings and complicated residential building shapes on wind loads has not been frequently investigated. Since wind-resistant design and construction are often not utilized in developing countries, the available studies of building arrangements are not necessarily appropriate for Asian and African housing. The study will begin with a state-of-the-art review of regional building practices. Current building practices will be critiqued, and a programme of analytical, physical and numerical studies proposed to evaluate alternate design methodologies.

(b) Wind-related risk and cost/benefit analysis

Types of structures, different construction methods and geographic, meteorological and cultural characteristics must be examined. If cost were not a factor, all structures could be built to resist a large wind hazard. However, economic realities cause builders, engineers, and administrators to make design and construction choices based on probable wind-related risks, costs and benefits of sturdier designs. Research engineers must join with economists, meteorologists and statisticians to develop a design approach which will permit the "optimum" selection of design criteria from available alternatives. This task will examine:

(i) Probabilistic assessment of wind data taking meteorological and topographical parameters into consideration;

(ii) Aerostatic and aerodynamic characteristics of non-engineered and engineered structures, the associated failure mechanisms of structures and the costs of revised construction; and

(iii)   A probabilistic evaluation of the benefits of
        design changes on structural safety against
        wind loads;

(iv)   Specifications for a regional uniform building
        code.

This task will gather national practices and code
information, identify commonalities and differences,
and propose a uniform code structure for wind effects
suitable for analysis and design on a regional basis.

It is expected that the above three tasks will require
a minimum of three years for communication among
interested research groups, review of data,
examination of new research results and incorporation
of results into code recommendations.

3.3.3   Potential Benefits

Since wind-related damage has frequently burdened the
economies of nations, it is in their own interests to
mitigate wind hazards and thus conserve human and property
resources.

An acute shortage of housing, particularly in most of the
developing countries of Asia and Africa, has made mass
housing a common social and economic problem.   It is
desirable that minimal resources be used to repair and
renovate mass housing structures that could be damaged by
frequent severe winds.   Yet, large losses are incurred
because of the failure of poorly designed or constructed
housing under extreme winds.

Cooperative studies of the type of materials and methods of
construction that will provide better resistance to wind
damage are mutually beneficial to all countries. Knowledge
about the wind risks and benefits of improved construction
techniques will help planners distribute community
resources.   This same knowledge will benefit insurance
carriers and should reduce premium costs.

It is obviously inefficient to limit the exchange of
engineering consultation and advice due to the presence of
conflicting and confusing national codification practices.
In some cases there are contradictory provisions.
Coordination will lead to improvement in code preparation,
lower construction costs and greater reliability.

3.4   Project 4
Preparation of Wind Engineering Training and Workshop Materials

3.4.1   Project Goal

The goal is to prepare guidelines, list of topics and
teaching aids for disseminating knowledge on wind
engineering practices among meteorologists and design
professionals.   These resources will be used to present

wind engineering workshops and symposia to train new staff and upgrade existing employees.

3.4.2 Background and Strategy

Although the topic of wind hazards and wind engineering design is of great importance to all countries, there are only a few national institutions which offer structured training in these areas, despite universal interest in this topic.

Experts in wind engineering will be requested to prepare written and visual-aid course materials suitable for presentation to short courses, workshops and symposia. These materials will be coordinated into a complete programme which can be distributed to participating countries. Since very few countries possess experts in all aspects of wind-related hazards, the pooling of knowledge should provide an opportunity for a region-wide improvement in wind-related engineering practices.

It is also expected that as research results emanate from the cooperative research projects listed earlier, the new information should be disseminated through updated workshop materials prepared for this task.

3.4.3 Potential Benefits

New engineering information is only useful if it reaches the administrators and engineers making construction decisions. This task is an integral part of the entire research programme described in the flow chart in Figure 1. Education, practice, criticism, code revision, and re-education are necessary for a dynamic engineering profession.

4. CATEGORY B PROJECTS

The following list of Category B titles have been proposed for future consideration.

Wind Characteristics

1. Severe thunderstorm meteorology

2. Regional analysis of tropical cyclones

Model Studies

3. Cross-facility validation of physical-modelling facilities

4. Physical-model studies of sand movement to prevent desertification

Codes and Design

5. Low-cost housing vulnerability

    6.   Shelter design for people and property

    7.   Vegetative and man-made shelter belts

    8.   Response and protection of transmission lines

Pre- and Post-Disaster Risk Analysis

    9.   Urbanization effects on wind hazards

    10. Cost-benefit analysis of mitigation techniques

Education and Workshops

    11. Community education programmes

REFERENCES

1. Indo-US Workshop on Wind Disaster Mitigation, Structural Engineering Research Centre, Madras, India. December 1985.

2. US-Asia Conference on Engineering for Mitigating Natural Hazards Damage. Asian Institute of Technology, Bangkok, Thailand. December 1987.

3. World Federation of Engineering Organizations Symposium on Alleviation of Natural Disasters. Arusha, Tanzania. September 1991

14. Terrain evaluation methods for predicting relative hazards from mass movement, fluvial erosion and soil erosion in the developing world

J. H. CHARMAN and J. S. GRIFFITHS, Engineering Geology Ltd, UK

ABSTRACT

The developing countries contain, almost by definition, large remote regions, isolated from efficient logistical support and where very little is known about the ground conditions. Rural and urban communities are particularly susceptible to natural hazards resulting from normal but enhanced geomorphological processes of landscape formation, such as soil erosion, landsliding, fluvial erosion or flooding. This is the result of many factors including: population pressures causing the development of marginal land for agriculture resulting in problems of soil erosion from forest clearance programmes, overgrazing or inappropriate farming practices; or the need for access to water leading to habitation in flood risk zones.

In addition, civil works associated with rural development projects may inadvertently increase the risk, for example roads or irrigation canals may cause extensive landsliding as a result of poor design and construction practises such as slope undercutting, inefficient spoil disposal, or vegetation clearance. Such linear structures can cover long distances and encounter a range of natural hazards.

Whatever the form of development, effective land assessment, planning and management can significantly reduce the potential risk from unexpected natural hazards of disastrous proportions. Experience in working in remote environments has demonstrated that use of terrain evaluation techniques involving desk study, remote sensing interpretation and field mapping, are a quick and relatively cost-effective reconnaissance method for obtaining information on the natural hazards that will affect all aspects of the development. By identifying these hazards at an early stage in the project they can readily be incorporated in the design, and allowed for during construction and throughout their working life.

This paper describes the methods of identification, classification and assessment of natural hazards using terrain evaluation techniques. Four case studies are described, undertaken by the authors in the Himalayas of Bhutan/Nepal, Pakistan and Ethiopia. Suggestions are also made about suitable investigations which can be undertaken to quantify hazards and enable protective or mitigating measures appropriate to the needs of the local community to be carried out.

1. INTRODUCTION

Many rural communities live under the threat of major natural events; they often have no knowledge of the nature of such processes or whether the activities that they carry out as part of their everyday life enhance the risk or can be modified to reduce such risk.

There is also a continuing programme of development in increasingly remote and isolated parts of the world. Very little is likely to be known about the ground conditions at the proposed development site, and problematic accessibility limits the scope of possible investigation methods. Linear structures in particular are most susceptible to the problems of unforeseen ground conditions as they cover long distances over variable terrain with a range of natural hazards. They can require, therefore, not only higher than anticipated costs of construction, but an extensive ongoing commitment to maintenance. It is evident, therefore, that an evaluation of the type and magnitude of natural hazards is of prime importance in assessing the cost associated with a new development.

Natural hazards to development in remote regions can be evaluated at four levels :

- reconnaissance for feasibility studies and preliminary design;
- site specific for detailed design;
- on-going assessment during construction;
- post-construction as a forensic exercise if failures have occurred.

The cost of both the investigation and the consequences of incorporating the results in the design increases significantly with each of these levels. In remote regions the most cost effective method of taking natural hazards into account in design is to identify their extent and magnitude at the feasibility stage. This requires the use of the specialised reconnaissance technique of terrain evaluation including natural hazard assessment. This method is evaluated for three particular hazard types: landslide; fluvial erosion; and soil erosion.

2. TERRAIN EVALUATION STUDIES

The basis of terrain evaluation is to subdivide the landscape into landform assemblages with similarities in terrain, soils, vegetation and geology (ref.1). Various general models of landforms and processes found in different types of environment, or morphogenetic regions, have now been developed by the engineering geological industry. Many of these basic models are compiled by Fookes & Vaughan (ref.2). The basic models present an idealised version of the landscape and processes found in the various regions. However, in any particular site study the basic model must be modified and adapted to fit the local conditions. Examples of adapted models developed during actual site evaluations undertaken by the authors are presented in Section 3.

A terrain evaluation study can be subdivided into four stages:

- desk studies
- remote sensing interpretation
- field mapping
- presentation

2.1 Desk Studies

The desk studies require the compilation and collation of all available literature about the site and similar environments. This enables the site to be placed in its general environmental context as well as establishing the nature of potential site specific natural hazards. At this stage the general terrain model applicable to the site can be established.

2.2 Remote Sensing Interpretation

As an adjunct to the desk studies, a highly cost-effective method of data collection which should be employed prior to going into the field is remote sensing interpretation. In the past this has been limited to the interpretation of aerial photographs, however, the advent of modern satellite imagery, in particular the LANDSAT Thematic Mapper and SPOT multi-spectral scanners, has led to an explosion in the amount of information available. These modern scanners allow spatially corrected images at scales up to 1:25,000 to be prepared. The images can then be interpreted using the techniques of terrain evaluation, including both broad scale land systems classification and more detailed geomorphological mapping methods.

The interpretation of the remote sensing data allows the proposed site for development to be placed in the overall landscape zone or zones based on the identified terrain model. Each land unit or zone has characteristics which necessitate a particular engineering approach. Therefore, once a site has been identified as lying within a certain zone(s), the range of potential hazards likely to be encountered can be identified.

2.3 Field Mapping

After making an interpretation of the remote sensing information it is necessary to evaluate the site specific hazards by carrying out a "ground-truth" mapping exercise. This is normally carried out as a walkover survey by a small team of specialists experienced in terrain evaluation techniques, who are familiar with the environment under investigation and have knowledge of the end-product requirements.

The methodology of "ground truth" mapping is described in detail in Cooke & Doornkamp (ref.3). The aim of the work is to provide a description of the landform units identified during the desk study and remote sensing interpretation stages and check their distribution in the field. With each landform unit it will be necessary to compile data on: the landscape facets which combine to make up the terrain systems identified; the soils, vegetation and geomorphological processes active in each facet; an identification and evaluation of the natural hazards to any potential development within each facet.

Once the broad scale terrain units have been identified, site specific studies of particular areas should be carried out whenever there are defined development plans. At this stage more detailed work using the techniques of geomorphological mapping should be employed. This involves the site specific identification of landforms, their distribution, composition and evolutionary development plus an assessment of the efficiency of contemporary natural processes in changing the existing environmental conditions.

Normally for this work the broad scale land systems mapping would be undertaken at scales of 1:1 million to 1:25,000, whereas geomorphological mapping would require working at scales between 1:25,000 and 1:500.

2.4. Presentation

To report on reconnaissance investigations the most effective means of presentation is in the form of a hazard or geomorphological map, block diagrams and accompanying tables. The block diagram must be schematic but representative of the types of terrain encountered in the field area with the various processes and typical natural hazards displayed in their correct spatial context. The accompanying map identifies the actual location of the various natural hazards, whilst the tables provide details of specific hazards and the risk they represent. A series of case studies based on this approach are presented in the following sections.

The most recent refinement in the presentation for terrain evaluation studies is the use of Geographical Information Systems (GIS). This involves the use of specialised spatial databases which can compile, analyse and reproduce data from all facets of the environment. This allows data collected during the terrain evaluation exercise to be integrated with other relevant information on demography, meteorology, land use, etc. to provide an overall model of the controls on development in a region. This extremely powerful tool, as it develops, will allow for greater control on the nature and extent of any exploitation in remote regions and will provide one very effective method for anticipating certain natural hazards. The technique is exemplified in this paper in a study of soil erosion in Ethiopia.

3. CASE STUDIES IN TERRAIN EVALUATION

3.1 Bhutan/Nepal: Landslide Hazard Mapping for Highways and Hill Canals

The Himalayan mountains are one of the world's most active young fold mountain belts. They are still forming today and are associated with extremely active landscape forming processes. The tropical climate is conducive to intense weathering of the parent rocks and rapid erosion under intense monsoonal rainfall is, therefore, widespread. Landsliding is probably the most damaging of the erosion processes and presents a high hazard to the community and to the sustainability of any development.

Landslides not only occur as part of the natural process of landscape evolution, they are often induced by road or canal construction. Using terrain evaluation techniques the landscape along project alignments can be classified to define landslide areas and permit the areas at risk from future activity to be evaluated.

A basic terrain model for mountainous regions has been established (ref.4). This model, adapted for local conditions (refs.5-7), is presented in Figure 1. The mountain model divides the landscape into five main zones. The projects described traversed Zones 3 and 4 and these in turn were sub-divided into units which displayed similar engineering characteristics in terms of design and construction practise.

For these projects an initial desk study and aerial photograph interpretation allowed the differentiation of the landscape into zones. These were presented on a base map comprising a set of 1:50,000 SPOT satellite images. Field mapping confirmed the initial interpretation and particularly defined the land units. At the same time, using a pro forma, additional factors were recorded and a scoring system adopted to provide a numerical evaluation of relative hazard. Such factors included the following:

     Natural and Cut slopes
          rock or soil type, and discontinuity pattern
          slope angle and regularity of profile
          slope condition (stable, potentially unstable, failed, overhanging)
          existing slope support and condition
          degree of vegetation cover
          water conditions
          rehabilitation or maintenance needs

     Fill slopes
          slope angle and regularity of profile
          slope condition
          existing slope support and condition
          degree of vegetation cover
          water conditions
          rehabilitation or maintenance needs

This Terrain Evaluation and Hazard Assessment allowed both natural and construction induced instability or potential instability to be identified and rated. Maintenance could then be directed to priority areas to give the most cost-effective use of available manpower resources.

3.2 Talli Village, Pakistan; Fluvial Erosion Hazard

In drylands most settlements are located close to the water sources needed to provide water for both agriculture and human

consumption.   Talli village in Baluchistan is typical of many
rural situations in the dryland environment.   The village is
located on the edge of the Chaker River alluvial fan with the
farmlands irrigated by ephemeral stream flows which occur two
or three times a year as 'flash floods.'   Ephemeral stream
flow channels on alluvial fans are unstable systems subject to
braiding with anastomosing distributaries, and are associated
with large sediment loads, large sediment sizes, high flow
velocities and high stream power.

In the Talli Village area the traditional method of using the
water from flash flood flows is to construct 2-3 metre high
earth bunds across the main channel and to divert the flow to
fields using a network of artificial drainage channels and
canals.   The method of determining who has access to the water
and for how long is based on traditional Islamic Water Rights
where the Landowner furthest upstream on the left bank of the
river has first rights to as much water as he requires before
he breaches his bund.   The requirement for the Talli Village
irrigation project was to replace the earth bunds by the
construction of a more resilient flow diversion weir which
would allow a higher proportion of water to be channelled into
the irrigation network in a controlled manner.

The main design problem for the weir was to identify a site
within the alluvial fan where it could be located without
being by-passed by the laterally eroding and migrating
ephemeral stream channels of the Chaker River.   These
processes had already resulted in the destruction of one weir
and had eroded large sections of the existing canal
distribution network.   The full scope of the investigations
for this aspect of the project (ref.8) involved evaluating the
behaviour of the channel network through time in order to
establish the likely pattern of future behaviour.   The basis
of the work was a terrain evaluation map produced from an
interpretation of a 1:40,000 scale uncontrolled photo-mosaic
from an aerial survey flown in 1950.   This interpretation is
presented in Figure 2 and highlights the pattern of
distributaries of the Chaker River on the alluvial fan to the
east of the village.

The pattern of distributaries identified on the interpretation
of the photo-mosaic was compared with the results of a limited
survey in 1984, a geomorphological survey in 1988 and a
topographic survey in 1991.   These various surveys
demonstrated that the Chaker River had maintained an overall
stable location on the southern limits of the fan and that
this should provide the location for the flood irrigation
weir.   The 1988 geomorphological survey, however, did
establish that in the southern limits of the fan the Chaker
had developed a beaded pattern, typical of ephemeral stream
channels (ref.9), in which the broader open stretches of
channel slowly migrating downstream through a process of
lateral scour.   The area of interest is shown in Figure 4,
with the main scour hollow associated with this beaded pattern
clearly defined and it's rate of erosion demonstrated by a
series of surveys.   However, the conclusion from the
geomorphological study was that the proposed location of the
weir which is shown on Figure 3 would have a design life of 30
to 40 years based on the identified channel erosion patterns.

172

Given the difficulties of construction and generally working on unstable ephemeral stream channels this design life was deemed acceptable by the engineers.

3.3 Awash Valley, Ethiopia: Soil Erosion Hazard

The continuing failure of the rains in sub-Saharan Africa has caused widespread suffering through drought and famine. One aspect of this has been an increasing pressure on existing agricultural land leading to large-scale problems of soil erosion. In an assessment of soil erosion in the Awash Valley in Ethiopia (ref.10) terrain evaluation techniques were central to the main phase of data collation and analysis. In this case the 110,000 km^2 Awash Valley was being studied by Sir William Halcrow & Partners (Consulting Engineers) for the development of a water resources master plan. As part of this work it was necessary to set up a system for estimating soil erosion rates and modelling the effects of soil conservation measures within the catchment.

Prior to the studies undertaken for the master plan, a major land systems analysis for the whole country at a scale of 1:250,000 had been carried out (ref.11) based on an interpretation of 71 LANDSAT images, with extensive field checking. This comprehensive study had identified 380 land systems in the country, 89 being present in the Awash Valley, each with a recurrent pattern of terrain facets comprising topographic units of uniform geology, slope, soil type, vegetation and land use. Typical descriptions for two of the main land units, (major river gorges, canyons and escarpments; and high to mountainous relief hills) are shown in Figure 4.

The data provided by the land systems mapping was utilised to calculate the erodibility of the various soil types within each terrain facet based on the FAO procedure for estimating soil erosion (ref.12). In these studies soil erodibility was shown to be a function of: soil type; soil grading; and slope. Data on these items were all provided by the land systems mapping.

Soil erosion, however, is a product of soil erodibility (Er) and rainfall erosivity (R), attenuated by the land cover factor (ie existing vegetation and land use). Data from rain gauges around the Awash catchment was used to produce rainfall erosivity maps based on the FAO procedure. The land cover factor was estimated using the descriptions of vegetation and land use compiled for each terrain facet and based on values already evaluated for Ethiopia (ref.13).

With the separate components of the FAO procedure for soil erosion estimation being able to be calculated, a raster based geographical information system (GIS) was developed using dBase III+ software to calculate the spatial pattern of soil erosion in the catchment. The model was cross-referenced to a terrain information database which contained data on soil type, average slope, soil erodibility, average soil depth, land use and vegetation type. An example of the output from the GIS which presents initial soil erosion estimates is shown in Figure 5.

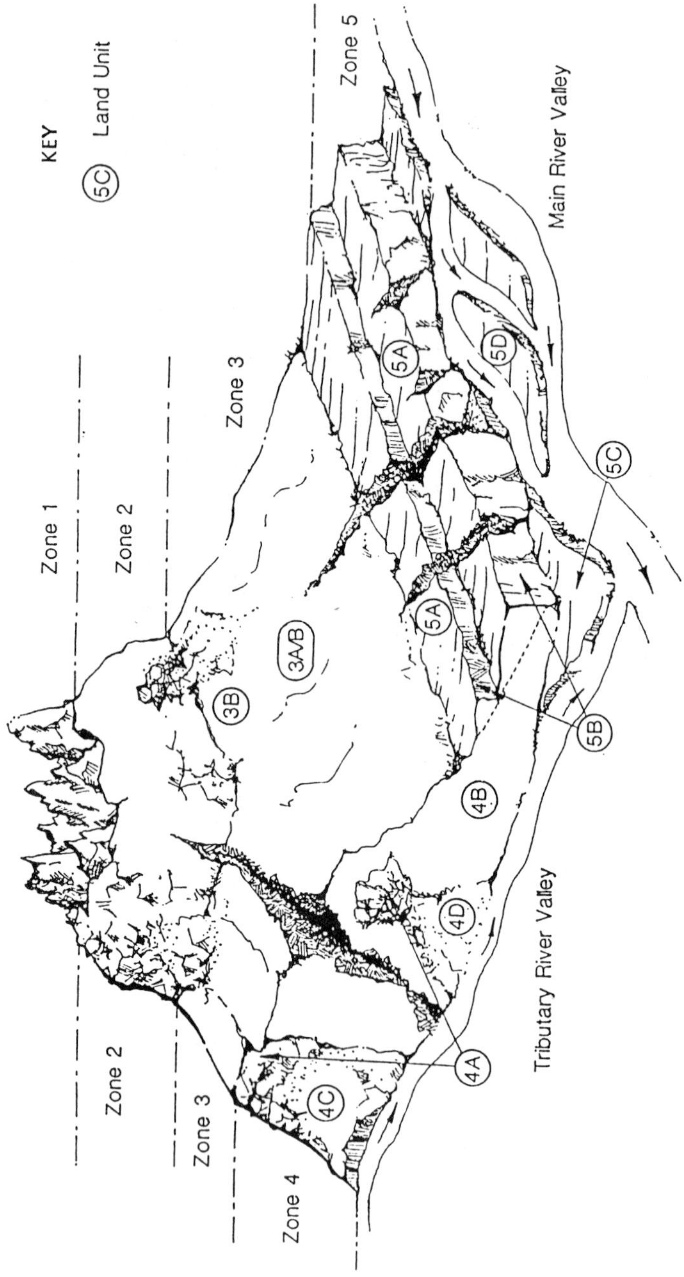

Fig. 1. (below and facing page). Mountain zone classification (adapted from Fookes et al., 1985)

ZONE		LAND UNIT
1	high altitude glacial and periglacial zone subject to glacial erosion, mechanical weathering, rock and snow instability, and solifluction movements with thin rocky soil, boulder fields, glaciers, bare rock slopes, talus development, and debris fan accumulation;	
2	free rock face and associated steep debris slopes subject to chemical and mechanical weathering, mass movement, talus creep, freeze-thaw, and debris fan accumulation;	
3	degraded middle slopes and ancient valley floors forming a low-angle erosional surface subject to chemical weathering, soil creep, sheetflow, gullying, and stream incision;	3A — Ancient Erosional Terrace. Covered with in-situ weathered profile of soil up to 3m. thick. Slope angle generally <35°. Relatively stable. Often farmer terraced. Surface water erosion high.
		3B (4D) — Degraded Colluvium. Transported slope debris or landslide debris comprising gravel, cobbles, boulders bound in silt/clay matrix. Slope angle <35°. Relatively stable. Often farmer terraced. Variable permeability.
4	high angle active lower slopes with chemical and mechanical weathering, large-scale slope instability, gullying, over-steepened slopes and basal undercutting, sub-surface water erosion, and talus development;	4A — Bare Rock Slopes. Steep slope angles often >60°. Stability dependant on orientation of discontinuities, i.e. beddingjoints.
		4B — Rock slopes with shallow (<2m) loose debris cover. Slope angle 45°-60°. Shallow instability and debris slides. Mass instability as 4A.
		4C — Active Colluvium. Thick landslide debris often with tow being eroded seasonally by river. Slope angle >35°. Actively degrading, highly unstable.
		4D (3B) — Degraded Colluvium. See 3B but less stable.
5	valley floors associated with fast flowing, sediment laden rivers, sequences of river terraces, and an extensive fluvial landscape.	

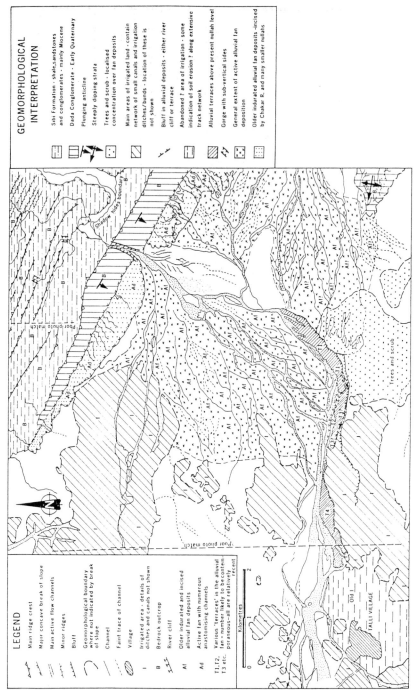

LEGEND

⌒⌒ Main ridge crest

⌢⌢ Major concave break of slope

⌣⌣ Minor ridges

⌒ Bluff

Geomorphological boundary where not indicated by break of slope

⌒ Channel

⌒ Faint trace of channel

⬭ Village

I Irrigated area - details of ditches and canals not shown

B Bedrock outcrop

River cliff

Al Older indurated and incised alluvial fan deposits

Ad Active fan with numerous anastomising channels

T1,T2, T3 etc. Various 'terraces' in the alluvial fan - number likely to be contemporaneous - all are relatively recent

Kilometres
0   1   2

GEOMORPHOLOGICAL INTERPRETATION

Sibi Formation - shale,sandstones and conglomerates - mainly Miocene

Dada Conglomerate - Early Quaternary

Plunging anticline

Steeply dipping strata

Trees and scrub - localised concentration over fan deposits

Main areas of irrigated land - contain network of small canals and irrigation ditches/bunds - location of these is not shown

Bluff in alluvial deposits - either river cliff or terrace

Abandoned ? area of irrigation - some indication of soil erosion ? along extensive track network

Alluvial terraces above present nullah level

Gorge with sub-vertical sides

General extent of active alluvial fan deposition

Older indurated alluvial fan deposits -incised by Chakar R. and many smaller nullahs

Fig. 2. Talli Village geomorphological interpretation

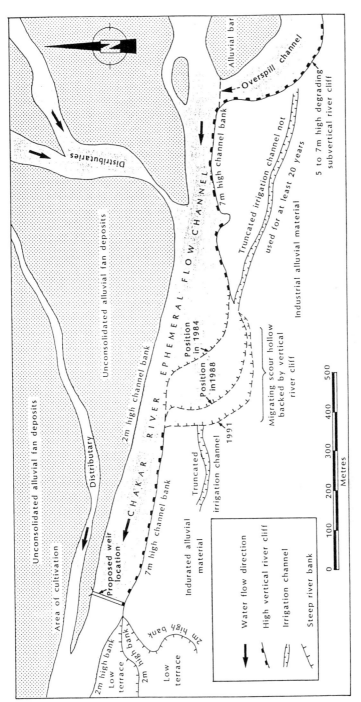

Fig. 3. Proposed weir location in relation to scour hollow on the Chakar River

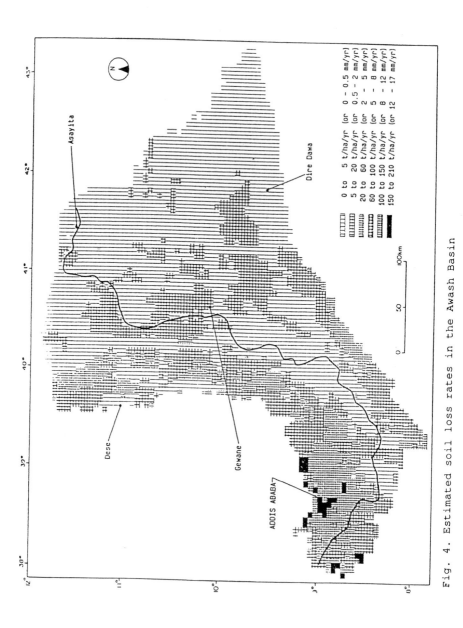

Fig. 4. Estimated soil loss rates in the Awash Basin

The GIS was also used to model the effects of land degradation by changing the values for land cover factor of individual cells to show the effects of increasing the amount of intensive agriculture and in reducing the amount of forest. Conversely, reductions in soil erosion rates were also calculated by assessing the effects of structural soil conservation measures, such as terracing, bunding, and trash lines, in reducing slopes.

The GIS model, developed from initial data collection procedures using terrain evaluation techniques of land systems mapping, therefore, was used to identify the areas where soil loss was greatest, the areas which would be most sensitive to changes in land use, and the areas where soil conservation measures would be most beneficial.

4.   CONCLUSIONS

The remoteness of many development sites and communities presents logistical difficulties in getting site investigation plant to site before construction is to start. Furthermore, design and construction methods must be appropriate to local skills. If not, maintenance will be outside the capability of the community and the project will be unsustainable. In this context the obvious requirement is for more comprehensive reconnaissance level studies.

The use of terrain evaluation techniques is particularly well suited to this approach. Terrain evaluation provides a feasibility level methodology to Terzaghi's observational method (ref.14). By providing a technique for identifying potential hazards at a very early stage in the design of the works typical details and alternative designs can be prepared and incorporated into the construction programme. Experience has also shown that local people in remote areas possess an intrinsic understanding of the nature of the terrain on which they depend. Terrain evaluation techniques are quickly accepted and understood and allow effective local input into site assessment and design.

The interrelationship between landforms, geomorphological processes and these facets of construction are complex and dynamic. The natural hazards that will be encountered by any new development can have an important impact on the sustainability of the whole project. Whilst these hazards can be evaluated by conventional ground investigation procedures it is suggested that terrain evaluation and natural hazard assessment applied at the feasibility stage are a very cost-effective means of obtaining data critical to the financial planning and costing of the project. By using remote sensing interpretation and field mapping techniques, the logistical problems of actually setting up investigation plant in remote, inaccessible and hostile environments are avoided. The data obtained allows the potential hazards to be identified at an early stage thus enabling alternative design details to be prepared prior to the commencement of work on-site.

Fig. 5. (below and facing page). Awash Valley, Ethiopia: descriptions of two main land units

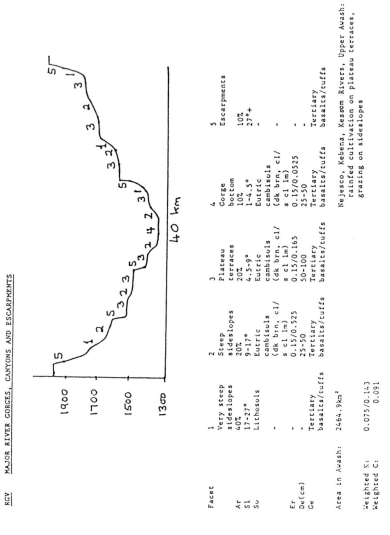

RGV MAJOR RIVER GORGES, CANYONS AND ESCARPMENTS

Facet	1	2	3	4	5
	Very steep sideslopes	Steep sideslopes	Plateau terraces	Gorge bottom	Escarpments
Ar	40%	20%	20%	10%	10%
Sl	17-27°	9-17°	4.5-9°	1-4.5°	27°+
So	Lithosols	Eutric cambisols (dk brn, cl/ s cl lm)	Eutric cambisols (dk brn, cl/ s cl lm)	Eutric cambisols (dk brn, cl/ s cl lm)	-
Er	-	0.15/0.525	0.15/0.165	0.15/0.0525	-
De(cm)	-	25-50	50-100	25-50	-
Ge	Tertiary basalts/tuffs	Tertiary basalts/tuffs	Tertiary basalts/tuffs	Tertiary basalts/tuffs	Tertiary basalts/tuffs

Area in Awash: 2464.9km²

Weighted S: 0.075/0.143
Weighted C: 0.091

Nejesco, Kebena, Kesem Rivers, Upper Awash: rainfed cultivation on plateau terraces, grazing on sideslopes

RH3V HIGH TO MOUNTAINOUS RELIEF HILLS

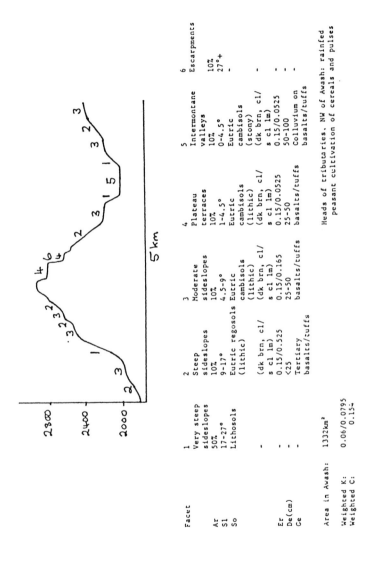

Facet	1 Very steep sideslopes	2 Steep sideslopes	3 Moderate sideslopes	4 Plateau terraces	5 Intermontane valleys	6 Escarpments
Ar	50%	10%	10%	10%	10%	10%
Sl	17-27°	9-17°	4.5-9°	1-4.5°	0-4.5°	27°+
So	Lithosols	Eutric regosols (lithic)	Eutric cambisols (lithic)	Eutric cambisols (lithic)	Eutric cambisols (stony)	-
	-	(dk brn, cl/ s cl lm)	(dk brn, cl/ s cl lm)	(dk brn, cl/ s cl lm)	(dk brn, cl/ s cl lm)	-
Er	-	0.15/0.525	0.15/0.165	0.15/0.0525	0.15/0.0525	-
De(cm)	-	<25	25-50	25-50	50-100	-
Ge	-	Tertiary basalts/tuffs	basalts/tuffs	basalts/tuffs	Colluvium on basalts/tuffs	-

Area in Awash: 1332km²

Weighted K: 0.06/0.0795
Weighted C: 0.154

Heads of tributaries, NW of Awash: rainfed
peasant cultivation of cereals and pulses

NATURAL DISASTERS

ACKNOWLEDGEMENTS

The authors would like to thank Engineering Geology Ltd for
supporting the submission of this paper, in particular the
helpful advice and comments provided by M K Sanders and
P F Stevens, and the drawings prepared by Mrs M Newland.

REFERENCES

1. ANON. Land surface evaluation for engineering purposes.
Report of the Working Party of the Geological Society.
Quarterly Journal of Engineering Geology Vol.15, No.4, 1982.

2. FOOKES P.G. and VAUGHAN P.R. A handbook of applied
geomorphology. Surrey University Press. 1986.

3. COOKE R.U. and DOORNKAMPE J.C. Geomorphology in
environmental management - an introduction. Clarendon Press,
Oxford. 1974.

4. FOOKES P.G., SWEENEY M., MANBY C.N.D. and MARTIN R.P.
Geological and geotechnical engineering aspects of low-cost
roads in mountainous terrain. Engineering Geology Vol.21.
1985.

5. CHARMAN J.H. Geotechnical survey and design training manual
for hill irrigation schemes in Bhutan. Ministry of Agriculture
and Forests, Royal Government of Bhutan. 1989.

6. CHARMAN J.H. Bhutan: Forestry III Preparation: Roadbank
Stabilisation Component. Confidential report to the World Bank
by Engineering Geology Ltd. 1990.

7. CHARMAN J.H. A manual for environmental protection measures
for hill irrigation schemes in Nepal. Ministry of Water
Resources, His Majesty's Government of Nepal. 150 pages. 1993.

8. GRIFFITHS J.S. Assessment of ephemeral stream channel
stability for the design of a flood irrigation weir on the
Chakar river in Baluchistan. Proceedings BGRG Conference on
Geomorphology in a Changing Environment, Royal Holloway New
College. 1993.

9. THORNES J.B. Channel changes in ephemeral streams:
observations, problems and models. In "River Channel Changes"
ed. K.J.Gregory. Wiley. 1977.

10. GRIFFITHS J.S. and RICHARDS K.S. Application of a low cost
database to soil erosion and soil conservation studies in the
Awash basin, Ethiopia. Land Degradation and Rehabilitation.
Vol.1 241-262. 1989.

11. HENRICKSEN B.L. Geomorphology and soils of Ethiopia.
FAO/UNDP/ETH/78/003, LUPRD, Addis Ababa. 1984.

12. FAO. A provisional methodology for soil degradation
assessment. Food and Agriculture Organisation, Rome. 1979.

13. BOERWINKLE E. and PARIS S. Methodology used in the development of a soil loss rate map of the Ethiopian Highlands. EHRS Field Document No. 5. LUPRD, Addis Ababa. 1984.

14. PECK R B, 1969. Advantages and limitations of the observational method in applied soil mechanics. Ninth Rankine Lecture, Geotechnique Vol.19, No.2.

15. Prediction of exceptionally severe storms

W. H. LYNE and A. M. RADFORD, Meteorological Office, UK

1. INTRODUCTION

The world meteorological community has an important role to play in the IDNDR, and this has been recognized in the Plan of Action of the World Meteorological Organization (WMO) (ref.1). This identifies the Organization playing a leading role in the mitigation of disasters caused by:

a. tropical cyclones;
b. floods;
c. tornadoes and severe thunderstorms;
d. other severe weather phenomena such as storm surges, major snowstorms and dust storms;
e. landslides and avalanches;
f. droughts.

Specific projects connected with these topics are prominent in the WMO Long-term Plan (ref.2), and one aspect, contained in the Public Weather Services Programme (PWSP)(ref.3), is the exchange of information on hazardous weather between countries. In the context of IDNDR, the exchange of information from the more advanced centres to those in the developing world is particularly relevant and is a feature of this paper.

The capabilities of the more advanced forecasting centres are briefly described in section 2 together with the types of products available and their means of communication. In particular, the global numerical weather prediction model employed by the Regional Specialized Meteorological Centre (RSMC)at Bracknell has shown some skill in the prediction of tropical cyclones and this is described more fully in section 3. RSMC Bracknell currently sends advisory messages on the track and evolution of tropical cyclones to selected countries, and an extension to this service to include other exceptionally severe weather is described in section 4. This has been offered by RSMC Bracknell as a contribution to the PWSP of WMO and to the IDNDR.

Natural disasters. Thomas Telford, London, 1993

2. FORECASTING AND COMMUNICATIONS WITHIN WMO

Many of the major National Meteorological Centres (NMCs) within the WMO now run complex numerical weather prediction models capable of providing a large amount of information for all or part of the globe. RSMC Bracknell has three operational atmospheric models ranging from a very high resolution mesoscale model for the United Kingdom, to a global model with a horizontal resolution of approximately 100 km. In addition, two marine models are also run to provide predictions of wave and swell, one for the European continental shelf, the other for the globe. A model is also run to predict the occurrence of storm surges in coastal waters of the UK.

The output from these models, supplemented by other sources of data such as satellite imagery, enables forecasters to be aware of the development of storms which could give rise to severe weather in all parts of the globe. In particular, the global atmospheric model at Bracknell has shown skill in forecasting the development and track of tropical cyclones, and this is described in section 3

An important component in the forecasting and warning process is the transmission of information to other national and regional meteorological centres. Central to this is the capacity of the WMO Global Telecommunication System (GTS) which is the primary means by which data, both observational and forecast, are exchanged. RSMC Bracknell disseminates a large number of bulletins over the GTS providing forecast information on a regular grid for up to five days ahead. The highest resolution grid on which global data is currently supplied is 2.5° latitude x 2.5° longitude, and the data are disseminated in GRIB, a binary code form.

The capacity of the GTS in developing countries can be substantially less than that between the more advanced centres. This, together with a lack of processing power, is a serious obstacle to their being able to take advantage of the information contained in coded bulletins. This is being addressed within Africa and the Middle East by the Meteorological Data Distribution (MDD) programme of EUMETSAT (European Organisation for the Exploitation of Meteorological Satellites). Data from meteorological centres are relayed to the two uplink stations at Bracknell (facsimile products) and Rome (digital products) for transmission via the Meteosat satellite to user stations. The purchase of user stations has largely been funded by the National Meteorological Services of developed countries, for example under the Voluntary Aid Co-operation Programme of WMO, and by various aid agencies. The number of user stations in Africa is now growing fairly quickly and the UK Met. Office has supplied four which are currently installed and working and is in the process of procuring another four. In this way products from advanced centres such as Bracknell can be used in countries which would otherwise have been unable to receive them. An example of a MDD facsimile product currently being produced at Bracknell is shown in figure 1.

A feature of some storms is that they are on a scale smaller than can be adequately resolved by the current model and bulletin grids. This is especially true of tropical cyclones, but information on their track and evolution can often be inferred from the model generated fields. An example of the information the model can provide is given in figure 1 in which the low centre shown near 15°S, 90°E provides a forecast of the position of tropical cyclone Harriet. The low centre about 20° further to the west is tropical cyclone Farida. This demonstrates the value of a system such as MDD, but information on tropical cyclones can also be conveyed in plain language advisory messages. RSMC currently issues these to selected centres for the southern Indian Ocean, the South Pacific and the North-West Pacific during their respective cyclone seasons.

3. TROPICAL CYCLONE FORECASTING AT BRACKNELL

The forecasting of tropical cyclones at Bracknell has been described earlier by Hall (ref.4), but the main features are reproduced here together with more recent verification results.

3.1 Analysis of tropical cyclones

Tropical cyclones are typically of the order of 750-1000 km across although in areas such as the North-West Pacific they may span as much as 2000 km. The area of extreme winds usually extends to no more than 50-100 km from the centre (e.g. Willoughby et al)(ref.5). Meteorological processes occur on a variety of scales in a cyclone, ranging from intense convection in the extreme conditions of the inner core to interaction with large-scale atmospheric features. This has led several centres to use a limited-area model embedded within a global one (e.g. Iwasaki et al)(ref.6), and this usually provides the best forecasting solution. However, the interaction with the large-scale flow can be a dominating influence in the movement and development of tropical cyclones, and this means that a global model alone can give good guidance of their evolution. Forecasts of actual intensity are usually poor due to the inability of the model to resolve the fine-scale structure within the cyclone itself. This is apparent from the representations of cyclones Harriet and Farida in figure 1.

The movement of tropical cyclones can be very erratic and often depends on subtle interactions between the tropical and mid-latitude large-scale flows. It is therefore extremely important that the initial position of the cyclone's centre is correctly identified in the model's analysis. Tropical cyclones form and intensify over the open ocean where there is seldom any high quality ground-based data with ships and aircraft diverted well clear of the system. Remotely sensed data from satellites is usually the only information available to numerical models from the vicinity of the cyclone, and consist mostly of upper-level cloud track winds. Satellite radiance data are of less value due to the weaker coupling of the mass and wind fields in tropical latitudes.

RSMC Bracknell devotes considerable effort into the manual quality control of data presented to the assimilation system. In particular, forecasters have the opportunity to accept, reject or support data, and to create, where applicable, bogus data in data sparse areas. In this way the model's analysis of a system such as a tropical cyclone can be adjusted to correspond with the forecasters view of its location and intensity. Advisory messages from world-wide monitoring centres provide information on the cyclone, but forecasters are also influenced by available satellite imagery from which the location of its centre can sometimes be accurately judged.

Two special facilities are available to forecasters to assist them in the creation of bogus data for tropical cyclones. The first is used when the forecaster wishes to initiate or intensify a circulation in the model. The centre of the circulation is first identified, and then the surface pressure and the wind speed at 850 hPa are specified on a circle, usually of 2.5° radius, around this point. The model then generates a set of bogus data around this circle at four levels in the vertical, including the surface. There is also the option of generating bogus relative humidity observations at the upper levels. The data are based on a crude conceptual model which assumes a symmetric circulation. No mean motion or steering of the cyclone is incorporated at the moment.

The second facility is used to reposition a tropical cyclone already established in the model. The required displacement of the cyclone is supplied by the forecaster and the model then generates a set of bogus data based on the model's own three-dimensional structure. This enables the cyclone structure to be largely preserved while adding knowledge concerning the system's location.

The actual central pressure and core winds of the system cannot be represented by the model and no attempt is made to insert such values as bogus data; the main effort is to ensure that the location and horizontal scale is correctly represented. This is important because tropical cyclones are steered by the large-scale flow and interact with it.

3.2 Verification of tropical cyclone tracks

A semi-automated scheme has been developed to verify the forecast positions of tropical cyclones. The actual locations of these are taken from the advisory messages received from tropical cyclone monitoring centres over the GTS, and the forecast positions are located from the model's relative vorticity field at 850 hPa.

Verification results for the last five years are presented in figure 2. All global model forecasts starting from initial analyses at 00 and 12 UTC have been verified, and the mean errors in cyclone positions have been plotted against forecast period. No particular tendency has been identified for the errors to be less in one basin than in another and the mean errors for all basins are given in the figure. They show a substantial interannual variability, but it should be noted that the initial error at the time of analysis is only a little greater than the grid length of the model. This is as accurate as might be expected. In a study of cyclone forecasts for the North-West Pacific, Chan and Kay (ref.7) identified a number of performance characteristics of the UK model including a greater skill than the corresponding CLIPER (climatology-persistence) forecasts at lead times beyond 24 hours.

An example of a cyclone forecast is given in figure 3. This shows the actual and forecast tracks of hurricane Andrew which caused such devastation in the Bahamas and parts of Florida and Louisiana in August 1992. The reported positions of the hurricane at 00 UTC are shown together with the 72-hour forecasts from those times The track was well forecast on the whole, although there was a tendency for it to be placed too far to the north on occasions. The forecast speed of movement also tended to be a little too slow.

3.3 Forecasts of tropical cyclone formation

The semi-automatic verification scheme has revealed several occasions when tropical cyclones were present at the later stages of a forecast despite no circulation being apparent in the initial analysis. In some cases the analysis time was several days prior to the first report of the tropical disturbance from which the storm developed. Hall (ref.8) has investigated forecasts of cyclone formation in the North-West Pacific in the period July to December 1991. A forecast was considered successful if the model predicted a disturbance with central pressure at least 6 hPa lower than the monthly average value at that location, and within 10° longitude and three days of an actual disturbance reaching the intensity of a tropical depression. Most of the forecasts started from an initial analysis which did not contain any circulation representing a reported tropical depression.

The hit rates for all the forecasts, expressed as the percentage successful, are given below. Also given are the hit rates for random forecasts of formation in the same period at three separate longitudes chosen to have the same probability of formation at the given longitude as actually occurred. Considering the difficulty in defining the event of tropical cyclone formation, especially in the model

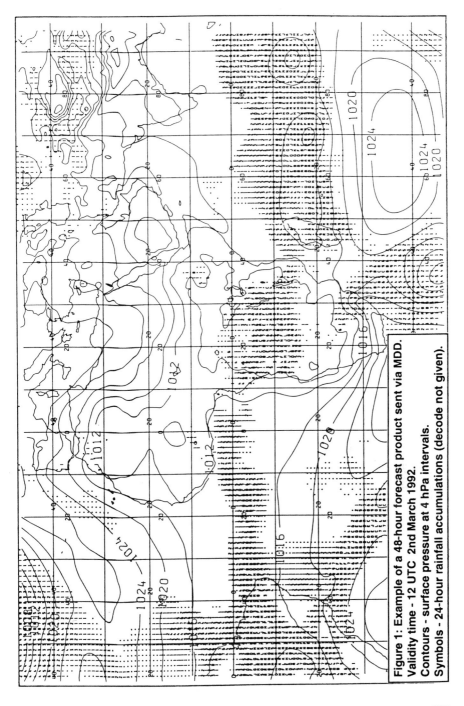

Figure 1: Example of a 48-hour forecast product sent via MDD.
Validity time - 12 UTC 2nd March 1992.
Contours - surface pressure at 4 hPa intervals.
Symbols - 24-hour rainfall accumulations (decode not given).

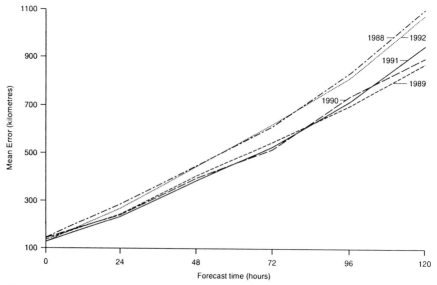

Fig. 2. Annual mean errors in the forecast positions of tropical cyclones

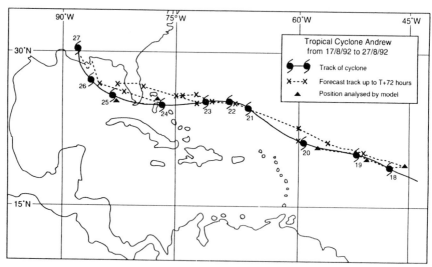

Fig. 3. Actual and forecast tracks for tropical cyclone Andrew

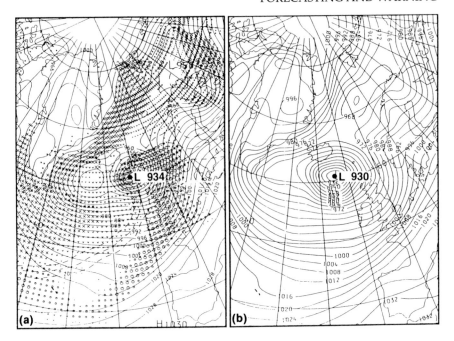

Fig. 4. 72-hour forecast (a), and analysis (b) for 12 UTC 10th
January 1993. Solid contours: surface pressure at 4 hPa
intervals. Symbols and dashed contours: precipitation-rate and
snow probability lines (decode not given)

forecasts, there is clearly a marked degree of skill in the
forecasts.

1-day forecasts	88%
2-day forecasts	86%
3-day forecasts	60%
4-day forecasts	48%
5-day forecasts	54%

Random at 120°E	25%
Random at 140°E	37%
Random at 160°E	27%

4.   WARNINGS OF EXCEPTIONALLY SEVERE STORMS

As was mentioned in section 2, RSMC Bracknell currently
issues plain language advisory messages to selected centres
on the development and movement of tropical cyclones in the
southern Indian Ocean, the South Pacific and the North-West
Pacific. However, information on exceptionally severe
weather is not restricted to these basins or to tropical
cyclones alone. The global model also provides information

on mid-latitude storms and other synoptic scale systems
giving rise to exceptionally severe conditions such as heavy
and prolonged rain or snow. The marine models are also
capable of providing additional information of wave and
swell heights. The models cannot be expected, though, to
handle mesoscale systems such as severe tornadic
thunderstorms. These occur on a scale smaller than the
models' resolution.

RSMC Bracknell has therefore made an offer through WMO to:

a. Extend the current range of plain language tropical
   cyclone advisories to include those areas not at present
   covered by existing bulletins, i.e. North-East Pacific,
   North-West Atlantic/Caribbean and the northern Indian
   Ocean.

b. Generate plain language advisories, similar to those
   issued for tropical cyclones, for extratropical storms of
   unusual severity. The advisories might be issued up to
   several days ahead and would provide advice on the
   expected tracks and intensities of the storms. Additional
   information concerning expected wind speeds and
   precipitation might also be included if felt appropriate.

This offer was made as a contribution to the Public Weather
Services Programme of WMO and to the IDNDR.

These bulletins would be made available on request, through
the GTS, to all National Meteorological Centres (NMCs) and
RSMCs responsible for issuing forecasts and warnings of
severe storms. The information supplied would be largely
based on direct output from the models, and its
interpretation would remain the province of the centre in
whose area of responsibility the severe weather was forecast
to occur. The centre would also continue to be the
responsible authority for the issue of severe weather
warnings within its area. The advisories would provide them
with more information to assist them in this task.

A proposal has also been made by RSMC Bracknell that coded
bulletins should be developed which would contain only those
data in excess of specified threshold values. By employing
the compression facilities offered by the WMO binary code
form GRIB, the bulletins would be able to contain
information on exceptionally severe weather at or near the
model's resolution (0.833° latitude by 1.25° longitude at
RSMC Bracknell). This proposal is currently being considered
within WMO, but it is unlikely to be of immediate benefit to
some developing countries because of the need for them to be
able to handle binary code forms. The plain language
advisories do not give rise to this problem.

An example of the capability of the model to provide
information concerning extratropical storms was provided
early in 1993 when a depression of record depth occurred to

the north of the British Isles. This gave rise to winds exceeding 100 mph (45 m/s) at times and coincided with the wrecking of the oil-tanker Braer on the Shetland Isles. The heavy seas led to the break up of the tanker but also helped to disperse the oil. The 3-day forecast of the surface pressure pattern for 12 UTC on the 10th January is shown in figure 4a and the verifying analysis in figure 4b. Also appearing in the forecast are symbols showing the expected extent and location of the precipitation. The forecast was excellent. (Note that the actual central pressure of the depression was about 15 hPa lower than shown by the global model's analysis in figure 4b. The higher resolution limited-area model was able to capture the extreme depth of the system, but its analysis (not shown) would not have provided a sensible basis for assessing the global model's forecast).

REFERENCES

1. Eleventh World Meteorological Conference, Geneva, 1-23 May 1991. Abridged report with resolutions. WMO-No.756, WMO, Geneva, 1991, 123-126.

2. The WMO Long-term Plan: overall policy and strategy 1992-2001. Third WMO long-term plan, part I. WMO-No.768, WMO, Geneva, 1992.

3. The WMO Applications of Meteorology Programme, 1992-2001; third WMO long-term plan, part II, vol. 4. WMO-No.764, WMO, Geneva, 1992, 4-9.

4. HALL, C.D., HUNT, J.C.R., RADFORD, A.M., CARRUTHERS, D.J., and WENG, W.S. Forecasting tropical cyclones and near surface wind conditions. ICSU/WMO International Symposium on Tropical Cyclone Disasters, Beijing, October 1992. To be published.

5. WILLOUGHBY, H.E., CLOS, J.A., and SHOREIBAH, M.G. Concentric eye walls, secondary wind maxima, and the evolution of the hurricane vortex. J. Atmos. Sci., 1982, vol. 39, 395-411.

6. IWASAKI, T., NAKANO, H., and SUGI, M. The performance of a typhoon track prediction model with cumulus parametrization. J. Met. Soc. Japan, 1987, vol. 65, 555-557.

7. CHAN, J.C.L., and KAY, W.K. Performance of the UK Meteorological Office global model in predicting the movement of tropical cyclones. City Polytechnic of Hong Kong, Research Report AP-92-16, 1992.

8. HALL, C.D. Operational forecasts of tropical cyclone formation in the western north Pacific in 1991. UK Met. Office, Central Forecasting Technical Note No. 7.

16. Flood hazard mitigation in peninsular Malaysia

N. W. CHAN, Flood Hazard Research Centre, Middlesex University

INTRODUCTION

Peninsular Malaysia lies approximately between latitudes 1°N to 7°N and longitudes 100°E to 105°E. It covers an area of 131,795 km². The climate is equatorial with uniformly high temperatures all year round (mean monthly temperature is about 26.7°C). The mean annual rainfall is high and varies from about 150 cm to more than 350 cm. In general, rainfall decreases as one moves from the east coast to the west coast. In the east coast, the mean annual rainfall can be as high as 400 cm. The bulk of this rainfall is deposited during the Northeast Monsoon Season from November to March (Ref.1). In the west coast, most of the rains fall during the two short inter-monsoon seasons in April and October where convectional rain storms occur frequently.

The topography of the peninsula is characterised by various fold mountain ranges in a predominantly northwest to southeast direction. A central mountain range, the Titiwangsa Range, forms the backbone of the peninsula. It is flanked by seven other mountain ranges. Average height ranges from about 1500 meters to 2000 meters. Near the coasts and rivers are flat alluvial plains with heights no more than one or two meters above sea level. It is in these lowland plains that most of the population is concentrated.

The heavy all year round rainfall in the Malaysian peninsula has given rise to a more than 100 river systems, though there is no single large river dominating the drainage pattern. The Titiwangsa Range is the main divide which determines whether a river flows eastward into the South China Sea or westwards into the Straits of Malacca. Due to the nature of its topography, the river courses are relatively short. The gradients of the rivers in the upper courses are steep, some drop about 1200 meters in less than 24 km before they emerge on to the coastal flood plains. In the lower stretches and the flood plains, the river gradients are gentle and flat, giving rise to widespread meandering patterns. Although the year-round precipitation ensures perennial stream flow and no river course is ever completely dry at any one time of the year, the torrential and localised nature of the rainfall causes rapid

Natural disasters. Thomas Telford, London, 1993

fluctuations in the river discharge. Consequently, the occurrence of floods is not uncommon (Ref.2).

THE FLOOD HAZARD

Historical floods

Although its neighbours Indonesia and the Philippines experience earthquakes, volcano eruptions and typhoons, Malaysians are fortunate in that there are no such natural hazards in the peninsula. The flood hazard is the only significant natural hazard that affects Peninsular Malaysia. While localised flooding occurs almost every year in one place or another, widespread and extensive floods in the peninsula have occurred regularly with a frequency of once in a few years. In the distance past, major floods in 1886, 1926, 1931, 1947, 1954, 1957, 1965, 1967 and 1971 have caused extensive damage to public utilities, crops and properties, disruption of social and economic activities, breakdown of essential services, outbreak of diseases and even the loss of lives. More recently, extensive floods have also occurred in 1973, 1979, 1983, 1986, 1988 and 1991. In the highly developed urban areas, flash floods are also a common hazard during torrential convection storms which occur all year round (Ref.3). The major flood-prone areas in the peninsula are mostly located in the coastal plains and riverine areas (Fig.1).

Flood damage

The costs incurred by the Malaysian Government in rescue and flood relief operations, as well as rehabilitation of public works and utilities is substantial. It is estimated that the damages for an annual flood, a 10-year flood and a 40-year flood are M$3.0 million, M$18.0 million and M$44.0 million respectively. Very little is remembered of the 1886 flood except that it was called the "Storm Forest Flood". This was because the flood, accompanied by gale force winds, destroyed several hundred sq.km of lowlying forests in the Kelantan River and Besut River flood plains. The 1926 flood was perhaps the biggest flood in living memory. During this flood most parts of the peninsula were affected. The 1971 flood was so serious that it was declared a national disaster by the Prime Minister. During this flood, most parts of the peninsula suffered damages on an unprecedented scale. The federal capital of Kuala Lumpur (M$34 million flood damage) and the Pahang River Basin (M$30 million flood damage) were the two worst hit areas. The 1967 flood was also a big one causing the most damage in the Kelantan, Terengganu and Perak river basins. The damage estimated for the Kelantan River Basin alone was M$78 million. More recently, the 1986 flood in Kelantan and Terengganu caused an unprecedented postponement of the public school examinations (Ref.4). A summary of flood damage for selected floods is shown in Table 1.

Types of flooding

In general, flood types in Peninsular Malaysia may be classified into the following categories:

195

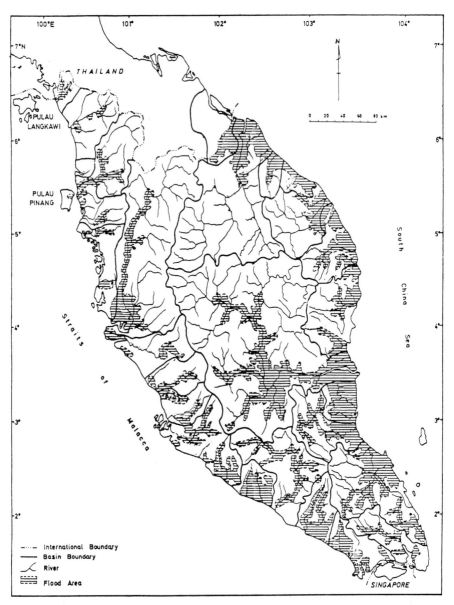

Fig. 1. Flood-prone areas in peninsular Malaysia (after Japan
International Cooperation Agency, 1982)

Table 1 : Flood   Damage   for   Selected   Floods   in   Peninsular
         Malaysia

Flood Event (Year)	(Place)	Damage (M$million)	Death	Persons Evacuated
1967	Kelantan R. Basin	78.4	38	320,000
1967	Perak R. Basin	60.8	0	280,000
1967	Terengganu R. Basin	15.8	17	78,000
1971	Pahang R. Basin	37.7	24	153,000
1971	Kuala Lumpur	34.3	24	NA
1984	Batu Pahat R. Basin	18.0	0	8,400
1988	Kelantan R. Basin	29.8	19	36,800
1991	Peninsular Malaysia	NA	11	NA
1992	Peninsular Malaysia	NA	12	NA

(Source: Drainage and Irrigation Department   Malaysia
and Malaysian National Security Council)

(1)   Overbank   flooding due   to overbank   flow as   a result   of
      insufficient channel capacity;

(2)   Tidal flooding which is   the combined result of high tides
      and back water effect; and

(3)   Inland flooding due to poor drainage.

FLOOD MITIGATION

Pre-1971

In   Peninsular   Malaysia,   the   Government   is   the   main   body
responsible for   flood mitigation. However,   prior to the   1971
flood, flood   mitigation was not even   mentioned as a   function
of any agency/department. Although   the Drainage and Irrigation
Department   (DID)   was   entrusted   with the   responsibility   of
providing drainage and irrigation, the responsibility of flood
mitigation   was not   part of   its function   (even   though flood
mitigation   is closely   related to   drainage). Because of   its
role   in   drainage   and river   conservancy,   the   DID   employed
mostly   structural   measures   of   flood   control. This   was
inevitable because the DID   was an agency entirely dominated by
engineers.

The Malaysian   Meteorological Service (MMS) was responsible for
forecasting the   weather, but it   was never   entrusted with the
responsibility of forecasting   floods. Because of this, all   it
did   was to   forecast heavy   rain spells.   In the   case of   the
Public Works Department .(PWD),   flood mitigation measures would
mean building   stronger   and   higher bridges,   building   roads
higher than   the   normal   flood mark,   or   even   building
alternative   roads which   avoided the   flood   plains. Only   the
Police Department, the   Welfare Department and the Ministry of

197

Health could be said to employ some form of non-structural flood mitigation measures. The Police Department was involved with the dissemination of flood warnings and rescue operations. The Welfare Department only moved in during and after a flood, mostly to provide relief. And the Health Department's concern was really the control of diseases rather than flood mitigation of any sort. As a result, flood mitigation measures prior to 1971 were almost entirely structural.

Whenever flooding occurred, each and every Government agency was responsible for the protection, rehabilitation, relief and carrying out of all other works related to the flood hazard within its jurisdiction. There was no central controlling body to monitor and coordinate the work. As a result, there was little team work between the Government agencies and often there was overlapping of responsibilities between two or more agencies, frequently resulting in confusion.

Post-1971

Despite its disastrous nature, the 1971 flood was really a blessing in disguise. It exposed the inadequacies of flood protection measures and the non-existence of a central body to plan, manage and monitor all aspects of flood mitigation in the peninsula. Furthermore, it showed that rapid development of flood plain regions since independence had substantially increased flood damage potential, particularly in urban areas. As a result, the Government embarked on a new approach towards comprehensive flood mitigation in the peninsula. A Water Resources Committee, headed by the Prime Minister's Department was set up to tackle the flood problems and other water related issues. Based on the recommendations of this committee, the flood mitigation strategies introduced were:

(1) The establishment of flood hazard institutions:

(a) The Permanent Commission on Flood Control:

This commission was established by a decision of the Malaysian Cabinet on 21st December 1971. Its immediate task was to study short-term measures to prevent the occurrence of floods and long-term measures for flood mitigation. As such, its main objective is to prevent floods from occurring. However, in the event of unavoidable flooding, its objective is to minimize flood damage in terms of loss of life and property. It is headed by the Minister of Agriculture with the DID serving as the secretariat.

(b) The National Disaster Relief and Preparedness Committee (NDRPC):

The NDRPC is headed by the Minister of Information and has its secretariat at the National Security Council in the Prime Minister's Department. The committee is responsible for coordinating all relief operations before, during and after a flood. The NDRPC is theoretically responsible for all the operations at the national, state, district, mukim and village levels (Fig.2). In reality, however, it coordinates operations at the national level and overlooks operations at the state

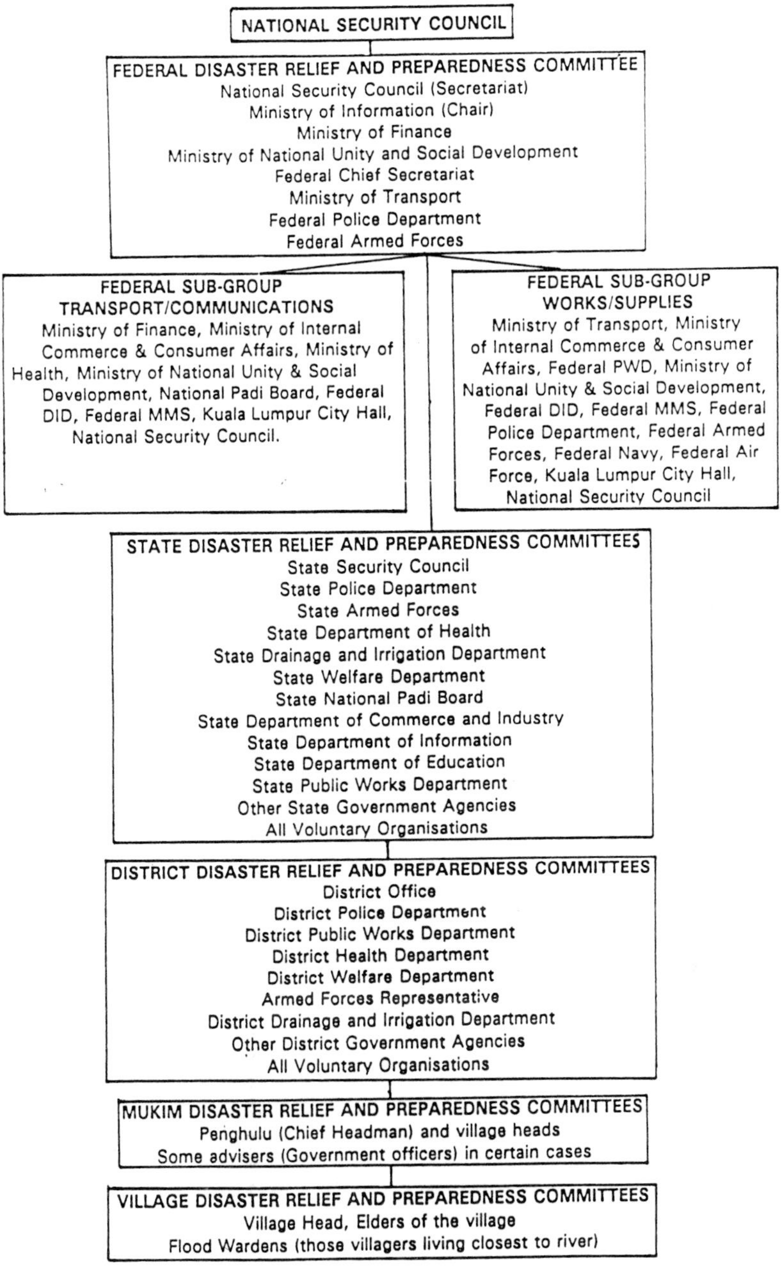

```
                    ┌─────────────────────────────┐
                    │   NATIONAL SECURITY COUNCIL  │
                    └─────────────────────────────┘
        ┌──────────────────────────────────────────────────┐
        │ FEDERAL DISASTER RELIEF AND PREPAREDNESS COMMITTEE │
        │        National Security Council (Secretariat)     │
        │            Ministry of Information (Chair)          │
        │               Ministry of Finance                  │
        │  Ministry of National Unity and Social Development  │
        │            Federal Chief Secretariat               │
        │             Ministry of Transport                  │
        │           Federal Police Department                │
        │             Federal Armed Forces                   │
        └──────────────────────────────────────────────────┘
```

FEDERAL SUB-GROUP TRANSPORT/COMMUNICATIONS	FEDERAL SUB-GROUP WORKS/SUPPLIES
Ministry of Finance, Ministry of Internal Commerce & Consumer Affairs, Ministry of Health, Ministry of National Unity & Social Development, National Padi Board, Federal DID, Federal MMS, Kuala Lumpur City Hall, National Security Council.	Ministry of Transport, Ministry of Internal Commerce & Consumer Affairs, Federal PWD, Ministry of National Unity & Social Development, Federal DID, Federal MMS, Federal Police Department, Federal Armed Forces, Federal Navy, Federal Air Force, Kuala Lumpur City Hall, National Security Council

```
        ┌──────────────────────────────────────────────────┐
        │ STATE DISASTER RELIEF AND PREPAREDNESS COMMITTEES  │
        │               State Security Council               │
        │              State Police Department               │
        │                State Armed Forces                  │
        │            State Department of Health              │
        │       State Drainage and Irrigation Department     │
        │             State Welfare Department               │
        │             State National Padi Board              │
        │     State Department of Commerce and Industry      │
        │           State Department of Information          │
        │           State Department of Education            │
        │           State Public Works Department            │
        │          Other State Government Agencies           │
        │             All Voluntary Organisations            │
        └──────────────────────────────────────────────────┘
        ┌──────────────────────────────────────────────────┐
        │ DISTRICT DISASTER RELIEF AND PREPAREDNESS COMMITTEES│
        │                  District Office                   │
        │             District Police Department             │
        │           District Public Works Department         │
        │             District Health Department             │
        │             District Welfare Department            │
        │             Armed Forces Representative            │
        │      District Drainage and Irrigation Department   │
        │           Other District Government Agencies       │
        │              All Voluntary Organisations           │
        └──────────────────────────────────────────────────┘
        ┌──────────────────────────────────────────────────┐
        │ MUKIM DISASTER RELIEF AND PREPAREDNESS COMMITTEES  │
        │     Penghulu (Chief Headman) and village heads     │
        │  Some advisers (Government officers) in certain cases│
        └──────────────────────────────────────────────────┘
        ┌──────────────────────────────────────────────────┐
        │ VILLAGE DISASTER RELIEF AND PREPAREDNESS COMMITTEES│
        │         Village Head, Elders of the village        │
        │ Flood Wardens (those villagers living closest to river)│
        └──────────────────────────────────────────────────┘
```

Fig. 2. Structure of the Federal Disaster Relief and Preparedness Committee in peninsular Malaysia (source: National Security Council of Malaysia)

level. Much of the operations in each state is left to be run by the respective state authorities. The main task of the NDRPC is to ensure that assistance and aid are provided to flood victims in an orderly and effective manner from the national level downwards.

(c) The Drainage and Irrigation Department:

Although river conservancy has always been a traditional function of the DID, flood mitigation was only officially designated as an additional function in 1972 (Ref.5). With these two functions going hand in hand, the DID is now responsible for the maintenance of river channels free from foreign obstructions, preventing silt from reaching the river, de-silting of river beds, diversion of river channels for mining and other purposes, river improvement works, river training and the construction and maintenance of other engineering structures for flood protection.

(2) The establishment of a flood disaster relief machinery:

This machinery was set up to ensure that all assistance and aid can be brought to the flood victims as quickly and as efficiently as possible. It is coordinated by the National Security Council (NSC) and the NDRPC is a part of this machinery (Fig.3). When the MMS and DID has forecasted an impending flood, the machinery will be activated. However, the full machinery will only be activated when floods occur in several states or when a state experiences a massive flood which cannot be adequately handled by the state authorities. In the event of massive and widespread flooding seriously crippling several states, then the NSC will advise the Honourable Prime Minister who may then decide whether or not to declare the flooding as a national disaster.

At the federal level, the NSC is the secretariat for the Flood Disaster Relief and Preparedness Committee (FDRPC) which comprises members from the Ministries of Information, Finance, National Unity and Social development, Transport, the Federal Chief Secretary, the Federal Police Department and the Federal Armed Forces. The FDRPC coordinates all relief operations from the Malaysian Control Centre in Kuala Lumpur. At the state level, there are 11 State Flood Relief and Preparedness Committees (SFRPC) for Peninsular Malaysia. Each state is given funds by the Federal Government every year to enable it to run its own flood relief operations. At the district level, there are several district committees under each state, depending on the number of districts in a particular state. Each district will have its own District Flood Relief and Preparedness Committees (DFRPC) which receives funds and directives from the SFRPC. Below the district level, there are several Mukim[1] Flood Relief and Preparedness Committees (MFRPC), again depending on the number of mukims in each

---

[1] A "mukim" is an administrative unit just below that of a district. A district is made up of several mukims. Likewise, a mukim is made of several villages, the latter being the smallest administrative unit.

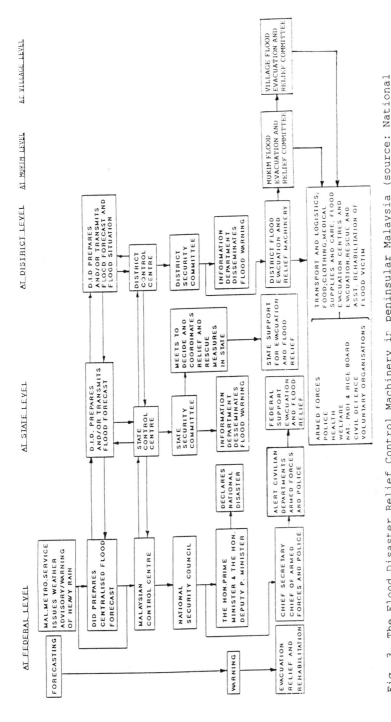

Fig. 3. The Flood Disaster Relief Control Machinery in peninsular Malaysia (source: National Security Council of Malaysia)

district. Each MFRPC is headed by a penghulu.[2] Finally, there are many Village Flood Relief and Preparedness Committees (VFRPC) under each mukim. Each VFRPC is headed by a ketua kampung[3].

(3) The collection of hydrological and flood data:

The importance of accurate hydrological data in the planning, design and implementation of flood mitigation methods cannot be underestimated, especially with reference to flood forecasting. Accurate hydrological data forms the basis of all aspects of water resource planning and management. Recognising this importance, the Malaysian Government has invested substantially in a programme to expand, update and improve the hydrological network in the peninsula. New procedures on data collection and processing are also constantly being introduced. The hydrological data bank is now fully computerised. This affords easy access and manipulation of the data which is now used for a variety of purposes. In terms of flood mitigation, it includes flood forecasting, flood analysis, design flood estimation and flood mapping. Other areas using hydrological data are water resource planning and management, drainage and irrigation, domestic water supply, generation of hydro-electricity, agriculture, land use planning, recreation and related researches.

(4) The carrying out of river basin studies, water resource studies and specific flood mitigation studies:

Since the 1971 flood, the Government has commissioned a number of river basin studies where major floods have occurred. These studies were aimed at understanding the hydrological characteristics of these basins, particularly with reference to its flood characteristics. By doing so, master plans for general water resource management (including flood mitigation) could then be prepared for each basin. To date, river basin studies which have been completed in the peninsula include the Kelang River Basin Study for Kuala Lumpur (1974), the Pahang River Basin Study (1974), the Kelantan River Basin Study (1978), the Terengganu River Basin Study (1978), the Batu Pahat River Basin Study (1984), the Johor River Basin Study (1985), the Golok River Basin Study (1985), the Besut River Basin Study (1990), the Krian River Basin Study (1990), and the Pinang River Basin Study (1991).

With the help of the Japan International Cooperation Agency, the Government also carried out a National Water Resources Study which was completed in 1982. Under this study, flood studies in other river basins not previously studied were carried out. The results of this study is now being used to develop a comprehensive and coordinated water resources development programme for the peninsula. One of the salient

---

[2] A "penghulu" is the Malay term for headman to a group of villages. However, in some areas the term is used synonymously with "ketua kampung" or village head.

[3] "Ketua kampung" is literally translated as village head, "ketua" being head and "kampung" being village.

features of this study is the formulation of a 20-year plan for flood mitigation works in 31 river basins and many other flood prone areas in the peninsula. Under this plan, a total of 573 km of river channel will be improved, 10 multi-purpose dams will be constructed, 74 km of flood bypass will be constructed, 11 ring bunds around urban centres will be built, and 10,000 people in flood-prone areas will be resettled. The cost of the entire plan is about M$2 billion. When fully completed it will provide protection to some 1.6 million people in the peninsula.

Specific flood mitigation studies have also been conducted to alleviate flooding in strategically important flood-prone areas in the peninsula. To date, the studies completed include the Cukai Flood Mitigation Study (1978), the Lower Perak Flood Mitigation Study (1980), and the Kangar Flood Mitigation Study (1983). Other studies aimed at flood alleviation include the Sewerage and Drainage Master Plan Studies for urban centres in the peninsula. These include studies for Kuala Lumpur, Kelang and Port Kelang, Butterworth and Bukit Mertajam, Alor Setar, Johor Bahru, Seremban, Melaka, Kuantan, Kota Bharu, Kuala Terengganu, Port Dickson and Muar. The completed master plans are of immense value to Government authorities and the private sector in terms of future land use planning in the areas concerned.

(5) The implementation of flood mitigation projects:

From past flood experiences, the Government is aware that providing costly structural (engineering) protection to the masses is not the only means of reducing the flood hazard. To date, flood mitigation strategies adopted represent a multi-disciplinary approach. All strategies can be grouped under two types of flood mitigation measures: structural measures and non-structural measures. The former represents all those measures involving the construction of engineering structures while the latter includes those measures which are non-engineering in nature. Non-structural measures are usually used in areas where structural measures are either too costly or are not economically justified. In most cases, non-structural measures are used to supplement structural measures.

(a) Structural measures:

(i) Improvement of river channels:

This is one of the oldest methods and is still the most widely used in the peninsula. Perennial silting of river channels have raised the river bed in relation to the flood plain. In many instances, the flood plain level may be below that of the river level, flooding being avoided by a raised natural levee (in some cases by an artificial embankment) on both sides of the river. As a result, the river bed has to be constantly dredged to deepen it. The rate of dredging should at least keep up with the rate of silting. River channels can also be improved by canalization. This latter method reduces the volume of discharge in the main river channel. As a result, flood flows can be contained.

(ii) Construction of levees or embankments:

Usually, this method is applied hand in hand with dredging and canalization. The sand and silt from the river bed is dumped on both sides of the river bank resulting in the formation of two raised river banks or levees. In urban areas, however, dumping of sand and silt is not feasible because of the constricted nature of river banks in such areas. Consequently, concrete embankments may have to be built.

(iii) Construction of flood diversion channels:

This method involves the construction of artificial channels along the main river channel to divert part of the discharge during flood flows. Diversion channels are built just before the main river enters a flood-prone area. This method is only feasible if the intended diversion channel is not too long. Otherwise, the cost of construction may be too high.

(iv) Construction of flood retention ponds:

A flood retention pond can be easily built in an area where there is a depression. Otherwise, it may prove too costly. In many cases, old mining depressions are ideal locations for the building of such ponds. Artificial retention ponds are like huge reservoirs. A small channel with a gate joins the retention pond to the main river. The gate can be opened during flood flows.

(v) Use of natural and man-made ponds for flood attenuation:

Man-made ponds such as disused mining pools and park lakes are ideal for flood storage. If flood flows can be diverted into such ponds and lakes, then flood peaks can be attenuated. The outflow from such ponds can also be regulated. This method has great potential for large urban areas such as Kuala Lumpur and Georgetown.

(vi) Construction of polders/ring bunds/tidal bunds:

This method requires the construction of a raised ring bund surrounding the area that is being protected. It is only applied in localised areas with a high damage potential and where it is not economically feasible to carry out an overall basin protection. A good example of poldering is the flood mitigation scheme of Pekan on the estuary of the Pahang River. Tidal bunds are built in coastal and estuarine areas to control tidal flooding. They are effective on the west coast of the peninsula which is sheltered from both the monsoons.

(vii) Construction of multi-purpose dams:

The building of dams solely for the purpose of flood mitigation in Peninsular Malaysia is seldom if not never economically justified. As a result, multi-purpose dams have been built. These dams serve a variety of functions. They generate hydro-electricity, provide water supply, regulate flood peak flows and can be used for recreational purposes. Some examples are Kenyir Dam in Terengganu, Chenderoh and Temengor Dams in Perak, Pedu and Muda Dams in Kedah, Klang

Gates and Langat Dams in Selangor, and Machap and Sembrong Dams in Johor.

(b) Non-structural measures:

(i) Legislation:

In Peninsular Malaysia legislation with respect to flood mitigation is rather vague. There are a few laws touching on flood mitigation but only in an indirect manner. For instance, the Waters Enactment 1920 provides that "the entire property in and control of all rivers in any State is and shall be vested solely in the Ruler of such State". With respect to flood mitigation, the Waters Enactment contains provisions for:

(1) prohibiting the construction of buildings and structures in the vicinity of a river or a declared flood channel "except in a case which may be expressly authorised by any other law" or "except in accordance with the terms of a written permission by the State Authority";

(2) allowing the Ruler of a State, if he is satisfied that the bed of any river is insufficient to contain flood waters, to declare by notification in the Gazette that the abutting land of such river shall be a flood channel and be subjected to the State's control;

(3) empowering the State ruler to put a stop to all illegal acts and interference with the bank of a river; and

(4) the issuance of a written authorization from the Ruler-in-Council for the construction of any revetment or erection of any building or structure within 15.2 meters of a river bank or within any flood channel.

The National Land Code also contains some provisions for dealing with flood control. In Malaysia, land is the property of the State. As such, the State authority has the right to reserve land for any public purpose by notification in the Gazette. Since flood mitigation is considered a public purpose, certain flood-prone areas may be set aside as "reserved land" and thereby not to be developed.

The Mining Enactment 1929, the Drainage Works Ordinance 1954 and the Land Conservation Act 1960 also touches on flood mitigation indirectly. All have provisions for the regulation of land and river use. However, the term flood mitigation is not spelled out clearly and the approval of land and river use is clearly left to the discretion of the authorities concerned.

(ii) Restriction of development:

This measure is a case of "prevention is better than cure". In areas where the building of flood mitigation structures cannot be economically justified, the planning authority may use this as a measure to avoid rather than control floods. Recently, the information gathered through flood risk analysis and flood mapping in the peninsula (Ref.6) has made it easier for

205

planners to restrict development in crucial flood-prone areas.

(iii) Flood risk analysis:

Expanding urban areas due to increased economic development have resulted in increased runoff, subsequently giving rise to increased flooding. Flood risk analysis is a technique of flood mitigation aimed at monitoring such changes in economic development in relation to flood peaks. Flood risk maps are prepared to help the authorities, particularly planners in the approval of development projects. They also help the public, particularly developers and property buyers, appraise certain properties in flood hazard areas.

(iv) Land use change:

Changing the type of crop can have a drastic effect on the runoff pattern. For instance, by converting padi land into oil palm can substantially increase surface cover and thereby reduce runoff. Another method is to cultivate cover crops such as peanuts or sweet potatoes between rows of rubber or oil palm trees. Other common cover crops planted in between rows of coconut trees are coffee and cocoa. The planting of such cover crops is not only beneficial as a measure of flood control but it also nourishes the soil and provides the farmer with a source of additional income.

(v) Resettlement of population:

As far as the Government is concerned, this measure is only used as a last resort when all flood mitigation measures do not seem to work. This measure is very costly for the Government because alternative land (and houses in many cases) will have to be allocated to each household that is being resettled.

(vi) Flood proofing:

Malaysians are very proud of their cultural heritage. There is a campaign to preserve old Malay palaces and mosques, Chinese shop-houses, Indian temples and old Portuguese, Dutch and British colonial buildings. Where such buildings happen to be located in flood-prone areas, all efforts are channelled to flood proof them. Flood proofing includes the construction of protection works to prevent flood waters from entering the individual buildings. This usually entails the building of a flood wall or a raised bund around the building. However, there are other methods such as raising the floor of the building, building a higher threshold across the doors, and replacing wooden stilts with concrete ones. Many individual property owners in flood-prone areas have also flood proofed their properties.

(vii) Flood insurance:

While insurance has been widely used as a means of flood protection in many countries in the west, particularly the United States and the United Kingdom, it is not well developed in Malaysia. In Malaysia, factory owners can insure the building structure as well as its contents (usually production goods) against flood damage but there is no specific insurance for individual house owners against such damage. Usually, the flood damage clause is incorporated as a sub-clause in the fire policy of the house. In this sub-clause, only the structure of the building is covered. House owners in flood-prone areas can take up special insurance against flood damage to house contents but the premium charged by insurers may be too high for its justification. Because of this limitation, there is great scope for the further development of flood insurance.

(viii) A sound watershed development and management policy:

While it is arguably difficult to control seasonal floods caused by the Monsoons, their severity can nevertheless be reduced. So too are flash floods caused by over-development and deforestation. In order to reduce if not control flooding, the solution lies in a sound watershed development and management policy. To date, less than 60 % of the total area in Peninsula Malaysia is still covered by natural forest. The Government (through the Forestry Department) has a long term plan for reafforestation in the National Forest Policy adopted in 1977. In this policy, development programmes in forested watershed are closely monitored. The country's forestry programme is also based on one of sustainable utilization rather than all-out exploitation.

(ix) The implementation of flood forecasting and warning systems:

Before the 1971 flood, flood forecasting methods were only used in a few of the major river systems. These were rather crude forms of forecasting based on simple stage-correlation whereby the river level at an upstream station is used to predict the level at a downstream station, usually located in a populated flood-prone area. Warning is then issued when a certain preset critical level at the upstream is exceeded. For instance, the river level at Kuala Krai is used to predict the river level at Kota Bharu. All these are done manually.

Since the 1971 flood, flood forecasting and warning systems have gradually been improved. The Government has pumped in a lot of funds to upgrade the hydrological infra-structure which supports flood forecasting and warning systems. There are now 42 telemetric rainfall stations, 47 telemetric river level stations, 119 manual rain gauges, 56 flood notice boards, 23 automatic sirens, 83 fixed VHF radio stations, and 63 mobile VHF radio stations throughout the peninsula. As a result of these new infra-structure, real-time flood forecasting has been made available for the Kelantan, Pahang, Perak, Klang, Batu Pahat, Muar and Johor rivers.

(x) Educating the masses:

Through its many agencies, the Government has set up various information programmes to educate the masses on how to response when a flood occurs. For instance, the Police tell the people when to move. The Welfare Department instructs the people where to go for shelter, food, clothing and other needs. There are also leaflets and posters distributed to people in flood-prone areas telling them what to do during a flood. The ketua kampung and his village committee are briefed by Government officers well in advance of any flood. The committee in turn briefs the village folks.

CONCLUSION

As a developing country, Malaysia's flood mitigation policy can be described as commendable, particularly since 1971. Since the First Malaysia Plan (1971-1975), the country's expenditure on flood mitigation has increased substantially. From a mere M$14 million in this plan, it has shot up to a massive M$700 million for the Sixth Malaysia Plan (1991-1995), a 50 fold increase over a 20 year period. Even after discounting inflation, the real increase is still substantial. With the many structural and non-structural measures being implemented for flood control and for flood relief, the country is moving in the right direction towards a comprehensive programme of flood mitigation. Yet, there are many areas which can still be improved.

While the total number of telemetric stations for rainfall and river flow in the peninsula seems large enough, a closer scrutiny would expose the inadequacies of uneven distribution. Most telemetric stations are located in populated areas while the sparsely populated areas, especially highland watershed areas, do not have enough telemetric stations. The MMS and DID have also not utilised remotely sensed rainfall (radar[4] and satellite sensed rainfall) as an input in its forecasting models. This could have been deliberately overlooked because of the high cost involved but real-time flood forecasting cannot be detached from the usage of such techniques.

Although the DID is officially recognised as the authority on all aspects of river use and management, it has no legislative authority or enforcement powers when it comes to rivers. All such powers are still vested with the respective State Authorities or the District Offices. Given the present status quo, the States will never relinquish their stranglehold on their rivers. At the moment, all the DID can do is to give advice to the State authorities when a certain project concerning a river is proposed. There is even no provision that a State authority needs to seek advice from DID's expertise. Even if it does, it may not adhere to DID's recommendations. So the only way to be certain that flood mitigation is given due consideration in any project is to make the DID one of the authorities that approve or reject the proposals. This would be difficult as legislation would have to be passed by the Federal Parliament.

---

[4] The MMS has used radar to predict rainfall in a qualitative way. The current radar can tell the meteorologist whether a certain region has rain or not. What it cannot do, however, is to tell the meteorologist how much rain the region is getting. Given the importance of time in the issuance of flood warning, this quantitative sensing of rain is vital to flood forecasting as it increases the lead time (time between the issuance of a warning and time when a flood occurs).

While there are some laws governing the regulation of river use and have some bearing on flood mitigation, they are not sufficiently clear or forceful enough as measures of flood mitigation. These laws were formulated mainly for the purpose of regulating and managing single sectoral water use. New laws must be passed to enable the authorities to have direct control in all aspects of water use which may affect flooding. This include laws that specify clearly water rights administration, water resource development, flood plain management and all aspects of flood mitigation. Alternatively, the existing laws should be updated with a stronger emphasis on flood mitigation.

REFERENCES

1. Chan N.W. Angin Monsun dan Kemusiman Hujan di Semenanjung Malaysia, Perantara 8(4), August, 1990, 22-6.

2. Douglas I. Aspects of water balance of catchments in the Main Range near Kuala Lumpur. Transactions, First Aberdeen-Hull Symposium on Malaysian Ecology, University of Hull, Department of Geography, Misc. Ser. No. 11, 1971, 23-35.

3. Jahi J.M. Flash flood problems and human responses to the flash flood hazard in Kuala lumpur area, Peninsular Malaysia. Akademika 26, January, 1985, 45-62.

4. Sooryanarayana V. Floods in Malaysia. Paper presented at The Working Group on Tropical Climatology and Human Settlements of the 26th Congress of the International Geographical Union, Sydney, August 1988.

5. Lim T.K. Malaysian rivers and floods. Paper presented at the Seminar Tebatan Banjir, Kuala Lumpur (Malaysia), 14 - 17 November, 1988.

6. Law K.F. Flood risk analysis and mapping in Malaysia. Paper presented at the Seminar Tebatan Banjir, Kuala Lumpur (Malaysia), 14 - 17 November, 1988.

17. The use of radar-based rainfall forecasts in operational flood warning

C. G. COLLIER, METSTAR Consultants, and P. D. WALSH
and C. M. HAGGETT, National Rivers Authority, UK

1. Introduction

The development of relatively inexpensive minicomputers, and digital communication systems in the later 1960's, provided the impetus in many developed countries for the deployment of digital radar systems, firstly within research projects and later within operational networks. In western Europe over the twenty years between 1970 and 1990 the number of operational digital weather radars increased from one to over one hundred (ref 1).

This activity was stimulated in part by the success of research projects aimed at assessing the potential of radar for making measurements of precipitation, for example the Dee Project in the UK (ref 2-3). This project led to the North West Radar Project, which demonstrated the feasibility of continuously operating a radar system totally unmanned at a remote location (ref 3).

Following these successful projects, the water industry in England and Wales, with the Meteorological Office, developed a cost-benefit analysis which justified the joint funding of an operational network of radars providing coverage over the whole of the UK (ref 4-5). The deployment of operational radars began in the late 1970's and was completed in 1991. The current network, including radars in Northern Ireland and Scotland, funded here in part by the Meteorological Office and other government agencies, comprises 13 Siemens Plessey 5.6cm (C-band) wavelength radars as shown in Figure 1.

Whilst the radar network in the UK was being developed in order to serve both hydrologists locally, and a range of users through the provision of composite imagery generated by the network centre at the Met. Office, Bracknell, (ref 6), work began at the Met. Office Radar Research Laboratory, located at the Royal Signals and Radar Establishment, Malvern, to develop very-short-range forecasting techniques based upon the radar network and satellite imagery, (ref 7).

Natural disasters. Thomas Telford, London, 1993

Fig. 1. Location and coverage of radars contributing data to the UK radar network. The range of the circles is 210 km

NATURAL DISASTERS

This work led to the development of the FRONTIERS system (ref 8-9), the current version of which is outlined later in this paper.

Since the Dee Project, meteorologists and hydrologists had worked closely together to assess the potential of weather radar for measuring areal precipitation in near real-time (ref 10-11), to develop a robust operational radar system (ref 12) and to use the radar data as an integral part of operational flood forecasting systems (ref 13). With the development of the FRONTIERS system in the early 1980s work began to assess the accuracy of radar-based rainfall forecasts and how best to use these forecasts as direct input to river flow forecasting models. Each new radar installation in England and Wales was planned and managed by consortia comprising Met. Office and appropriate water industry representatives. Research initiatives were largely taken by these consortia, the Institute of Hydrology and a few university groups notably that at the Dept of Civil Engineering, University of Birmingham, later to be transferred to the University of Salford. With the creation of the National Rivers Authority this close cooperation has continued.

Following an initiative taken by the Institute of Hydrology, a Natural Environmental Research Council (NERC) Committee for Hydrological Uses of Radar Data was established involving the representatives of several agencies. This committee was able to formulate and encourage the implementation of a NERC Special Research Topic called HYREX aimed at providing funding for radar hydrometeorological studies. Subsequently the committee has become an Inter-Agency committee and continues to provide a focal point for radar hydrometeorological R&D. In addition the Met. Office and the National Rivers Authority have jointly pursued R&D projects aimed at clarifying the current performance of FRONTIERS forecasts within operational flood forecasting systems. The work is summarized later in this paper. Of particular importance are the lessons learnt on the how to use radar data and what its limitations are. The relevance of this knowledge to using radar in developing countries will be discussed in the final section.

2. Flood Warning in England and Wales

Under the Water Resources Act 1991, the National Rivers Authority has the power "to provide and operate Flood Warning Systems". The responsibility is a permissive not a mandatory duty, although in practice the Authority has established such systems in all of its nine regions. However the NRA is the only body to have these powers, but does not usually issue warnings direct to the public. Warnings are issued to the police and local authorities who are in a better position, through their ability to deploy people locally, to carry out this task and to assist members of the public. The NRA operational role in flood warning is essentially one of monitoring, forecasting and prediction using a wide range of hydrometeorological information. This arrangement dovetails well with the emergency planning arrangements for civil emergencies, under which the police and local authorities would take control of, for example, any evacuation and temporary accommodation arrangements.

The purpose of the flood warning service is to minimize danger to the public and reduce financial losses from flooding by providing timely, accurate and reliable warnings of impending flooding enabling those at risk to take remedial action. This is achieved by the coordinated action of a number of agencies who need to operate in an integrated manner in order to achieve the optimum benefits for those whom the system is designed to serve.

The NRA also has operational responsibilities for flood defence schemes, including pumping stations, flood storage basins, and would be the lead agency in any physical response to mitigate the effects of flooding through emergency repairs to flood embankments and similar defences. It therefore requires flood forecasts to achieve effective operational responses to flood threats and flooding.

Historically communities became establised at crossing points of rivers on their flood plains. There are therefore many towns throughout England and Wales with potential flood risks.

3. Current flood warning procedures

The National Rivers Authority, through its Flood Warning Service carries out continuous 24 hour monitoring of river conditions and uses weather forecasts to give it early warning of the need to prepare flood forecast and warnings. In the NW region telemetered data are collected every 15 minutes from about 70 river gauges, 20 rain gauges and 4 tidal level recorders. There are fed in to flow forecasting models and alarm message generated for the attention of duty staff when ever actual or forecast levels exceed predetermined threshold levels. These enable the NRA to forecast flood risk for North West England and, through the Police and Local Authorities, to issue warnings to people and property at risk from flooding.

The monitoring of rainfall and river levels is carried out by the Duty Officers either in a specially equipped flood forecast room or outside office hours during normal weather conditions, from home using portable computer terminals. When weather forecasts or conditions deteriorate and there is a possibility of tidal or inland flooding, the flood forecast room is opened and would thereafter be continuously staffed.

The NW Regional Flood Warning Scheme which is, discussed here as an example, gives warnings, where practical of potential flooding from either river or tidal sources (not discussed here). When flooding from rivers is forecast, specific warnings are issued for pre-defined flood risk zones and at specific stages during the development of the flood as it is forecast. Appropriate action is then taken by Police and Local Authorities in the areas previously determined by the National Rivers Authority.

Warnings of flooding from rivers in "formal" flood risk zones (ie where specific plans have been prepared) are initiated by an advanced warning to the Police when there is a distinct possibility that flooding is possible. This is not made public but enables the police to prepare for the next stage since if river level forecasts continue to rise, Amber or Red Flood Warnings would need to be issued to the inhabitants in the areas at risk and action can be taken to deploy. The passing of the flood is followed by a "Stand Down" message when there is no further role to be played by the police in issuing warnings and river levels can safely be predicted to drop below the danger level.

4. Provision of heavy rainfall forecasts by the Meteorological Office

In the United Kingdom heavy rainfall forecasts are issued by Meteorological Office Weather centres to their local NRA regions in England and Wales, to River Purification Boards and Hydroelectric Power generating companies in Scotland and to Government departments in Northern Island. Occasionally severe weather warnings involving precipitation are also issued to the general public via television and radio. The forecasters at these Weather Centres use various aids to help them reach a decision on the expected quantities of rain relying on numerical model forecasts as guidance for periods beyond about six hours.

Traditional techniques based upon studies of the synoptic situation at the surface and upper levels are used with varying degrees of complexity at individual Centres. One of the most comprehensive procedures has been developed by the forecasters at Manchester supplying information to the NRA North West Region in the form of expected events of significant rainfall over the catchments in the region. This service has been in place for over 20 years. During this period the forecasters have devised techniques and knowledge of how to judge which synoptic weather patterns will lead to significant falls of rain across part of the region (ref 14-15).

More recently radar imagery has become available and the continuity of radar composite images is now used as an additional aid for 0 to 6 hours lead times. During the last two years assessments have also been carried out at London and Manchester of the utility of the current generation of radar-based extrapolation forecasts generated by the FRONTIERS system. These forecasts will be discussed later in this paper.

5.   Radar data and radar-based rainfall forecasts

Conventional in situ observations of the atmosphere are too
widely spaced to identify many of the phenomena which lead
directly to weather. Forecasters require information on a
fine scale in order to recognize characteristic patterns,
and make concomitant fine scale analyses. Of particular
importance is precipitation data as this information enables
forecasters to make detailed heavy rainfall forecast of
importance to hydrological flow forecasting. Radar data
enable precipitation systems to be identified when
conventional observations provide only limited data.

Over the last twenty years or so there has been considerable
activity aimed at developing mesoscale numerical models of
the atmosphere. These models have been unsuccessful at
reproducing physical processes determined as locally forced
responses to large-scale meteorology (see for example ref
16-17). However, it has become clear that short-range
forecasting using mesoscale data will not be completely
successful unless these data can be assimilated in a way
which ensures that the information content of the data is
retained. Since there are limitations on both model
resolution which can be used effectively, and the data
retention which can be achieved at present,
observation-based forecasting methods are still found to
provide a basis for generating heavy rainfall warnings.

Since 1984, when the national radar network became
operational, all regions in the NRA have made increasing use
of radar data as an aid to improve flood prediction and
flood warning. However, the ways in which this information
is used can vary considerably, from subjective assessments
of general weather conditions to full integration into flood
forecasting systems. Over the last five years there has
been a marked trend in the NRA away from the use of radar
data in a qualitative way on stand-alone systems to more
quantitative applications with the integration of data with
regional telemetry and forecasting systems. This move to a
more integrated approach in data capture and processing has
given the opportunity to use information from a wider
network of rain-gauges to locally calibrate data in
real-time thereby increasing the accuracy of the measurement
of areal rainfall and hence flood forecasting generally.

Weather radar then is a key element in many flood
forecasting systems operated by the NRA. However, its use
in isolation does limit the maximum warning time available
to the rainfall-runoff lag of the subcatchment in question.
In the upper reaches of urban and steeply sloped catchments
these lag times can be very short, less than an hour in some
cases, and in such circumstances there is a need for
quantitative rainfall forecasts to extend lead times.

At present two approaches to rainfall forecasting are being
evaluated by the NRA.

215

NATURAL DISASTERS

FRONTIERS -   Making use of data generated by the Met.
                      Office giving forecasts out to 6 hours
                      ahead on a 5km grid, updated every 30
                      minutes (ref 8-9, section 6.1).

LOCAL FORECASTS -   Regional based systems providing
                      forecasts up to 2 hours ahead on a 2km
                      grid, updated every 15 minutes.
                      Developed by the Institute of Hydrology
                      and University of Salford (section 6.2)

Both system will be used in tandem, with the higher
resolution forecasts, which are required particularly for
flood forecasting over urban areas and small rural
catchments, providing a valuable complement to the national
FRONTIERS product. It is envisaged that forecasts from both
systems will be used to generate flood forecasts
operationally with the local system generating rainfall
predictions up to 2 hours ahead and FRONTIERS from 2 to 6
hours ahead.

One example of this approach is the NRA Thames Region system
known as CASCADE (a Catchment Assessment System Concerned
with the Accurate Dissemination of Effective flood
warnings). At its heart lies a VAX 4000-400 computer which
collects data from the weather radar installation at Chenies
in Buckinghamshire every 5 minutes, 55 raingauges and 111
river gauges.

A local radar calibration scheme has been developed and run
operationally since 1989 which calibrates radar images by
reference to rainfall recorded by the rain-gauge network.
This enables the accuracy of rain-gauge rainfall data to be
combined with the spatial characteristics of radar rainfall
measurements.

Data from two radar-based rainfall forecasting models are
used by the system to generate instantaneous and
accumulation forecasts. A local rainfall forecasting system
developed by the Institute of Hydrology generates rainfall
predictions out to 2 hours ahead and the national FRONTIERS
system out to 6 hours ahead.

Many of the rivers in the Thames Region, especially those
draining London, are fast responding and the disruptive and
damaging effects of flooding are potentially very high. The
provision of reliable, accurate and timely flood warnings in
such circumstances are especially important. Weather radar
and radar-based rainfall forecasts are important elements in
such a system in this part of England.

6. Assessment of radar-based rainfall and flood forecasts

6.1 FRONTIERS forecasts of rainfall

FRONTIERS forecasts have been assessed routinely since

January 1990 using a number of different indices (ref 18).
These indices have also been evaluated for persistence
forecasts that is leaving an image stationary for the entire
forecast period. At T + 1 hour FRONTIERS beat persistence
with the gap widening during 1991 as the forecasters became
more familiar with the operating procedures. At T + 3 hours
the gap between the FRONTIERS forecasts and persistence is
narrower.

The forecast accuracy was found to improve as the area over
which rainfall accumulations are averaged is increased.
Twenty-one of the worst FRONTIERS forecast cases have been
investigated and the main problem in each case identified.
The use of persistence inappropriately, and development
adequacy of the rainfall pattern, feature significantly in
this analysis.

Recent work suggests that there is a large difference
between the performance of the FRONTIERS forecasts in
convective and frontal synoptic situations. It is not
difficult to understand why this is so when one considers
the rapid changes of intensity and movement which occur in
convective systems. This is illustrated by the 2km x 2km
radar data over the Lee river catchment (North London) shown
in Figure 2. Here a convective cell develops rapidly from
hour to hour and a band of heavy rain moves first to the
east and then back to the west. No forecasting procedure
based purely on extrapolation can cope with such changes.
In spite of this, forecasts of frontal rainfall can be of
great use for lead times up to six hours ahead.

6.2 Local forecasts of rainfall

The highest spatial and temporal data resolutions have been
used to make very-short-period forecasts (for a review see
ref 20). Although many procedures have been devised, one of
the most robust is that based on the cross correlation of
one image with another image at a subsequent time (see for
example ref 21). This technique has been adapted to use
with the 2km x 2km radar data available from the UK radar
network (ref 22) and has been integrated into an operational
flood warning system (ref 23) (Section 6).

Analysis has revealed that such a local forecasting
technique based upon high resolution data can out perform
the FRONTIERS system (based on 5km x 5km, 30 minute data)
within the first two hours of a forecast. Beyond two hours
ahead the wider spatial coverage of the radar network and
the use of satellite data enables rainfall to be moved into
the area of interest from a significant distance upwind.

6.3 Assessment of radar-based flood forecasts

Rainfall-runoff models may act to filter the quality of
rainfall forecasts so that deficiencies in rainfall
forecasts may not always translate directly to errors in

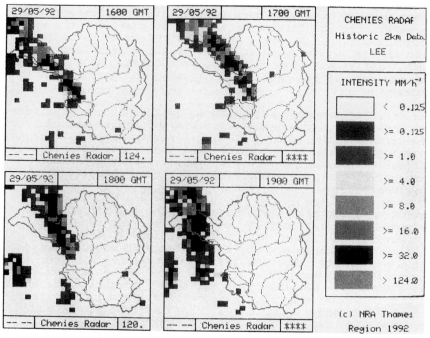

Fig. 2. 2 km x 2 km radar data over the Lee catchment (North London) on 29 May 1992

flow forecasts. Considerable work has been undertaken by the NRA to assess the quality of river flow forecasts made using several different hydrological models. Of particular interest are the results produced by the NRA Thames Region.

The NRA Thames Region have carried out a detailed evaluation of the FRONTIERS rainfall forecasting system over the period October 1990 to February 1993 to ascertain whether such forecasts will enhance flood forecasting and flood warning in the Thames Basin. FRONTIERS accumulation data have been available for input to rainfall-runoff models. Initially, rainfall forecasts were used to run the Isolated Event Model (IEM) which is a rainfall-runoff, non-linear storage model currently used for flood forecasting in London and the Lee Valley (Haggett et al, 1991). The model is being used to evaluate FRONTIERS forecasts in three river catchments of varying size and land-use:-

Silk Stream at Colindeep Lane - small urban catchment (29 km²) in north-west London

Beverley Brook at Wimbledon Common - medium sized urban catchment (43.5 km²) in south-west London

Roding at Loughton - large rural catchment (269 km2)
in Essex

Rainfall accumulation data are averaged over the 2km grid
squares that make up each of the river catchments listed
above. The analysis followed the fixed lead time, variable
origin approach to enable comparisons to be made between the
accuracy of rainfall forecasts with different lead times.
For each event, this initially involved compiling a rainfall
profile of all one hour ahead forecasts (T + 1) and using
this information to generate corresponding flow forecasts at
each gauging station. The procedure was then repeated for
all other forecast lead times, comparing the resultant error
statistics at each stage.

A number of error statistics were used in the analysis, but
the Root Mean Square Error (RMSE) formed the basis for
comparison between modelled and observed flows and may be
defined as:-

$$RMSE = \left\{ 1/N \sum_{i=1}^{N} \left(\frac{Fi}{Gi}\right)^2 \right\}^{1/2}$$

Where Fi is the forecast flow in cumecs
      Gi is the gauged flow in cumecs and
      N is the total number of flow values

In addition to flow forecasts generated from FRONTIERS data,
forecasts were also produced from observed rainfall, both
rain-gauge and radar subcatchment, for each event. This
enabled inherent model errors to be determined and provided
a yardstick for assessing the performance of the FRONTIERS
forecasts.

During the first year of the evaluation very few significant
rainfall amounts were recorded and this, coupled with poor
data availability, meant that only 5 events on average were
suitable for analysis in the study catchments. In contrast,
1992/93 was a much wetter year and data availability
increased markedly with the result that on average 21 events
were available for analysis in the study catchments.

As well as presenting average statistics for all events in
each catchment some event selection was undertaken to
determine the performance of FRONTIERS for storms of
differing synoptic type and magnitude. Statistics were
produced (Table 1) therefore, for the following cases in
each catchment:-

(1) average flow RMSE for all selected events
(2) average flow RMSE for the 10 largest flood events
(3) average flow RMSE for frontal events*
(4) average flow RMSE for convective events*

*as defined by the Met. Office

NATURAL DISASTERS

In general, the following conclusions can be made following completion of the evaluation of the FRONTIERS product.

* In the two urban catchments studied there appears not to be a firm relationship between forecast accuracy and lead time. Indeed, in both cases the T + 1 forecasts produced larger RMSE errors than the T + 6 forecasts (Figure 3). In the rural Roding catchment, however, a firm relationship was demonstrated, with the errors increasing with lead time (Figure 4).
* On average, FRONTIERS forecasts performed well for all lead times when compared with model runs using observed rainfall data. However, there were wide variations in forecast performance between events for all three catchments studied.
* For the 10 largest events in each catchment, the RMSE errors were consistently higher when compared with the average errors for all events.
* In general, the flow forecasts generated by FRONTIERS for convective events produced higher errors than those generated by frontal storms.

Table 1: Average RMSE errors across all lead times

(a)	Roding	Silk Stream	Beverley Brook
All events	3.51 (12)	2.06 (27)	2.55 (23)
Ten largest events	4.03 (10)	3.79 (10)	2.73 (10)
(b)			
FRONTAL	2.54 (5)	1.45 (13)	2.56 (12)
CONVECTIVE	7.84 (1)	2.94 (8)	2.73 (8)

( ) number of events used in analysis

6.4 Prospects for future radar-based systems

In summary,

* FRONTIERS performs well on average and when compared with observed rainfall data. There is significant variation between events, however, and error statistics tend to mask these differences.
* a conclusive link cannot demonstrate between forecast accuracy and lead time for urban catchments. But can for larger rural catchment.
* FRONTIERS performs less well in extreme events than generally.
* FRONTIERS performs better for frontal events than for convective events.

220

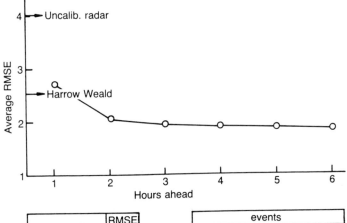

	RMSE
1 hour ahead	2·72
2 hour ahead	2·06
3 hour ahead	1·95
4 hour ahead	1·90
5 hour ahead	1·89
6 hour ahead	1·86
Harrow Weald	2·54
Uncalib. radar	4·03

events	
2. 30/03/92	24. 24/09/92
3. 14/04/92	25. 02/10/92
4. 27/04/92	29. 09/11/92
5. 30/04/92	31. 15/11/92
6. 09/05/92	32. 18/11/92
7. 29/05/92	37. 02/12/92
8. 30/05/92	39. 18/12/92
11. 30/06/92	40. 05/01/93
12. 01/07/92	41. 06/01/93
18. 13/08/92	42. 10/01/93
19. 25/08/92	43. 11/01/93
21. 18/09/92	44. 12/01/93
22. 22/09/92	45. 13/01/93
23. 22/09/92	

Fig. 3. Average flow RMSE for 27 events at Colindeep Lane using
Frontiers Forecasts

* Work, presented in section 8.2 suggests that a local
  forecasting advection procedure performs better than
  FRONTIERS for lead times up to 2 hours ahead; also
  better resolution (2km - 15 minute updates) for
  urban catchments. Local forecasts can be generated
  immediately on the users computer. FRONTIERS takes
  30-40 minutes to generate a forecast.
* Both FRONTIERS and local forecasting do not perform
  particularly well for convective situations. An
  alternative approach, other than advection, should be
  investigated.

Work is currently underway to blend radar-based forecasts
with numerical model predictions. A Met. Office project
known as NIMROD has began to address this matter. As yet it
is not clear whether such an approach will produce a
significant improvement at the spatial and temporal scales
required by hydrologists. In parallel with this activity

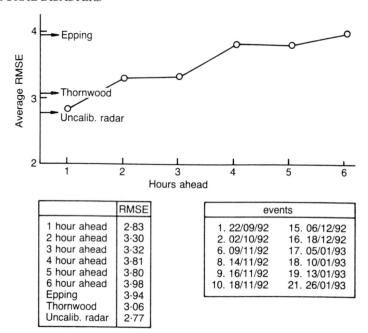

	RMSE
1 hour ahead	2·83
2 hour ahead	3·30
3 hour ahead	3·32
4 hour ahead	3·81
5 hour ahead	3·80
6 hour ahead	3·98
Epping	3·94
Thornwood	3·06
Uncalib. radar	2·77

events	
1. 22/09/92	15. 06/12/92
2. 02/10/92	16. 18/12/92
6. 09/11/92	17. 05/01/93
8. 14/11/92	18. 10/01/93
9. 16/11/92	19. 13/01/93
10. 18/11/92	21. 26/01/93

Fig. 4. Average flow RMSE for 12 events at Loughton using Frontiers Forecasts

the Met. Office are investigating the use of artificial intelligence techniques with high resolution radar, satellite and numerical model output. So far results are encouraging, and it is hoped that a joint project with the NRA will take this work to operational implementation. It is clear that to use the current forecasts produced by local forecasting procedures or the FRONTIERS system operationally it is important to put in place a procedure for recognizing when to use which approach. This may involve an assessment of the likely performance in terms of probability. The basis of such a procedure is the recognition of the weather type likely to occur over a catchment in the next few hours.

7. The role of radar in protecting vulnerable communities

So far we have presented work being undertaken in the UK to assess the operational potential of radar-based flood warning systems. We have shown that, for frontal rainfall, radar can produce very useful rainfall forecasts, and, via a rainfall-runoff model, forecasts of river hydrographs. Convective rainfall is more problematic. However, as illustrated by Figures 1 and 3, only radar is capable of mapping the details of rainfall fields in such situations. A real-time telemetering rain-gauge network would be required with a totally impractical density.

Flash flood situations are often associated with convective rainfall, hence work must continue to develop improved forecasting methods. Nevertheless, the most basic form of warning system can be achieved using radar imagery, and disseminating the knowledge that an event is beginning rapidly to users. The dissemination of warnings is a critical part of any operational flood warning system as discussed in section 3. This involves rapid communications and clearly defined lines of responsibility.

UK experience suggests that it is imperative that meteorologists and hydrologists work together in developing flood warning systems. It might appear to be unnecessary to stress this point, but it is only through close collaboration that robust systems can be developed. All too easily the performance of radar can be misunderstood, and its potential be overlooked.

References

1. CEC, 1992 Weather Radar Networking COST Project 73 Final Report of the Management Committee, Kluwer Academic Publishers, Dordrecht, ed. D.H. Neewsome, 254pp
2. DWRHP, 1977 Dee Weather Radar and Real Time Gydrological Forecasting Project, Report by the Steering Committee, publ Central Water Planning Unit, Reading, November, 172pp
3. Collinge, V.K. and C. Kirby, 1987 Weather Radar and Flood Forecasting, John Wiley & Sons Ltd, Chichester
4. NWC, 1983 Report of the Working Group on National Weather Radar Coverage, National Water Council, Met. Office, June, 31pp
5. Walsh, P.D., and G. Noonan, 1990 "Development of UK Weather Radar Network: Benefits in hydrological forecasts for flood warnings", in Economic and Social Benefits of Meteorological Services, WMO No 733, Geneva, 296-303.
6. Collier, C.G., 1980 "Data processing in the Meteorological Office Short period Weather Forecasting Pilot Project", Met.Mag., 109, No 1295, 161-177
7. Browning, K.A., C.G. Collier, P.R. Larke, P. Menmuir, G.A. Monk and R.G. Owens, 1982 "On the forecasting of frontal rain using a weather radar network", Mon.Wea.Rev., 110, 534-552
8. Browning, K.A., 1979 "The FRONTIERS plan: a strategy for using radar and satllite imagery for very-short-range precipitation forecasting", Met.Mag, 108, 161-184
9. Browning, K.A., and C.G. Collier, 1982 "An intengrated radar-satellite nowcasting system in the UK, in Nowcasting, ed. K.A. Browning, Academic Press, London, Chapter 1.5, 47-61
10. Collier, C.G., P.R. Larke and B.R. May, 1983 "A weather radar correction procedure for real-time estimation of surface rainfall", Quart.J.R.Met.Soc., 109, 589-608
11. Collier, C.G., 1986 "Accuracy of rainfall estimates by radar, Part I: Calibration by telemetering rain-gauges", J.Hydrology, 83, 207-223

12.   Collier, C.G., J.A. Cole, and R.B. Robertson, 1980 "The North-West Weather Radar Project: the establishment of a weather radar system for hydrological forecasting", Hydrological Forecasting, Proc. Oxford SYmp, April, IAHS Publ No 129, 31-40

13.   Noonan, G.A., 1987 "An operational flood warning systen", Chapter 8 in Weather Radar and Flood Forecasting, ed. V.K. Collinge and C. Kirby, John Wiley & Sons Ltd., Chichester, 109-126

14.   Holgate, H.T.D., 1973 "Rainfall forecasting for river authorities", Met.Mag., 102, 33-38

15.   Dalton, F., 1987 "Weather radar and a regional forecasting service", Chapter 7 in Weather Radar and Flood Forecasting, John WIley & Sons Ltd., Chichester, 97-107

16.   Pielke, R.A., 1982 "The role of mesoscale numerical models in very-short-range forecasting", Chapter 4.1 in Nowcasting, ed. K.A. Browning, Academic Press, London, 207-221

17.   Carpenter, K.M., 1982 "Model forecasts for locally forced mesoscale system", Chapter 4.2 in Nowcasting, ed. K.A. Browning, Academic Press, London, 223-234

18.   Met. Office, 1992 Evaluation of FRONTIERS Forecast Precipitation Accumulation, Final Report March 1992, publ. by Met. Office and the NRA, 46pp (copy held in Nat.Met.Lib, Met.Office, Bracknell)

19.   Brown, R., G.P. Sargent, P.D. Newcomb, J. Cheung-Lee and P.M. Brown, 1991 "Development of the FRONTIERS precipitation nowcasting system to use mesoscale model products", Preprints 25th Int. Conf. on Radar Met., 24-28 June 1991, Paris, France, AMS, Boston, 79-82.

20.   Collier, C.G., 1990 "Objective methods of extrapolating patterns", Proc. Workshop on the Use of Satellite Data in Nowcasting and Very Short Range Forecasting, 16-20 July 1990, publ. EUMETSAT, EUM PO7, 49-62

21.   Austin, G.L. and A. Bellon, 1974 "The use of digital weather records for short-term precipitation forecasting", Quart.J.R.Met.Soc., 100, 658-664

22.   Borrows, P.F., R.J. Moore, C.M. Haggett, M. Crees, D.A. Jones, D.S. Hotchkiss and K.B. Black, 1992 "Development of a weather radar based rainfall forecasting technique for real-time operational use", in International Weather Radar Networking Final Seminal of the COST Project 73, Kluwer Academic Publishers, Dordrecht, 243-249

23.   Haggett, C.M., G.F. Merrick and C.I. Richards, 1991 "Quantitative use of radar for operational flood warning in the Thames area", in Hydrological Applications of Weather Radar, ed. I.D. Cluckie and C. G. Collier, publ. Ellis Horwood, Chichester, 590-601

18. The ILP's global seismic hazard assessment program for the UN/IDNDR

D. GIARDINI, Istituto Nazionale di Geofisica, Italy, and
P. W. BASHAM and M. J. BERRY, Geological Survey of Canada

INTRODUCTION

The United Nations, recognizing natural disasters as a major threat to human life and development, designed the 1990-2000 period as the International Decade for Natural Disaster Reduction (UN/IDNDR; UN Res. 42/169/1987); the Decade goals are to increase worldwide awareness, foster the prevention and reduce the risks of natural disasters, through the widespread application of modern science and technology. As the first, necessary measure toward the implementation of risk reduction strategies, the Scientific and Technical Committee (STC) of the UN/IDNDR has endorsed international demonstration projects designed to improve the assessment of natural hazards (earthquakes, volcanoes, tropical hurricanes, floods, ...).

Earthquakes adversely affect large parts of the Earth, and vulnerability to disaster is increasing as urbanisation and developments occupy more areas that are prone to the effects of significant earthquakes. In order to minimise the loss of life, property damage and social and economic disruption caused by earthquakes, it is essential that reliable estimates of seismic hazard be available to national decision makers and engineers for land use planning and improved building design and construction. Among the spearhead programs endorsed in the UN/IDNDR context is the proposal of the International Lithosphere Program (ILP) for a Global Seismic Hazard Assessment Program (GSHAP), with the sponsorship of the International Council of Scientific Unions (ICSU).

The GSHAP proposal embodies many of the strategies and priorities of the IDNDR, filling a critical gap cited by many countries in attempting to assess properly the seismic hazard of their territory for the implementation of risk mitigation strategies. The program promotes a regionally coordinated, homogeneous approach to seismic hazard evaluation; the ultimate benefits will be national assessments of seismic hazards, available before the end of the Decade. The implementation of sound seismic hazard estimations into policies for seismic risk reduction will allow a focus on the prevention of earthquake effects rather than intervention following the disasters.

NATURAL DISASTERS

GLOBAL SEISMIC HAZARD

Earthquakes are the expression of the continuing evolution of the Earth planet and its surface. Earthquakes are the most deadly of the natural disasters affecting the human environment; indeed catastrophic earthquakes have marked the whole human history, accounting for 60% of worldwide casualties associated with natural disasters (Figure 1); a relatively small country like Italy averaged more than 100,000 casualties for each of the last three centuries.

Earthquakes occur worldwide; while gigantic events (M>8.5) happen only rarely and in restricted areas of the globe, large and moderate earthquakes (6.5<M<8.5) may take place in all continental areas, if with very different frequency; smaller seismic events (5<M<6.5) occur virtually everywhere. The average global seismicity records every year 1 very large event (M>8), 10 large events (M>7), 100 moderate events (M>6) and more than 1,000 smaller earthquakes (M>5).

The economic damage inflicted by natural disasters (Figure 2) and by earthquakes is increasing with time. The long-term effects of a catastrophic earthquake (the disruption of the economic chain, the human resettlement, the reconstruction to modern standards) may last decades and absorb a considerable part of a national budget; the reconstruction of the Irpinia region (Central Italy) after the 1980 event has exceeded $M 50,000 to date, and the predicted damage which would be inflicted today by the repetition of the great 1923 Tokyo earthquake would total a fourth of the annual national budget of Japan.

Global seismic hazard and vulnerability to earthquakes are increasing steadily as urbanisation and development occupy more areas that are prone to the effects of significant earthquakes; the uncontrolled growth of megacities in highly seismic areas around the world is often associated with the construction of seismically unsafe buildings and infrastructures, and undertaken with an insufficient knowledge of the existing seismic hazard. Moderate and even small earthquakes may turn catastrophic in earthquake prone areas with poor building construction practice, as proven by the frequent occurrence of devastating, small (m~6) earthquakes, as the 1960 event in Morocco (10,000 casualties) and the 1972 event in Nicaragua (5,000 casualties).

While short- and mid-term earthquake prediction may one day be able to reduce significantly the death toll of earthquakes, the environmental effects (collapse of buildings and infrastructures, disruption of the productive chain, human resettlement) can be reduced only through a long-term prevention policy in earthquake-prone areas based on: (a) the assessment of seismic hazard and risk, (b) the implementation of safe building construction codes, (c) the increased public awareness on natural disasters, (d) a strategy of land-use planning taking into account the seismic risk and the occurrence of other natural disasters.

The assessment of seismic hazard is the first link in the prevention chain and the first step in the evaluation of the seismic risk, obtained by integrating the hazard – the measure of the danger associated to the recurrence of earthquakes – with local amplification factors tied to soil condition and with the intrinsic value and vulnerability of the existing buildings and infrastructure. Seismic hazard is assessed by most

226

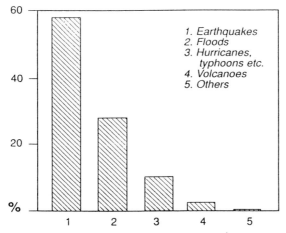

Figure 1. Casualties related with different types of natural disasters in the 1900-1976 period (percentage data from the IDNDR Office).

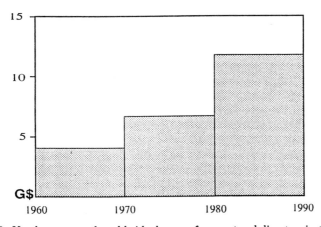

Figure 2. Yearly average of worldwide damage from natural disasters in the last three decades (data from the IDNDR Office).

nations as the preliminary step toward the adoption of building construction codes. The GSHAP and the UN/IDNDR provide an important chance to improve the global seismic hazard assessment by: (1) coordinating national efforts in multi-national, regional projects, (2) reaching a consensus on the scientific methodologies for the seismic hazard evaluation and (3) ensuring that the most advances methodologies be available through technology transfer and educational programs.

GSHAP OVERVIEW

The GSHAP proposal by ILP has been endorsed as a demonstration project by the UN/IDNDR (III UN/IDNDR/STC; Geneva, March 1992) with the support of international scientific agencies (ICSU, IUGG, IUGS, IASPEI) and of UNESCO. The primary goal of GSHAP is to ensure that national agencies be able to assess seismic hazard in a regionally coordinated fashion and with the most advanced methods. The ultimate benefits will be national assessments of seismic hazards for use in risk mitigation strategies.

The program is coordinated at global level and implemented at regional and local scale, with a regionalized approach based on the establishment of Regional Centres to: (a) assist national efforts, (b) compile homogeneous regional data bases, (c) ensure the needed coordination in across-boundaries hazard assessment, and (d) provide a framework for data exchange and the implementation of unified assessment procedures. While the Regional Centres represent the backbone of the program, much of the initial work will be done at the national level to ensure that all of the appropriate data bases on historical and instrumental seismicity, strong motion and macroseismic data and knowledge of earthquake characteristics are assembled. A large portion of the budget will be devoted to ensuring the participation of relevant scientists from the developing countries in the regional workshops and in the joint hazard assessment at the Regional Centres.

The principal targets for GSHAP are the developing countries located in active earthquake belts. By mid Decade a computer-based model of earthquake potential and ground shaking potential will be available at each Regional Centre, to produce seismic hazard maps at appropriate regional and national scales. A training and educational program will be conducted at the Regional Centres, focussing on: (a) the compilation of geophysical data bases, (b) the assessment of seismic hazard, (c) the use of hazard evaluation in the reduction of seismic risk, (d) the technology transfer of the data bases, hazard model and computational programs to participating national agencies.

The role of the global GSHAP coordination is to promote the establishement of homogeneous criteria to deal at each Regional Centre with the four main components of seismic hazard assessment: earthquake catalogues, seismotectonics and earthquake source zones, strong seismic ground motion and seismic hazard computation. To ensure continued assistance and support and to emphasize the North-South transfer of technology and knowledge in hazard assessment, a restricted group of hazard experts under the lead of the GSHAP Coordinator will assist in the establishment and operation of the Regional Centres.

The GSHAP is coordinated with other seismic hazard programs undertaken by international organizations (e.g. IASPEI, ICSU, IUGG PAIGH, ESC, HABITAT, UNESCO) and with the initiatives of the international earthquake engineering community (IAEE; WFEO/UATI). It will incorporate the results of three ILP projects: the World Stress Map, the World Map of Active Faults, and Paleoseismicity of the Late Holocene, initiated to improve understanding of the earthquake process and to integrate other geophysical and geological information to provide a firmer basis for the assessment of seismic hazards.

The first year of GSHAP implementation has been launched with a Technical Planning Meeting, held in Rome in June 1992, concentrating efforts in: (a) establishing a regional subdivision of the world and selecting Regional Centres in all continents, (b) devising homogeneous procedures for assembling databases and assessing seismic hazard, (c) initiating activities in test areas with high seismic hazard, (d) obtaining support and resources for the program, (e) nominating the Steering Committee and determining the managing structure of the program. Following this preparatory phase (1992-1993), GSHAP will consist of two phases; the first two-year phase (1993-1994) will target specific areas where the multi-national approach will be applied and comparative tests will be conducted to evaluate the performance of selected methodologies in different seismo-tectonic environments; the second two-year phase will expand the regional coverage of GSHAP and transfer the technology of the hazard computational capability from the Regional Centres to participating countries.

PRODUCTS

The most important seismic hazard product that will become available in each of the Regional Centres by mid Decade will be a computer-based model of earthquake potential and ground shaking potential that can be utilized to produce seismic hazard maps at any required regional and national scale. To this purpose GSHAP will strive to establish homogeneous regional guidelines for: (a) the creation of unified seismic catalogues, (b) the definition of seismotectonic models, earthquake source zones and earthquake recurrence rates, (c) the treatment of strong-motion data bases. While this constitutes only the preliminary step needed for hazard assessment, it is potentially one of GSHAP's major achievements.

The computation of seismic hazard at Regional Centres will provide a forum for the comparative evaluation of existing methods and approaches in the assessment of hazard error and uncertainty. The global GSHAP coordination is aimed at selecting a suite of approaches to be implemented at all Regional Centres to: (a) deal in homogeneous fashion with different seismotectonic environments, (b) produce hazard estimates at appropriate national scales and (c) depict various ground motion parameters meeting different engineering or national requirements.

As the present lack of a regional framework is cited as a severe worldwide limitation to seismic hazard assessment, the establishment of the Regional Centres will be a crucial achievement of GSHAP; these Centres are expected to remain in place as a resource to build upon and improve in future years, updating the hazard model as new geoscience information becomes available. Through its training and educational program, conducted at the Regional Centres, GSHAP seeks to foster the widespread

229

application of advanced knowledge and methodologies in hazard assessment and its use in seismic risk reduction. An important product expected by mid Decade is the transfer of the data bases, hazard model and computational programs to any participating national agency for further detailed studies within their own countries.

Finally, in addition to the national implementation, GSHAP will produce by 1996 a series of regional seismic hazard maps at continental scale, to provide a useful global hazard reference framework.

TARGETS

The principal targets for GSHAP will be the developing countries located in active earthquake belts, that do not have adequate national programs for seismic hazard evaluation.

Countries with moderate seismic hazards, which they may not normally estimate and take into account, will also benefit from GSHAP; this will be especially true for regions with rare, but potentially very damaging earthquakes, where the hazard estimation can be based on knowledge from similar regions worldwide.

Countries that have both high seismic hazards and advanced national assessment programs will also be important targets for the program; their active participation will be a key to ensuring regional coordination, high technical and scientific standards, and ultimately the success of the program.

International funding and relief agencies will be provided with a reference framework of global seismic hazards which, coupled with vulnerability studies, can guide their efforts in the latter part of the Decade.

COORDINATION

The GSHAP is proposed by ILP, a program established by ICSU with joint sponsorship by the International Union of Geophysics and Geodesy (IUGG) and the International Union of Geological Sciences (IUGS); the links with the geological and geophysical fields ensure that the ILP structure is suited to secure the integration of seismology with other geophysical and geological information required in the assessment of seismic hazards. GSHAP will maintain close coordination with the ILP structure and programs and with the international hazards projects conducted in various regions of the globe.

GSHAP will provide a framework for enhanced cooperation in multi-national seismic hazard assessment by building on existing capabilities and assessment efforts at national and regional scales. GSHAP will sponsor the compilation of national and regional data bases to common standards and will support the implementation of hazard and risk assessment at national scale. Special emphasis will therefore be placed on obtaining close working relationships with the appropriate national seismological agencies and institutes, as these are the bodies that have the local seismological expertise and are ultimately responsible for championing the hazard assessment with local and national planning agencies.

As GSHAP is a program developed for the UN/IDNDR, it will integrate with other programs established for the Decade by international scientific organizations (IUGG, IASPEI, ICSU). GSHAP has been endorsed by the International Association of Seismology and Physics of the Earth's Interior (IASPEI) as one of the main contributions of the seismological-geophysical community to the Decade, with resolutions of the IASPEI Committee for the IDNDR (Geneva, March 1992) and of the European Seismological Commission (ESC; Prague, September 1992) and with the establishment of a ESC/GSHAP liason committee.

To ensure that the program's seismic hazard products are appropriate to the needs of low-cost, earthquake resistant design and construction, a particular necessity exists to coordinate GSHAP purpose and activities with the international earthquake engineering community (WFEO/UATI, IAEE). At the 10 World Conference of Earthquake Engineers (Madrid, July 1992) GSHAP has been identified by the International Association for Earthquake Engineering (IAEE) as an important reference for the World Seismic Safety Initiative, an initiative in preparation for the UN/IDNDR.

REGIONAL STRUCTURE

The key to the GSHAP implementation is the establishment of Regional Centres to act as focal points for activities in seismic hazard assessment, hosted by main geophysical institutions in all continents (Figure 3): 1. North and Central America (UNAM, Mexico City), 2. South America (CERESIS, Santiago), 3. Central Europe (GFZ, Potsdam), 4. Western Mediterranean Basin (CNPCRST, Rabat), 5. Continental Africa (University of Nairobi), 6. Middle East (IIEES, Teheran), 7. Northern Eurasia (IPE, Moscow), 8. Central-Southern Asia (SSB, Beijing), 9. East Asia-Oceania (PHILVOLC, Manila). This regional structure stems from considerations of seismo-tectonic homogeneity and political geography and is intended to maximize the transfer of advanced technologies. Regional boundaries are not intended to be rigid; national agencies in bordering areas will contribute to more than one Regional Centre.

GSHAP test areas, characterized by different tectonic environments and varying levels of seismic hazard, have been designed in all continents (Figure 3) for the initial implementation of the program's goals and methodologies: South America, the Guatemala-Panama portion of Central America, Spain-Maghreb, the Adriatic plate (Mediterranean), the Central Rift system in Eastern Africa, Eastern Turkey-Iran, North India-Tibet-Burma, Indonesia-Philippines. The list is not final and will be integrated by Regional Centres with any area of interest.

MANAGEMENT

The GSHAP is coordinated at global level but implemented at regional and local scale; the overall operation and administration of the program is conducted at four levels: Steering Committee, Coordinating Centre, Regional Centres and National Agencies (Figure 4).

1. Steering Committee

A Steering Committee has been named by ILP and includes directors of national

231

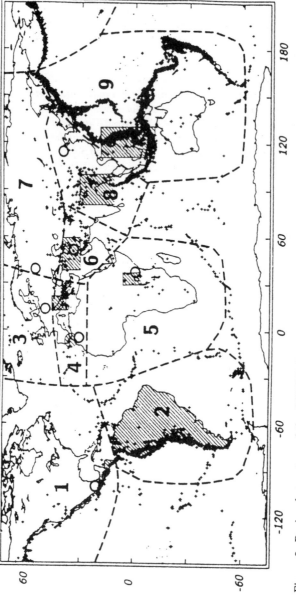

Figure 3. Regional structure of the GSHAP. Regions are identified by number in the text; dashed areas identify GSHAP designed test areas; circles mark the location of the established Regional Centres.

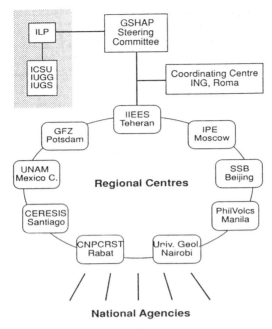

Figure 4. Management structure of the GSHAP.

and international seismological associations and leading authorities in seismic hazard assessment: H. Gupta (India), Chairman, P. Basham (Canada), Secretary, N. Ambraseys (UK), D. Ben Sari (Morocco), M. Ghafory-Ashtiany (Iran), A. Giesecke (CERESIS), G. Grandori (Italy), D. Mayer-Rosa (Switzerland), R. McGuire (USA), G. Sobolev (Russia), G. Suarez (Mexico), P. Zhang (China), D. Giardini (Italy, GSHAP Coordinator) and a representative from Japan. The Steering Committee will serve for the five-years duration of the program with the following duties: (a) provide overall guidance and scientific direction to the GSHAP, (b) assist in obtaining support and resources for the implementation of the program objectives and regional structure, (c) oversee the action of the Coordinating and Regional Centres, (d) represent GSHAP in international organizations and meetings, (e) provide worldwide leadership and regional assistance in the implementation of GSHAP, (f) develop and approve all technical specifications and strategies of the program.

2. Coordinating Centres

A Coordinating Centre and a program Coordinator have been established by ILP at the Istituto Nazionale di Geofisica of Rome, with the following tasks: (a) ensure global coordination in the GSHAP action implementation and action, (b) assist in obtaining support and resources for the implementation of the program objectives and regional structure, (c) represent GSHAP in international organizations and meetings, (d) prepare progress reports for the Steering Committee, (e) organize the publication

233

and dissemination of GSHAP plans and results at global level, (f) coordinate the development of technical specifications and strategies for the program, (g) supervise the action of a restricted group of international experts in the establishment of the technical procedures and operation of the Regional Centres.

3. Regional Centres

The GSHAP activities are conducted mostly at regional and national level. Each Regional Centre is headed by a Regional Coordinator, a respected scientist with recognized leadership in regional seismotectonics and hazard assessment and assisted by a panel of experts drawn from the region. The following activities are conducted under the responsability of the Regional Coordinator: (a) establish the Regional Centre: physical location, equipment, personel, (b) identify and activate an operative network of national correspondents in all nations in each region, (c) prepare a five-year plan detailing the structure and goals of each Regional Centre, (d) organize meetings of national representatives to review existing efforts and schedule regional activities, (e) prepare and submit funding requests to secure support and resources, (f) identify test areas for the implementation of the GSHAP multinational approach and assemble joint regional geophysical datasets, (g) represent GSHAP in regional organizations and meetings, (h) prepare progress reports for the Coordinator, (i) organize the publication and dissemination of GSHAP plans and results at regional level, (j) cooperate in devising technical specifications and strategies of the program.

4. National Agencies

As the ultimate benefits of the program will be improved national assessments of seismic hazards, the national seismic agencies are the bodies that have the local seismological expertise and will be responsible for championing the hazard assessment with local and national planning agencies and with the international groups. On them rests the responsability and merit of transforming the GSHAP operating framework into a fruitful program.

TECHNICAL PROCEDURES

GSHAP aims at establishing the consensus of the scientific and engineering community on a wide set of criteria for seismic hazard assessment suitable for application in different seismotectonic regimes around the world. The preparatory phase of the GSHAP has, among its key objectives, the definition of a preliminary set of technical specifications to be implemented and tested at the Regional Centres in the first phase of the program, to deal in homogeneous fashion with the basic elements of modern seismic hazard assessment, grouped into four main categories: 1. earthquake catalogues, entailing an as comprehensive as possible description of past earthquakes, 2. earthquake sources, the geological features that can be assumed to produce future earthquakes, 3. earthquake effects, the ground shaking and other effects that earthquakes will produce, 4. hazard computation, the calculation of ground-shaking parameters of engineering use, usually with an associated probability of occurrence, at a specific site or throughout a region.

1. Earthquake Catalogues

The most fundamental information for a hazard assessment is the record of past earthquakes in a region as captured by the earthquake catalogues. Among the important concerns are the completeness of the catalogues (whose details must degrade as one goes back in time) and whether sufficient studies have been conducted to estimate the earthquake sizes and locations in order to assess the implications of a modern recurrence. There are no established standards on the specific contents of the seismic catalogues and on the standardization of parameters such as those that specify earthquake size.

2. Earthquake Sources

A description of future earthquakes is based on a combination of the knowledge of past earthquakes and of the geological features (faults) on which they occurred. As it is often difficult or impossible to associate earthquakes with specific faults, a seismogenic source may be described as a geographical area of assumed uniform earthquake occurrence. Among the characteristics of earthquakes sources that must be defined are the rates at which the earthquakes are occurring within each source as a function of size, and the largest earthquake that can occur within each source.

3. Earthquake Effects

The assessment of seimic hazard is based also on the measure of the ground shaking produced by the passage of seismic waves. The shaking will vary with earthquake size, with distance from the earthquake source, with the characteristics of the rocks through which the waves pass, and with the local foundation conditions, e.g., rock or soft soil. The ground shaking was characterized in the past by direct measure of the damage caused by the earthquake (the seismic intensity) and most recently by instrumental values of ground acceleration; the data used to characterize ground shaking is very variable in quality and quantity around the world. Conversely there are also a variety of ground shaking parameters that can be displayed on hazard maps, for example, to represent ground shaking effects important to design and construction of different types of structures; the choice for an individual country may be tailored on the basis of parameters traditionally used in national building codes. A goal of the GSHAP approach is to select reference parameters for regional hazard maps in order to provide comparisons of hazard over broad regions of similar seismotectonic characteristics.

4. Seismic Hazard Computation

Seismic hazard computation methods fall into two general categories: historic and deductive methods. "Historic methods" are based on the historical record of earthquake occurrences; they are of simple conception, as they do not require geological interpretations of earthquake sources, and ideally applied to seismic catalogues spanning periods longer that the local seismic cycles. "Deductive methods" are based on the characterization of the seismogenic structures (faults and areal sources) and account for hypotheses such as migration of seismicity and seismic "gaps" (locations at which a large earthquake is overdue). The methodological choice may depend largely on the availability and completeness of the seismological, geophysical and geological data bases; often it reflects also the philosophical inclination of the analyst. With either method it is important to clearly define the variability of the seismic hazard analysis, to quantify for the end user the degree of confidence in the estimate.

The development of the technical specifications for the hazard assessment in the GSHAP framework has been conducted by: (i) requesting recommendations from recognized world authorities in the four hazard elements; (ii) eliciting technical reports from established international commissions and groups; (iii) holding a Technical Planning meeting in Rome in June 1992, with the participation of 70 hazard experts from 27 countries and in representation of main international seismological agencies. A Technical Volume has been prepared, collecting the detailed reports and recommendations.

PLAN OF ACTIVITIES

The first year of GSHAP activities was devoted to: (a) define the technical procedures, the regional structure, the plan of activities and the funding strategy of the program, (b) start activities at the Regional Centres, (c) obtain the needed endorsements and (d) establish connections with existing initiatives in seismic hazard assessment. This preparatory phase initiated with the Technical Planning meeting and the installation of the Steering Committee (Rome, June 1992) and ends with the second meeting of the GSHAP Steering Committee (Mexico, April 1993), scheduled to evaluate the status and prospectives of the GSHAP and to take final decisions on all the program technical procedures. Following this preparatory phase, the program schedule has been planned to develop in two phases.

First Phase : 1993-1994

The first phase will target specific areas where the multi-national approach will be applied and comparative tests will be conducted to evaluate the performance of selected methodologies in different seismo-tectonic environments, through: (1) organizational meetings held at the Regional Centres, to be attended by technical specialists and representatives of national seismological agencies of each area and by appropriate members of the Steering Committee and of the Coordinating Centre, (2) the continuing effort by the Coordinating Centre and the Regional Centres, assisted by experts of the international geophysical community, to establish homogeneous criteria for the compilation of regional data bases and for handling the four basic elements of hazard assessment, (3) the compilation of national data bases following GSHAP specifications and their transfer to the Regional Centre, (4) the assemblage of regional data bases and development of seismic hazard model for test areas, (5) the program evaluation by the Steering Committee and the Regional Coordinators.

Second Phase : 1994-1996

The second two-years phase will complete the regional coverage of GSHAP through: (1) a second round of meetings at the Regional Centres to review preliminary seismic hazard estimates of the test areas, (2) the continuing action at the Regional Centres expanded to the whole regions, (3) the compilation of national data bases following

GSHAP specifications and their transfer to the Regional Centre, (4) the assemblage of data bases and development of seismic hazard model for the whole regions, (5) the technology transfer of the hazard computational capability from the Regional Centres to participating countries, (6) the publication of the regional hazard products, (7) a final review meeting, attended by the Steering Committe, the Regional Coordinators and participants to the Technical Planning meeting of 1992, (8) the formulation of plans for the maintenance of the capabilities at the Regional Centres into the future.

BUDGET

Even if the assessment of seismic hazard is a statutory activity of most of the national and regional agencies taking part in GSHAP, a consistent program budget is required to secure the key elements of the program: (1) the regional and global coordination, (2) the operation of the Regional Centres, (3) the training program, (4) the participation of national scientists in the Regional Centres activities and meetings, (5) the test area esperiments, (6) the publication of the hazard products, (7) specific national efforts in the compilation of geophysical and geological data bases. Assuming an average expense of $ 100,000 per year for each Regional Centre, the overall budget for the whole GSHAP operation can be crudely estimated to be of the order of $M 5. At present GSHAP seeks resources to support the operation of the test areas and Regional Centres; the funding scheme followed in GSHAP is based on four steps: (a) funding and development agencies are identified which can be interested in sponsoring activities in one area or Regional Centre, (b) contacts are established by the Coordinating Centre to introduce the GSHAP framework and explore possibilities, (c) a detailed proposal to sponsor activities in a region or in a test area is submitted by the Regional Centre, upon verification by the Coordinating Centre; (d) international agencies (ICSU, UNESCO, ILP, UN/IDNDR) provide support where appropriate. Several initiatives in this framework are already under way and specific proposals have been submitted to funding agencies.

19. The new physics and earthquake prediction

I. G. MAIN, University of Edinburgh

ABSTRACT

Major advances have recently been made in understanding the process of earthquake generation in the crust as a "self-organised critical phenomenon". Models of earthquakes have been produced where a variety of local non-linear interactions, in response to external tectonic forcing, spontaneously produce an ordered state with structure on all scales, similar to that seen in second-order phase transitions elsewhere in physics. A wide class of such models naturally produce such diverse phenomena as the Gutenberg-Richter frequency-magnitude law, the observed fractal distribution of mapped active faults, and the fractal correlation of earthquake hypocentres. The concept of the Earth organising itself into a critical state is also a possible explanation for why seismicity is so easily induced by relatively small, local stress perturbations (0.1 MPa) compared to the total tectonic load (100-400 MPa), e.g. due to dam impoundment, reservoir drawdown or mining. Models with specified finite boundaries produce "characteristic earthquakes", representing an avalanche of failed elements percolating across the whole model.

The strong non-linearity in the physics is bad news for earthquake prediction in the sense of predicting a precise magnitude and time of occurrence, since these models represent an ordered state, on the boundary of chaos, where long-term prediction is inherently unattainable. However, the implications for quantitative earthquake hazard evaluation based on earthquake recurrence statistics are much more positive. First, the common assumption of stationarity in evaluating the hazard now has a physical basis - i.e. that the Earth has already organised itself (albeit with some element of short-term fluctuations) into a stationary state representing a dynamic equilibrium near the critical point. Secondly, fractal fracture systems by their very nature also have large stable blocks similar to those seen in the Earth's crust, though these need to be identified over long timescales. Finally the enhanced probability of occurrence of characteristic earthquakes (where they exist) can now be seen as a result of a percolation network given a characteristic dimension by the finite width of the Earth's brittle crust.

Natural disasters. Thomas Telford, London, 1993

INTRODUCTION

The Earth's convective engine produces energy at a rate of about 40 terawatts, some 1% of which is converted into earthquakes. As far as we can tell this process has been going on throughout most of geological time, and is likely to continue into the future, albeit with slowly diminishing rates as the Earth cools. Such convection results in a fragmented thermal boundary layer - the lithosphere - which generally moves in a steady and predictable way, giving rise to the notion of plate tectonics. However this steady (linear) tectonic forcing is not reflected in the recurrence rates of the great earthquakes through which most of the tectonic energy is dissipated. As a result our attempts to predict the occurrence of individual earthquakes have been disappointing. This is not surprising in view of (a) the nonlinearity and unpredictability of the underlying dynamics of the processes of fracture and friction, and (b) the limitations in coverage and resolution of the data available on which to base predictions.

This paper concentrates on an examination of the physical reasons for this unpredictability in behaviour over one or a few cycles, and the more predictable statistical properties of the system over longer timescales. The good news is that the common assumption of stationarity of the earthquake process ("the past is the key to the future") in generating probabilistic estimates of future seismic hazard is confirmed by recent discoveries. In contrast the ultimate goal of the prediction of the place, size and time of an individual major earthquake remains as elusive as ever.

DISTRIBUTION OF EARTHQUAKES IN SPACE, TIME AND SIZE.

Earthquakes are not randomly distributed throughout the Earth's lithosphere, but form clusters which appear self-similar on a range of scales between the resolution of the hypocentre locations and the finite width of the Earth's seismogenic crust. The clustering is found to have a power-law spatial distribution

$$P(R \leq r) \approx r^{D_2} \qquad (1)$$

where P is the probability of finding a distance r or less between two hypocentres and D_2 is the correlation dimension. Such distributions are found both on the laboratory scale (ref.1) and on a crustal scale (ref.2). The degree of clustering is quantified by the exponent D_2, which is one of the fractal dimensions of the system (refs. 3,4).

Earthquakes are also clustered temporally, as Smalley et al. (ref.5) showed by plotting the probability that an interval of time τ contains an earthquake increases with τ as

$$P(\tau) \approx \tau^{D_0} \qquad (2)$$

where $0<D_0<1$, and D_0 is the capacity dimension of the time series. Thus the temporal behaviour is also fractal, with a greater degree of clustering than would be expected from a random Poisson process. This implies that individual

239

earthquakes are not completely unrelated, and therefore interactions are important.

For many years it has been known that the distribution of earthquake magnitudes is log-linear, obeying the Gutenberg-Richter law

$$\log N(M \geq m) = a - bm, \tag{3}$$

where N is the number of times a magnitude m is equalled or exceeded in a given time interval, and a and b are constants. Again this relation is found on all scales, from laboratory experiment (ref.6) to plate-rupturing faults (e.g. Fig. 1), with $b \approx 1$ (refs.7,8). Since magnitude is a logarithmic measure of radiated energy or seismic moment, it can be shown that (3) is a consequence of a power-law distribution of earthquake source length l

$$N(L \geq l) \approx l^{-D}, \tag{4}$$

where D=2b for the usual case when the seismometer period is matched to the peak in recorded ground velocity for the events of interest (ref.9). Thus in general $D \approx 2$. The exponent D is not a fractal (capacity) dimension in the strict sense of Mandelbrot (ref.3), though it has been included in a more general definition commonly used in geology and geophysics (ref.4). In general D is neither equal to the correlation dimension nor the capacity dimension of the seismic sources, though it may be in special cases.

Almost all earthquakes result from slip on faults, and it is no surprise that fault systems also exhibit scale-invariance (Fig. 2). For systems such as Fig. 2 with a single throughgoing fault we find $D \approx 1$ (ref.10). The lower value of D (c.f. $D \approx 2$ from seismic studies) results from the individual faults in Fig. 2 being large enough to break the whole brittle thickness of the seismogenic layer. Thus strict scale-invariance would be expected to break down for earthquakes larger than the width of the brittle crust, as found by Pacheco et al. (ref.11). If the fault width scales approximately with its length, as suggested for normal or thrust faults (ref.12), and the width is constant for a given seismogenic zone, then we might expect the repetition of "characteristic earthquakes" to occur at a particular scale (ref.13). For a larger area with a variety of seismogenic widths we would simply expect a change in slope b. On a global scale an increase in b is observed (ref.11), but on the scale of a single throughgoing fault b often decreases above this length scale (Fig. 2 and ref.14).

In summary earthquakes are not randomly distributed in space, time or size, but have an ordered distribution with structure on all scales. Exceptions include the transition from earthquakes which are "smaller" to "larger" than the seismogenic width in a particular area, and these may or may not relate to "characteristic" earthquakes.

THE NEW PHYSICS

The statistical mechanics of earthquakes is not that of a system at thermodynamic equilibrium, otherwise the distribution

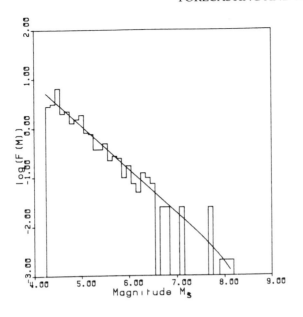

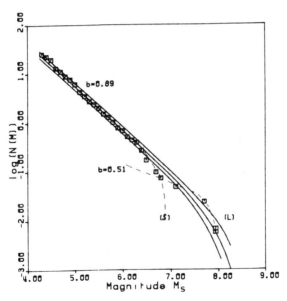

Figure 1. Discrete (upper diagram) and cumulative (lower diagram) frequency-magnitude distribution for southern California (after refs.7,8). The instrumental data (40 years), when constrained by the seismogenic slip rate, scales well with palaeoseismic data (M≈8) obtained on a scale of 2000 years or so. Earthquakes large enough to break the seismogenic crust (L) may scale differently than smaller events (S).

(a) California faults showing evidence of activity in latest 15 m.y.

100 km

(b) Dasht-e Bayez earthquake fault, Iran

100 m

(c) Clay deformation in a Reidel shear experiment

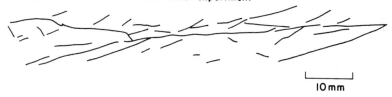

10 mm

(d) Detail of shear box experiment

1 mm

Figure 2. Similarity of fault systems on a variety of scales (after ref.10).

of earthquake energies would be a Boltzmann exponential rather than the observed power-law implied by the Gutenberg-Richter law. Main & Burton (refs.7,8) used Shannon's information theory to derive a gamma distribution of earthquake recurrence statistics

$$N(E \geq E_0) \approx \int_{E_0}^{E_{max}} E^{B-1} \exp(-E/E^*) \, dE \qquad (5)$$

where B=D/3 and E* depends on the long-term energy release rate, proportional to an analogous "tectonic temperature". For a system at thermodynamic equilibrium B=0, and the Boltzmann exponential is recovered. However, a Boltzmann distribution would hold only if earthquakes could be treated as point processes occurring completely at random in space, size and time, with no memory of the location of a previous earthquake. The mere observation of earthquake recurrence on faults forces us to neglect this null hypothesis.

A similar distribution to (5) exists for the seismic moment, allowing long-term observation of fault slip rates to be used to constrain the extrapolation of earthquake recurrence statistics from instrumental catalogues, as carried out in Fig. 1. To some extent this alleviates the systematic changes in scaling caused by the finite width of the seismogenic crust (ref.14).

Nevertheless the first-order feature of earthquake scaling is the power-law distribution of source length or energy implied by the Gutenberg-Richter law. Where else in nature do we observe this behaviour? The answer is in systems near a critical point, for example the melting of a solid at zero heat capacity, or the magnetisation of a magnetic mineral as it cools below the Curie temperature (ref.15). However these systems require precise tuning of the state variables (e.g. pressure and/or temperature) to produce fractal structures and power-law scaling.

In contrast some systems spontaneously organise to a critical point, without the presence of such fine tuning, in order to balance energy input and output on long timescales. The classic example of a "self-organised critical phenomenon" is a sandpile (ref.16). Grains of sand are added to a surface until a critical slope of the pile of sand is reached, at which point a power-law distribution of sand avalanches is observed. Overall the rate of sand input and output is balanced, but individual avalanches occur in discrete bursts which represent fluctuations about this average state.

This analogue has been suggested as a convincing explanation for earthquake phenomenology (refs.17,18). Similar fractal distributions are found irrespective of whether individual earthquakes are modelled as frictional slip (ref.17) or the nucleation of fractures (ref.19) The important property of the local dynamics is its non-linearity rather than its precise form. Fig. 3 shows the predicted frequency distribution of earthquake energies from a two-dimensional spring-slider block model produced by a computational cellular automaton with nearest neighbour interactions, analogous to single grain-grain contacts in the sandpile model (ref.20). Realistic b-values of 1 or so are obtained only when some finite dissipation (non-conservation) of the sliding force (normally a loss of about 20%) is introduced. An example of the fractal structure of a two-dimensional crack model, (after ref.21) is shown in Fig. 4.

The concept of the Earth organising itself into a critical state is a possible explanation for why seismicity is so easily induced by relatively small, local stress perturbations (0.1 MPa, e.g. ref.22) compared to the total tectonic load (100-400

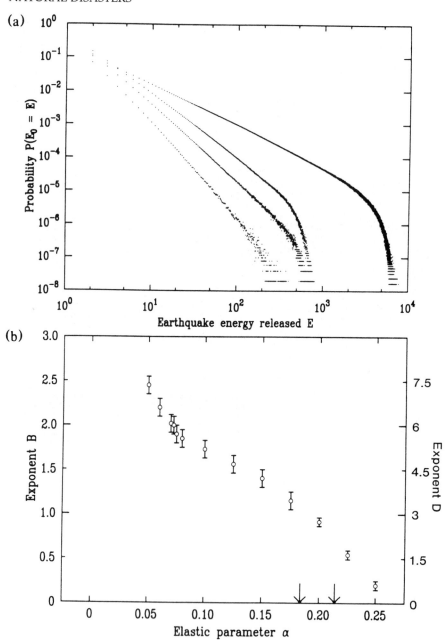

Figure 3. Frequency distribution of earthquake energies from a slider block cellular automaton (after ref.20). The degree of force dissipation (non-conservation) is expressed by the elastic parameter α. For 4 nearest neighbours complete conservation occurs when $4\alpha=1$. This figure is reproduced in this form with permission from the American Physical Society.

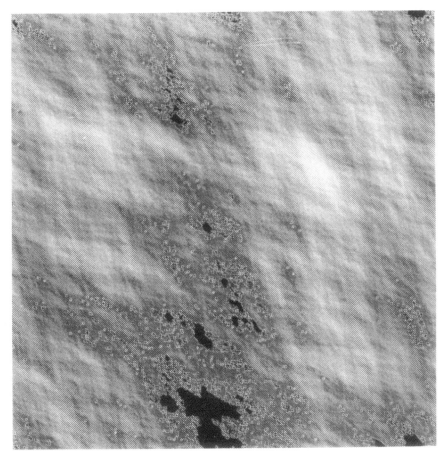

Figure 4. A snapshot of fractal cracks growing in a cellular automaton based on fracture mechanics (after ref.21). The background tones of grey represent the effective strengths of individual elements at a particular time, and the black areas represent elements broken in the plane of the crack. No scale bar is given since the predicted fracture pattern has no specific characteristic length.

MPa). Examples include dam impoundment, reservoir drawdown or mining. It is also interesting to note that finite size effects also have a bearing on the statistics of the models. For example the distributions of Fig. 3 show a deviation from power-law scaling at high energies, consistent with the gamma distribution (eq. 5). Similarly experiments with sand piles have produced "characteristic" avalanches reflecting the size of the table used in the experiment (ref.23).

In summary the model of self-organised criticality (SOC) explains much of the phenomenology of earthquakes, but it does not lead very easily to any discrimination between the various microscopic processes thought to be operating (friction/fracture etc.), since the macroscopic structure has a similar fractal character which may in some sense be "universal" to many physical systems (ref.15). Nevertheless some strong, non-linear, dissipative, local interactions are required to produce the apparent order observed on larger scales.

IMPLICATIONS FOR EARTHQUAKE PREDICTION (IN THE STRICT SENSE)

Much confusion abounds in the literature over what exactly constitutes the "prediction" of an earthquake. Here we will take this to mean the prediction of the location, time of occurrence and size of a future earthquake, together with properly-constituted error bounds for these parameters. This implies that the statistical significance of any specific prediction needs to be compared with the long-term probability of occurrence at the same locality. The discussion above suggests that the Earth has already evolved to a critical state, representing a dynamic equilibrium between the relatively constant input and intermittent release of tectonic energy. Thus we may expect future earthquakes to occur on existing faults, with new faults growing relatively slowly over several cycles. This is exactly what was found for the 1980 El Asnam (Algeria) sequence of earthquakes (ref. 24). Despite this predictability of location Thatcher (ref. 25) showed that few earthquakes in the circum-Pacific belt consistently recur in a precise way on the same fault segment, implying that the "characteristic earthquake" model may not hold in detail. Nevertheless the prediction of the location and a range of possible sizes of a single future earthquake, based on past occurrence, does at least have some physical as well as empirical justification.

The more difficult question is how to predict the time of occurrence of large events with sufficient confidence. First of all the strong non-linearities involved imply a degree of growing unpredictability with time (ref.26), so that even small changes in stress at a local level may rapidly evolve to major events if (a) the system is near criticality to start with, and (b) the dynamics involved is non-linear. I.e. even if we could sample the fault surface directly with a dense network of ideally-placed instruments, our capacity to predict would rapidly diminish with time. This loss of predictability is analogous to the behaviour of a deterministic chaotic system, although self-organised criticality is a state only at the bounds of chaos, with ordered fluctuations which imply a degree of predictability which decays more slowly than a chaotic system. For example frictional slider-block models do show precursory variations in space and time of the overall rate of activity (ref.27).

Under controlled laboratory conditions systematic changes in the fractal scaling exponents D and D_2 have been observed which are related to failure (refs.1,28), and can be explained by models of crack ensembles based on fracture mechanics (refs.29,30). However in these experiments the observed fluctuations in scaling are due to systematic variations in the chemical free energy associated with failure by stress corrosion cracking, analogous to variations in the conservation parameter α in Fig. 3. Similar variations in seismic b-values and correlation dimensions have been suggested at a much lower resolution (based on windows including one hundred events or so, compared with tens of thousands in the laboratory) in field examples (refs.19,31,32), almost always associated closely in time with the major events. Thus if the inherent problems of catalogue homogeneity can be overcome, short-term prediction may be possible, based on the recognition of systematic patterns of changes in scaling exponents. However even this may need at least an order of magnitude increase in the quantity of data, since for example the 90% confidence limits in a seismic b-value determination is of the order $\pm 2b/\sqrt{N}$, or ± 0.2 for typical values of $b \approx 1$ and $N \approx 100$, compared with the total observed variation of b of the order ± 0.5. The necessary increase in data quality over reasonable timescales will require the more common use of three-component, broadband, downhole seismometers, with higher signal to noise ratios than presently possible with surface instruments.

So far we have concerned ourselves mainly with the physics of an earthquake population as a complex system, and have concluded that the ultimate goal of prediction on long enough timescales to give a sensible warning may prove to be inherently impossible. Despite this there is some suggestion that coherent short-term precursors may be associated with systematic fluctuations about the average state of self-organised criticality. Intermediate-term precursors (e.g. coda Q anomalies or geodetic precursors) present a more difficult problem since they naturally fall in between the range of short-term predictability and long-term unpredictability. However, a much more serious problem in this case is the definition of what constitutes an "anomaly" in any geophysical signal which may have a temporal noise spectrum which itself may be coloured (e.g. 1/f), giving rise to "flickers" in the system which may or may not be related to the underlying dynamics. If we filter a large data base of geophysical signals we are almost bound to find apparently good examples of precursors - just by chance.

Applying a fairly rigorous testing procedure, a panel of experts recently convened by IASPEI could find only three earthquakes for which an unambiguous, intermediate-term precursor could be found, despite the proliferation of such "observations" in the literature. Nevertheless the possibility of intermediate-term prediction remains an open question at this stage, but requiring a probabilistic rather than a deterministic approach for the foreseeable future.

IMPLICATIONS FOR SEISMIC HAZARD EVALUATION

If the Earth has already evolved to a state of self-organised criticality, then one of the basic assumptions of seismic hazard analysis - that of stationarity - now has a strict physical basis. In this hypothesis the future probability of earthquake occurrence may be "predicted" in a statistical sense, knowing the past occurrence rates from instrumental, historical, geological or geodetic data. Given our understanding of SOC, however, it is important to include several cycles in any estimate of future earthquake occurrence,

247

almost inevitably requiring the use of palaeoseismic data (ref.33) or tectonic slip rates (refs. 7,8). Fig. 1 is an example where both methods are in good agreement, but more work is needed to test the generic validity of this approach. Such long-term data can be matched with shorter term instrumental catalogues most effectively when earthquake source sizes are measured on the seismic moment scale.

The fractal nature of earthquakes as a self-organised critical phenomenon naturally results in deformation being concentrated in clusters, with concomitant large areas which are unaffected by large events (ref.4). Since earthquakes occur in a self-similar manner on a wide range of scales (ref.34), we would expect some activity everywhere, but with variations in the size of the maximum earthquake from place to place. The attainment over long timescales of a self-organised critical state implies that fluctuations in the faulting pattern are likely to occur only slowly. This allows the location of future events to be predicted with some degree of confidence, but only when data are available over several cycles. In practice this will produce problems in intraplate areas with low annual probabilities of the occurrence of large events. We can be reasonably confident that a seismically "quiet" area delineated by the present-day earthquake occurrence is likely to stay quiet only if we have independent confirmation from a database which includes information from several maximum earthquakes.

It is important however to realise that any predictable spatial order is likely to be fractal rather than Euclidean. Thus the common practice of seismic zonation into Euclidean blocks may be to some extent artificially smoothing out the true distribution of seismic hypocentre potential, analogous to the spatial aliasing inherent in any contouring scheme. For example, mountains often don't appear fractal on contour maps, although the greater spatial resolution of aerial photographs clearly shows this property. The potential seismic hazard, however, is also a function of the local seismic attenuation, which will tend to smooth the resulting maps of seismic hazard, in the sense of the likely probability of ground motion. In contrast the site conditions may reflect the local geology, which may also have a fractal structure, implying that site-specific estimates of the hazard are desirable.

Nevertheless the idea of self-organised criticality gives a firm scientific rationale for many the standard procedures which underlie probabilistic seismic hazard evaluation, notably that of stationarity, albeit as a metastable state with ordered or random fluctuations. As a result we can be more confident of our predictions of seismic hazard, but only when a long enough data base is used. Our estimates of the long-term hazard will gradually improve as more data becomes available from historical archives, palaeoseismic studies and a comparison of present-day crustal deformation from geodetic studies with palaeomagnetic determinations of tectonic slip rates. This study highlights the pressing need to extend this database.

CONCLUDING DISCUSSION: PROTECTING VULNERABLE COMMUNITIES

The advances in scientific understanding described above have clear implications for the future direction of seismic hazard mitigation. The good news is that there now exists a rational physical basis for estimates of future seismic hazard based on past recurrence. The bad news is that earthquake prediction in the strict sense may be inherently unattainable, although there is some indication that short-term predictability exists during ordered fluctuations about the critical state. The clear message is that we do not serve the needs of vulnerable communities well by assuming 'a priori' that earthquake prediction is even a feasible goal. This is an open question at the moment. Nor should we oversell the utility of particular techniques which do not satisfy rigorous statistical tests in an objective peer review process with clear guidelines. For example the recent IASPEI exercise has shown just how difficult it can be to prove scientifically the mere existence of even a few precursors, despite the welter of literature where such claims have been made.

In contrast, our understanding of earthquakes as a _process_ has improved dramatically, to the point where we can be much more confident of our estimates of future hazard, especially when data is used on timescales covering several cycles. Much more work needs to be done to extend this database, using geological (palaeoseismic), geodetic (including satellite-based systems) and geophysical (palaeomagnetic) data, since this is the single most important requirement which emerges from our new understanding of seismogenesis. The more common use of broadband, three-component instruments in quiet borehole sites is also an important first step to improving the statistics of short-term recurrence rates and estimates of the fractal geometries of hypocentres. The fractal distribution of earthquake hypocentres itself may have an impact on the standard procedure of seismic zonation into Euclidean blocks. Similarly the fractal nature of geological outcrop may lead to large fluctuations in damage over small areas, highlighting the need for more site-dependent studies.

ACKNOWLEDGEMENTS

I am grateful to Zeev Olami for permission to reproduce Fig. 3, and to Bob Pearce, Jeremy Henderson & Patience Cowie for numerous discussions on these topics, as well as for specific comments on the manuscript.

REFERENCES

1. HIRATA T., SATOH H. & ITO K. Fractal structure of spatial distribution of microfracturing in rock. Geophysical Journal of the Royal Astronomical Society, 1987, vol. 90, 369-374.

2. KAGAN Y.Y. & KNOPOFF L. Spatial distribution of earthquakes: the two-point correlation function, Geophysical Journal of the Royal Astronomical Society, 1980, vol. 62, 303-320.

3. MANDELBROT B.B. The fractal geometry of nature, Freeman, New York.

4. TURCOTTE D.L. Fractals and chaos in geology and geophysics, Cambridge University Press, Cambridge UK.

5. SMALLEY R.F., CHATELAIN J.L., TURCOTTE D.L. & PREVOT R. A fractal approach to the clustering of earthquakes: Applications

to the seismicity of the New Hebrides, Bulletin of the Seismological Society of America, 1987, vol. 77, 1368-1381.

6. SCHOLZ C.H. The frequency-magnitude relation of microfracturing in rock and its relation to earthquakes, Bulletin of the Seismological Society of America, 1968, vol. 58, 399-415.

7. MAIN I.G. & BURTON P.W. Information theory and the earthquake frequency-magnitude distribution, Bulletin of the Seismological Society of America, 1984, vol. 74, 1409-1426.

8. MAIN I.G. & BURTON P.W. Long-term earthquake recurrence constrained by tectonic seismic moment release rates, Bulletin of the Seismological Society of America, 1986, vol. 76, 297-304.

9. KANAMORI H. & ANDERSON D.L. Theoretical bases of some empirical relations in seismology, Bulletin of the Seismological Society of America, 1975, vol. 65, 1073-1095.

10. MAIN I.G. PEACOCK S. & MEREDITH P.G. Scattering Attenuation and the Fractal Geometry of Fracture Systems, Pure & Applied Geophysics, 1990, vol. 133, 283-304.

11. PACHECO J.F., SCHOLZ C.H. & SYKES L.R. Changes in the frequency-size relationship from small to large earthquakes, Nature, 1992, vol. 355, 71-73.

12. PURCARU G. & BERCKHEMER H. Quantitative relations of seismic source parameters and the classification of earthquakes, Tectonophysics, 1982, vol. 84, 57-128.

13. SCHWARTZ D.P. & COPPERSMITH K.J. Fault behavior and characteristic earthquakes, Journal of Geophysical Research, 1984, vol. 89, 5681-5698.

14. MAIN I.G. Earthquake scaling, Nature, 1992, vol. 357, 27-28.

15. BRUCE A. & WALLACE D. Critical Point Phenomena: Universal Physics at Large Length Scales, in Davies, P., Ed., The New Physics, Cambridge University Press, 1989, 236-267.

16. BAK P., TANG, C. & WIESENFELD K. Self Organised Criticality: An Explanation of 1/f Noise, Physical Review Letters, 1987, vol. 59, 381-384.

17. BAK P. & TANG C. Earthquakes as self-organized critical phenomena, Journal of Geophysical Research, 1989, vol. 94, 15635-15637.

18. SORNETTE A. & SORNETTE D. Self-organized criticality and earthquakes, Europhysics Letters, 1989, vol. 9, 197-202.

19. HENDERSON J.R, MAIN I.G., MEREDITH P.G. & SAMMONDS P.R. The evolution of seismicity at Parkfield: observation, experiment and a fracture-mechanical interpretation, Journal of Structural Geology, 1992, vol. 14, 905-913.

20. OLAMI Z., FEDER H.J.S. & CHRISTENSEN K. Self-organized

criticality in a continuous, nonconservative cellular automaton modelling earthquakes, Physical Review Letters, 1992, vol. 68, 1244-1247.

21. HENDERSON J., MACLEAN C., MAIN I.G. & NORMAN M. A fracture-mechanical cellular-automaton model of seismicity, Pure & Applied Geophysics, 1993 (submitted).

22. SEGALL P. Earthquakes triggered by fluid extraction. Geology, 1989, vol. 17, 942-946.

23. PRADO C.P.C. & OLAMI Z. Inertia and break of self-organized criticality in sandpile cellular automata models, Physical Review A, 1992, vol. 45, 665-669.

24. KING G.C.P. & YIELDING G. The evolution of a thrust fault system: processes of rupture initiation, propagation and termination in the 1980 El Asnam (Algeria) earthquake, Geophysical Journal of the Royal Astronomical Society, 1984, vol. 77, 915-933.

25. THATCHER W. Order and diversity in the modes of circum-Pacific earthquake recurrence, Journal of Geophysical Research, 1990, vol. 95, 2609-2623.

26. RUNDLE J.B. A physical model for earthquakes 1: Fluctuations and interactions, Journal of Geophysical Research, 1988, vol. 93, 6237-6254.

27. SHAW B.E., CARLSON, J.M. & LANGER, J.S. Patterns of seismic activity preceding large earthquakes, Journal of Geophysical Research, 1992, vol. 97, 479-488.

28. MEREDITH P.G., MAIN I.G., & JONES C., Temporal variations in seismicity during quasi-static and dynamic rock failure, Tectonophysics, 1990, vol. 175, 249-268.

29. MAIN I.G. A modified Griffith criterion for the evolution of damage with a fractal distribution of crack lengths: application to seismic event rates and b-values, Geophysical Journal International, 1991, vol. 107, 353-362.

30. MAIN I.G. Damage mechanics with long-range interactions: correlation between the seismic b-value and the two point correlation dimension, Geophysical Journal International, 1992, vol. 111, 531-541.

31. HIRATA T. A correlation between the b-value and the fractal dimension of earthquakes, Journal of Geophysical Research, 1989, vol. 94, 7507-7514.

32. SMITH W.D. The b-value as an earthquake precursor, Nature, 1981, vol. 289, 136-139.

33. SIEH K., STUIVER M. & BRILLINGER D. A more precise chronology of earthquakes produced by the San Andreas fault in southern California, Journal of Geophysical Research, vol. 94., 603-624.

34. SCHOLZ C.H. The Mechanics of Earthquakes and Faulting, Cambridge University Press, Cambridge UK, 1990.

20. Predicting volcanic eruptions using microgravity, and the mitigation of volcanic hazard

H. RYMER, Department of Earth Sciences, Open University

ABSTRACT

Recent well publicised volcanic eruptions have stimulated a new era of concern among volcanologists to understand the eruption trigger mechanisms and environmental implications of volcanism. About 50 volcanoes erupt each year. However, a much smaller number presents a significant risk to lives, property and economies. Among these, several 'laboratory volcanoes' have been selected by the IDNDR task group of IAVCEI (The International Association for Volcanology and Chemistry of the Earth's Interior) for intensive, multi-disciplinary study.

The Volcano Geophysics Group at the Open University has been developing a high precision microgravity technique for monitoring active volcanoes. It consists of measuring the acceleration due to gravity to 1 part in 10^8 and relative elevations to an accuracy of 1 cm. Points in the regions of interest are compared with a stable reference point. The method has been used to construct models for the sub-surface structure (or plumbing system) at several volcanoes, and to record changes before eruption. It is important to understand 'how a volcano works' when it is not erupting, so that changes in its 'normal' behaviour can be recognised easily before the beginning of an eruption. This paper presents case histories from a variety of volcano types.

Taken in isolation, data from any one type of measurement are ambiguous, but microgravity monitoring with ground deformation is a powerful tool for eruption prediction. Many hazardous volcanoes remain poorly monitored, and even where good data sets exist, there are difficulties in recognising eruption precursors and the required hazard mitigation. Promoting constructive public understanding and response to the threat of volcanic hazard also presents a significant problem.

INTRODUCTION

The worst eruption in terms of the loss of human life occurred in 1815 in Indonesia, when Tambora erupted killing 92,000 people. Although this is a smaller number than the numbers

Natural disasters. Thomas Telford, London, 1993

killed in the worst hurricane (500,000 in the Ganges delta in 1970) or the worst earthquake (up to 800,000 in Tangshan, China in 1976), an eruption of the same size at present would be far more devastating if there was no warning given. The problems are not the same for all countries; some developing countries have large numbers of active volcanoes, and many developed countries have no active volcanoes or earthquake regions at all. However, the economic chaos caused by a relatively small eruption in a developed country may be much larger than that caused by a larger eruption in a less developed country.

At least 50 volcanoes erupt every year. Many eruptions go unnoticed because they are in remote locations where direct observations are difficult and communications are poor. Although only 4% of eruptions involve deaths, many more may result in globally significant climatic changes. There are about 40 volcano observatories worldwide. While some are able to support comprehensive surveillance systems, most, due to a lack of personnel and resources cannot afford detailed monitoring of volcanoes except when a crisis has already occurred. Volcanic hazards may be classified broadly into two types; locally significant and globally significant hazards.

Locally Significant Hazards:

Although there are many different types of volcanic eruption (see below), the local area is always affected by volcanic activity for anything up to several tens of square kilometres. For example, lava flows consist of rivers of molten rock travelling at between 1m and 30km per hour (depending on the type of volcano) for distances up to several tens of km at temperatures of up to 1000^0 C. The more explosive eruptions tend to eject large quantities (0.1 - 10's of km^3) of ash and rock fragments into the atmosphere and much of these fallout locally. Ground surges may follow collapse of an eruption column forming a glowing cloud of volcanic debris. These eruptions are known as nuees ardentes. Most eruptions are accompanied by some gas release, and this may escape into the upper atmosphere and have global consequences (see below), or it may form aerosols with water vapour at lower elevations and cause acid rain which falls locally. Eruptions may be triggered by earthquakes and vice versa.

Globally Significant Hazards:

The very smallest of eruptions may have no effect outside the active crater of the volcano. Eruptions occurring on islands or close to the sea may produce tsunami (tidal waves) with effects reaching tens or even hundreds of km. Large eruptions, where several tonnes of gas are released have been found to be of global significance. For example, Mt Etna (Sicily) ejects about 13 Mt (Megatonnes)of CO_2 per year on average into the atmosphere. It is therefore equivalent, in terms of greenhouse gas production, to a 1000 MW coal fired power station. Etna also produces some 1.4 Mt of SO_2 per year. This gas is believed to contribute to global cooling by absorbing incoming solar radiation preventing it from reaching the Earth's surface. The recent eruption of Mt Pinatubo (Philippines) ejected 15 Mt of SO_2 and there is evidence that on average this caused surface temperatures to fall globally by about 0.1° C. Volcanic chlorine was once considered to play an important role in the destruction of the ozone layer. However, detailed studies on the fate of hydrochloric acid aerosols ejected from Pinatubo reveals that they rain out locally and are not transported to the upper atmosphere [ref. 1]. The chlorine that destroys ozone is largely of anthropogenic origin (in the form of CFCs used as propellants and coolents), but it is activated by sulphuric acid aerosols of volcanic origin. Thus there is a complex and as yet poorly understood relationship between human pollutants, volcanic eruptions and global climate.

RISKS ASSOCIATED WITH VOLCANIC HAZARDS

Risks related to the globally significant hazards are difficult to quantify since the hazards themselves are still poorly defined. However, the local risk arising from lava flows and more explosive volcanic eruptions are clearly burning and burial. Gas release may cause asphyxiation by inhalation locally and asthma more regionally. Acid rain may produce skin disorders and all these phenomena will be devastating to wildlife and farm land for the duration of the eruption and sometimes much longer (see examples below).

If there are significant quantities of ground water involved, risk may extend well beyond the immediate fallout region of the euption. For example, the relatively minor eruption of Nevado del Ruiz (Colombia) in 1985 resulted in the loss of some 22,000 lives as the glacier on the top of the volcano melted. Water rushed down the river valleys removing loose material from the banks. The muddy torrent rushed downslope at 30 km per hour to cover the village of Armero to a depth of 3 m. A similar muddy torrent (known as a lahar) resulted in the death of about 900 people after the eruption of Mount Pinatubo in 1992. Other risks locally that exist in volcanic areas relate to the temporary breakdown of communications and services. Clean water, sewage disposal and food distribution facilities are quickly disrupted by the effects of flooding, ash fallout and even lava flows blocking transport routes. Economic hardship caused by the destruction of farmland and live stock can have the same effect. The risk of famine and disease particularly in poor, vulnerable communities that are remote from the emergency services is high.

A relatively new risk has become apparent in the past decade. The June 1982 eruption of Galunggung volcano (Java) produced lahars and nuees ardentes reaching 5 km and extensive ash falls tens of cm thick up to 10 km from the vent. A British Airways jet carrying 240 people flew about 150 km WSW of the volcano at 11 km altitude and encountered the ash cloud. All four engines stalled, and the plane lost 7.5 km of altitude before the engines could be started again - an emergency landing was successfully made. There are several other examples of near miss aviation disasters where commercial international flight paths and volcanic ash plumes intersect. The Alaska Volcano Observatory and some others now regularly communicate with air traffic controllers to alert them on the progress of ash plumes. In some cases, the best information on plume height and drift comes to the observatories from the pilots themselves. Over the ten year period 1975-1985, about 100 eruption plumes penetrated the air traffic range (6-10 km elevation).

EDUCATION

There is an urgent need for education in regions of volcanic risk towards 'disaster preparedness'. In many instances, local populations are totally ignorant of the potential dangers of nearby volcanoes and of the risks involved in an eruption. In some cases, there is knowledge at official levels, but it is not communicated to the population. Sometimes the problem is simply one of communication, sometimes one of politics and sometimes one of logistics and resources.

For example, a hazard map for Nevado del Ruiz volcano had been drawn up a month before the eruption, and the 'extremely dangerous' situation of Armero village highlighted. Despite this, the village was not evacuated and one of the largest natural catastrophes in terms of the loss of human life, property, agricultural land and live stock occurred. If the local population had understood the risks of even a small eruption, if early warning systems had been set up in the valleys above the town to alert people of the approaching lahar as recommended a month earlier by volcanologists, or if officials aware of the risks had instigated evacuation procedures, the disaster might have been lessened.

It is certain that the death toll resulting from the eruption of Pinatubo in 1992 would have been much greater if officials had not evacuated towns and villages (including the US Clarke Air Force base). The presence of the air force base was doubtless instrumental in the awareness and preparedness of the volcanic risk in this case.

In response to a directive from the U.S. National Academy of Sciences, the International Association for Volcanology and Chemistry of the Earth's Interior (IAVCEI) set up an IDNDR task group. The group selected several 'laboratory volcanoes' for intensive, multi-disciplinary study. The European Science Foundation (ESF) also selected 10 decade laboratory volcanoes. It is still rather early to assess the success of these initiatives, but several meetings, workshops and research programmes have been funded on the basis of the IDNDR. To name but two of many examples;

(i) a workshop was organised in Pasto, Colombia in January 1993 that brought together around 100 volcanologists from Britain, the US, Latin America, Russia and many other countries to discuss volcanic hazard and to establish geophysical and geochemical monitoring networks on nearby Galeras volcano, one of the IAVCEI laboratory volcanoes. Galeras erupted unexpectedly during the meeting killing 6 of the scientists including Geoff Brown from the Open University (UK) while working inside the crater. This tragic event was sadly not unique and several volcanologists are lost each year in similar disasters. A positive feature of these events has been that the focus of attention by volcanologists is shifting from the purely scientific investigation of volcanism, towards the humanitarian, disaster prevention and hazard mitigation aspects. Thus studies into hospital facilities for coping with sudden very large numbers of casualties and the training of local officials in disaster preparedness and evacuation procedures in regions of high risk are coming under scrutiny. The continuous, automated geophysical and geochemical monitoring of volcanic activity is also being seriously considered for the first time.

(ii) The European Community has funded collaborative research programmes on Mount Etna (Sicily), Piton de la Fournaise (Reunion Island), Teide (Tenerife), Santorini (Greece) and Furnas (Azores), five of the ESF laboratory volcanoes. The aims are to try to characterize quiescent and background activity and through careful observations of eruption precursors, eventually to predict larger, more significant eruptions.

VOLCANIC ACTIVITY

The hazard from a volcanic eruption depends on the type of volcano, the time since the last eruption of that volcano, the geographical location, the local climate and the time of year. Broadly, volcanoes may be divided into 3 types on the basis of the chemistry of the rocks they erupt and on their typical mode of eruption (see below). The longer a volcano is dormant between eruptions, the larger the eruption tends to be, so that while Kilauea (Hawaii) and Etna (Sicily) are well known active volcanoes, since they erupt almost continuously, the risk to the human population is negligible. The risk to property and the local environment is not diminished however. The location and timing of a volcanic event affects its hazard since wind directions and strengths in the upper atmosphere vary with latitude and season, so that an ash eruption might be transported round the globe at one time, but would remain confined to a small region at another time. Local climate also plays an important role here. It has already been pointed out that the devastation of the town of Armero resulted from the melting of a glacier on the top of Nevado del Ruiz volcano. The eruption that caused the melting was itself quite minor.

Types of volcano

Most of the world's active volcanoes are located below sea level on the spreading ridges of the east Pacific and the mid-Atlantic. These volcanoes do not pose a serious threat to human life, and the vast majority have not yet been seen or in any way studied. Volcanoes on land fall broadly into 3 groups; (a) basaltic extensional rift volcanoes, (b) andesitic stratocones and (c) large silicic calderas.

(a) Basalt is a volcanic rock type that is characteristically rather more fluid than others and the volcanoes that erupt basalt tend to build up into shield shaped edifices that are broad and low, with smooth gentle slopes (Figure 1). Basaltic volcanoes often erupt both from summit craters and from rifts or fissures in their flanks. Eruptions are often spectacular, involving glowing rivers of lava and fire fountains, but the lavas follow valleys where available in a predictable way, and the threat to human life is neglable. Typically, a basaltic lava flow will travel at between 1 and 100 m per hour and it flows predictably enough that it can to an extent be controlled.

Indeed the 1991-1993 lava flow from Etna that threatened the village of Zafferana 10 km downslope was successfully diverted using earth dams and explosives. Basaltic volcanoes tend to erupt almost continuously for extended periods, and although they account for most of the active volcanoes at any one time, are perceived as being of only limited risk.

(b) Andesite is a more silica rich and typically gas rich rock than basalt. It is rather more viscous than basalt, and so when volcanic gases become trapped inside the molten rock, they cannot escape quietly, but instead the pressure builds up until the gas is able to escape explosively. Volcanoes that erupt andesites are steep sided cones with deep summit craters formed either explosively or as a result of collapse after an eruption (Figure 2). Summit craters are sometimes able to retain water, as the andesite weathers to form impermeable clays effectively preventing rain water from leaking away. The resulting lake forms another hazard, as an eruption may release thousands of gallons of water suddenly, and the water may be contaminated with volcanic gases dissolved in it (see below). Andesitic lava flows tend to move more slowly than basaltic lava flows, but the viscous nature of the rock means that the flow is thicker, with steep sides, often several meters high, and the flow has sufficient inertia to overcome simple earth dams put in its path. Andesitic volcanoes erupt explosively and so pose a more serious threat to populations than their more effusive basaltic counterparts. Andesitic eruptions are usually triggered by the build up of gas pressure, and therefore do not tend to erupt continuously. Thus years or even centuries may pass between eruptions at a single andesitic volcano.

(c) As the silica content of rock increases, the viscosity and explosivity also increase. The most explosive and therefore potentially the most hazardous volcanoes are those that erupt the most silicic materials (called dacites and rhyollites). These volcanoes are characterized by a large explosion or collapse feature several km across called a caldera. There is often also a small resurgent cone or dome in the centre of the depression (Figure 3). Eruptions from calderas are less frequent than for basaltic or even andesitic volcanoes and typically occur every thousand to hundred thousand years. However, when eruptions do occur, the devastation is widespread and globally significant climate change may result from the enormous volumes of ash and aerosols injected into the atmosphere. The largest historic event of this type was at Tambora (Indonesia) in 1815 when 150 km^3 of ash and pumice were erupted. The eruption plume probably rose to about 50 km and the climate was disturbed worldwide for several months, global temperatures falling by up to 1° C. Crop failure resulted and famine and disease spread as far as Europe.

The average overall energy output of a volcano, whatever its type falls within the range 10^{18} - 10^{16} Joules per year (10^{10} - 10^{8} W or 10^{4} - 10^{2} MW). Thus the most devastating eruptions involve energy that has built up at this rate for thousands of years, and the smallest eruptions involve the continual release of energy at this rate. Perceived risk depends on some function of the probability and type of eruption and the value put on life and property. Thus on the timescale of human lives,

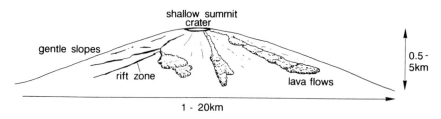

1.   An example of a basaltic rift volcano. Typically, the slopes are gentle, and although lava eruptions may be spectacular, they rarely pose serious risk to life.

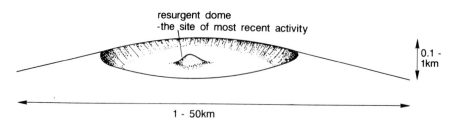

2.   Andesitic stratocone. The slopes of this type of volcano are steeper than those of the basaltic cone, and there is often a deep crater at the summit formed through explosive activity or collapse after eruption.

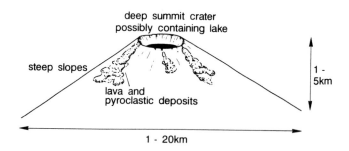

3.   A large silicic caldera is characterised by a depression in the ground often tens of km across, but only tens or hundreds of metres deep. It is formed as a result of violent explosive activity.

andesitic cones which erupt with moderate frequency present the greatest risk. Pyroclastic flows and surges, avalanches, nuees ardentes, mudflows and lahars are the characteristic hazards from these volcanoes (Figure 4).

VOLCANO MONITORING

Until relatively recently, the only way to monitor a volcano was to watch it and the amount of warning that could be given would depend on the communication between the lookout and the local population. For example, although Pliny the Elder was in a good position to assess the eruption of Vesuvius in 79 A.D., he was unable to provide any assistance to the fleeing people of Herculaneum and himself perished at Stabiae. Some people may have escaped by boat, but for most, there was insufficient time to evacuate.

Modern techniques of volcano surveillance involve the use of a wide range of physical and chemical measurements, some of which require lengthy laboratory work to analyse and some of which provide instant results. Each technique has advantages and draw backs of some kind, but the more methods that can be used at one time, the better the chances of detecting precursory variations and therefore of being able to provide a warning. The most appropriate techniques to use depend on the type and scale of the hazard envisaged.

A new technique, which has become known as microgravity monitoring, has been found to be capable of detecting precursory changes within a volcano that other techniques have not resolved. Microgravity has been used at about 30 volcanoes worldwide [summarised in ref. 2] and examples from each of the three types of volcano are given below.

EXAMPLES OF MICROGRAVITY PRECURSORS TO VOLCANIC ERUPTIONS

The precursor to an eruption will depend on the type of volcano. Basaltic volcanoes tend to erupt freely flowing lavas, and the precursors might be a swelling of the volcano associated with the intrusion of magma into the edifice and the corresponding mass increase (observed as a gravity increase). Andesitic volcanoes erupt explosively and so the precursors might be a build up in volcanic gas pressure beneath the surface or the intrusion of magma within the edifice. These would be seen as net microgravity decreases and increases respectively, possibly associated with ground deformation. Calderas erupt large volumes explosively and although a large caldera eruption has not been observed, it is thought that such an eruption may be triggered by the intrusion of hot basaltic magma into a reservoir of more silicic magma [ref. 3]. The silicic magma would become superheated and the dissolved gases would rapidly expand and escape to the surface. The bubbles would entrain hot magma that itself would be degassing rapidly. Magma intrusion should be detectable as a gravity increase, while increased gas content would appear as a gravity decrease.

Mount Etna, Sicily:

Etna is a large predominantly basaltic volcano that has been

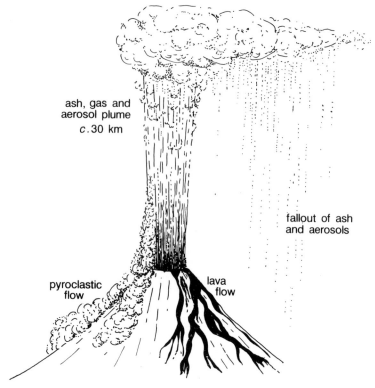

ash, gas and
aerosol plume
c.30 km

fallout of ash
and aerosols

pyroclastic
flow

lava
flow

4.   Potential hazards from an andesitic volcano.

active for at least 100,000 years, and throughout historic times
has been in almost continuous activity. Much of the activity is
concentrated in the summit area, but the vent for the recent
eruption (1991-1993) was on the south flank some 4 km from the
summit. For 16 months, lava poured from the vent at a rate of
about 10 cubic metres per second, making this by far the largest
eruption on Etna for 300 years. A smaller eruption occurred in
October 1989 and resulted in the formation of a 7 km long
fracture trending SSE from the summit. Microgravity and height
measurements were made at about 50 stations in the summit area
of Etna (Figure 5) in June 1990, and the measurements were
repeated in June 1991 [ref. 4]. Although the elevation changes
were negligible (less than 3 cm), large gravity increases were
observed around the summit craters and along an elongated zone
following the line of the fracture (Figure 6). The gravity
changes are orders of magnitude greater than expected on the
basis of elevation changes alone, and so must be related to a
subsurface mass increase. The mass increase was of the order of
10^{10} kg and was caused by an intrusion of magma into the
fractures left by the 1989 eruption (Figure 7). It had not been
known before this how deep the fracture went, or whether indeed
it remained open. There was no significant ground deformation
associated with this intrusion and because the magma migrated

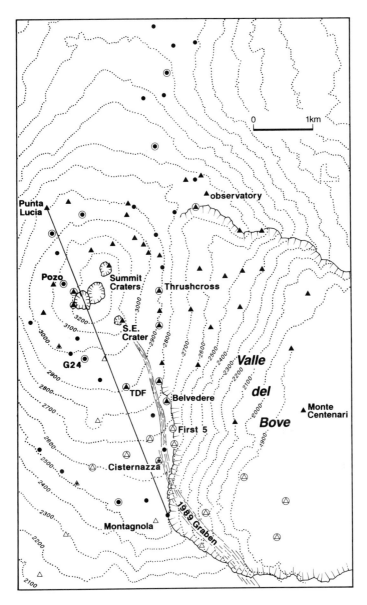

5.   Map showing the distribution of stations used for
microgravity and ground deformation monitoring in the summit
region of Etna.   [From ref. 4].

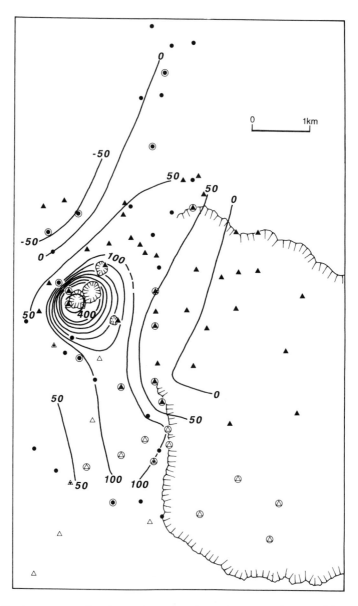

6.   Contour map showing microgravity changes observed between
June 1990 and June 1991.   The units are μGal, where 1μGal = 10^{-8}
ms^{-2}.   [From ref. 4].

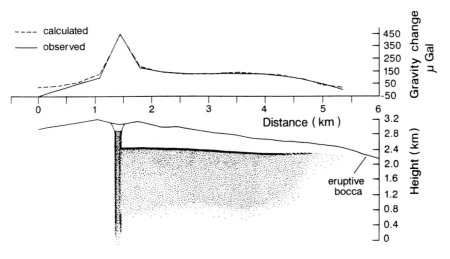

7.   Cross section through the summit of Etna along the profile
indicated on Figure 5.   The best fitting model for the observed
gravity changes involves a 4 m wide dyke and 50 m diameter
feeder pipe filling with magma at some time between the two sets
of observations, in June 1990 and June 1991.   [From ref. 4].

8.   Deployment of concrete blocks by helicopter in an attempt
to divert the 1991-1993 Etna lava flow from entering the village
of Zafferana.

263

passively into a pre-existing fracture, there was also no seismic signature. Thus the gravity increase provided the only clue that an eruption would follow. By April 1992, the lava flow had travelled about 10 km and almost reached the town of Zafferana. It was diverted by the use of explosives deployed by helicopter close to the vent (Figure 8).

Poas volcano, Costa Rica:

Poas is one of a chain of active andesitic volcanoes in Costa Rica (Central America). It has been active for about 50,000 years and is built on top of the remains of larger more silicic volcanoes. Its flanks are densely vegetated with rain forest and in the clearings the land is heavily cultivated with coffee, banana and strawberry plantations. The active crater supports a lake that is filled with rain water strongly contaminated by volcanic gases bubbling into it (Figure 9). Between 1965 and 1989, the lake remained fairly stable although its level changed by a few metres with the seasons. Typically the temperature of the lake was about 60° C and the pH less than 1. Microgravity and elevation monitoring from 1985 indicated a gradual increase in sub-surface mass beneath the lake, although until 1987 no change was visible at the surface [ref. 5]. After this time, the lake level began to fall, and the temperature began to rise. Falling lake level would cause a decrease in gravity, so the observation of continued gravity increase suggested a very large or shallow mass increase. It was known from previous gravity and seismic investigations that the summit crater at Poas was underlain by a magma feeder pipe [ref. 6]. The microgravity increases were interpreted [ref. 7] in terms of dendritic intrusions reaching up from the frozen carapace of the feeder pipe towards the lake bottom (Figure 10). An earthquake may have caused the carapace to fracture allowing magma to seep upwards. The heat of the intrusion caused the lake to evaporate more rapidly than it could be replenished by rainwater, and the lake gradually disappeared until by April 1989, the 70 m deep lake had been reduced to a boiling mud pool (Figure 11). A small explosive ash eruption ensued, but the greater hazard came from the continued degassing of the magma intrusion. When the lake was present, it dissolved the gases seeping into its bottom sediments. In the absence of the lake, the gases vented directly into the atmosphere, which in the tropical climate rapidly formed aerosols. Sulphuric and hydrochloric acid aerosols were carried by the wind down the western flank of the volcano. Vegetation was devastated as the aerosols fell out as acid rain. The aerosols were sufficiently small by the time they reached the nearest towns to be breathed in by people, causing significantly increased incidents of asthma and skin disorders. Although the magma intrusion was detected in advance of the eruption, the extent of the hazard and therefore risk is only now becoming apparent. Only further experience will enable us to recognise the diversity of hazards related to volcanic eruptions.

Rabaul, Papua New Guinea and Campi Flegrei, Italy:

A caldera eruption has not occurred since volcano monitoring techniques have been developed. However, although a caldera eruption is less likely to occur during a human life time, its

9.   Active crater of Poas volcano, Costa Rica. The crater is
approx. 200 m deep and 1 km wide. The lake at the bottom has
been the site of recent activity.

effect would be so devastating that calderas in regions of dense
population are monitored closely. There were crisis during the
1980s at two such calderas, Rabaul and Campi Flegrei [refs. 8-
10]. In both cases, the ground rose up by over a metre and
gravity decreased (as would be expected for an elevation
increase), but not by as much as it should if the gravity change
could be attributed solely to the height change. Thus in both
cases, an overall increase in sub-surface mass occured (approx.
10^{11} kg), but in neither case did an eruption follow. Thus
while it seems that magma was added to the large reservoir of
silicic magma beneath the calderas, there was apparently not
enough to cause the catastrophic superheating expected to
precede an explosive eruption. Although the amount of ground
uplift was large enough to be alarming, the calculated increased
volume of magma was small (few per cent), and so the risk in
fact was small. In both cases people were evacuated from the
area temporarily.

265

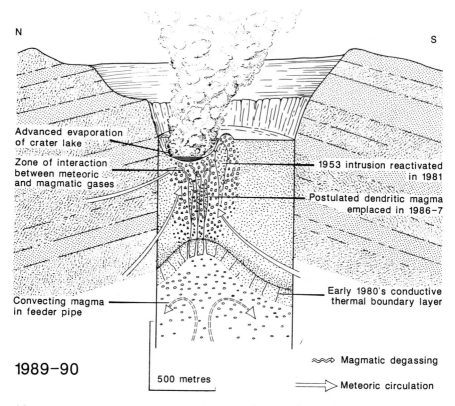

N

S

Advanced evaporation
of crater lake

Zone of interaction
between meteoric
and magmatic gases

1953 intrusion reactivated
in 1981

Postulated dendritic magma
emplaced in 1986–7

Convecting magma
in feeder pipe

Early 1980's conductive
thermal boundary layer

1989–90

500 metres

≈≈≈> Magmatic degassing

⇒ Meteoric circulation

10. Cross sectional model through the summit area of Poas
volcano, illustrating the intrusion of magma from the feeder
pipe to a region just below the lake, observed through
microgravity increases between 1985 and 1989.

11. The crater lake at Poas disappeared by April 1989 and since
then the lake bottom has been covered by a series of boiling mud
pools and fumaroles venting volcanic gases directly into the
atmosphere.

TABLE 1 Fatality statistics from historic volcanic eruptions. (From ref. 11).

Volcano	Country	Year	Primary cause of death				
			Pyroclastic flow	Debris flow	Lava & mud flow	Post-eruption starvation	Tsunami
Kelut	Indonesia	1586		10,000			
Vesuvius	Italy	1631			<18,000		
Etna	Italy	1669			<10,000		
Merapi	Indonesia	1672	300				
Awu	Indonesia	1711		3,200			
Oshima	Japan	1741					1,480
Cotopaxi	Ecuador	1741		1,000			
Makian	Indonesia	1760					
Papadajan	Indonesia	1772	2,960				
Lakagigar	Iceland	1783				9,340	
Asama	Japan	1783	1,150				
Unzen	Japan	1792					15,190
Mayon	Philippines	1814	1,200				
Tambora	Indonesia	1815	12,000			80,000	
Galunggung	Indonesia	1822		4,000			
Nevado del Ruíz	Colombia	1845		1,000			
Awu	Indonesia	1856		3,000			
Cotopaxi	Ecuador	1877		1,000			
Kratatau	Indonesia	1883					36,420
Awu	Indonesia	1892		1,530			
Soufriére	St. Vincent	1902	1,560				
Mont Pelée	Martinique	1902	29,000				
Santa Maria	Guatemala	1902	6,000				
Taal	Philippines	1911	1,330				
Kelut	Indonesia	1919		5,110			
Merapi	Indonesia	1951	1,300				
Lamington	Papua New Guinea	1951	2,940				
Hibok-Hibok	Philippines	1951	500				
Agung	Indonesia	1963	1,900				
Mount St. Helens	U.S.A.	1980	60				
El Chichón	Mexico	1982	>2,000				
Nevado del Ruíz	Colombia	1985		>22,000			
	TOTALS		65,140	53,900	28,000	89,340	53,090

SUMMARY AND CONCLUSIONS

Volcanic hazard ranges from the emission of greenhouse gases and the resultant effect on the global climate, to lava and mud flows, to ash falls, to gas release. The risk depends on the proximity of the volcano to populations and economically important regions, as well as on the timing of the eruption.

The successful mitigation of volcanic hazard involves the identification of high risk volcanoes, the assessment of hazard, the monitoring and forecasting of eruptions and the training of local officials in the management of a volcano emergency.

There are several techniques used in monitoring volcanic activity, and the more techniques that are available, the better the chances of success. Experience has shown that while each technique has advantages and drawbacks, the combined use of microgravity and ground deformation observations is applicable across the range of volcano types and the range of potential volcano hazards.

REFERENCES

1.Volcanism and Climate change. American Geophysical Union Special Report May 1992
2.RYMER, H. Microgravity change as a precursor to volcanic activity. Journal of Volcanology and Geothermal Research, in the press.
3.SPARKS, R.S.J., Sigurdsson, H and Wilson, L. Magma mixing: a mechanisms for triggering acid explosive eruptions. Nature, 1977, vol. 267, 315-318.
4.RYMER, H., Murray, J.B., Brown, G.C., Ferrucci, F and McGuire, W. Magma eruption and emplacement mechanisms at Mt Etna 1989-1992. Nature, 1993, vol. 361, 439-441.
5.RYMER, H. and Brown, G.C. Gravity changes as a precursor to volcanic eruption at Poas volcano, Costa Rica. Nature, 1989, vol. 342, 902-905.
6.BROWN, G.C., Rymer, H. and Thorpe, R.S. The evolution of andesite volcano structures: new evidence from gravity studies in Costa Rica. Earth and Planetary Science Letters, 1987, vol. 82, 323-334.
7.BROWN, G.C., Rymer, H. and Stevenson, D. Volcano monitoring by microgravity and energy budget analysis. Journal of the Geological Society. London, 1991, vol. 148, 585-593.
8.MCKEE, C., Mori, J. and Tali, B. Microgravity changes and ground deformation at Rabaul caldera, 1973-1985. Geological Survey of Papua New Guinea Report no. 87/29.
9.BERRINO, G.,Corrado, G., Luongo, G. and Toro, B. Ground deformation and gravity changes accompanying the 1982 Pozzuoli uplift. Bolletin Volcanologique, 1984, vol. 47-2, 187-200.
10. BERRINO, G., Rymer, H., Brown, G.C. and Corrado, G. Gravity-height correlations for unrest at calderas. Journal of Volcanology and Geothermal Research, 1992, vol. 53, 11-26.
11. TILLING, R. Introduction and overview. In Volcanic Hazards. Short course in Volcanology Volume 1. (Ed. R. Tilling) American Geophysical Union. 1989, 1-8.

Keynote paper. A national disaster preparedness service

D. J. OAKLEY, Consultant, UK

ABSTRACT: FLOODS AND CYCLONES are experienced at specific localities. Effective preparedness and response action will also need to be locally-based. There is a need to define more clearly the preparedness activities that are locally appropriate. Local perceptions of risks will be significant. There is also a need to devise and establish national level support systems that will enable locally-based groups to effectively prepare.

Two-storey house construction in England is the most flimsy to be found in Europe. Loads on timber beams are conveyed to walls via a bearing of a few centimetres. The structures have little inherent stiffness. In an earthquake of any magnitude most would collapse.

The next earthquake in England does not figure very high on the worry lists of very many people; except the designers of dams and other long-life structures. We get on with our lives; occupied with more pressing concerns than the next earthquake in Nottingham or Tunbridge Wells.

This behaviour of ours in regard to earthquake risks here at home offers a crude model for obtaining understanding of the perceptions of others - individuals, households and national governments - in countries whose territories are exposed to earthquakes even of high magnitude and frequency - or floods, cyclones, landslides and volcanic eruptions.

In the less developed countries many more directly pressing matters occupy the foreground of people's concerns: the stability of government; patron/client relationships and the landless poor; feeding the family this week and obtaining work in an urban world.

Households are directly vulnerable to the vagaries of the monsoon rain, landlordism, personalised politics, landlessness and illiteracy. Floods and high winds, eruptions and earthquakes may come frequently but nothing can be done about this. Except to appeal for funds to organise relief at the time of a disaster event. At the national level connections are seldom made between the levels of social and economic

Natural disasters. Thomas Telford, London, 1993

development, the form of social structure, cultural expectancies and the uneven pattern of economic development. Disaster and development are not seen to share a common agenda.

Once a 'nothing-to-do-except-organise-relief-syndrome' has become established in national life it becomes difficult for those officials who act on this 'successful strategy' to consider the alternative strategy of preparedness for, and the prevention and mitigation of, the disaster event. Other government business is more pressing. Also, preparedness and mitigation measures suggest new expenditure lines in the Five Year Plan and in the Annual Development Budget. This at a time when capital investment is being reduced in accord with an internationally pressured, structural adjustment programme.

NATIONAL PREPAREDNESS AND PROTECTION STRATEGY

Aligning local and national effort into the adoption of a preparedness and protection strategy may be no easy task. Such a strategy has to make its way in the face of the adopted 'relief management policy'; and in the face of competing claims of national policies for poverty alleviation, integrated rural development, food security agriculture, economic structural adjustment and environmental protection. The policies and priorities of Aid Agencies and International Banks will also influence the balance of national priorities adopted by a particular government.

The national committee formed to give expression of the policy insights of the INTERNATIONAL DECADE FOR NATURAL DISASTER REDUCTION may have been established with fanfare and then quietly forgotten. Huge human and economic losses nothwithstanding the 'relief-after-the-event' strategy is still tenaciously held. At the household level in a rural subsistence economy, preparing for a possible disaster event can be seen as an unaffordable luxury. Daily deprivations are more pressing.

OPERATIONAL REALITIES

Given that the operational situation for a professional adviser on disaster preparedness may contain a wide mixture of perceptions and responses: and all grounded in experience, an easy acceptance of the preparedness and prevention policies embodied in the IDNDR programme is not to be expected in the less developed world. This being so it becomes necessary that we who seek to encourage their adoption have a generalised appreciation of what this can mean for a district council, a regional committee or a national level board. The agenda that has to be covered should be public knowledge. That which we seek to enable them to undertake should be clear.

If we are not agreed on this operational agenda then it becomes difficult to organise the team effort that is required. This among the advisers themselves and between them and national or local committees and implementors. There is much learning required of the professional advisers when entering a new national situation. Their knowledge and skills are of little use if they cannot be geared into the local

271

administrative framework. Any changes demanded by the specific tasks of disaster management have to be kept to a minimum. The creation of new public sector posts is fraught with difficulty in many countries. Structural adjustment policies frequently demand that public sector employment be held to the present establishment or severely cut. Such a policy can overwhelm the case for the appointment of a few disaster management professions to key posts. There are to be no new posts.

A professional disaster adviser should avoid stumbling into such face-offs by displaying the wider sweep of preparedness and disaster mitigation strategy as being a policy attitude that penetrates programmes and projects that are to be implemented in any event and within other programmes. But unless examined for their potential impact on risk-raising or risk-reduction may have other than a mitigating effect: i.e. land drainage schemes, river embanking or urban development on low-lying land. Not every element of a preparedness and mitigating strategy will generate new expense. Rather it will change the balance of expenditure; and possibly lead to the justification of needed disaster professionals in high places; by pointing to the savings in life and post-disaster economic recovery costs that could ensue from their appointment to a central DISASTER MANAGEMENT UNIT and to preparedness organisations at provincial and local level.

THE AGENDA FOR PREPAREDNESS AND PROTECTION

The idea of an agenda to structure policy search and debate is one that administrators in government can work within. Attached to this paper is an examplar agenda for the consideration of a National Disaster Preparedness Service for a country subject to large scale riverine floods: Pakistan. In the development of the agenda advantage has been taken of experience in Vietnam, Bangladesh and Mauritius. The agenda is to be used stealthily in the working committee life of those seeking to establish such a Service. It may be apposite for a committee to take the agenda as a whole. It may be more useful to take it in stages over a year or two; delegating parts to special study groups, provincial bodies, metropolitan councils and local level groups.

A NATIONAL DISASTER PREPAREDNESS SERVICE with an associated DISASTER MANAGEMENT TRAINING INSTITUTE could offer support to the local preparedness groups, documentation and survey skills. And also offer administrative access to the large-scale operating organisations whose actions change local environments through irrigation, flood control works and sea defence constructions.

The basis of this advisory service would be a sharing of an understanding of the concept of a 'natural disaster cycle'. This to be identified as NATURAL HAZARD ANALYSIS, VULNERABILITY ANALYSIS, DISASTER PREVENTION ACTION, DISASTER MITIGATION ACTION (structural and non- structural), PRE-DISASTER PREPAREDNESS PLANNING (including forecasting and spread of warnings), EMERGENCY SERVICES ORGANISATION (including search and rescue), DEPRIVATION ASSESSMENT AND CRITERIA, DAMAGE ASSESSMENT CRITERIA AND TECHNIQUE, RELIEF

TABLE: 1

AGENDA FOR THE CONSIDERATION OF THE ESTABLISHMENT OF A

NATIONAL DISASTER PREPAREDNESS SERVICE [NDPS]

---

1. The tasks of DISASTER MANAGEMENT AND OF PREPAREDNESS AND PROTECTION can be thought of as making up a 'cycle' of management events. It is the objective of a NATIONAL DISASTER PLAN OR SERVICE to complete and command the whole of the management cycle from the Federal to local level; both in planning and operational terms. This command would seek a man/environmental equilibrium leading to the diminishing of risks from natural hazard.

2. The cycle or repeating agenda is presented here under five organising themes:

> HAZARD MITIGATION AND PROTECTION
> PREPAREDNESS AND EMERGENCY RESPONSE
> ASSESSMENT AND REHABILITATION
> RECOVERY AND RECONSTRUCTION PLANNING
> IMPLEMENTATION MANAGEMENT

A: HAZARD MITIGATION AND PROTECTION

A:1 NATURAL HAZARD ANALYSIS
- o flood sequence, duration and frequency
- o hazard mapping (including landslides, earthquakes etc)
- o database management and design of open access

A:2 RISK AND VULNERABILITY ANALYSIS
- o people and animals
- o urban and rural areas
- o structures of post-disaster significance
- o vulnerability mapping i.e. human activity in wide river beds or behind positions where the planned breaching of river dykes is to be expected to protect water control structures

A:3 DISASTER PREVENTION
- o articulation of a National Preparedness policy
- o integration with Sustainable Economic and Social Development planning and programming
- o integration with Environmental Management Policy
- o integration with National Conservation Strategies
- o appropriate legislation
- o planning and organisation (seen as professional activity) located at a range of levels

---

continued

Table 1 - continued

---

    o public awareness programmes implemented
    o wide distribution of hazard and vulnerability maps

A:4 DISASTER MITIGATION AND PROTECTION
    o extend PREVENTION activities into five year plan
       preparation
    o resolve any conflicts with economic and structural
       adjustment policies
    o ensure Project Feasibility Documents include questions
       on:
        – environmental impact on local region
        – conservation implications
        – risk analysis of the project to be carried out i.e.
           disaster-prone high or low
        – ramifications in the local regional setting
    o in the design of structures; site, specify and detail
       to resist identified hazards
        – engineered structures, specifically those of
           post-disaster significance
        – non-engineered structures e.g. of earth and
           roundwood poles
        – review the 'design flood' used in technical design

B: PREPAREDNESS AND EMERGENCY RESPONSE

B:1 PRE-DISASTER PREPAREDNESS
    o check annually that plans remain relevant
        – the NATIONAL DISASTER PLAN
        – the FLOOD CONTROL COMMISSION PLAN
        – PROVINCIAL EMERGENCY PLANS
        – DISTRICT EMERGENCY PLANS
        – the MODEL DISTRICT DISASTER PLAN (issued from
           National level)
        – sector plans for:
           . industry
           . agriculture/food security
           . health etc
           . Red Crescent and Red Cross
           . private charities/NGOs
    o undertake every five years a searching review of
       disaster planning assumptions and of the experience of
       putting them in action
    o review regularly the effectiveness of the flood and
       rain forecasting arrangements
    o review regularly the efficiency of the means of
       disseminating warnings

B:2 SPECIFIC DISASTERS AND THE INSTITUTIONAL MEMORY
    o record the history of each disaster in terms of the
       history of events, their scale and duration; the loss
       of life and damage caused at particular locations,

---

continued

Table 1 - continued

together with a failure analysis of the cause of flood
in each river reach or area receiving direct rainfall
- by type of flood
  . area rainfall
  . hill torrent
  . riverine
  . due to operational factors
  . due to planned dyke breaching
  . and combinations and sequences of the foregoing
o review and analyse the performance of the emergency
  services at Federal, Provincial and District level on
  a 'no-fault' basis (drawing from C2 following)
o apply knowledge gained from the flood casebook studies
  to the annual and periodic reviews of the PREPAREDNESS
  SERVICE as a whole

C: ASSESSMENT AND REHABILITATION

C:1 DISASTER DAMAGE ASSESSMENT
  o regard recording of damage by local administrations as
    being 'initial' and to be followed by a more technical
    assessment as soon as possible
  o establish criteria of assessment and failure analysis
    for each environmental system i.e. river reach;
    forested watersheds; infrastrucuture control system
    i.e. dyked rivers; sector i.e. rural economy and rural
    housing; agriculture
  o professionalise through organisation and training the
    recording and assessment of damage to:
    - national, provincial and local economies
    - regional development agendas
    - environmental protection measures
    - conservation measures
    - urban growth plans
    - life-line systems of communication and service
    - buildings having post-disaster significance

C:2 RELIEF OPERATIONS
  o review and redefine in relation to this agenda the
    duties of the DISASTER MANAGEMENT UNIT in the Prime
    Minister's Office (or other office of government).
  o record and analyse the performance of emergency relief
    services at each level on a 'no-fault' basis
  o use analysis to improve relief organisation at each
    operational level
  o study the lessons to be learnt from self-help action
    at local level

C:3 REHABILITATION
  o recognise this as being a re-entry stage to a
    reinvigorated social and economic development strategy

continued

Table 1 - continued

---

    o give preference to developmental support action rather
       than to compensatory payments
    o where compensatory payments are made examine the
       impact on the funding sources and upon future funding
       of planned development projects

D: RECOVERY AND RECONSTRUCTION PLANNING

D:1 RECOVERY
    o Identification of the recovery agenda:
      - renewal of agriculture and its diversification
      - renewal and possible redesign of infrastructure
         components and local lifeline systems of water
         delivery, energy and communication
      - revitalise local economies employing all local
         assets including those of human resource
      - identification of local financing:
         . governmental
         . private
         . local community contributions
           i.e. for labour digging drainage ditches or
           for compartmentalisation of irrigation areas
      - identification of needs for foreign assistance:
         . finance
         . technical assistance
         . institutional twinning
      - arranging loan agreements and negotiating grants
      - institutionalisation of reconstruction management:
         . delegation of programme management at the
           Federal level between Disaster Management
           Office: the Planning and Development Division
           and Finance Division
         . monitoring
         . evaluation of programme and contribution to
           regional and developmental progress

D:2 PLANNING AND DEVELOPMENT
    o In undertaking the Planning and Development appraisal
       at Federal and Provincial level search the project
       documentation to establish economic and technical
       efficiency in all dimensions:
      - function
      - system contribution (irrigation, highway)
      - service in the geographic region
      - positive within the urban growth and overall
         settlement policy
      - no negative environmental impact
      - supports conservation of natural resources
      - lowers disaster risks

---

continued

Table 1 - continued

D:3 PROGRAMMING
    o Define programming and operational context:
       - seek to reduce risks through mitigating design and
          operational action
       - set actions in their regional or sub-regional
          setting: i.e. establish operationally the concept
          of human settlement strategic planning
       - assess developmental contribution of 'repair'
          approach as against a redesign based upon a failure
          analysis
       - review local and sub-regional hazard map and
          vulnerability map in the light of changes planned;
          and again when changes completed

D:4 SETTLEMENT AND REGION
    o Integrate at the geographic and sub-geographic region
       level reconstruction proposals in relation to plans
       for town expansion, new towns studies and proposals to
       establish rural service centres. Left unexamined all
       could be so sited as to lead to an increase in
       disaster risks. In settlement planning generally bear
       in mind the extensive urban growth to be expected in
       the next two decades due to:
       - increase in population growth
       - accelerated movement of rural peoples to urban
          sites
       - conflicts of land use as urban growth demands land
          that is now under irrigation

D:5 ENGINEERING AND ARCHITECTURAL DESIGN
    o Review the 'design flood' adopted for specific areas
       and zones in the light of recent events and reassessed
       flood risks
    o Ensure engineering and architectural proposals for
       repair of damaged structures are professionally
       appraised for feasibility and economy in the light of:
       - the estimated economic life of the structure
       - viability after the flood of the system of which
          the structure forms a component:
           . irrigation
           . river control
           . flood flow measurement
           . road section of a highway upon an unstable slope
           . bridge crossing point where bridgeworks were
             swept away in 1992, 1993, 1994 etc.
           . post-disaster buildings of significance
             i.e. flood control centres, hospitals

D:6 CONSTRUCTION PHASING
    o Study and review the implications of phasing of
       construction works over three year, five year and ten
       year programmes:

---

continued

Table 1 - continued

- heightened risk of flooding in construction zones
  while works remain incomplete:
  - canal and river flood by-passes
  - main drainage canal systems i.e. left and right
    bank drains in Sindh, Pakistan
- delays caused by material shortages and cost
  overruns as the building materials market is
  stressed by national construction activity in
  railways, motorways, flood reconstruction and urban
  expansion

D:7 SUSTAINABLE DEVELOPMENT AND SPECIAL CONCERNS
  o Examine reconstruction action in areas of special
     concern: e.g. rebuilding in the rural environment set
     in the context of encouraging self-reliance and
     employment generation
  o In context of urban growth and regional settlement
     patterns

E: IMPLEMENTATION MANAGEMENT

E:1 ADOPT A LEAD CONCEPT
  o Apply the principle of 'encouraging self-reliance in
     the disaster response' to the organisation of a
     government PREPAREDNESS SERVICE which offers
     administrative, technical and training support
     throughout a disaster management system:
     - community-based organisations assisted by Local
       Union Councils and NGOs
     - Union Councils assisted by Districts
     - Districts assisted by Provincial Disaster
       Committees
     - Provincial Planners assisted by Federal support and
       information services

E:2 BUILD CAPACITY AND CAPABILITY
  o Appraise the capacity and capability of the existing
     organisations allocated duties in the face of
     disasters and in relation to the five themes of this
     Agenda (para 2 above).
  o Recognise the strengths of particular organisations
     and persons and build on these
  o Raise capability through attaching professionally
     staffed support units at critical points through the
     PREPAREDNESS SERVICE
  o Redefine and re-allocate duties to each body (as
     reformed) and prepare with each body revised Terms of
     Reference which establish clearly relationships with
     other entities in counter-disaster action
  o Ensure linkages between the entities are functional by
     giving shared responsibilities to agencies within some

---

continued

Table 1 - continued

particular administrative 'clusters'; reflecting the
five themes:
- hazard mitigation
- preparedness and emergency management
- assessment and rehabilitation
- recovery and reconstruction
- implementation management
o Appoint Senior Liaison Officers for each cluster of
administrations to formally liaise with other clusters
i.e. hazard mitigation group with reconstruction
group.
o Ensure continuity of information flow up and down the
SERVICE from local to federal level through planned
regular 'horizontal flow' and 'vertical flow'
meetings. Information and decision stemming from the
meetings to be published together with studies and
research papers in a quarterly JOURNAL OF DISASTER
MANAGEMENT having Senior Liaison Officers as an
advisory panel to the Editor.

E:3 PROFESSIONAL SUPPORT UNITS
o Establish at the level of the PRIME OR CHIEF MINISTER
a professionally staffed DISASTER MANAGEMENT UNIT
o To ensure the reduction of disaster risk and to
improve integration in programme and project design
between Sectors establish REGIONAL DEVELOPMENT
MONITORING UNITS at the University in each Province.
Ensure there is easy access to the data base that is
constructed and that each Draft Project Document is
submitted for comment as to its regional impact to a
MONITORING UNIT.
o Encourage the Institute for Sustainable Development
(or similar) to include studies on the
inter-relationship of frequent disaster on development
intention at Federal, Provincial, local and sector
level. Give a special attention to the growth of
population and of urban growth upon the changing
relationships between disaster risks and development
programming. Feed the information gleaned into the
quarterly JOURNAL OF DISASTER MANAGEMENT.

E:4 MONITORING AND REVIEW

o establish and implement procedures to ensure the
relevance and inter-action of the components of the
disaster cycle.

OPERATIONS MANAGEMENT AND EVALUATION, REHABILITATION AND
RECONSTRUCTION PLANNING.

Preparedness planning is the design and selection of
adjustments and interventions in this cycle.

NATURAL DISASTERS

Within the orientation of the 'offering of a service' the staff of the NATIONAL DISASTER PREPAREDNESS SERVICE would operate nationally, provincially, at district and local levels to:
- help define with communities the nature of their vulnerability
- help ensure the most effective use of scarce resources
- encourage the establishment of Local Emergency Preparedness Offices
- offer a consulting service in the preparation of local plans and in their implementation
- advise on the undertaking of mitigating actions
- offer training opportunities and manuals
- assist in public education

The NATIONAL DISASTER PREPAREDNESS SERVICE could administratively form part of the operating programmes of already existing agencies having national responsibility for aspects of planning and development.

The preparedness and protection programme would be administered by a national committee advised by the Director and staff of a DISASTER MANAGEMENT UNIT located in the Chief or Prime Minister's Office. The staff of the unit, together with key professional advisers in provincial and regional protection agencies, would offer guidance to representative committees and to sector agencies such as forestry, irrigation and sea defence. All have a concern for aspects of preparedness and protection. The officers of the service would also undertake disaster impact studies, as a component of environmental impact studies, of the projects proposed for implementation within development programmes. The staff would also be enablers of the forging of working relationships in preparedness action with non-governmental organisations.

LOCAL GROWTH POINTS

The concept of a national service may not necessarily grow from the centre of government. The inititative may come from a particularly vulnerable community, district or province who move ahead of a national recognition of need: as happened in Papua New Guinea where a province most exposed to volcanic eruptions laid the way for a national strategy. Initiatives of this kind do not always originate within local government but can stem from the work of the Red Cross or Red Crescent societies at a local level; or from the work of a non-governmental organisation who has seen the necessity to move beyond the offering of relief assistance to communities who experience disaster frequently from flood or high wind.

As has been hinted the agenda embodies a hidden agenda. That is the recognition and belief that disaster is experienced at a local level and that this is where the front line of mitigation work, preparedness organisation and emergency response must also be located. A particular attention has to be given to encouraging local participation in preparedness planning by identifying and making public a range of methods whereby local initiatives can be financed. Project Finance can be assembled from a spread of sources including local house-to-house collection, freely offered labour on constructional tasks (food for work), special local taxes, national, provincial, district and zone exchequer contributions; all aided in specific circumstance (to be defined) by grants-in-aid and soft loans from international sources - bilateral, non-governmental and private commercial.

Other levels of this agenda seek to identify the local level tasks and the provincial and national contexts in which they are to be met. This can lead to the definition of the type of support service that the local level agencies need if they are to prepare effectively and maintain their preparedness.

The objective of the NATIONAL DISASTER PREPAREDNESS SERVICE is to support the initiatives and organisation of 'self-reliant' local preparedness organisations. This is to be done in the awareness that self reliance is a concept foreign to dependency cultures. Further the concept of 'community' can mean little beyond its utility as an organising idea. The community on the ground at any particular location may be faction-ridden and highly fragmented: a victim of its social, economic and physical environment.

Despite these difficulties it could be said that national and international disaster relief operations are needed to the extent that local and national preparedness planning and management is not pursued. Preparedness planning brings an additional benefit. It is supportive of personal and community development.

The adoption of a PREPAREDNESS SERVICE, approached locally and nationally, offers a policy change for those countries which now invest in a relief-based response to disaster.

For those attending the Conference the idea of an agenda presenting the width and breadth of a NATIONAL DISASTER PREPAREDNESS SERVICE may provide a home for the idea they are to present in a paper or verbally in discussion. Some of these ideas may need testing beyond the research environment that gave them birth; first in pilot projects and then more widely. Simplicity in application, ease of maintenance and overall economy of effort will be factors in moving from the new base in knowledge to an executive format that can be applied in practice. This journey time may take many years before application reduces the risk to vulnerable communities of danger from a specific natural hazard.

Acknowledgement. This paper is presented in a personal capacity. It is derived, however, from experience gained while serving on advisory missions organised by the CEC, UNDRO Geneva and UNCHS Nairobi.

21. Computer simulation and zonation of lava flow hazards

G. WADGE and I. McKENDRICK, University of Reading

INTRODUCTION

Lava flows are unusual among volcanic hazards in that they are, normally, sufficiently slow-moving to enable mitigating action to be taken along their paths. These actions take the form of the evacuation of settlements, erection of barriers, the use of explosives and the chilling of the flow with water (Refs 1-2). There is, however, no known method of preventing lava from reaching the surface once an eruption has started, merely changing its spatial position on the surface. Engineering effort may be ruled out because diversion puts a different group of people at risk.

Being able to predict where and when the lava flow will advance would obviously be a major help to mitigation efforts. Unfortunately, such prediction is made very difficult by the complex nature of lava flow morphology and dynamics and variations in the rate of lava effusion. Large central volcanoes may erupt up to tens of thousands of lava flows during their lifetimes. Of course, anywhere on such a volcano will probably be overrun by lava at some time during the construction of the edifice. At any one time, however, the likelihood of inundation is variable spatially. This likelihood is of concern for planning authorities in the medium- to long-term.

In this paper we describe methods of applying a computer programme to simulate lava flow - FLOWFRONT to these two distinct hazard assessment tasks. As a case example we take the village of Zafferana Etnea on the southeast flank of the Etna volcano.

COMPUTER SIMULATION OF LAVA FLOW

Lava flows are fluids whose rheological behaviour changes during the process of cooling, crystallisation and the loss of volatiles (e.g. ref.3). Eruptions often produce flow-fields of complex shape that are partly a function of variable effusion rate (ref. 4) and topography. Attempts to simulate the flow of lava and the resulting deposits using computer programs (e.g. refs. 5-7) have used highly simplified physical models because

Natural disasters. Thomas Telford, London, 1993

there is no consensus for the theoretical basis that explains all the observed features of lava flow-field development.

The program we use here , FLOWFRONT, is capable of reproducing some of the important characteristics of a simple isothermal Bingham fluid flowing over digital topography - in particular the thickening and widening of flow on lower slopes. A full description of the program is given by Young and Wadge (ref. 7). FLOWFRONT uses a cellular automaton-type algorithm which calculates at each iteration whether lava will advance downslope at the current margins of the flow in terms of whether the simulation cell is of one of three types. FILLABLE types are empty cells that may receive lava from ACTIVE type cells which become LAVA type cells once their contents above a minimum threshold are distributed downslope. The algorithm is only concerned with the front of the flow and transport to the front is implicit. This speeds up the computations greatly compared to simulations involving the whole flow body but at the cost of any ability to model effects of thermo-mechanical continuity of the flow as a whole.

FLOWFRONT requires a number of parameters to be set. The main ones are (i) critical thickness of flow specified for a given slope angle (determined by the yield strength of the flow) , (ii) a minimum thickness of flow, and (iii) the effusion rate history expressed as the volume of lava to be supplied to the front at each iteration. The simulated flow moves over a digital elevation model (DEM) of the topography and the resulting thickness of lava is displayed. The current implementation of the program is on a workstation where flows of several thousand iterations can be run in a few minutes and the parameters reset in a few seconds.

METHODS OF APPLICATION

To use any computer simulation as a predictive tool for the assessment of the advance of lava flows requires: (i) an available DEM of the area at an appropriate accuracy, (ii) knowledge of the location of the lava vent , and (iii) knowledge of the ambient flow characteristics; the effusion rate and rheology. The first two of these requirements are relatively straightforward, it is much more difficult to obtain accurate field estimates of the ambient flow characteristics.If these requirements were all met a predictive model of the position of the lava flow for a few days to weeks in advance could be created.

Not only is the physics of the flow of lava incompletely understood but the processes that control the timing and location of lava-producing eruptions are also poorly known. In this case the best source of information from which to derive maps of the probability of inundation by future lava flows is the record of earlier flows. In particular, the subset of the most recent historical lava flows for which fairly complete information on planimetric shape of the flow-field, and its volume and duration are known. Given this information it is possible to create maps of the potential for inundation for the volcano using Monte Carlo simulation, though the method is

283

essentially independent of both the simulation algorithm or the type of hazard.
The methodology of both these applications is described in Wadge et al .(ref. 8).

Retrospective Simulation of the 1991-92 Etna Eruption

The eruption that began on December 1991 on southeast flank of Etna (and continues at the time of writing (March 1993)) is the longest and probably most voluminous eruption in the past 300 years on the volcano. In the first month of activity the lava flow had reached a distance of 5.5 km along the southern wall of the Valle del Bove (ref. 9; Figure 1) It had also destroyed a water-supply for the town of Zafferana Etnea 2.5 km further downslope. Because of the threat to this town an earthen barrier 250 m long and 20 m high was constructed at the end of the Val Calanna (Fig. 1) in an attempt to check the progress of the flow. By this time lava flows were already beginning to override one another closer to the vent. The barrier was eventually surmounted by lava in early April and by April 15 had flowed down the narrow valley of the Portella di Calanna to reach its maximum distance of 7.5 km. Although more lava

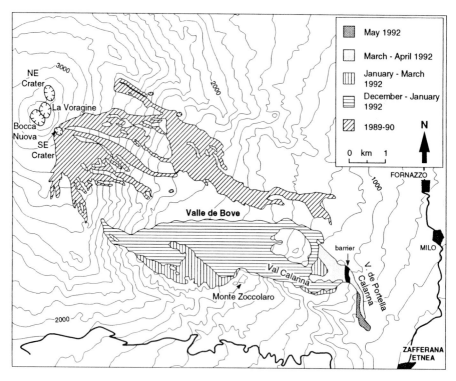

Figure 1. Sketch map of the early development of the 1991-93 Etna lava flow. The maximum distance was achieved in April 1992 (after map in ref. 9).

reached this far in May and some isolated buildings were
destroyed, Zafferana Etnea itself was not entered (Fig. 2).
Succeeding lava flows build up a complex flow-field but were
restricted to areas much closer to the vent.

This pattern of early high effusion rate flow reaching its
maximum distance or close to it within the first few weeks, and
succeeded by a longer period of lower effusion rate flow
contributing to the more proximal parts of the lava flow-field
is typical of many eruptions of Etna (ref. 8). Using the
parameters shown in Table 1 a simulation of the first 4 weeks of
the eruption (Fig. 1) gives the results shown in Figure 3. The
simulated flow does not go round the northern side of the Monte
Calanna, but apart from this it is a reasonably good fit to the
actual flow (Fig. 1). However, as Wadge et al. (ref.8) argue,
FLOWFRONT is sensitive to parameter values that can be estimated
only approximately from field observations (e.g. thickness and

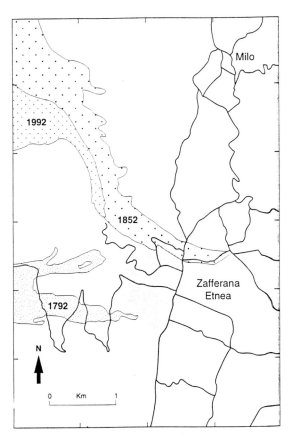

Figure 2. Sketch map of the region around Zafferana Etnea. The
lines show the road network. Of the three historical lava flows
in this region only the one of 1852 entered the town.

285

Figure 3. A retrospective FLOWFRONT simulation of the 1991-92
lava flow after the first four weeks. Compare with figure 1. The
original display is in colour.Model parameters are : 500
iterations at 80,000 m³ / iteration (constant effusion rate);
vent position = 310,297; critical thickness = 8.5m at 6 degrees
slope, minimum thickness = 1.5m).

Table 1.   FLOWFRONT parameters to model first month of the
           1991-92 Etna lava flow.

Number of Iterations	500
Volume supplied to front per iteration	80,000m³
Critical flow thickness	8.5 m
Critical slope angle	6°
Minimum flow thickness	1.5 m

flow rate). Hence although retrospective modelling can produce
reasonable simulations the value of the method used in a
predictive, operational manner is likely to be reduced because
errors in the simulated length and area of the flow will make
the results too inaccurate as the basis for detailed mitigation
efforts.

Monte Carlo Simulation of Lava Flow Hazard Potential on Etna

The most useful way to estimate lava flow hazard potential is to create a map that shows the current probability that each point on the volcano will be inundated by a lava flow. The hazard from lava flows comes from eruptions on the flanks of the volcano; flows from the summit craters are too short to threaten human habitation. There have been 35 such flank eruptions in the period 1763-1989 for which details are known.

This catalogue of eruptions forms the basis of the probabilistic method for estimating the potential for lava flow inundation. There are four steps to the method (Fig. 4).

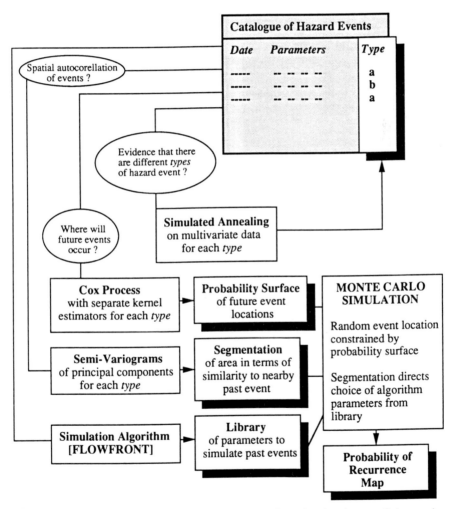

Figure 4. Schematic method of Monte Carlo simulations of hazard recurrence maps based on a catalogue of past hazard events.

(i)   We suspect from previous work (e.g. ref. 10) that there are
two "types" of flank eruptions. Type-A eruptions are short-
lived with high eruption rates (total volume/duration), produce
relatively narrow flow-fields and can occur anywhere on Etna.
Type-B eruptions are long-lived with low eruption rates, produce
broad flow-fields and are restricted to the eastern flank of
Etna, centred on the Valle de Bove. Using the techniques of
simulated annealing on multivariate statistics we can
successfully classify all of the 35 eruptions unequivocally into
one of these two types (ref. 8).

(ii) The spatial distribution of earlier eruption vents is used
to create a surface that expresses the probability of future
vents. Distance-weighted counts of eruption vents at each point
are made using separate kernel estimators for each eruption
type. Type-A and type-B estimates are scaled to ensure that the
proportion of the two types in the simulated data is consistent
with that observedwhen these probability maps are used to
generate more eruptions from the same spatial distribution
(using the so-called Cox Process).

(iii) The previous step ensures that we can initiate both types
of simulated lava flows in the appropriate places but gives no
indication of the eruptive properties of the lava flows. To
assess this we test the historical catalogue for properties of
spatial autocorrelation between lava flows from neighbouring
vents using semi-variograms of principal component values from
the multivariate data. Type-A eruption vents exhibits
significant autocorrelation, and so the model space is segmented
into areas considered to be similar to the nearby historical
event.

(iv) For each of the 35 flank eruptions retrospective FLOWFRONT
simulations of the lava flow-fields are created and the
parameters for each are stored in a library.

Using the probability surface, the segmentation based on
autocorrelation and the library of FLOWFRONT parameters, Monte
Carlo simulations of lava flows on Etna can be run. Random
choices of vent position are constrained by the probability
surface. The most appropriate historical eruption for the
simulated vent is chosen from the segmentation and the
appropriate FLOWFRONT parameters used from the library. In this
way large numbers of simulated lava flows can be generated.

Figure 5 shows the results of a Monte Carlo run of 380 simulated
lava flows, equivalent to 2,454 years of historical activity.
Every time a cell in the model is occupied by a simulated flow
the count is incremented. The sum total of inundations gives a
measure of the probability of future inundation. For example, a
place inundated 5 times in 2,454 years has a recurrence
probability of once every 491 years or 0.002/year.

Lava Flow Hazard for a Single Community

Planning concerns are usually focused on individual communities.

The hazard evaluation in Chester et al. (ref.11) identified 18
towns on Etna of which Zafferana Etnea had the highest
vulnerability to lava flows. Most of these towns are ancient
settlements and hence one would expect them to be sited in
relatively safe positions.

Although the boundaries of Zafferana Etnea are not rigorously
defined in Figure 2, the town has only been entered once by an
historical lava flow, in 1852. This gives an observed
probability of inundation of once every 35 eruptions or
0.0286/eruption. What is the equivalent probability of a lava
flow simulated by our method entering the town? This can be
calculated using the Binomial Theorem. For 35 simulations (the
same number as the historical catalogue) this lies between 0.0
and 0.0857 and between values of 0.011 and 0.047 for 380
simulations as in Figure 5, at the 95% confidence level. For
more simulations these limits narrow around the 0.0286/eruption
value.

A more useful measure of the hazard faced by Zafferana Etnea is
one based on the area of town inundated. The 1852 flow covered
about 17% of the town. The simulations of Figure 5 covered, in
aggregate, 107% of the town's area. In terms of an areal
inundation recurrence rate, the historical data figure is 0.075%
of the town's area/year. For the 380 simulations result the
figure is 0.044%/year. Were the appropriate data available
these inundation recurrence rates could be used to estimate
value at risk.

SUMMARY

Computer simulations of flowing lava can be used as a basis for
assessing the hazard to populated areas lying in their paths. A
celluar automaton-type simulation program ,FLOWFRONT,has been
used to model ,retrospectively, the behaviour of the lava flows
of Etna, in particular the lava flow of 1991-93. The value of
this program, and indeed any others that require parameter
setting based on field observations of flow properties, is of
limited accuracy for predictive purposes.

In a probabilistic framework, however, simulation algorithms
like FLOWFRONT can be used to create maps of long- to medium-
term hazard from lava flows for a whole volcano; in this case
Etna. We demonstrate that a statistically-based method using
data from a catalogue of historical lava flow eruptions can be
used to explore any suspected class structure in the data and
derive a vent probability surface and a segmentation based on
the nearest, most similar, historical eruption that can be used
to constrain a Monte Carlo simulation. Each simulated flow uses
the FLOWFRONT parameters most appropriate to its spatial
location. The resultant maps give a measure of the relative
potential for inundation by a lava flow given the behaviour of
the volcano in the past. We stress that this method is
independent of the simulation algorithm used and, to an extent,
of the type of hazard. It could be applied to any situation
where a catalogue of spatially heterogeneous hazard flow events
was available.

289

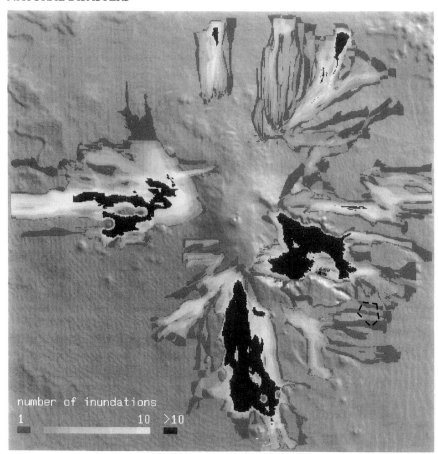

number of inundations
1   10 >10

Figure 5. Results of the probabilistic method of mapping lava
flow hazard recurrence for Etna. 380 Monte Carlo simulations of
lava flows using the FLOWFRONT algorithm were used. The original
display is in colour.The area of the town of Zafferana Etnea is
shown approximately by the dashed outline on the southeastern
flank of the volcano. The image is about 31 km square.

Hazard assessment based on Monte Carlo simulation allows a much
longer period of behaviour to be simulated, which should give a
more representative pattern of behaviour. For the community of
Zafferana Etnea, a series of 380 simulations indicates that the
areal inundation recurrence rate for the town of 0.044% of the
town's area /year is less than that derived from the one
observed lava flow to enter the town in 1852 of 0.075%/year.

ACKNOWLEDGEMENTS

This work was carried out under NERC contract F60/G6/12.

290

REFERENCES

1. BLONG R.J. Volcanic hazards. Academic Press, London, 1984, 424pp..
2. TILLING R.I. Volcanic hazards and their mitigation : progress and problems. Reviews of Geophysics, 1989, vol.27, 237-269.
3. CRISP J. and BALOGA S. A model for lava flows with two thermal components. Journal of Geophysical Research, 1990, vol. 95, 1255-1270.
4. KILBURN C.R.J. and LOPES R.M.C. The growth of aa lava flow fields on Mount Etna, Sicily. Journal of Geophysical Research, 1988, vol. 93, 14759-14772.
5. BARCA D., CRISCI G.M., DI GREGORIO S., MARABINI S. and NICOLETTA F.P. Nuovo modello cellulare per flussi lavici:colate di Pantelleria. Bolletino GNV, 1988, IV, 41-51.
6. ISHIHARA K., IGUCHI M. and KAMO K. Numerical simulation of lava flows on some volcanoes in Japan. In, Lava flows and domes. FINK J.H. (ed.) IAVCEI Proceedings in Volcanology, vol. 2, 1989, 174-207.
7. YOUNG P.A.V. and WADGE G. FLOWFRONT: simulation of a lava flow. Computers and Geosciences, 1990, vol. 16, 1171-1191.
8. WADGE, G., YOUNG P.A.V. and MCKENDRICK I. Mapping lava flow hazards using computer simulation. Journal of Geophysical Research, in press.
9. SEAN. Etna.Smithsonian Institution-Global Volcanism Network Bulletin, 1992, vol. 17, no. 4, 10-11.
10. WADGE G. The variation of magma discharge during basaltic eruptions. Journal of Volcanology and Geothermal Research, 1981, vol. 11, 139-168.
11. CHESTER D.K., DUNCAN A.M., GUEST, J.E. and KILBURN, C.R.J. Mount Etna: the anatomy of a volcano. Chapman and Hall, 1985, 404 pp.

24. Management oversight risk tree analysis as a tool for the evaluation of emergency plans

H. C. WILSON, Department of Industrial Technology, University of Bradford

Abstract

A description of a modified Management Oversight Risk Tree (MORT) analysis technique for the evaluation of emergency or crisis management plans is presented.

The technique identifies those areas of management response that are critical for the correct implementation of crisis and emergency plans. The explanation is illustrated by reference to the activation of recent plans to some of major incidents. The technique is shown to be simple and effective in use.

INTRODUCTION

A disproportionate amount of time and resources are expended on the exercising of crisis and emergency plans which have not been pre-evaluated from a human factors view. Crisis and emergency management plans seldom fail to perform due to breakdown of immediate hardware resources. In the public sector fire appliances, ambulances, police vehicles, hospital operating theatres, accident and emergency units and the plethora of used in an emergency are in routine use and are usually adequately maintained. In the industrial and commercial sector fire fighting equipment, computers, communication equipment, data acquisition and retrieval systems are maintained in high degree of operational readiness. The operation of a plan frequently fails due to the omissions and oversights that occurred during the plan creation stage. Not a failure of hardware but a failure to realise the extent of planning, foresight, and training required which involves human resources.

These omissions and oversights are not deliberate acts of sabotage but stem from the inability to visualise the extent of the response that may be required.

The are many excellent analytical systems for the identification of potential and actual hardware errors, such as Event Trees, Fault Tree Analysis, Failure Mode Effect Analysis, and Failure Mode Effect and Criticality Analysis which have a rightful place in the armoury of the crisis manager. The limitation of these systems is that seldom take into account the fact that people are involved and people are extremely variable, much more so than a fire pump or a police siren. When the starter button on an electrical pump is depressed the pump will either function properly or fail. When someone is told to go and do something the range of potential outcomes is staggering. Is in the anticipation of these outcomes, and in the prevention of negative outcomes, that the present system, the modification of the Management Oversight and Risk Tree, should be given consideration.

Management Oversight and Risk Tree (MORT)

The MORT analysis system was developed within the power generation system of the United

Natural disasters. Thomas Telford, London, 1993

States of America to evaluate those failures and omissions that could, would or did lead to the occurrence of critical incidents (1). A critical incident being defined as an event that could or did lead to damage to people or property. Thus it was used to evaluate near-misses as well as actual damage producing incidents.

MORT Diagrams
MORT has eight major levels of activity and other sub-levels which may be added at any stage deemed necessary by the investigator. In this MORT has a wide degree of flexibility. The diagrams are composed of symbols which are similar to, but not totally identical to, those used in the classical Fault Tree analysis which are subject to an ANSI code on logic diagrams. The symbols which consist of events and gates are shown in Figure 1. MORT uses three main headings which are shown in Figure 2; the top event is successful implementation and the subsequent three sub-headings cover the areas of specific oversights or omissions (S factors); general characterisation of the management systems (G factors); and assumed risks (R factors). R factors will not be considered here and the text will concentrate on the S and G factors which are more pertinent to the topic under discussion.

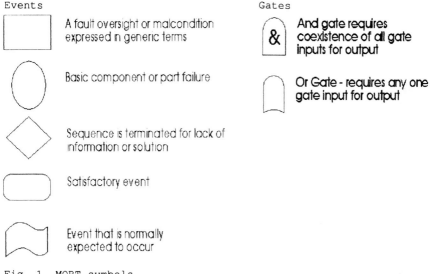

Fig. 1. MORT symbols

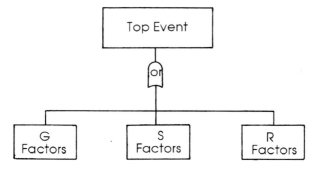

Fig. 2. Basic MORT investigation tree

NATURAL DISASTERS

The classical MORT diagram (Figure 3) has 13 major topic areas depicted by upper cases letters.

The system is a top-down logic tree, i.e. it begins with the critical incident and works down through various branches identifying the primary and secondary causes. It is two basic parts.

a) Hardware
As this is a basic fault and event tree it is a standard technique which is in frequent use and as such will not be discussed in detail. Other more elaborate analytical techniques as mentioned previously, could be substituted for the prescribed method. The research presented here concentrates mainly on the software and reference to hardware will be made only where necessary.

b) Software
As stated above, MORT is a top-down logic tree and is ideal for the identification of those human factors and other components that have not received the consideration necessary to prevent or mitigate a critical incident.

The development of the MORT technique presented here is that certain elements of the logic tree have been reversed and redescribed to allow the identification of those components that which are critical to the successful implementation of the crisis management plan. This allows a diagnostic evaluation of the human factors involved in the plan prior to exercising or initiation.

The MORT Technique
The MORT technique supplies the investigator with a disciplined method of pre-implementation analysis of a crisis or emergency management plan. The model used described here identifies nearly 300 basic problems that relate directly to causes or preventative measures. These 300 basic problems underpin about 100 generic problems representing successively broader areas of management. The method is similar to an inverted Fault Tree but lends itself to identify generalised failures, e.g. management omissions and uncertainties, which are not consistent with the standard Fault Tree methodology which is usually applied to one specific incident. The term Fault Tree implies blame whereas the investigation should be targeted towards identification of cause, mitigation, and prevention. MORT is based on the degree of adequacy of an action. Actions are described as Adequate, Less Than Adequate (LTA), or may be described as inadequate information for judgement. The procedure is similar to applying fuzzy logic in that adequacy is subjective rather than empirical.

In its simplest form MORT is a diagram which arranges the necessary program elements in an orderly and logical manner and structures the associated literature and current best practice into three level of relationship, viz.;

1) Criteria
Judgement rationale from the MORT text. There are thousands of criteria to judge adequacy when a step is well done or LTA.
2) Basic Events (Causes)
1500 possible causes which are the steps required to fulfil a function
3) Generic Events (Problems)
98 generic problems which are the functions necessary to complete a process.

Through this basic system the operator is able to identify the simple decision points in an analysis enabling detection of omissions, oversights, and defects.

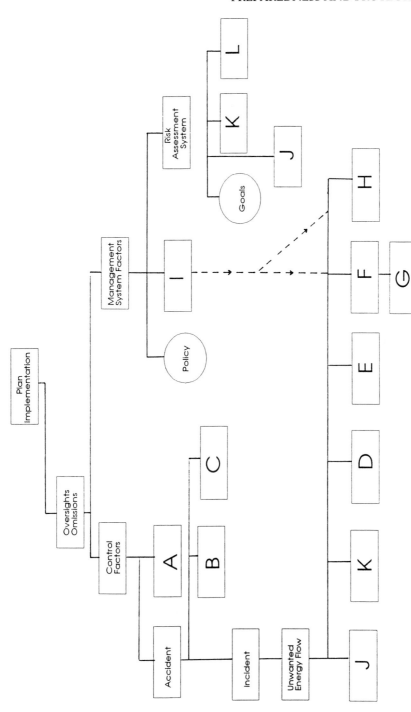

Fig. 3. Management oversight risk tree

NATURAL DISASTERS

A) Amelioration Tree

B) Barriers Tree

C) Persons/Objects in Energy Channel Tree

D) Operational Readiness Tree

E) Maintenance Tree

F) Supervision Tree

G) Task Performance Error Tree

H) Services Tree

I) Implementation Tree

J) Information Systems Tree

K) Hazard Analysis Process Tree

L) Safety Program Tree

M) Human Factor Review Tree

Trees B and C are not truly relevant to the immediate topic and will be omitted but are essential when reviewing a critical incident.

MORT Guidance Points

A) Amelioration Tree

Amelioration limits the consequences of what may immediately occur and reduces the significance of those consequences when and where ever possible. Consideration is given to factors such as; are amelioration functions pre-planned as opposed to being allowed to occur fortuitously at the time of the plan implementation (planning vs. luck); will the scope the plan adequately cover the type and severity of any accident ("all hazards" planning vs. specific scenario planning); are the available resources adequate for execution of the plan in either form (designated vs. available).

D) Operational Readiness

Is the adequacy of the preparations verified according to the original design of the plan, including operational specifications, i.e. does it meet the mission statement ?; is the conduct of an operational readiness review required, i.e. has the plan been sitting on the shelf gathering dust or is dynamic ?, are the criteria used for determining readiness adequate, i.e. who judges operational readiness, i.e. who verifies readiness, internal or external adjudication and are those people competent to make that decision ?; is a "who does what" plan prepared for each element of the main plan, i.e. planned activity vs. availability ?

E) Maintenance Tree

Is there adequate maintenance or inspection of resources, processes, utilities, operations etc., consider the number and diversity of people and resources that will be used ?, i.e. all elements of the plan should be maintained at similar levels; If relevant, has maintenance been split into preventative and inspection dependent maintenance, i.e. a fire appliance has preventative maintenance performed as a routine function according to a prescribed schedule whereas stocks of blankets, dried food will require inspection dependent maintenance.

F) Supervision Tree.
MORT attempts to assess management's role in service to the institution of supervision, not the person. The emphasis throughout is to determine why the management system could fail and not which individual within the management team could fail. Is management organised in such a manner that they can control all processes ? Does the crisis management team have sufficient information, technical and otherwise, to allow them to make policy decisions ?Is the help and assistance given to supervisors adequate to enable them to fulfil their roles ? During the operation of an emergency or crisis plan many personnel will be involved in roles outside their normal remit and require a higher degree of supervisory support. Does management have a feedback system to inform them on the adequacy of their control systems so that they modify their policies to ensure optimal and performance ? If the supervisor has recently been transferred to this role, is there a protocol for the transfer of information from old to new supervisor ? In the event of a serious incident how frequently will the supervisor inspect the site for safety ? e.g. chemical spills, transportation accidents, floods, etc. where personnel could be at risk. Will the incident site be maintained in an adequate state ? Site of serious incidents must be maintained as a "scene of crime" and evidence must be preserved.

G) Task Performance Error Tree. Many well run organisations, including industrial and commercial concerns, use a system of job safety analysis (JSA) as a level of performance excellence. This JSA is not only aimed at personnel safety during operation but also at excluding operational errors from performance of any task. Perhaps a better description would be "task evaluation analysis". Does the task analysis, whatever its nature, meet the established tests of method, participation, written record and review. In the construction of a plan it is essential to prescribe the main tasks and how they should, in broad terms, be performed, e.g. press releases, handling the media, care of the injured etc. the performance methods recorded and a review of their efficiency performed both during and after the event. Is a pre-task briefing given and is that briefing adequate for the task ? For example, does the briefing include recent changes to equipment and personnel ? Will task assignments be given to best qualified personnel ? For example, how often do we see on news items fire brigade personnel removing rubble from the site of a disaster. This is a waste of their specialised training, perhaps local authority, or commercial, construction personnel should be used for this task. Personnel should never be used for an unfamiliar task solely on the basis of their immediate availability. Will personnel have received specific task training ? Will those handling calls from the media or distressed relative have been trained in their roles ? Media response teams are often volunteers whose normal duties would not include this aspect of an emergency response. When dealing with distressed relatives perhaps use should be made of personnel from some of the voluntary caring organisations such as CRUSE, or the Samaritans etc. who have extensive training and experience in this field of response. During the rescue phase of disaster management personnel at the site should be protected by barriers and controls to allow them to concentrate fully on their tasks. Interruptions by relatives or media personnel will hinder the rescue and those involved in this stage must be protected. Protection of the rescue workers should also be extended to cover well-meaning senior personnel who are not immediately involved in that stage of the rescue process. Is there provision in the plan to "sweep clean" the immediate site to remove and re-allocate personnel not immediately involved in that stage of the operation ?

H) Services Tree. Does upper level management provide the necessary supportive services and guidance needed at lower organisational levels for high performance ? Has the necessary information been sought out and disseminated to all concerned ? Has use been made of information services such as university departments, regulatory authorities, professional organisations etc. when compiling the information? Were training methods assessed for effectiveness ? Were the training programs validated ?

I) Implementation Tree. Does the overall plan fulfil the policy statement ? Have problems relating to the implementation of the plan been related back to senior management ? Is implementation a continuously balanced effort designed to correct defects and generally proactive rather than reactive ? Are management systems and methods adequate to provide taut control and wise guidance to ensure high performance ? Is there a clear written statement of responsibility of the line organisation, from the top individual through the first line management to the individual respondent ? Has this statement been distributed throughout the organisation and is it clearly understood ? Has the intent of the statement been implemented ? Is there an efficient system for the transmission of information to the senior management ? Does senior management provide information needed at lower organisational levels ? Are the budgets adequate, not only for the investigating group, but also for those groups also involved in the implementation of the plan ? Are plan elements implemented in a timely manner ? Are there delays in introducing solutions to problems into plans and if so, can these delays be minimised ? Has top management shown interest in lower level program activities through personnel involvement ? Is their concern known, respected and reflected at all management and employee levels ?

J) Information Systems Tree. Is the information flow adequate ? Is there adequate technical information available ? Often relevant information exists but it is not communicated to the person who needs it. Is there previous case studies and examples that can be used ? Is the list of experts to contact for information adequate ? Do those experts know that they are on the list ? Are there studies directed to the solution of known problems ? Has there been research into prevention ? Are internal communications adequate ? Who sends what information and to whom ? Are external communications adequate ? Who is to obtain information from external bodies ? Is the method of data storage, retrieval, searching and processing adequate ? Is the monitoring of the plan adequate ? Who performs the monitoring and to whom are the findings made available ? Are changes in the plan communicated to all concerned ? Who is responsible for this communication ? Is the plan subject to external audit ? Are the auditors competent to perform this function ? At what organisational level do they report ?

K) Hazard Analysis Process Tree. One aspect of emergency planning that is often overlooked is the safety of the response personnel. It is futile to risk the lives of respondents in a rescue attempt as the bad press it will receive will negate any possible good that it may have achieved. Lack of definition is a major weakness in most organisations. Have goals and tolerable risks been defined for safety and is there any conflict between the two ? Are the goals and acceptable risks well defined and accepted ? Does the organisation have the necessary skills in-house to be able to adequately assess the risks or is there a need to employ profession consultants ? Is at least the minimum level of human factors capability needed for an operation, available and used ? Are the response personnel aware of what is required, when to act and when the task has been completed ? Has an attempt been made to predict which human errors are likely to occur and corrective procedures implemented to prevent their occurrence been made ?

L) Safety Programme Tree. Has the aspects of safety been adequately considered ? Many simple processes carry an element of danger and these have to be considered. A full tea urn precariously balanced on a ledge has the potential to severely injure many people. Safety is the correct attention to small details. Have the ideals of a safety program been discussed at all organisational levels ? Are safety procedures documented in operating manuals and schematics ? Is safety training adequate ? Consider the competency of the trainers and adequacy of the training methods employed. Does the safety program encompass all forms of hazard ?

M) Human Factors Review Tree. This section may be fitted into any of the preceding sections as thought necessary. Are the professional skills available adequate for the function ? Is the task described to the respondents prior to task allocation ? Is the task better done by a human or a machine ? Will the task requirements be adequately considered ? Has there been dry-run training in each of the elements of the plan ? Have procedures been revised in accordance with changes in the plan ? Does the phraseology and language used in the writing of the plan consider different, intellectual, and reading abilities ? Have the semantics of the words in the plan been considered ? (Technical jargon cannot be excluded entirely but should be minimised and where inclusion is necessary an explanation of the term should be given.) Have the procedures in the plan been verified ? Are instructions in the plan easy to perform in a crisis situation ? Do the procedures give clear and precise instructions for anticipated emergency conditions ? Do procedures in the plan have steps performed in a sequence according to criteria ? Do personnel selection criteria assure the capability, both physical and mental, which is necessary and sufficient to perform the procedures ? Has training been preplanned ? Does it specify demonstration and exercising of the plan in a hands-on manner ?

These are some of the guidance points that should be considered in the evaluation of a plan. Others may be added at appropriate points in each of the trees and some trees may be added into others where deemed necessary. The above list is not meant to be exclusive but is given as an indication of the depth of investigation that the MORT system is capable of developing.

As the MORT analysis progresses through the responses to the pre-set questions the investigator depicts each item using the following code

GREEN	Good or Adequate
BLUE	Insufficient or Unknown Information
RED	Less Than Adequate

The action points are those items which are coloured BLUE or RED and after a very short period the system beings begins to depict those areas of the plan which require addressing. If an area is predominantly RED then information transfer blocks can be added below each event box to allow further detailed analysis of the failure events.

TEMPORAL PHASES of a CRITICAL INCIDENT

The objective of a crisis or emergency response plan is to prevent, or at least limit the effects of, a critical incident. Such incidents and events do not occur spontaneously but are the build up of a sequence of events or omissions which can be identified. There are six temporal phases that can be identified in any incident.

Quiescent Period

This period may last for many years. It is the period between similar event during which there is a slow progress towards a re-occurrence. It could be used to study, and perform research into, the preceding critical events. Unfortunately what occurs is usually less than the minimum to prevent the re-occurrence.

Prodomal Period

This period may last several years but usually only lasts for a short period, days or often hours. There are overt warnings of impending crisis and emergency preparedness measures can and should be implemented but seldom are.

"The Flip Over"

The very rapid change from the prodomal period to the cataclysmic. Immediately prior to this phase there is an opportunity to prevent the occurrence from happening.

Cataclysm

A very short period of time with the release of tremendous forces of an intensity that can flatten buildings or produce death.

Rescue Phase

Fires are fought, lives are saved, the injured are taken off to hospital for treatment, temporary housing and shelters are provided, evacuation is carried out. These events will happen provided that there is in existence a well prepared emergency plan, if this is lacking then no mitigation of the event will occur.

Recovery Phase

This situation will last until the effects on the community affected has passed and the community has returned to normal. Often this phase will last for years. Again, the effectiveness of this phase will depend on planning as it has to begin immediately after the cataclysmic event and it will not, nor cannot, occur spontaneously.

All of these phases are considered during the MORT evaluation and using some of the guidance points and the evidence from recent disasters can illustrate the effectiveness of this technique.

A). Amelioration. The weather conditions prevailing at the time of the Braer incident were fortuitous as the storm broke up the oil slick, if however, the weather had been calm then the effects of the incident would have exceeded those of the Exxon Valdez. In the aftermath of Chernobyl the resources available within the UK, and other European countries, were shown to totally inadequate to deal with the situation.

D) Operational Readiness Tree. In the light of the events after the Chernobyl incident it is justified to state that the UK readiness system for dealing with nuclear fall-out needed reviewing and the criteria for the system that was in existence was inadequate.

F) Supervision Tree. If UK peacetime emergency planning as a whole is considered then many of those responsible for the preparation and implementation of those plans do not have this area of responsibility as a full time function. The role of local authority emergency planning officer is often an add-on to another function. This limits the amount of time that can be devoted to the preparation of those plans. At the Kings Cross Tube Station fire the command of the situation was undertaken by the fire service. The incident commander changed three times within a space of a few minutes as more senior officers arrived at the scene. It is not being suggested that these changes had any effect on the outcome of the incident but in other circumstances it is not difficult to imagine the potential for the loss of critical information at change overs. Not all organisations are as effective as the fire service at this task.

G) Task Performance Error Tree. It may seem incongruous that an emergency plan should not include all of the essential elements required for its smooth operation yet this does occur. At the Kegworth air crash the police were overwhelmed by the number of visitors to the site, press, relatives, voyeurs etc., who arrived within a short period of time. For many of those who will be involved in an emergency it will be the first experience of working in an extremely stressful and often hazardous environment. Planning must take into account that supervision will have to be increased to prevent those involved being injured.

H) Services Tree. Many plans are prepared purely as a list of telephone numbers of key personnel. Plans are often prepared without obtaining the necessary basic information. The problems associated with crowd control and the reaction of the public to hazardous situations are often overlooked when plans are being drawn up. In these situations whether there will be panic depends on many factors such as available escape routes, loss of vision due to smoke or adequate lighting, immediate responsibilities such as a detached member of the family - a mother frantically seeking her lost child during a fire is not a calm individual and panic can spread rapidly. Many local authorities in the UK are faced within increasing financial restrictions and when cut backs are necessary it is the soft options which suffer. Emergency planning is a soft option and the financing of many has been cut drastically over the past few years.

I) Implementation Tree. One of the major faults that was uncovered at the inquiry into the Kings Cross fire was the lack of control by the management of London Underground. From the inquiry it was evident that the management of London Underground were poorly trained for the roles they had to perform and that they lacked support from their senior management.

J) Information Systems Tree. London Underground had experience of many smaller fires that could have been used for the creation of an effective emergency and prevention plan. Similarly, there have been several incidents of crushing incidents at football matches and other large events from which lessons could have been learnt. Many university departments have done or are at present performing research into crowd related matters and this information is freely available to interested parties. Similar research establishments have investigated chemical fires and their effects. At a recent table-top exercise which used a chemical spillage from a road tanker as its scenario to evaluate a county wide plan, one of the players found to his dismay that unknown to him he had been placed on 24 hour call-out by his employer. Monitoring of plans is usually done in-house by those personnel involved in its creation. This system will not detect errors such as those in above. Monitoring of plans must be done by external personnel.

MORT REQUIREMENTS

The requirements necessary to perform a MORT analysis are very simple:

The Plan to be investigated
The MORT diagrams
The MORT question sheets
Three coloured pens, one each of blue, green and red
Sheets of blank paper and above all else -
Honesty

In common with all investigative techniques MORT is only as good, or as bad, as the personnel using it. If the investigator does not answer the questions honestly, then MORT will fail. In all new MORT analysis the investigator should arrive at the end with many blue items, some red and a few green. It is working towards the conversion of the red and blue to green that requires skill.

SUMMARY

From the above it can be seen that the MORT system can be used to evaluate plans that have been created for emergency and crisis management. These plans require such evaluation prior to being dry-run exercised and certainly prior to being used in anger. It is not suggested that all of the failure points have been identified, or can be identified, prior to the event but the implementation of the MORT system will considerably reduce the risk of plan failure during a critical time.

REFERENCE
1) W G Johnson, J. Safety Research, 7 (1), (1975), 4 - 15

25. Use of disaster magnitude scale to analyse natural disasters

A. Z. KELLER and A. AL-MADHARI, Disaster Prevention and Limitation Unit, University of Bradford

INTRODUCTION

In order to compare disasters arising from different sources it is useful to use quantitative measures. For this purpose Keller (1) introduced the Bradford Disaster Scale (BDS) which is based on the logarithm of the number of fatalities involved in the occurrence of a disaster. It has been shown that the method is useful for disaster analysis and hazard identification and quantification; it can also be used as a tool for structured and strategic planning.

Whilst death is the most significant and most easily identified consequence associated with disaster, other consequences such as injuries, cost of damage, social disruption, psychological trauma and environmental impact cannot be neglected. Due to the complexity of these consequences, a comprehensive quantitative measure to satisfy all planning needs is difficult to formulate.

The approach developed in this paper and elsewhere Keller (2,4,5) is to consider consequences existing in a multidimensional manifold and to formulate scales for each of these dimensions. Consequences of disasters can then be considered as a vector whose components are given by individual scale values for each dimension.

In accordance with this philosophy, somewhat simplistically, an initial two-dimensional consequence space is assumed. The scales adopted for these dimensions are fatalities and re-insurable cost of disaster.

In the present paper, the consequences of natural disasters arising from earthquakes, floods and abnormal weather conditions including hurricanes tornadoes, cyclones and storms are studied. For simplicity the latter category of natural disasters resulting from abnormal weather conditions will be referred to in the reminder of the present paper as a "climatic"

In order to avoid unduly large and difficult to handle data sets, a disaster is defined as:

302

" An event localised both in time and space such that either 10 or more fatalities occur and/or total re-insurable damage cost exceeds $1 M (US) as a result of the event "

This definition is an extension of the original definition given in Keller (1) which is expressed only in terms of fatalities. Again, the threshold values of 10 fatalities and $1 M (US) are pragmatic and not absolute and are chosen for convenience of producing clean and manageable data sets. For example, Keller (3,6) in an analysis of disasters in the oil and chemical industries, because of the relative small number of disasters having detailed documentation, used a fatality threshold of 5. Similarly, in Keller (2,4), in dealing with disasters of a global nature, because of the very large number of disasters involved and the possible under-reporting of "small" disasters, a fatality threshold of 20 was assumed.

In earlier papers (2,4,6), a probabilistic model is developed in which inputs for the model are frequency of occurrence and magnitudes of disasters of the particular type being studied. Expressions derived from the model include the return period for disasters having magnitude equal or greater than a particular value. This method has been applied by Keller (2,4) to disasters of general nature that have occurred in the geographical areas of the USA, Europe and the UK. In a more structured application the method has also been applied by Keller (6) to the disasters referred to above which have occurred during the period 1970-1987 within chemical and allied industries. As described in (2,4) the method has since been extended to allow for analysis of re-insurable losses for disasters in both the USA and Europe.

In the present paper the method is applied to the following disasters of natural origin.

Earthquakes
Floods
Climatic

FATALITY SCALE

On the Bradford Disaster Scale magnitude is defined by taking the common logarithm (base 10) of the number of fatalities resulting in a disaster.

A similar form of scaling based on common logarithms has been previously used by Richardson (7); further reference to this scaling technique can also be found in Marshall (8).

Supplementary to magnitude scaling a classification system, Keller (1), has been introduced for analysis of large data sets where fatality data values are not necessarily precise.

COST SCALE

In a similar way to the fatality scale a cost scale can be defined where the magnitude of the cost component is the common logarithm of the re-insurable losses in $ M (US).

NATURAL DISASTERS

STATISTICAL MODELS

Assume that the magnitudes of disasters are described by a probability density function $f(m)$. For the three cases studied in this paper, it has been found that a statistical distribution that well describes the behaviour of fatalities is the exponential probability density function (pdf) given by

$$f(m - m_0) = \begin{cases} \beta e^{-\beta(m-m_0)} & \text{if } m \geq m_0 \\ 0 & \text{if } m < m_0 \end{cases} \quad (1)$$

and where m_0 is the threshold magnitude

It has been shown that in previous papers (2,4,6) that this distribution is also appropriate for describing fatalities occurring in other types of disasters both natural and man-made. Values of β obtained in these previous studies are given in Table (1)

Corresponding to (1), the following Weibull pdf $f(m_c)$ can be used to model recoverable insurance losses

$$f(m_c) = \begin{cases} \eta \dfrac{m_c^{\eta-1}}{\tau^\eta} e^{-(\frac{m_c}{\tau})^\eta} & m_c \geq 0 \\ 0 & \text{otherwise} \end{cases} \quad (2)$$

where m_c is the common logarithm of the recoverable insurable cost. Because the unit of measurement is $ M (US) and the threshold is $1 M (US) $m_0 = 0$. η and τ are shape and scale parameters respectively.

The pdf (2) has been previously used in studies of disasters that have occurred in the USA and Europe (2,4). Values of η and τ obtained in these previous studies are given in Table (2).

STATISTICAL ANALYSIS

Data sets were constructed for the three types of natural disasters: earthquakes, floods and climatic. Data covering the years 1982-1990 were obtained from tables published by Swiss Re (9)

Maximum likelihood estimates from the data, of the parameters β, η and τ were obtained. These values are given in Tables (1) and (2) together with estimated annual disaster occurrence rates. Graphical demonstrations of the probability distribution fits to the observed data are given in Figures (1-6).

304

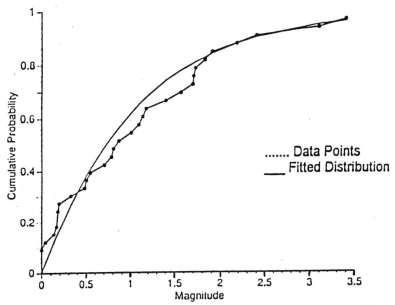

Fig. 1. Fatalities of earthquake disasters world wide (1982–1990)

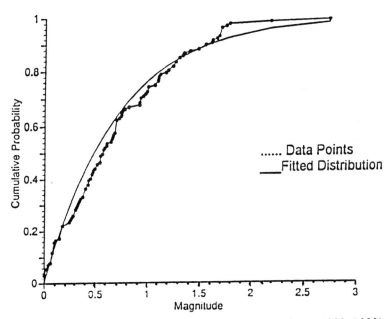

Fig. 2. Fatalities of flood disasters world wide (1982–1990)

305

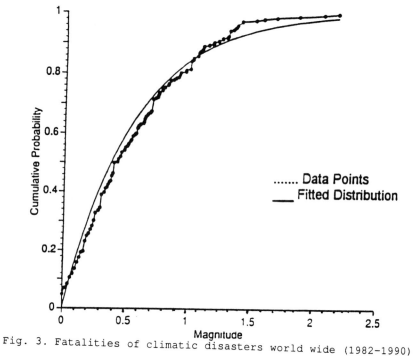

Fig. 3. Fatalities of climatic disasters world wide (1982-1990)

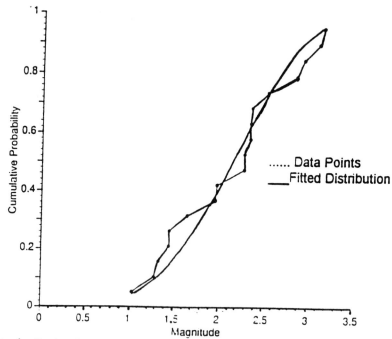

Fig. 4. Cost of earthquake disasters world wide (1982-1990)

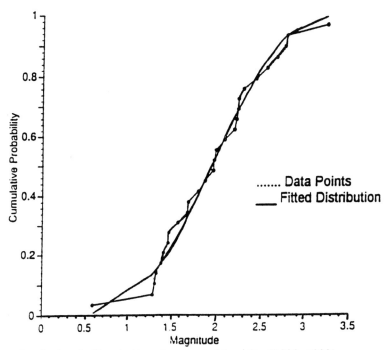

Fig. 5. Cost of flood disasters world wide (1982-1990)

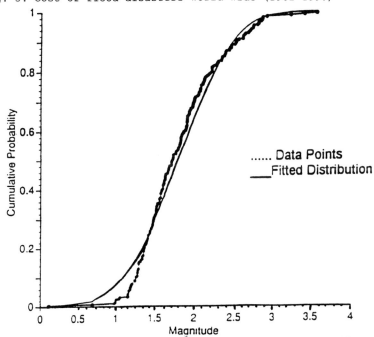

Fig. 6. Cost of climatic disasters world wide (1982-1990)

NATURAL DISASTERS

CALCULATION OF RETURN PERIODS

Fatality.

Values of return periods for disaster of magnitude greater than m were calculated using the formula

$$t_R = \frac{1}{\lambda\ R(m)} \tag{3}$$

where

$$R(m) = \begin{cases} e^{-\beta(m-m_0)} & \text{if } m \geq m_0 \\ 1 & \text{if } m < m_0 \end{cases} \tag{4}$$

and λ is the annual occurrence rate of disasters classified by fatalities

Re insurable Cost

Values of return periods for disasters of magnitude greater than m_c is given by

$$t_R = \frac{1}{\lambda_c R(m_c)} \tag{5}$$

where

$$R(m_c) = \begin{cases} e^{-(\frac{m_c}{\tau})^\eta} & \text{if } m_c \geq 0 \\ 1 & \text{if } m_c < 0 \end{cases} \tag{6}$$

and λ_c is annual rate of occurrence of disasters classified by re-insurable cost. Derivations of (3) and (5) are given in Keller (2,6).

Return periods for earthquakes, floods and climatic disasters were calculated using equations (3) and (5) and the distribution parameter values given in Tables (1) and (2). These return periods are given in Figures (7-12).

CONCLUSIONS

The following conclusions can be drawn from the present study.

1- As shown by the β and λ values in Table (1) natural disasters such as earthquakes, floods and climatic disasters are between one and two magnitudes worse than technological disasters and constitute approximately 35% of all disasters.

308

Table (1). Disaster fatality parameters

Disaster Type	Annual disaster rate λ	β
Oil and Chemical** 1970-1987	9.61	2.50
UK * 1960-1990	2.90	2.71
World Wide * 1970-1990	109.10	2.18
Third World * 1970-1990	96.55	2.10
USA * 1970-1990	5.75	2.80
European * 1970-1990	12.25	2.78
Earthquake 1982-1990	3.56	0.97
Flood 1982-1990	14.00	1.45
Climatic 1982-1990	25.30	1.85

* Disasters of all types

** World-wide

Table (2). Disaster insurable cost parameters

Disaster Type	Annual disaster rate λ_c	η	τ
World Wide * 1982-1990	96.89	2.92	1.72
Third World * 1982-1990	16.11	2.55	1.67
USA * 1982-1990	26.67	3.25	1.83
European * 1982-1990	32.55	3.22	1.67
Earthquake 1982-1990	2.00	3.80	2.36
Flood 1982-1990	3.11	3.77	2.15
Climatic 1982-1990	28.55	3.75	1.98

* Disasters of all types

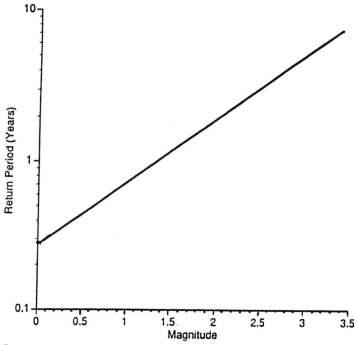

Fig. 7. Earthquake disaster fatalities (1982-1990)

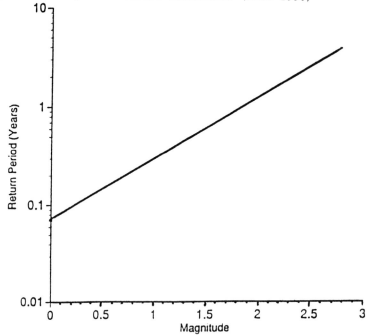

Fig. 8. Flood disasters fatalities (1982-1990)

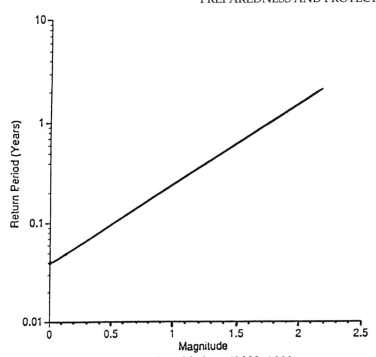

Fig. 9. Climatic disasters fatalities (1982–1990)

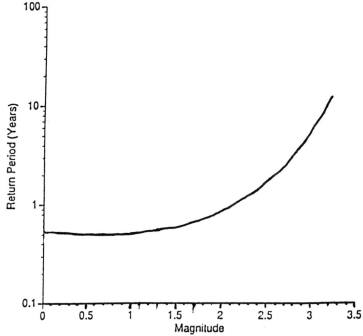

Fig. 10. Earthquake disasters recoverable insurable losses
(1982–1990)

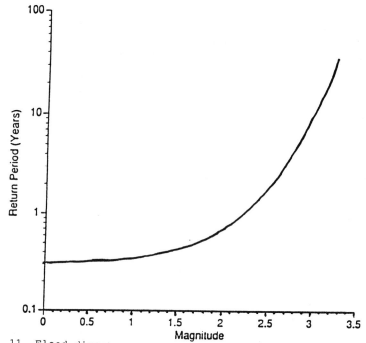

Fig. 11. Flood disaster recoverable insurable losses (1982–1990)

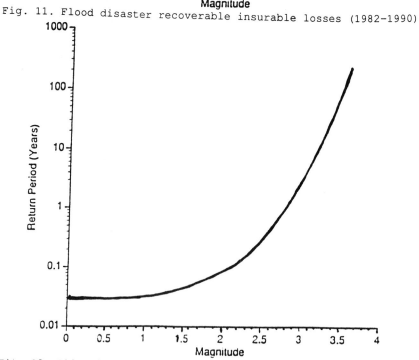

Fig. 12. Climatic disasters recoverable insurable losses (1982–1990)

2- Again, Table (1) indicates that climatic disasters occur approximately seven times more frequently than earthquakes and nearly twice as frequently as floods. Moreover, the fatality magnitudes are between 0.4 and 0.9 magnitude worse.

3- With regard to insurable cost because of consistency of shape parameter η as indicated in Table (2), there is a suggestion that there is also a consistency of factors present in climatic disasters, floods and earthquakes which require further investigation and possible identification.

4- Constancy of τ in Table (2) indicates that the expected or average value of re-insurable cost are essentially the same for all types of natural disaster. This is because the parameter τ is directly related to the mean value.

5- There is a large difference between the annual rates of occurrence of "fatality" and "cost" disasters, as given by λ and λ_c in Tables (1) and (2) for floods; this would suggest that there is major under-insuring for flooding which would not be a surprising phenomena for third world countries where most flood disasters occur. A similar result but to a lesser extent is indicated for earthquakes.

RECOMMENDATION

Provided that the validation of the methods presented here are acceptable, further studies with these methods should now be carried out on natural disaster data classified into sets with much narrower taxonomy particularly relating to geographical areas and type of disasters. These analyses would enable detailed risk assessment for any type of natural disaster to be carried out for particular geographical locations with regard to frequency and magnitude of damage including fatalities and cost. Such assessments would allow a greater realistic planning for provision of resources for given areas with regard to emergency services, medical supplies and training locally of medical and other staff. National governments and international agencies such as the United Nations and international voluntary aid organisations would be able to draw on these assessments to assist them with their own individual planning.

REFERENCES

1). Keller,A.Z. The Bradford Disaster Scale. In "Disaster Prevention and Limitation; Proceedings of the 1st. DPLU Conference, 12-13th September 1989, University of Bradford, Keller,A.Z. and Wilson, H.C. (Eds.)", The British Library, London, 1990.

2).Keller, A.Z. Wilson, H.C and Al-Madhari,A. Proposed Disaster Scale and Associated Model for Calculating Return Periods for Natural Disasters of Given Financial Magnitude. International Conference Technological Innovations in Civil Protection . Exhibition of Technological Products Tecpro 93. Florence, Italy, March 17-20,1993

3). Keller,A.Z. and Wilson, H.C. An Evaluation of Chemically Related Disasters using the Bradford Disaster Scale. 'IChemE' Hazards XI, Manchester 16-18th April, 1991.

4). Keller,A.Z., Wilson, H.C. and Al-Madhari,A. Proposed Disaster Scale and Associated Model for Calculating Return Period For Disasters of Given Financial Magnitude. M.O.R.E. 8 Seminar, Liverpool, 3-4th March, 1992.

5). Keller, A.Z. and Wilson, H.C. The Bradford Disaster Scale and Flood Disaster Prediction. International Invitationary Seminar, Middlesex polytechnic, London, October 1989.

6). Keller,A.Z., H.C.Wilson and A.Al-Madhari, Proposed Disaster Scale and Associated Model for Calculating Return Period for Disasters of Given Magnitude. Presented at 'Cindynics', European Symposium of Hazard Science, Cannes, 29th-31st January, 1992.

7). Richardson,L.F. Statistical of Deadly Quarrels. Atlantic Books, London, 1960.

8). Marshall,V.C. Major Chemical Hazards. Ellis Horwood Ltd., London, 1987
Keller and Al-Madhari

9). Sigma, Swiss Reinsurance Group, Zurich, Switzerland (Issues for period 1970-1990).

314

26. Prediction of risks in developing countries with sparse river flow data

J. R. MEIGH, J. V. SUTCLIFFE and
F. A. K. FARQUHARSON, Institute of Hydrology, UK

ABSTRACT

River flooding has always been a major cause of death and destruction of property, and poorer people in developing countries are particularly vulnerable. While other disasters cause greater loss of life, the total numbers affected by floods are far greater than by other disasters.

Alleviation of flooding damage can be achieved by engineering works, by zoning according to risk, or by installing flood warning systems. For these first two, estimates of flood magnitudes for various levels of risk are a necessary preliminary. However, in developing countries, the ability to do this is often hampered by a sparse flow data network and short records. This paper discusses the regional flood frequency analysis approach to these problems. This provides the ability to make reliable and rapid flood estimates at sites with little or no local flow data. Some examples of such regional studies are given.

The paper also discusses the alternative approach of installing flood forecasting systems. This approach is valuable when engineering solutions are too expensive and the relocation of the vulnerable population is impracticable. It is essential that the forecasting system is supported by an effective means of warning the population at risk and by efficient mechanisms for evacuating the inundated areas and moving or safeguarding property.

INTRODUCTION

River flooding has always been a major cause of death and destruction of property. In an examination of the major natural disasters in 1990, Berz (ref.1) showed that floods accounted for 123 of the 420 events (29% of the total) and resulted in 2535 deaths (5%) and US\$ 4200 million (9%) economic loss. In Latin America from 1900 to 1988 floods accounted for 42% of the natural disasters, for 5% of the people killed and 26% of the damage, although river and coastal flooding are not distinguished (ref. 2). While the numbers of people killed by floods are relatively small compared to other natural disasters, the total numbers affected in some way by flooding exceed all other disasters.

NATURAL DISASTERS

While floods are natural events, caused either by seasonal rainfall surplus or by unusually heavy storms, the damage and loss of life they cause are aggravated by man-made factors. Among these are increasing urbanisation and deforestation causing rapid runoff and increasing the frequency and intensity of floods; the restriction of waterways by uncontrolled development; the development of flood plains for agriculture; and the increasing occupation of flood plains particularly by poorer people in cities. These last two factors mean that floods now cause increased damage and loss of life. In other words, many communities have become more vulnerable to these natural disasters.

River flood plains have always been attractive to agricultural communities, and the availability of relatively flat and fertile land in proximity to water led to settlement and indeed to some of the earliest civilizations. In some of these long-settled flood plain regions, a balance between areas of settlement and of cultivation has been approached, which takes into account the advantages of flood-plain settlement and the risks of inundation. In other areas this balance has not been achieved. For instance, in the Yellow River valley in China sediment transported by the river has raised the channel well above the surrounding country, so that vertical stratification of cultivated areas and settlements is not possible.

Alleviation of flood damage

There are three approaches to reducing or averting the damage and loss of life caused by flooding:

- Engineering works to protect flood-prone areas
- Zoning of areas according to risk and the relocation of population and industry away from high risk areas
- Forecasting and warning of impending floods so that lives and movable property can be saved.

Engineering works include construction of flood embankments and channel widening and straightening; these measures are only likely to be feasible in urban areas or over limited reaches. Flood retention ponds and use of storage reservoirs to provide attenuation are other possibilities, although these are unlikely to be practical in cases where flooding is caused by seasonal rainfall surplus. Bridges and culverts need to be designed to pass flood flows, and the appropriate design of buildings, taking into account flooding risks, can also reduce damage.

The zoning of areas according to the risk or frequency of inundation can be used to minimise the likelihood of loss of life or damage. This is done by allocating areas to pasture, perennial agriculture or housing using contours which correspond to levels of flooding expected once in 2, 10 or 100 years, for example. This approach would often require the relocation of population away from flood-prone areas and may be politically and financially impracticable, especially in some developing countries where the poorest people live in the highest risk areas.

Both these approaches to alleviating flooding problems require reliable estimates of flood magnitudes at a variety of levels of risk. Part 1 of this paper discusses techniques for this and concentrates on the method of regional flood frequency analysis. This relates flood behaviour to the physical and climatic characteristics of the catchments, and allows flood estimates to be made for basins without flow records. Thus it is applicable in regions where the density of the river flow gauging network is low, and is especially valuable in developing countries. The method provides preliminary estimates at a large number of sites, and also gives reliable estimates for more extreme events compared to traditional single site frequency analysis.

A further stage in the analysis is often required: the derivation of peak water levels from the peak flows. This can be done using calibration curves at gauging stations and interpolation by contours in simpler cases. More complex situations require a hydraulic analysis based on the physical characteristics of the river reach and flood plain; this issue is beyond the scope of this paper. Once levels have been derived, the end product of the whole analysis could be a floodplain map with contours representing not levels but frequency of inundation.

The third approach to alleviating flood damage is to install flood forecasting and warning systems; this topic is discussed in part 2 of this paper. Flood forecasting is particularly attractive when engineering solutions are too expensive and it is impractical to move the population from the areas at risk. Systems are based on the telemetry of rainfall and river flow data and the use of models which run in real time. They provide forecasts of flows and river levels over a short period in the future, from a few hours to a matter of days ahead.

PART 1   FLOOD ESTIMATION

The usual problem to be solved in flood estimation is to find the peak flow at a particular site which corresponds to a predefined risk of occurrence. The level of risk is the probability of that flow being equalled or exceeded in any one year. This annual probability is expressed in terms of the return period of the event; that is, the expected interval between occurrences. Thus a flood having a probability of 0.01 of being equalled or exceeded in any one year has a return period of 100 years. The return periods used at a site depend on both the type of structure or problem and on the damage and loss of life expected if the design flow is exceeded. Typical values range from 20 or 50 years for road culverts to 10,000 years or more for major dams, especially if upstream of settled areas.

Broadly, there are two approaches to flood estimation problems: rainfall-runoff modelling and statistical methods. This paper concentrates on the statistical methods. Rainfall-runoff methods are used for major projects where estimates of the complete flood hydrograph are needed. Analysis of rainfall intensities is carried out to determine storm rainfall amounts and durations for a range of probabilities. These provide inputs to a rainfall-runoff model, calibrated using periods of observed flow and rainfall, which is then used to derive the flow hydrograph for the design flood event. This approach is more complex and has a larger data requirement than statistical methods.

Although the statistical approach only provides peak flows, estimates can more easily be made with sparse data. There are two types of analysis: single site and regional flood frequency analyses. Regional analysis can rapidly provide estimates at a large number of sites, and can be used at sites with very short or even no flow records. Thus, it is particularly advantageous in developing countries where flow gauging stations are often few and records short. In these situations, the only alternatives are a range of empirical techniques which have poor reliability. The regional method provides preliminary estimates which are adequate in many cases. Even where detailed studies using the rainfall-runoff approach are needed, regional analysis provides a valuable additional technique with which to compare the answers.

Single site flood analysis

Before discussing regional flood frequency analysis, it is useful to consider single site analysis. Where there is a river flow gauge with a reasonably long record at or near the site, the traditional approach has been to make the flood estimates based on the data at that site only. This involves extracting the peak discharge value for each year of record, ranking the data, and assigning a probability to each value according to its rank. Next a frequency distribution is selected and fitted to the data. The flow corresponding to the required return period can then be read from the fitted curve. An example is shown in figure 1; this shows two different frequency distributions fitted to the 21 years of data for the river Tati in Botswana.

While the single site approach is appropriate in some cases, there are major disadvantages. First, an estimate is often required for a return period much longer than the period of data, requiring considerable extrapolation of the curve. As can be seen from figure 1, this can be unreliable. The two distributions seem to fit the data equally well, but when used to estimate a flood with a return period of 100 years, say, they give very different results. At the much longer return periods needed in some studies, the uncertainty produced by extrapolation becomes extreme.

A second frequently occurring problem is outliers in the data. This problem is a result of the inherent variability of the flooding process, and is again illustrated by figure 1. While most of the data points seem fairly consistent, the largest flood of the record lies far from either fitted curve. It might be thought that this is an extreme event which had a much lower probability of occurrence than indicated by the probability based on its rank in the 21 year record. If this were so, it should have been plotted to the right, but its correct position cannot be known until a much greater period of data has been collected. (In some cases, local historical evidence may be available showing that this flood is the highest over a longer period.) It is extremely difficult to know what importance to give to the outlier, and thus the choice of the most appropriate curve is uncertain, with a consequent high degree of uncertainty in the resulting flood estimates.

In many countries, especially developing countries, the data network is sparse and there is often no suitable flow record nearby; hence, it is impossible to apply the single site

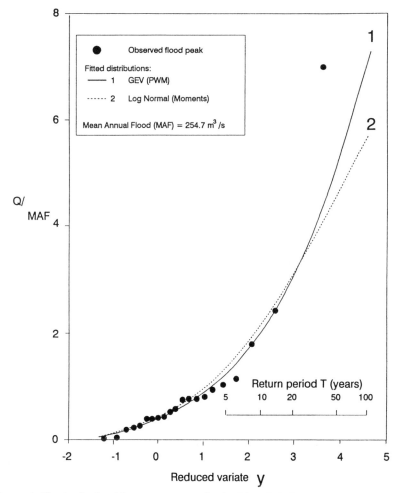

Figure 1 Single site flood frequency curves for the River Tati, Botswana

analysis. The regional flood frequency analysis approach overcomes these problems.

Regional flood analysis

Regional flood frequency analysis makes use of all the flow records within a region considered hydrologically homogeneous. By combining records, equations are developed which allow flood estimates to be made at sites with short or no records. To some extent, it also reduces the problems discussed above which can occur with single site analysis. One of the first major applications of regional flood frequency analysis was the flood study based on over 500 flow records in Britain and Ireland (ref. 3). Sutcliffe (ref. 4) considered the applicability of the

methods developed in the study to other countries, and showed
that, while the empirical findings were not applicable elsewhere,
the methods were.

Because the regional method uses all the flow records in the
region, the total record length is the sum of the lengths of the
individual records; thus, flood estimates at high return periods
can be made with greater confidence. It must be pointed out that
the individual site records are unlikely to be truly
statistically independent; in other words, a major flood is
likely to occur at the same time at more than one site, and this
would seem to reduce the validity of the approach. Nevertheless,
it has been shown (ref. 5) that regional analysis is more
accurate than the single site approach even when there is
considerable intersite dependence, so this issue need not worry
us unduly.

A regional flood analysis consists of three stages:

1.   Selection of the region to be studied
2.   Development of equations to estimate mean annual flood
3.   Development of flood frequency curves for the region

Selection of the region

Clearly, if a method is to be applied at any site within a
region, it is necessary that the whole region can be treated as
homogeneous. We need to be reasonably confident that all points
in the region would show similar flood behaviour. Unfortunately
these conditions are very difficult, if not impossible, to
determine in a rigorous manner. Some studies have attempted to
determine criteria to define homogeneous regions, but these are
not feasible to apply in most practical situations (ref. 6). The
records available for a particular study are invariably made up
of a number of long plus many short records, and many of the
records are often not of the best quality. While clearly
erroneous data must be excluded, it is usually necessary to
accept some lower quality records for a reasonable size of
database. This, combined with the inherent variability of the
flooding process, means that when rigorous testing procedures are
applied, they usually show that any selection of sites is not
homogeneous.

In practical situations, then, the hydrologist must fall back on
more subjective techniques, and this has been our approach in a
number of studies (refs 7, 8, 9). Initially, an assessment of the
expected hydrological behaviour of the region is carried out.
This is based on as much information as possible; the minimum is
maps of topography and mean annual rainfall, and an assessment
of the climate type. Additionally, maps of geology, soils, land
use and vegetation are examined where available. The assessment
is based on knowledge of typical hydrological behaviour under a
range of conditions; for instance, steep catchments with shallow
soils typically produce more extreme floods than lowland areas;
arid regions typically have a more variable flooding regime than
humid ones; areas affected by tropical cyclones are subjected to
more intense storms than other climate zones. This initial
impression is then supplemented by comparison of the flood
frequency curves for each individual site. These should show
broadly similar characteristics but allowance must be made for

natural variability and for outliers in the data. Some records which do not fit closely to the general pattern can be allowed, but it is a matter of judgement how much discrepancy between individual sites is permissible. An example of individual site records in a region is shown in figure 2; this is for 10 stations in Botswana. The curves are broadly similar, with only one markedly steeper and one markedly shallower than the main group. The plot shows straight lines between the observed points for each station rather than the fitted curves to give a better indication of variability.

So far geographical regions have been considered, but they can often be sub-divided on the basis of physical characteristics; for instance, large catchments may have a different flood frequency curve to small ones. An extension of this approach is to ignore geographical regions, and to define the regions solely on the basis of catchment characteristics or climate. A study of warm arid and semi-arid areas widely distributed throughout the world showed that they had broadly similar flood characteristics, and could be treated as a single region. Thus, an initial flood estimate, at least, can be made for any arid or semi-arid catchment worldwide using the single set of regional equations (ref. 8). Similarly, it was found that the very largest basins in the world all exhibited rather similar behaviour and could be treated together (ref. 10). However, these examples seem to be special cases and such approaches do not appear to be generally applicable. In most cases we must still depend on regions defined geographically.

Estimation of the mean annual flood

For each flow record the series of annual maxima is extracted, and the mean of these values is the mean annual flood (MAF). For each catchment a set of physical and climate characteristics is also determined. The minimum data needed are the catchment area (AREA) and mean annual rainfall (AAR). Ideally a range of other characteristics should also be obtained. A regression analysis is then carried out to determine an equation for estimation of MAF based on these catchment characteristics. AREA is always found to be the most significant variable, and others have lesser importance. The characteristics should be chosen to represent the different factors relevant to flooding, and these may vary from region to region. For instance, in the UK besides catchment area, measures of drainage density and river slope, the proportion of lakes, a soil index and the net one-day rainfall of 5-year return period were all found to be significant; in heavily urbanised areas the urbanised proportion of the catchment had to be taken into account (ref. 3). In a similar study of Java and Sumatra the characteristics used were area, slope, the proportion of lakes and the mean annual maximum catchment one-day rainfall (ref. 11). Other characteristics might sometimes be necessary. For instance, in regions with wet rice cultivation, the proportion of the catchment covered by paddy fields could be considered, while in forested regions, the proportion of forest might be significant.

In many cases a full set of catchment characteristic data is not easily available. Even when they are, AREA is always dominant. This is illustrated by the study of Java and Sumatra; table 1 shows the change in the coefficient of determination, R^2, as variables are gradually introduced into the regression. In many

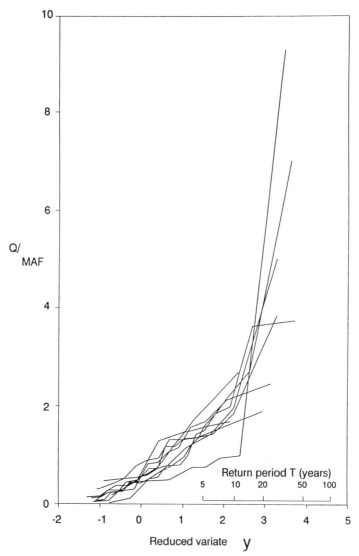

Figure 2 Comparison of flood frequency curves at individual sites within a region

studies, good results can be obtained using only AREA, and MAF regressions based on AREA only have achieved R^2 of up to 0.92 (ref. 8).

MAF equations as discussed above provide a useful means of estimating MAF when no data are available at the site of interest. Where a long, reliable flow record is available, it is preferable to estimate MAF from the local data rather than from the regional equation.

TABLE 1

Effect of additional independent variables in a
MAF regression

Independent variables	R^2
AREA only	0.788
AREA, APBAR	0.881
AREA, APBAR, AREA2	0.885
AREA, APBAR, AREA2, SIMS	0.888
AREA, APBAR, AREA2, SIMS, LAKE	0.889

All variables were transformed by taking $\log_{10}$: AREA =
catchment area;APBAR = mean annual maximum catchment 1-day
rainfall; AREA2 = $(\log(\text{AREA}))^2$; SIMS = river slope; LAKE =
proportion of lakes. (Source: ref 11)

Flood frequency curves for the region

The next stage is to determine the flood frequency curve, or
curves, for the region. The annual flood peak values are made
non-dimensional by dividing each value by the MAF for that site.
The data for all the sites are then grouped together and a
frequency distribution is fitted to them. There are a large
number of distributions which could be tried. However, we have
generally used only a single distribution, the general extreme
value (GEV) distribution. This is a three parameter distribution
which allows flexibility in the shape of the curve meaning that
a wide range of flood regimes can be modelled. We have found it
to be generally suitable in all circumstances investigated. The
method of fitting the distribution is also significant, and we
have generally used the method of probability weighted moments
(PWM) (ref.12). This has been found to be robust and reliable,
and has the advantage that it does not put too much weight on the
extreme floods which may be outliers.

Having fitted the curve for the region, one more stage of
analysis can be carried out. This is to examine whether there is
appreciable variation between groups of sites within the region.
It is often found that small catchments produce more extreme
floods than large ones. The sites can be divided into two or more
groups on the basis of catchment area, and the distribution
fitted separately for each. If an appreciable difference is found
between the curves, then two or more regional flood frequency
distributions can be defined. To investigate this further, it is
also worthwhile to examine the individual site curves - these can
often be seen to fall into two rather different groups,
justifying the separation of the two groups of sites. Other
catchment characteristics, such as rainfall, are also sometimes
found to give useful separation of curves within a region.

Application of the regional method to a particular site

When these analyses have been completed, the results can be used
to produce flood estimates for particular sites in the region.
The MAF equation is used to determine the MAF, but, if observed

TABLE 2

Regions for which regional flood studies have been carried out

Study region	Number of stations	Station-years
Australia (Queensland)[*][1]	30	475
Brazil (Rio Grande do Sul)	57	1209
Czechoslovakia	16	774
Denmark	62	1946
Hungary & Yugoslavia[*]	12	348
India (Kerala)	76	1171
Indonesia (Java & Sumatra)	95	1009
Iran[*]	25	343
Jordan[*]	6	57
Kenya[*]	19	338
Korea[*]	24	542
Malawi	28	509
Papua New Guinea	50	450
Saudi Arabia & Yemen[*]	30	378
South Africa & Botswana	103	3884
Sri Lanka	13	280
Thailand (excl. southern peninsula)	109	2012
Togo & Benin	19	443
Zimbabwe[*][3]	68	1355
Arid and semi-arid areas worldwide[1]	162	3637
West Africa[2]	224	4200

[*]Study region covers only part of the country.
(Source: ref 7, except [1]ref 8, [2]ref 9, [3]ref 16)

flow data are available at the site or nearby, the MAF is calculated from these instead. The appropriate regional flood frequency curve is then applied to deduce the flood for the required return period. Unless there is an exceptionally long observed flow record at the site, the regional curve is preferred to a single site curve. In most cases no local flow data will be available and the application of the method is straightforward.

Examples of regional flood studies

We have used the methods described above to develop regional flood frequency curves for many different parts of the world. Table 2 lists some of the countries or regions that have been studied; in some cases the region studied comprised only part of the country, and this is indicated by an asterisk against the country name. We have only listed those regions for which there was reasonably good coverage of data. Thus the curves developed can be considered to give a reasonably good preliminary flood estimates for the specified regions. The table lists the number of stations and of station-years (the total of the number of years of data at the individual stations) for each region.

In addition to the conventionally defined regions, there is also a curve which was developed for warm arid and semi-arid areas worldwide, as discussed above. Another grouping was based on a much larger region than usual. This is for West Africa, and the study used much of the available data from Guinea in the west to Cameroon in the east. Within this region, sub-regions were defined, based both on geographical parts of the region and on groups defined by catchment area and by mean annual rainfall.

Some examples of the regional flood frequency curves are shown in figures 3 and 4. In figure 3 a selection of curves illustrate the range of results obtained. It was not found necessary to sub-divide the stations on the basis of catchment characteristics in these cases. The figure illustrates the result that drier regions typically have steeper curves than more humid areas. This cannot be taken as a universal rule, and some regions appear to be

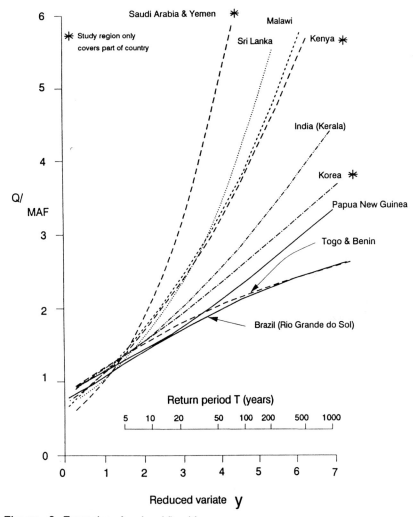

Figure 3 Examples of regional flood frequency curves

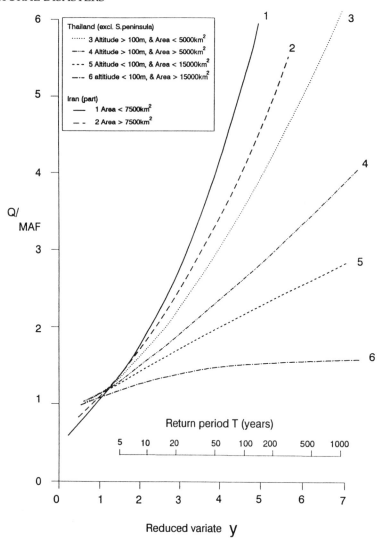

Figure 4   Examples of regional flood frequency curves for which stations
are divided into groups according to catchment characteristics

anomalous; for instance Sri Lanka, a relatively humid region, has
a rather steeper curve than might be expected.

In contrast to the regions in figure 3, a sub-division of the
catchments was needed for those in figure 4. For Iran a division
on catchment area was used. This illustrates the usual result
that small catchments have steeper curves than large ones. For
Thailand a more complex division was necessary; it was found that
the stations could be divided into two distinct groups: low-lying

areas near the coast, and those at higher altitudes. For convenience this division was taken as an altitude of 100 m at the gauging station. In the low-lying areas high discharges tend to flow out of the main channels into a network of subsidiary channels, producing a distinctly flat flood frequency curve. Within both of these two groups, a further sub-division was then defined on the basis of catchment area.

PART 2   FLOOD FORECASTING AND WARNING

There are situations where flood prevention by engineering methods is inappropriate, but it may be possible to reduce flood damage costs significantly through a combination of real-time flood forecasting and flood proofing measures.

Real-time flood forecasting involves collection of precipitation data over the catchment and of river levels and flows at a number of sites throughout the river system by telemetry. These data are used with mathematical models of the hydrological and hydraulic response of the river to produce short-term forecasts of discharges and resulting levels throughout the catchment. The observed river level or discharge data are used to provide a real-time self-correcting, or updating, facility for the models. Using modern computers, extremely sophisticated models may be run very rapidly to provide good quality forecasts of potential flood risk over the coming hours or days, depending upon the response time of the catchment. Telemetry data may be transmitted using radio, telephone or satellite, and weather radar can also provide valuable information on the spatial extent of rainfall. In other cases, rainfall estimates have been derived from cold cloud observations by satellite. When rain occurs, there is a significant time lag before river levels rise in the lower reaches of a river basin, and the bulk of the forecast lead time provided by real-time flood forecasting models is produced by this lag which varies with basin size. The forecast lead time may be extended through the use of rainfall forecasts, but the accuracy of such information can never be high.

The most widely used real-time flood forecasting system in Britain is the river flow forecasting system (RFFS), developed by the Institute of Hydrology (refs 13, 14). This software is written in a modular manner so that a suitable model configuration can easily be set up for any river basin, using an appropriate series of areal-rainfall, rainfall-runoff and hydraulic routing models, depending upon the data available and the required forecasting objectives. The system is currently applied to the Yorkshire region of the NRA, to a catchment in the Clyde Purification Board region, for the City of Lincoln and for a pilot study scheme in Hong Kong. The RFFS system takes inputs from both conventional telephone or radio telemetry and also from weather radar, and a series of short-term precipitation and storm-surge tide forecasts may also be used. One main advantage of the system is that the model configuration may be changed dynamically throughout a flood event. For example, when a flood situation develops in only a part of the river system, the RFFS allows the user to make forecasts and define a particular combination of models which is appropriate to this situation. This allows increased efficiency and speed of response.

NATURAL DISASTERS

Real-time flood forecasting cannot be applied directly to a catchment with no observed flow data, as models must be calibrated against recorded rainfall and flows. However systems can often be implemented very rapidly and after only a short period of data collection. They are also relatively cheap and very cost-effective. For example, the pilot scheme in Hong Kong is expected to have a payback period of about 10 years. If the intangible benefits of flood forecasting such as reduction in personal stress, ill-health and loss of life are also taken into account the payback period is reduced to only four years.

Flood forecasting indicates where flooding is likely within the next few hours or days. To be effective systems must be supported by means of warning the public, and people must be in a position to respond in a way that reduces flood damage. Not only can people leave the risk area, but given sufficient warning, farmers may move livestock and farm equipment to higher ground, and industry may be able to move stock and machinery in some circumstances. Schemes should involve a component for public education so that those at risk understand the types of warnings that may be issued, and know what responses the public services will make and how best to respond themselves.

A complementary means of reducing flood damage is through flood-proofing, where buildings are protected from incursion of flood waters, either through the construction of flood embankments around flood-prone areas, or through flood proofing individual buildings. Flood proofing will not always be feasible, but if hydrological analyses shows that particular buildings are flood-prone, modest expenditure on flood-proofing can often produce very dramatic savings in flood damage costs (ref. 15).

CONCLUSIONS

The regional flood frequency analysis approach (discussed in part 1) provides a means of estimating flood magnitudes which is particularly appropriate to developing countries. It provides the ability to estimate floods at long return periods, and in this it is generally more reliable than single site analysis. More importantly it provides a means of estimating at sites for which there are no flow data and it is also helpful when records are available at the site of interest. The method can be developed for areas where the flow data collection network is sparse and when the available records are short. The development of the methodology for a particular area requires a detailed examination of the available data and of the physical and climatic characteristics of the region, and is an exercise which requires considerable judgement on the part of the hydrologist. However, once the method has been developed it can be used to provide rapid estimates at a large number of sites. The method provides estimates which are adequate for many purposes, and only in detailed design of major projects or in cases where the complete flood hydrograph is needed are additional techniques required to supplement the analysis. The flood estimates provided are an essential input to any engineering solution or zoning approach to alleviating flooding problems.

We give examples of regional flood studies which have been carried out for a range of countries around the world, and these studies are continuing. We wish to take this opportunity to encourage individuals and organisations who would like a regional study to be carried out for a particular area to co-operate with us in providing sets of annual flood peak data and catchment characteristics information to be analysed.

The alternative approach to alleviating flooding problems is to use flood forecasting systems (discussed in part 2). This approach is valuable when engineering solutions are too expensive and the relocation of the vulnerable population is impracticable. Flood forecasting often provides a cost-effective means of minimising flood risk and associated flood damage costs. Because they can be implemented rapidly, and relatively cheaply, real-time flood forecasting schemes may well offer a better means of reducing flood risk in developing countries than traditional engineering solutions. Systems must be complemented by well structured dissemination systems; the public must be warned of imminent flooding in a timely manner and must have been educated on what actions to take.

REFERENCES

1. BERZ G., 1992. Munich Re's list of major natural disasters in 1990. Natural Hazards, 5, 95-102.

2. STILLWELL H.D., 1992. Natural hazards and disasters in Latin America. Natural Hazards, 6, 131-159.

3. NATURAL ENVIRONMENT RESEARCH COUNCIL, 1975. Flood Studies Report, 5 vols.

4. SUTCLIFFE J.V., 1980. Use of the Flood Studies Report overseas. Flood Studies Report - Five Years On, Inst. Civ. Engrs. Conf., Manchester, 7-11.

5. HOSKING J.R.M. and WALLIS J.R., 1988. The effect of intersite dependence on regional flood frequency analysis. Water Resour. Res., 24, 588-600.

6. WILTSHIRE S.E., 1985. Grouping basins for regional flood frequency analysis. Hydr. Sci. J., 30, 151-159.

7. FARQUHARSON F.A.K., GREEN C.S., MEIGH J.R. and SUTCLIFFE J.V., 1987. Comparison of flood frequency curves for many different regions of the world. In Regional Flood Frequency Analysis, ed. V.P. Singh, Reidel, 223-256.

8. FARQUHARSON F.A.K., MEIGH J.R. and SUTCLIFFE J.V., 1992. Regional flood frequency analysis in arid and semi-arid areas. J. Hydrology, 138, 487-501.

9. FARQUHARSON F.A.K., MEIGH J.R. and SUTCLIFFE J.V., 1993. Statistiques de la crue régionale en Afrique de l'Ouest, Hydrologie Continentale (in press).

10. ACREMAN M.C. and FARQUHARSON F.A.K., 1992. Flood frequency of the world's largest catchments. 3rd Int. Conf. on Floods and Flood Management, 145-156.

11. INSTITUTE OF HYDROLOGY, 1983. Flood Design Manual for Java and Sumatra. Report to Directorate General of Water Resources Development, Ministry of Public Works, Indonesia.

12. HOSKING J.R.M., WALLIS J.R. and WOOD E.F., 1984. Estimation of the generalized extreme value distribution by the method of probability weighted moments. Technometrics, 27, 251-261.

13. MOORE R.J., JONES D.A., BIRD P.M. and COTTINGHAM M.L., 1990. A basin-wide flood forecasting system for real-time flood warning, river control and water management. Int. Conference on River Flood Hydraulics, ed. W.R. White, Wiley, 21-30.

14. MOORE R.J. and JONES D.A., 1991. A river flow forecasting system for region-wide application. Conference of River Engineers, 8-10 July 1991, Loughborough University.

15. SMITH D.I. and HANDMER J.W. (eds.), 1986. Flood warning in Australia. Centre for Research and Environmental Studies, Canberra.

16. INSTITUTE OF HYDROLOGY, 1986. Flood estimates for Mazwikadei dam, Zimbabwe. Report to C.M.C. di Ravenna, Italy.

27. Windstorm model with applications to risk management

A. BOISSONNADE, Lawrence Livermore National Laboratory, USA, and W. DONG, Risk Management Software, USA

ABSTRACT

This paper presents the results of a sponsored applied research project conducted by a multi-disciplinary team to integrate state-of-the-art methods in wind and collateral (e.g., surge, wave, precipitation) hazard assessment and vulnerability prediction to assess hurricane risk to properties. The team, directed by Risk Management Software Inc., comprised researchers from universities and the risk management industry, insurance actuaries, management and financial risk consultants, and system analysts. The project team developed a methodology to assess losses to individual and groups of properties due to hurricanes, and to analyze these losses within the various financial frameworks utilized by risk managers. The methodology was developed to be flexible enough so it can be used with various levels of information on the exposed properties and their environment. For this reason, innovative tools were developed to access national geographically-digitized datasets and to distill them into usable formats. This methodology has been implemented in a PC-based Windows environment computer program and the results are presented as probability distribution curves of monetary losses over entire or selected regions, for all or selected types of properties. In addition, the methodology is flexible enough to study the propagation of financial risks to third parties such as reinsurers. An application is included as demonstration of the methodology and the type of results obtained.

INTRODUCTION

Natural disasters such as hurricanes occur every year. Each year, on the average, 100 tropical storms form in the world. About two-thirds of them grow into hurricanes, typhoons or cyclones. Of these storms 12% occur in the Western Atlantic ocean (3.3/year) and an average number of about 2 hurricanes make landfall each year along the U.S. coasts in the Gulf of Mexico and North Atlantic [1]. Of all natural hazards, hurricanes are the major contributor of catastrophic losses. Losses resulting from hurricanes are numerous and can be categorized as follows:

> Life and injury
> Property damage (structures and contents)
> Business interruption
> Other losses (economic and political implications).

NATURAL DISASTERS

Generally speaking, the more intense the storm is, the more extensive damage results. The Saffir-Simpson intensity scale is used to rate hurricanes and a summary of the storm characteristics plus observed and assumed coastal destruction values that are associated with each of the five intensity categories can be found in References [1] and [3].

Although intense hurricanes have landfalled on the U.S. coasts regularly, their consequences in terms of property damage have increased over the years. This trend has been vividly demonstrated in recent years with the damaging impacts of Hugo in 1989 and again of Andrew in 1992. Andrew wrought unprecedented economic devastation along a path through the northwestern Bahamas, the southern Florida peninsula, and south-central Louisiana. Southern part of Dade County, Florida, was particularly hit with peak gusts in excess of 160 mph, characteristics of a category 4 (on the Saffir-Simpson Scale) hurricane [2]. Andrew caused total damage assessed to be between $20 and $25 billion, with most of the damage occurring in Florida, making it the most expensive natural disaster in U.S. history.

Fortunately, Andrew was not the most devastating hurricane in terms of human losses. As of September 1992, a total number of 62 killed people was reported [2]. However, the number of disrupted lives was considerable. In Dade County, Florida, alone, this hurricane left up to 250,000 people homeless. The relatively low number of casualties is attributed to good hurricane preparedness and evacuation program [2]. Such an event in countries with poor hurricane preparedness would have likely resulted in thousand (or even hundreds of thousand [4]) casualties and could have caused economic disruptions on a scale that could effect the social stability of these nations.

While the number of hurricane casualties has decreased since the early 1900's in the United States as hurricane warning procedures and evacuation planning have improved, property damage has increased. The reasons for this increase are two fold [5,6]: the recent population and construction boom in the affected regions (a 400% increase in population along Florida coasts between 1950 and 1985), and inadequate urban planning and construction requirements.

For a long time, many organizations did not know how feasible it was to manage hurricane risk. The reasons for this are similar to those regarding how to manage earthquake risk [7]. They include the unpredictable nature of the event (occurrence and intensity), the perception that structures cannot resist hurricanes, and the inadequate technology to cost-effectively quantify the risk and its potential consequences.

Hurricane risk can be managed like any other risk by knowing as much as possible about the risk, its causes and consequences on the human lives and properties exposed to such a risk. This process is well known to risk managers and, in particular to the insurance industry. Prior to Hugo, the insurance industry was concerned with the occurrence over a small period of time of several multi-billion dollar damaging hurricanes in the United States [8] and methodologies were developed to assess impacts of catastrophic events (for example [9] and [10]).

Unfortunately, the knowledge necessary to assess the potential impacts of hurricanes needs to be retrieved from the technical expertise accumulated in diverse fields such as

332

meteorology and wind engineering; expertise which are fragmented, expensive to retrieve, and not readily available to the risk manager.

In addition, the paucity of information about the characteristics of the properties at risk (type, quality, value, surrounding topography, distance to coast, etc.) produces a challenge to this type of analysis due to the site-specific nature of damage. The development of tools to assist in the closing of this information gap requires both the existence of large national geographically-oriented datasets and the ability to access and distill them into usable formats. Only recently has technology brought both elements into being.

This paper presents a methodology developed by a multi-disciplinary team to create a hurricane risk model which brings update information to risk managers. The general approach is first presented, followed by a description of the different wind hazard and vulnerability models. Applications and an example are then presented.

GENERAL APPROACH

This study began in an effort to deal with 2 major questions: (1) How much damage would be done to individual or groups of properties due to hurricanes for which characteristics are known. The hurricane may be selected from a data base of historical hurricanes having occurred in the region under study or simulated from a selection of storms likely to occur in the area. (2) How much damage would be expected in given regions knowing the hurricane environment and financial risk structure of the exposed properties.

The first question deals with deterministic events because the characteristics of the storms are given prior to performing the analysis. The second question is stochastic in nature because of the randomness in the occurrence and nature of the events to be considered.

The primary technical objectives during the development of the methodology were:

1. The methodology should use state-of-the art analytical approaches to assess hurricane risk.

2. The methodology should maintain data information consistent with other types of risk analyses.

3. The methodology should account for all hazards associated with hurricanes and report to the user the impact of each one.

4. The methodology should remain flexible to be applicable on a site by site or a regional basis without excessive computational or input requirements.

5. The methodology should provide best available by-default information on hazards, property characteristics, and their vulnerability on a site-specific or regional basis to insure a level of consistency between analyses.

5. The methodology should accommodate a variety of input and output formats, and a variety of types of analyses.

6. The models should utilize site-specific information, either available from the user or from relevant data bases.

7. The models should propagate uncertainty at each step of the analysis and provide an assessment of this uncertainty in the output.

These objectives dictated the choice of an overall system architecture which could accommodate the use of various models and extensive library of data bases without impeding the performance of the analysis. For these reasons the system comprises three blocks: User Interface and Data Capture, Individual Peril Models, and Financial Risk Models.

The user interface module must be very flexible because it allows the user to enter different levels of information on the properties for which hurricane risk is assessed. Property characteristics may include precise location, value, age, and physical characteristics. On the other end, they may consist of regional aggregated values of properties characterized by social functions (for example, residential, non residential) or lines of business (for example commercial marine).

Depending upon the level of information provided, the procedure is to identify all relevant information to the properties as a function of the regions they are located within. To perform this task, extensive GIS data bases have been collected or developed. These data bases are used to provide site specific information to the user (graphics or tables) prior to performing the analysis.

For each of the hazards associated with hurricanes, and for which reliable state-of-the-art analysis techniques are available, the model performs an assessment of the hazard and of the risk, given the vulnerability characteristics of the structures defined in the input process.

In parallel to the hurricane hazard and structural characteristics, the financial risk characteristics of the properties are entered. These characteristics may vary with the case under study. They may simply consist of the total value of each property or the financial terms and conditions attached to the financial risk approach being considered.

HAZARDS

Hurricane systems can bring a variety of associated hazards beyond high pressure winds. In some historical cases, these collateral hazards have been far more costly and deadly than the direct effects of the storm itself. These hazards include: storm surge and waves, local flooding, missiles, and tornadoes or very localized highly turbulent wind conditions.

Storm surge and waves: Due to wind and pressure effects of hurricane events, the sea level becomes elevated beyond normal heights. Given the appropriate bathymetric conditions, a dramatic increase in sea level can occur. Wind-driven waves are added perils to structures close to the ocean.

Precipitation, local flooding: Rainwater, a meteorological characteristic of all hurricanes, is a double threat to structures. Once the structure's integrity has been compromised (windows broken, roof stripped, etc.), rainwater is free to enter the structure and damage its walls, ceilings, and contents, as has been often observed [6]. Local flooding is a second peril resulting from hurricane downpours. Even flood water levels of one or two feet can be causes of extensive damage to basements and contents.

Missiles: Although this peril is mainly associated with tornadoes, it is recognized that under the extreme winds of hurricanes, small objects can easily become airborne missiles and potential leading sources of extensive damage. These missiles can be naturally occurring objects, such as twigs, stones, and branches. Often, they are deadly pieces of failed constructions, such as roof shingles, pieces of glass, and plywood. These missiles can dramatically increase the damage of many structures and can initiate the failure of key elements, such as windows, alls, and roofs, resulting in more damage due to other hazards.

Tornadoes: Spotted observations of tornado-like phenomena have been observed during periods of extreme winds. Although their impact is very dramatic, they are localized and are poorly understood phenomena yet.

HURRICANE PERIL

Estimation of hurricane peril due to all hazards is a critical part of the hurricane risk model. The approach chosen in this study to model hurricane peril is two-fold. Sophisticated models have been developed to locally assess hazards due to wind and surge effects. However, there is yet not enough body of evidence to suggest that it is possible to model with relative confidence hazards associated with other perils. Therefore, these hazards are modeled as "modifiers," that is parameters which affect the hurricane risk as function of the hurricane-prone regions and storm parameters.

Wind Hazard: Wind hazard is represented by maximum wind speed and duration of the wind speed above a critical level, judged to be representative of the domain in which damage may occur. Wind speed is defined as peak gust, a wind speed averaged over 2 to 5 seconds.

Although several models have been developed for assessing extreme wind hazards, only a few models consider all the relevant meteorological storm parameters. Until the early 1980's, most engineering models used somewhat empirical relationships between central pressure of the storms (the lowest barometric pressure within the storms) and maximum observed wind speeds. With the compilation of scientific observations during hurricanes, meteorologists have developed wind field models which can more accurately predict wind speeds and wind patterns at the surface. Such a wind field model was used to predict surface wind speed given the characteristics of the storm and local terrain conditions, which are:

Storm parameters

- Storm direction
- Pressure distribution and maximum observed wind speed
- Forward speed
- Radius to maximum wind
- Landfall location

Local conditions

- Location of the site with respect to the storm track

NATURAL DISASTERS

- Distance of the site from the coast
- Local topographic conditions

Most of the listed storm parameters are available from current data bases of historical hurricanes. Other parameters are obtained statistically from observations on a regional basis. Note that hurricane parameters vary with regions and therefore care is exercised to preserve this regional dependency.

Distance of a site from the coast is a major parameter in the wind speed assessment in the first few miles inland as the winds coming on-shore attenuate. For this reason data bases have been created to retrieve this parameter, should it not be available to the user.

Although winds are undeterred by ground-level-conditions (except in extreme conditions, such as mountain ranges), wind speeds experienced at ground and building heights can be dramatically influenced by local topographic conditions. In general the rougher the local surroundings, the more the friction acting on the surface winds, causing a relative slowing of those. Two distinct categories of topographic conditions are considered: natural roughness and man-made roughness. Within each category, different levels of roughness are considered. For each of these, data bases are created for all coastal areas based on existing national GIS data bases.

Extensive data validation was performed at all phases of the wind hazard model by validating and calibrating predicted wind speed values against officially confirmed observed wind speed values at specific locations by using hurricane-predicted wind maps. An example of such validation is presented in Figure 1. Similar maps are used to validate user-generated storms.

Surge hazard: Surge hazard is characterized by its hydrostatic effect (surge level) and hydrodynamic consequences due to wave actions. Most sophisticated surge models [11] include the following parameters:

- Meteorological storm characteristics
- Storm direction
- Bathymetric and topographic elevations
- Flood protection structures
- Tide levels

These models use extensive finite difference or finite element types of analyses. For the scope of this study, a relatively simplified surge model was developed, accounting for the impact of the above parameters and validated/calibrated against results obtained from state-of-the art surge models and observed historical data (See Figure 2).

Detailed data bases on topographic elevations and local surrounding terrain conditions are developed at different levels of resolution (down to 100 meters in coastal areas) to be retrieved by users prior to analysis. These data bases are also being used in assessing potential flooding locations during heavy rainfall.

The hurricane hazard models are used to assess hurricane risk due to deterministic and stochastic scenarios. Deterministic scenarios are defined as cases where the storm characteristics are defined prior to analysis. They include:

336

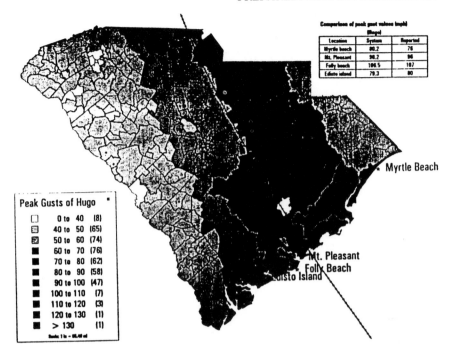

| Comparison of peak gust values (mph) |
| (Hugo) |

Location	System	Reported
Myrtle beach	80.2	76
Mt. Pleasant	98.2	96
Folly beach	106.5	107
Edisto island	79.3	80

Peak Gusts of Hugo

☐	0 to 40	(8)
	40 to 50	(65)
	50 to 60	(74)
■	60 to 70	(76)
■	70 to 80	(62)
■	80 to 90	(58)
■	90 to 100	(47)
■	100 to 110	(7)
■	110 to 120	(3)
■	120 to 130	(1)
■	> 130	(1)

Figure 1.   Model-Simulated Wind Speed; 1989 Hugo

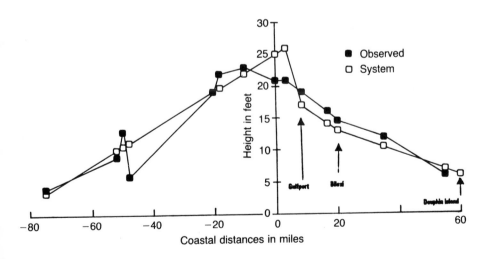

Figure 2.   Predicted versus Observed Surge levels; 1969 Camille

337

- Maximum historical storm
- Historical storm
- Modified historical storm
- Simplistic user-defined storm
- Complex user-defined storm

Storm characteristics may be defined prior to analysis by either selecting historical storms, specifying landfall location and storm intensity, or a detailed characterization of the storm parameters. For all scenarios, hurricanes are associated with a return period on the wind speeds they generate in a particular coastal area.

Stochastic scenarios are defined as cases where the randomness in hurricane occurrence, intensity, and location is modeled. The common approach is to use Monte Carlo simulation [12]. This approach is not adequate when the characteristics of the storms producing extreme winds need to be tagged and the dependency between coastal areas affected by the same storms need to be preserved. In addition, a large number of simulated storms are needed to consistently capture the randomness of the events. This is particularly important at the tail of the loss distribution used in assessing hurricane risk. For these reasons, a new methodology was developed in this project. Using the enhanced historical hurricane data bases, an exhaustive probabilistic modeling of the key characteristics of the storms was first performed for coastal segments. Then, an event tree approach was used to simulate hurricane characteristics at different locations of the coastline. Finally, storm paths were selected statistically from historical data bases using clustering analyses. In this fashion, it was possible to simulate the characteristics of the storms and their tracks.

Extensive comparisons of probabilities of exceeding wind speeds along the U.S. coast obtained with our methodology against results of previous methods (for example [12]) provided good agreement.

Results of stochastic analyses are used for estimates of annual expected losses, probability of exceeding given loss thresholds over time with confidence bounds, and expected maximum loss.

HURRICANE VULNERABILITY

Property vulnerability to various hurricane hazards is modeled in the methodology according to a variety of parameters. A summary of the inputs to building and content performance modeling is listed in Figure 3.

The methodology uses different classification types to match the different formats in which input data may be collected. Structures are either classified by social functions, structural type, or materials. Although there exist few relevant studies on wind vulnerability assessment of properties, there exist a large amount of untreated data which can be used to develop damage functions. However, to account for the multitude of situations, it is not feasible to assess vulnerability for detailed specifics. For this reason, hurricane vulnerability is assessed in a two-phase process.

First, generic damage functions have been developed for general classes of structures using input from past studies, wind engineering expert opinions, and available loss data. These

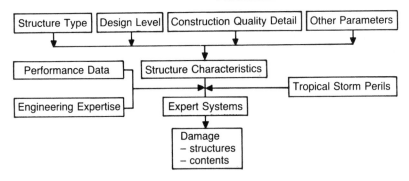

Figure 3. Performance Building Modeling

functions relate hurricane hazard values to damage ratio, defined as repair cost to total replacement cost, by specifying a mean value and an estimate of the variability about this mean value. Then, a series of modifiers have been identified based on past observations of hurricane damage. For each modifier, an assessment of their impact on mean damage ratio, and associated variability, of the generic damage functions has been performed using site-specific damage observations in different regions of the country over a broad band of structures.

Modifiers are classified into three types: site-specific dependent, region dependent, and hazard-dependent. Site-specific dependent modifiers include particular structural characteristics (e.g., roof type, anchoring, cladding, foundations) and equipment. Region-dependent modifiers include local construction practices and enforcement. Hazard-dependent modifiers quantify the increase or decrease in damage to properties as a function of the presence of certain levels of types of hazards (e.g., rain)

One of the innovative aspects in the hurricane vulnerability is the development of damage functions for contents. To this effect, the methodology models damage to contents as a function of the likelihood of the hurricane-induced hazards to physically reach contents and the sensitivity of these contents to those hazards, should they occur [13].

Extensive validation of the damage functions and modifiers are performed by comparing predicted damage with either damage assessed by engineering expertise or historical losses on a site and regional basis. Figure 4 displays a summary of damage ratios to wood frame structures during a rerun of hurricane Hugo.

FINANCIAL RISK

The methodology accommodates a multitude of financial situations within which losses are calculated. The simplest of all is the case where risk bearers carry all the risks incurred to the properties. The most complex of all is when risk bearers only carry a fraction of the property risk under complex agreements. Such a case might be one in which a fraction of the financial risk on properties is transferred to a third party, which in turn transfers a share of the risk to a fourth party, and so on (e.g. reinsurance). In such financial conditions, the

339

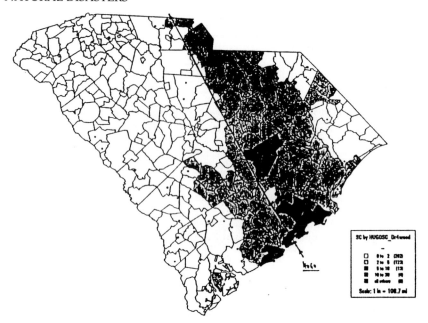

Figure 4.   Simulated Damage Ratio to Wood Frames, 1989 Hugo

methodology tracks individual parts of the total risk in the
financial loss calculations to each party.

APPLICATIONS AND DEMONSTRATION

Users are able to run a variety of loss analyses with the
model. Analyses will be either deterministic or stochastic, for
which models have been developed. The different user options
are:

Historical Storm Analysis: In this option, past hurricanes can
be run against a variety of exposed properties to identify their
impact. Maximum historical scenarios can be run to identify the
type of events which affect the most the properties under study.

User-defined Option: In this option the user can control the
type and level of hazard. Current or past events can be
recreated and "What-if" analyses can be made using storm
scenarios with specific input on the storms.

Average Risk Option: In this option, the system calculates
average losses given the exposed properties and their
characteristics over user-defined time windows.

Probability of Specified Loss Option: This option calculates the
probability of exceeding user-defined maximum losses associated
to given exposed properties over user-defined time window.
Conversely, given the probability of exceedance, the associated
maximum loss is assessed. In each case, the storms likely to
cause this level of loss are identified and can be rerun to
perform an uncertainty analysis.

For the purpose of demonstration, a hurricane risk assessment is being performed on an hypothetical population of structures in Florida, comprised of several thousand exposed properties for which individual locations are input (See Figure 5). In this particular case, it is assumed that the estimated total losses are presented in an aggregated format per zipcode.

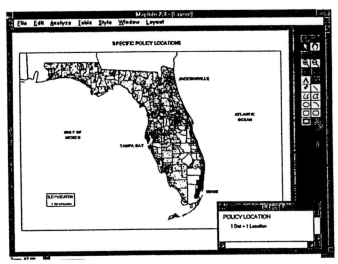

Figure 5.   Locations of Exposed Properties

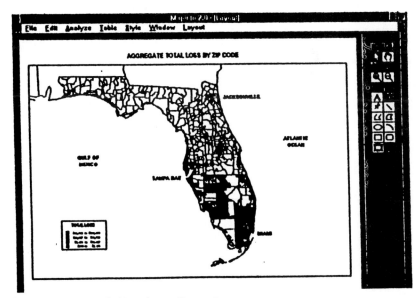

Figure 6.   Total Monetary Losses

NATURAL DISASTERS

The analysis option selected is to run a storm heading northwest landing near Miami. For each class of structures, damage ratios are assessed for all geographical locations. Hurricane hazards are first assessed and losses for each location are calculated. Total expected losses for the locations shown in Figure 5 are displayed in Figure 6. Tabular reports can be printed or stored in data bases for further analysis.

CONCLUSIONS

A procedure has been developed to assess hurricane risk in a systematic way by dealing with each individual component of the problem. These components are the hurricane hazards, the exposures at risk, and the consequences of the hazards on these exposures. For each of these components, state-of-the art information about hurricane occurrences, wind field models, surge models, structure characteristics, local topographic conditions, and behavior of structures was collected.

This procedure has been developed primarily for assessing financial losses to properties. However, it can be used to minimize risks whether high risk structures need to be identified or strengthening strategies need to be developed for such high risk structures.

Should it be hurricane or other hazards, the type of procedure described above provides a tool to help decision makers understand the risk and its relevance by properly informing them.

ACKNOWLEDGMENTS

The authors want to thank all the persons at Risk Management Software Inc. who contributed to this project. The first author, who is the technical director of the windstorm project, performed this study in affiliation with Risk Management Software, Inc. The authors acknowledge for their contributions Professor Alan Davenport and his staff at the University of Western Ontario, Canada, Professors Norris Stubbs and Dale Perry of Texas A&M University, and Professor Haresh Shah of Stanford University. Any opinions, findings, and conclusions expressed in this paper are those of the authors and do not necessarily reflect those of Risk Management Software, Inc.

REFERENCES

[1] Neumann, Charles, K. et al., "Tropical Cyclones of the North Atlantic Ocean, 1871-1986, with updates to 1990," Historical Climatology Series 6-2, National Climatic Data Center, Asheville, North Carolina, 1990.

[2] National Hurricane Center., " Preliminary Report (updated March 2, 1993) on Hurricane Andrew, 16-28 August 1992," National Hurricane Center, NOAA, southeast Regional Climate Center, 1993.

[3] Gray, Williams, M. and C.W. Landsea, " African Rainfall as a Precursor of Hurricane-Related Destruction on the U.S. East Coast," Bulletin of the American Meteorological Society, Vol. 73, No. 9, 1992.

[4] United Nations Centre for Regional Development, " Cyclone Damage in Bangladesh, Report on Field Study and Investigations on the Damage Caused by the Cyclone in

Bangladesh in 29-30 April, 1991," United Nations Centre for Regional Development, Nagoya, Japan, 1991.

[5] Sparks, Peter, R. "The Risk of Hurricane Wind Damage to Buildings in South Carolina, A White Paper," Coastal Hazards Advisory and Mitigation Project, Clemson University, 1990.

[6] Perry, Dale et al., "Hurricane Andrew-Preliminary Observations of WERC Post-Disaster Team," Wind Engineering Research Council, Inc., September 1992.

[7] Shah, Haresh, C. " Earthquake Risk Management Systems for Developing Countries," Colloquium on the Environment and Natural Disaster Management, Sponsored by the World Bank, Washington, D.C., 1990.

[8] All-Industry Research Advisory Council, "Catastrophic Losses, How the Insurance System Would Handle Two $7 Billion Hurricanes," All-Industry Research Advisory Council (renamed Insurance Research Council on 6/1990), November 1986, Oak Brook, Illinois.

[9] Friedman, Don G., "Natural Hazard Assessment for an Insurance Program," The Geneva papers on Risk and Insurance, Vol 9, No. 30, January 1984.

[10] Insurance Services Office, Inc., "Catastrophes: Accurately Projecting Losses," ISO Insurance Issues Series, December 1990.

[11] Jelesnianski Chester P., "SPLASH (Special Program to List Amplitudes of Surges from Hurricanes", NOAA Technical Memorandum NWS TDL-46, NWS, Silver Spring, MD, April 1972.

[12] Batts, Martin E. et al., "Hurricane Wind Speeds in the United States," NBS Building Science Series 124, National Bureau of Standards, may 1980.

[13] Stubbs, Norris and A. C. Boissonnade, "Damage Simulation Model for Building Contents in Hurricane Environment," Proceedings of the 7th U.S. National Conference on Wind Engineering, Los Angeles, CA, 1993.

28. A formalized decision-making procedure for the assessment of volcanic eruption threats using expert judgement

W. P. ASPINALL, Aspinall & Associates, UK, and G. WOO, BEQE Ltd, UK

SUMMARY

Volcanoes pose serious threats to life and to the socio-economic well-being of vulnerable nearby communities. Recent episodes have highlighted the serious difficulties and misunderstandings which can occur when, under great pressure and in the face of uncertainty, groups of working scientists endeavour to provide guidance on the possible course of future eruptive activity to political decision-makers or to the media. Often, straightforward consensus of opinion is not achievable; but publicly expressing contradictory scientific views can be confusing to the community at large and presents extra difficulties for officials anxious about public safety.

Once a volcano has come to life, any decision as to the level of threat is clouded by the profound degree of uncertainty in interpretation of the geophysical and geochemical processes being manifest. Given the present state of volcanological knowledge, the academic Earth scientist might prefer to reserve his opinion, yet the practical and ethical demands of decision-making in a potential life-threatening situation requires that his expert judgement is exercised. Although often not recognised as the case in the Earth sciences, use of expert judgement in such circumstances is implicit but is rarely, if ever, elicited in any structured way. As a result, opinions are susceptible to unexpressed biases; these may comprise excessive conservatism, particularly when responsibility for decisions falls publicly on one or two individuals, or even publicity-seeking exaggerations of impending cataclysmic violence.

High-consequence decision-making in the presence of uncertainty is a problem in many enterprises, such as space flight engineering, and techniques for the elicitation of expert judgement in such situations have recently been developed, based on the concept of an optimal "decision-maker", constructed out of the weighted judgements of a selected set of individual experts. The weights are assigned through a calibration procedure to test the informativeness and impartiality of individuals in making their judgements. A computer program is used to calculate the findings of the optimal decision-maker, the superiority of which over traditional methods of pooling expert opinions has been demonstrated in several trials, including meteorological forecasting exercises.

This impartial aid to critical decision-making would be very beneficial in the context of volcano hazard assessment because individual scientists would feel encouraged to state their true scientific opinions, which would not be quoted directly but would be incorporated as factors in the optimal decision-maker. With this formalised procedure, the views of all

Natural disasters. Thomas Telford, London, 1993

contributing experts can be taken properly into account, and unhelpful influences, such as publicity or personality conflicts, can be nullified. The workings of the procedure for eliciting expert judgements are illustrated in an hypothetical example of a volcanic crisis.

INTRODUCTION

In the last twenty years, the roles of Earth scientists in dealing with the threats posed to vulnerable communities by volcanic eruptions have been highlighted by a number of controversial and disastrous events. The violent and erratic nature of volcanoes has been accentuated by large losses of life amongst civilian populations and, recently, by the tragic deaths of a number of volcanologists whilst working in the field. Scientists who struggle to provide local communities with appropriate warnings of impending eruption, so that protective measures may be taken by the civil authorities, will not be encouraged in their endeavours by the apparent increasing trend to hold them legally responsible, even unto threat of imprisonment, for failure to predict an outbreak of activity (see, for example, ref. 1).

The difficulty of providing helpful advice to political authorities and the press, in the middle of a volcanic crisis and in the face of scientific uncertainty, was exemplified in 1976 by the evacuation of the population from around the Soufrière volcano in Guadeloupe, in the French West Indies, when abnormal seismic activity and steam venting developed near the summit of the mountain. During and after the episode, the volcanological arguments for and against the costly evacuation were topics of serious contention, and considerable acrimony, leading eventually to the French authorities convening an international scientific committee of enquiry into the issues.

The proper role of the Earth scientist, in such circumstances, was also discussed editorially and in correspondence in the literature (e.g. refs. 2 - 10), and included a call for the establishment of a deontological code (that is, a code of moral duty or obligation) to guide professional volcanologists. In the debate, the problems and pitfalls of attempting to present differing scientific interpretations and opinions to the public authorities were recognised, with at least one contributor (e.g. ref. 8) arguing the case for adopting a probabilistic basis for volcanic hazard assessment. Since the time of the Guadeloupe affair, significant strides have been made in hazard assessment methodologies: the basic meaning of probability in science has come under increasing scrutiny (see, for example, ref. 11) and, within the modern Bayesian paradigm, the very notion of objective probability is now dismissed as illusory. In investigating the reasonableness of modes of thought and behaviour under conditions of uncertainty, all that can be demanded is consistency among beliefs, and a rational relationship to objective data. It has been shown theoretically (ref. 12) that there is no essential distinction between probability assignments based on numerical frequencies and those based on judgements: both can be incorporated into a computation of hazard if the correct procedures are adopted.

Within this new, pragmatic framework, the role of expert opinion is central to the underlying formalism, especially where data are very sparse or very low probabilities of exceedance are being considered; in either case, extreme but plausible hypotheses which lack empirical support may have to be entertained. For decision-making, various methods have been devised to synthesise expert judgements through opinion pools, which are weighted combinations of individual judgements.

Observational monitoring of volcanoes has the important safety function of providing a factual basis for a real-time appraisal of the risks of eruptions and associated hazards, but any decision as to the current level of threat is clouded by the profound degree of uncertainty in

345

the interpretation of conditions which may give rise to life-threatening eruptions. At the purely scientific level, certain categories of volcanic outburst may be associated with a prior build-up of activity, but others may give only minimal premonitory signals of their development; prior knowledge of the history of eruptive patterns at the individual volcano, its geochemical features, and current indications of its seismic state, deformation, heat output and so on, can help, but their contributions to a prognosis are inexact. Given the present state-of-the-art, the academic Earth scientist might well prefer to reserve his judgement and await the outcome of the situation.

Yet the obvious demands of decision-making for protecting vulnerable communities requires that this expert judgement be exercised and, as is often the case in such circumstances, use of expert judgement is traditionally accepted as implicit, and not elicited in any structured way. Because of the absence of any formal procedure for the elicitation of expert judgement, results are susceptible to bias, particularly if the responsibility for making decisions falls on one or two individuals. On the other hand, the common practice of simply averaging the judgements of several individual experts fails to discriminate between them on any grounds, even though reason may exist to suspect the value of some of their opinions. Concern over simplistic methods of aggregating expert judgements leads on to the consideration of methods which involve some calibration of experts.

The issue of decision-making in the presence of uncertainty is a common problem in many areas of risk assessment: cancelling a space flight, for example, is a high-consequence high-profile decision and techniques for the elicitation of expert judgement in situations of great uncertainty have recently been developed for the European Space Agency (ref. 13). These are based on the concept of an optimal decision-maker, constructed numerically out of the weighted judgements of a selected set of specialist individuals with expertise in a variety of relevant disciplines. In the case of a volcanic crisis, seismologists, geologists, geodeticists, geochemists and geophysicists would be among those likely to be involved. The weights are assigned through a calibration procedure to test the informativeness and reliability of individuals in making their judgements and a computer program, EXCALIBR (ref. 14) can be used to implement the construction of the optimal decision-maker.

MATHEMATICAL FORMALISM

A salutary lesson learned from the elicitation of expert judgement in the context of risk analysis is that, however well qualified they may be, experts differ widely in their abilities to estimate parameter values and associated confidence bands. Some experts may be poorly calibrated, in the sense that their median estimates may be consistently biased and discordant with reality. Other experts may be over-confident in their views, in the sense that they assign unwarranted narrow uncertainty bands on their median estimates; still other experts may be uninformative, in the sense that they assign such broad, cautious uncertainty bands that little useful information is conveyed.

Recently, an elegant mathematical approach has been devised by Cooke to calibrate expert judgements (ref. 15). This method overcomes many of the technical difficulties which have beset previous attempts, while being convenient and efficient for practical use. In Cooke's approach, each expert is asked to assess the values of a range of quantiles for a given set of calibration parameters, as well as for the parameters of actual interest. An optimal decision-maker is then constructed on the basis of the performance of the experts on the calibration parameters. This construction is based on the mathematical theory of scoring rules to gauge the quality of experts. Although such scoring has been developed into a systematic way of rewarding the positive aspects of expert judgement, and is implicit in any modern performance-based human assessment, it was first conceived as a way of eliciting probabilities for rare events which could not be appraised by conventional statistical techniques.

The mathematical formalism is as follows:

Let q_e (e=1,2,...E) be the distribution of the E experts whose judgements are elicited for an uncertain parameter. Then if p_A denotes the analyst's distribution:

$$p_A = \sum w_e\, q_e \; ; \quad \text{where} \; \sum w_e = 1, w_e \geq 0. \tag{1}$$

For the discrete case, where a quantity can take n values, the entropy $H(p)$ is defined to indicate the lack of information in the distribution:

$$H(p) = -p_i \ln(p_i) \tag{2}$$

If s is a probability distribution over the same n values, the relative information of s with respect to p can be defined as:

$$I(s,p) = s_i \ln(s / p_i) \tag{3}$$

$I(s,p)$ is always non-negative, and $I(s,p) = 0$ if, and only if, s is identically equal to p. $I(s,p)$ is commonly taken as an index of the information learned (sometimes referred to as the index of surprise) if one initially believes p, and later learns s is correct.

Let $X_1, X_2,...X_M$ be the set of calibration variables; let $X_{M+1}, X_{M+2},....X_N$ be the variables of actual interest; let $f_1, f_2,....f_R$ be the quantile probabilities elicited and let G_{me} be the minimum information cumulative distribution for X_m, defined as the distribution for which the entropy is as large as possible, and which satisfies the constraint that the f_i quantile values agree with the assessments of expert e.

Indices of calibration and informativeness of expert e's assessments, respectively $C(e)$ and $H(e)$, can then be defined (ref. 15) in terms of $I(s,p)$ and G_{me}, and a corresponding weight w_e can be attributed to expert e according to the formula:

$$w_e \propto I_\alpha\,[C(e)] \cdot \{C(e)/H(e)\} \tag{4}$$

where $I_\alpha[C]$ = 0 if $C < \alpha$
$\quad\quad\quad\quad\quad$ = 1 if $C \geq \alpha$

The parameter α may be chosen to optimise the analyst's distribution p_A in equation [1]. With this definition, the weight assigned to expert e increases with the calibration index $C(e)$, and decreases with $H(e)$.

The availability of the free parameter α to optimise the analyst's distribution in a manifestly impartial manner, avoids critical judgement of the quality of individual experts, who might otherwise be self-conscious over public accountability. In practical applications, the calibration term $C(e)$ can vary over three orders of magnitude for a reasonably large group of experts, whereas the informativeness index $H(e)$ rarely varies by a factor greater than about three. There is a natural trade-off between calibration and informativeness: an expert can achieve good calibration by being uninformative. However, high informativeness is not a substitute for poor calibration and, in Cooke's scheme, informativeness modulates the calibration term, providing a quantitative means of distinguishing between experts of similar calibration.

This aid to decision-making would be very useful in the context of volcanic hazard assessment, for example, because experts could be encouraged to give their true opinions, which would not be attributed to them directly, but would be incorporated into judgements of the optimal decision-maker. Without this type of formal procedure, the adoption of traditional methods of gauging uncalibrated opinions may result in over-conservative biases which tend to arise when individual decisions are subject to external tensions. The algorithm is suitable for use in decision-making in other Earth sciences applications, such as earthquake hazard assessment (ref. 16) and mining safety (ref. 17).

APPLICATION TO AN HYPOTHETICAL VOLCANIC CRISIS

Suppose there to be a volcano, Volcan Inconnu, which has started showing signs of abnormal activity, and that a significant population lives in close propinquity to it. The local authorities are concerned about the hazards of eruption and can call on the advice of three Earth scientists stationed locally: say, a geologist (Harry), a seismologist (Tom) and a geochemist (Fred). Suppose also that the authorities are prepared to supplement this expertise by inviting three external specialists, Snowy, Jock and Dick, each of whom has experience in eruptions elsewhere, to participate in monitoring developments at the mountain. Of these six experts, perhaps two have real knowledge of Volcan Inconnu, such as its record of eruptive behaviour, the composition of its products or its recent history of seismic activity; the others, however, can bring extensive experience, in their own different disciplines, from other volcanoes and eruption sequences. The government has to decide whether or not to evacuate the vulnerable community, and needs as much time as possible to marshall its resources.

The key issue is how to extract a rational, unbiased assessment of the hazard posed by the volcano from the varied opinions of the experts. If the authorities were to rely solely on the opinion of the senior local man, they would effectively place an undue onus of responsibility on this individual for the eventual outcome of the episode; inevitably, this state of affairs must powerfully influence how he appraises and articulates his scientific opinion and those of his colleagues. On the other hand, if a suitable capability were available for synthesizing the experts' opinions, then an impartial measure of their consensus could be provided to the decision-makers.

For the purposes of this illustrative example, the experts are asked to anticipate the Volcanic Explosivity Index (VEI - see ref. 18) of the biggest explosion from Volcan Inconnu each day, up to six days ahead; the VEI is a logarithmic scale for volcanic eruptions, akin to a magnitude scale for earthquakes. (The experts could have been invited to predict the probability that fresh magma is ejected, the silica content of new material, the height of eruption column, the direction of flow of a nuée ardente (glowing avalanche), the volume of tephra airfall deposit, the greatest run of lahar (volcanic mudflow) or any number of other variables).

The formal elicitation of the experts' opinions would proceed as follows. An independent facilitator is needed to perform the calibration and conduct the elicitation. He must have a detailed understanding of the proper procedures for eliciting expert opinion and must be sufficiently cognisant with the science that he can understand the technical issues, even though he himself may have only limited experience in the subject. The experts would be provided with seed information from small datasets from a limited number of case histories from elsewhere (five fictitious volcanoes are used here) for which empirical results, termed realizations, are available (Cooke stresses the importance of keeping the calibration questionnaires brief and to the point); they are also presented with current data for the situation at Volcan Inconnu. The datasets could comprise any combination of seismic, geochemical and geodetic information, eruptive patterns from previous episodes, volumes of material ejected, rates of output, heat flow measurements, steam output and gas content, and so on. It would not matter unduly if some individual experts were personally familiar with the outcomes of some of the calibration cases, or if the datasets were incomplete in some aspects.

For each case, the expert would be invited to provide his lower 5%, 50% (median) and upper 95% values for VEI over the next six days, these quantile estimates being a convenient way of representing a probability distribution for the parameter being considered. Where an individual's degree of belief is vague, his probability distributions will tend to be broad and hence uninformative; where his degree of belief is full of conviction, his probability distributions will be peaked and informative. If, in the latter case, the expert's median value is close to the empirical result he will be well calibrated, if not, then his opinion is over-confident and may be significantly in error. Examples of inter-expert variation in the estimation of an arbitrary parameter are shown in Figure 1; the parameter has an expected value of 2.0.

The experts' estimates for the test cases are assembled and input to the computer program, for comparison with the five known realizations. The experts' indices of calibration and informativeness are quantified and these are then used to construct the optimal decision-maker. In the simulated example which follows, the quantity being assessed is the maximum VEI at two future time periods: 2 days ahead and 4 days ahead. The scoring results of the experts for the five test cases are given on Tables 1 and 2 for the two periods. For Day 2, Experts 1, 2 and 3 are equally well calibrated with Expert 3 (Fred) providing the most information and, hence, gaining the highest weighting in constructing the optimal Decision-Maker for this interval. The Decision-Maker is better calibrated than any individual expert.

The ranges of the experts' input values for the test cases for Day 2, the empirical realization ("Real") and the estimate given by the optimal Decision-Maker ("DM") for each case are depicted on the Input Data Range Graph on Figure 2. In most trial cases, Experts 4 and 6 either overestimate the VEI, or provide estimates of such wide uncertainty that they are uninformative and, as a consequence, the judgements of these experts are weighted out of the decision-making process.

There is some change in the scoring of the experts when they are asked to forecast further ahead to Day 4; the scoring results from the trial cases are summarised in Table 2. Now, only Experts 2 and 3 (Tom and Fred) are well calibrated with Tom providing more information than Fred for this longer range forecast, thus gaining the highest weighting in the construction of the Decision-Maker. Note that Expert 6 (Dick) appears to provide more information than the others but he is so poorly calibrated than he achieves a zero weighting in the decision-making process.

The calibre of the inputs provided by the experts, as exemplified by their ranges for the test cases on Figure 2, can be summarised: Experts 1, 2 and 3 produce helpful guidance on the problem; Expert 5 is very cautious in his opinion and contributes only at very low weighting to the assessment; Experts 4 and 6 rarely match the realizations in the tests, even with their extreme quantiles, and are, therefore, very poorly calibrated. On the strength of these scorings, it might be suggested that mythical Experts 4 and 6 would be better employed doing the cooking!

349

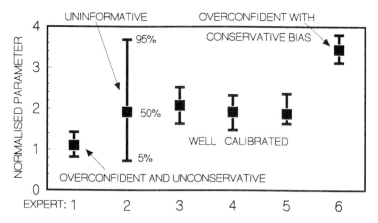

Fig. 1. Typical inter-expert variation in 5%, 50% and 95% estimates of a parameter

The solutions provided by the optimal Decision-maker are also recorded on Tables 1 and 2. VEI values are normally expressed as whole numbers but the results are given here to one place of decimals to allow comparisons to be made with the estimates obtained by the optimal Decision-Maker for the calibration cases. For Day 2, the median quantile evaluated by the Decision-Maker indicates a VEI = 2.2, with lower (5%) and upper (95%) quantiles of VEI = 0.5 and VEI = 5.9; this implies that the Decision-Maker expects the explosivity of Volcan Inconnu to be much less than any of the trial cases at the same elapsed time period. The Decision-Maker's expected figure for Day 4 is VEI = 5.0, with lower and upper quantiles of VEI = 2.1 and VEI = 7.9 respectively. Note that the latter median value is much higher than the earlier, and more violent than two of the trial cases, implying that the Decision-Maker expects the violence of the eruption to increase with time; the enlarged uncertainty manifest in the later forecast accurately reflects the increased collective apprehension of the experts in forecasting over a longer timescale. (It should also be recalled that the VEI is a logarithmic scale so these differences would be very large in practice).

From an inspection of Item 6 (target volcano) on the Input Data Range Graph (Figure 2), it can be seen that it would be very difficult to discern a clear consensus on the current situation from the experts' opinions, notwithstanding the coarse discretization and broad intervals of the VEI scale. If the expert opinions were simply aggregated with equal weights (a traditional but now discredited approach), the means for the two cases would be VEI = 2.9 and VEI = 4.7, respectively; the first is 0.7 of a unit of explosivity more alarmist than the Decision-Maker (equivalent to a factor of more than 5x in output of ejecta), whereas the second instance is 0.3 less (equivalent to half the predicted output). In the absence of the optimal Decision-Maker, such disparities could easily result in over-conservative decisions to meet the hazard on Day 2 whereas the risk on Day 4 may be inadequately perceived.

The solutions computed by the Decision-Maker would be the most appropriate values to set before the authorities for political decision-making or for broadcasting to the media; comparisons with the calibration eruptions could be used to set the estimates in context.

Table 1. Results of scoring experts and decision-maker's solution for day 2 of sequence

Case name : VOLCAN INCONNU - DAY 2   29. 3.93   CLASS system

Results of scoring experts.
Weights : global.   DM optimisation : yes.
Significance level : 0.060   Calibration power :   1.0

Expert name	Calibr.	Mean rel.infor. total	realiz.	Number realiz.	UnNorm. weight	Normalized weight no DM	with DM
1 HAL	0.32000	0.553	0.474	5	0.15177	0.31857	0.27083
2 TOM	0.32000	0.376	0.392	5	0.12529	0.26298	0.22357
3 FRED	0.32000	0.608	0.541	5	0.17298	0.36309	0.30868
4 SNOWY	0.00100	0.678	0.684	5	0	0	0
5 JOCK	0.06000	0.476	0.440	5	0.02638	0.05537	0.04707
6 DICK	0.04000	0.495	0.521	5	0	0	0
DM	0.73000	0.130	0.115	5	0.08397		0.14984

Resulting solution (combined DM distribution of values assessed by experts)

Item name	Quantiles of solution 5 %	50 %	95 %	Scale
1 MT ST SWITHIN	2.16	5.32	7.86	U
2 CERRO BRUJO	1.29	4.24	6.56	U
3 SAKE-JIMA	0.46	3.73	5.87	U
4 LYNFA MONS	0.53	4.39	7.25	U
5 MORNE MERDE	1.97	4.31	5.96	U
VOLCAN INCONNU	0.54	2.19	5.93	U

Table 2. Results of scoring experts and decision-maker's solution for day 4 of sequence

Case name : VOLCAN INCONNU - DAY 4   29. 3.93   CLASS system

Results of scoring experts.
Weights : global.   DM optimisation : yes.
Significance level : 0.730   Calibration power :   1.0

Expert name	Calibr.	Mean rel.infor. total	realiz.	Number realiz.	UnNorm. weight	Normalized weight no DM	with DM
1 HAL	0.04000	0.606	0.528	5	0	0	0
2 TOM	0.73000	0.662	0.772	5	0.56372	0.59220	0.42614
3 FRED	0.73000	0.511	0.532	5	0.38819	0.40780	0.29344
4 SNOWY	0.39000	0.462	0.467	5	0	0	0
5 JOCK	0.04000	0.666	0.600	5	0	0	0
6 DICK	0.00100	0.749	0.691	5	0	0	0
DM	0.73000	0.446	0.508	5	0.37096		0.28042

Resulting solution (combined DM distribution of values assessed by experts)

Item name	Quantiles of solution 5 %	50 %	95 %	Scale
1 MT ST SWITHIN	4.04	6.41	8.0	U
2 CERRO BRUJO	5.06	7.0	8.0	U
3 SAKE-JIMA	3.0	4.41	6.0	U
4 LYNFA MONS	5.06	7.0	8.0	U
5 MORNE MERDE	2.0	3.37	7.63	U
VOLCAN INCONNU	2.08	5.0	7.88	U

351

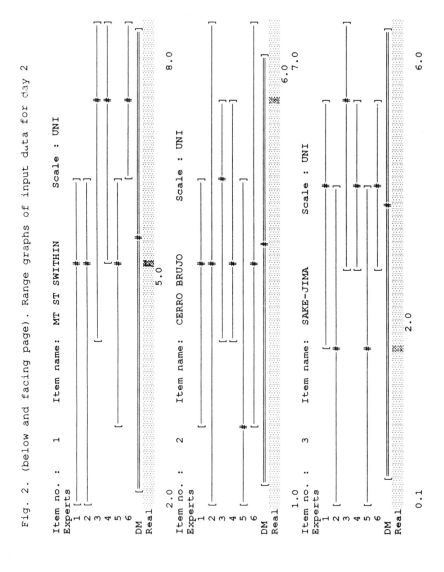

Fig. 2. (below and facing page). Range graphs of input data for day 2

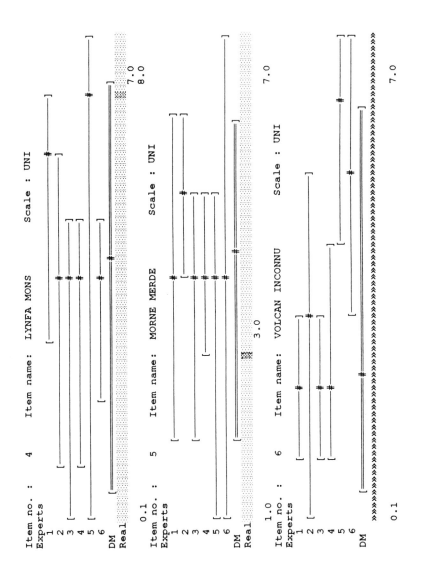

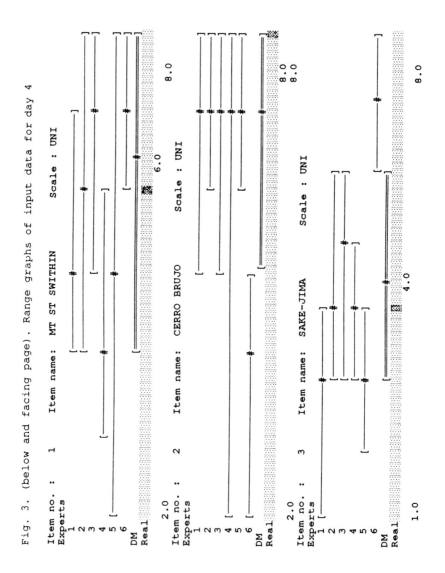

Fig. 3. (below and facing page). Range graphs of input data for day 4

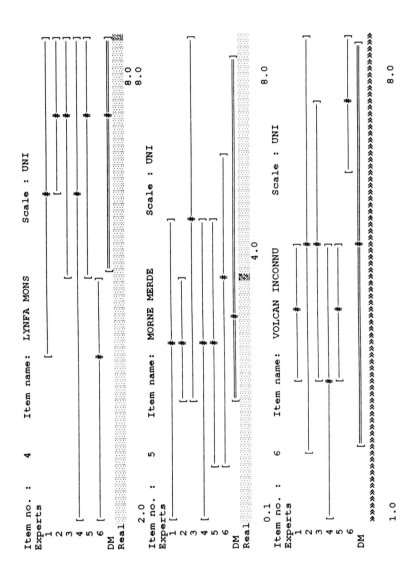

NATURAL DISASTERS

DISCUSSION

The formal elicitation of expert judgement should be an integral component of any hazard assessment. Because the elimination of bias and the treatment of uncertainty are both critical to the outcome, attention must be paid to the inherent tendencies of individual experts to exaggerate or under-estimate values, or to be over-confident or self-effacing in their responses. Calibration exercises allow these traits to be identified and quantified. Methods now exist for improved decision-making through the optimal fusion of expert judgements, taking into account the variability and informativeness of the selected experts.

Volcanic eruptions are considered to be one of the most serious natural hazards threatening vulnerable communities in the developing world. The severity of the problem is expected to increase as populations grow and the demand on land use increases. Progress has been made in developing applicable techniques for measuring all manner of volcanic phenomena locally and by remote sensing, and theories have been proposed to explain their physical causes. Yet, the fundamental volcanic processes are poorly understood and are probably deterministically chaotic in character (ref. 19); some volcanic episodes create grave threats to public safety whilst others cause little or no damage. In these circumstances, a probabilistic procedure is required which can incorporate both observational data of many kinds and the subjective degrees of belief of experts. The issue is one which is increasingly seen as sensistive when satellite imagery and remote sensing information is collected by agencies outside the affected territory.

The introduction of optimal decision analysis techniques, such as that described above, could systematically rationalize the important element of expert judgement in any volcanic hazard assessment, making maximum use of informed opinion. There would also be benefits in minimizing the impact of personality clashes within the scientific group, thereby reducing substantially the opportunity for embarrassing and confusing public disputes. Modern implementations of these techniques for using expert judgement are economic to execute in any evaluation made in the presence of scientific uncertainty, and almost invariably improve the accuracy and reliability of prognostications based on sparse data. These efficient decision tools could be invaluable aids in many aspects of both long-range disaster preparedness and the immediate management of natural catastrophes, especially in regions where local expertise is limited.

REFERENCES

1.   HADFIELD P. (1993) Mount Mayon blows without warning. New Scientist, 1860, 13 Feb. 1993, p8.

2.   Nature, Vol. 264, 9 Dec. 1976, p 500.

3.   TAZIEFF H. (1977) La Soufrière, volcanology and forecasting. Nature, 269, 96-97.

4.   BOSTOCK D. (1978) A deontological code for volcanologists? Editorial J. Volc. Geotherm Res., 4, 1.

5.   SIGVALDASON G.E. (1978) Reply to editorial. J. Volc. Geotherm. Res., 4, I-III.

6.   BARBERI F. and GASPARINI P. (1979) Letter to the Editor. J. Volc. Geotherm. Res., 6, 1-2.

7.   FISKE R.S. (1979) A deontological code for volcanologists? - a response to Derek Bostock's editorial. J. Volc. Geotherm. Res., 5, 211-212.

8.   TOMBLIN J. (1979) Deontological code, probabilistic hazard assessment or Russian roulette? J. Volc. Geotherm. Res., 5, 213-215.

9.   TAZIEFF H. (1980) Letter to the Editor. J. Volc. Geotherm. Res., 8, 3-6.

10.   FISKE R.S. (1984) Volcanologists, journalists, and the concerned public: a tale of two crises in the Eastern Caribbean. In: "Explosive volcanism: inception, evolution, and hazards", Nat. Res. Counc. (U.S.) Geophysics Study, National Academy Press, Washington D.C., pp 170 - 176.

11.   HOWSON C. and URBACH P. (1991) Bayesian reasoning in science. Nature, 350, 371-374.

12.   DE FINETTI B. (1970) "Teoria delle probabilita". Einaudi, Torino.

13.   COOKE R., FRENCH S. and VAN STEEN J. (1990) "The Use of Expert Judgement in Risk Assessment", European Space Agency, Noordwŷk, The Netherlands.

14.   COOKE R.M. and SOLOMATINE D. (1990) EXCALIBR: Software package for expert data evaluation and fusion in risk and reliability assessment. Report from the Technical University of Delft, The Netherlands.

15.   COOKE R.M. (1990) "Experts in Uncertainty: Expert Opinion and Subjective Probability in Science". Oxford University Press, 321pp.

16.   WOO G. (1992) Calibrated expert judgement in seismic hazard analysis. In: Proc. 10th World Conf. Earthq. Engng, Madrid, 333-338.

17.   WOO G. and ASPINALL W.P. (1993) Expert judgement in making decisions on mining hazards. In: "Rockbursts and Seismicity in Mines", Proc. 3rd Int. Symp. on Rockbursts and Seismicity in Mines, Kingston, Ontario. A.A. Balkema, Rotterdam, in press.

18.   SIMKIN T., SIEBERT L., McCLELLAND L., BRIDGE D., NEWHALL C. and LATTER J.H. (1981) "Volcanoes of the World". The Smithsonian Institution; Hutchinson Ross Pub. Co., Stroudsberg, Penn., pp 20-21.

19.   SORNETTE A., DUBOIS J., CHEMINEE J.L. and SORNETTE D. (1991) Are sequences of volcanic eruptions deterministically chaotic? J. Geophys. Res., 96, 11931-11945.

29. Reconditioning of existing adobe housing to mitigate the effects of earthquakes

L. ZEGARRA, Universidad Católica del Perú, and
A. GIESECKE, CERESIS, Peru

SUMMARY

Considerable work has been done throughout the world to produce new technology for adequate construction with adobe. However, such efforts do not mitigate the impact of future large earthquakes on existing adobe housing, since these technologies are not applicable, in general, for reconditioning older houses. It is therefore urgent and very important to address the problem faced by millions of people who live in adobe housing just hoping they are lucky enough to be spared during their lifetime the occurrence of a destructive earthquake.

The problems with adobe construction when subjected to ground shaking are due to non-engineered construction, the inherent mechanical limitations of the material, massive yet fragile and low-resistant walls, configuration defects that enhance the problem such as long walls without transversal bracing elements, excessive height from floor to ceiling, inadequate wall to wall and wall to roof joints, and foundations in soft soils. After each important earthquake a series of brochures and manuals are prepared and distributed, with an assortment of recommendations to improve the seismic resistance of adobe constructions, many of them with contradictory appreciations and, generally, without the benefit of laboratory or field tests to guarantee proper performance.

The basic concept of the CERESIS project is to evaluate and establish simple, low-cost procedures for reconditioning existing adobe housing, taking into account the type of soil on which they are built, the size, shape and construction characteristics, so that they will resist seismic excitation at least to the extent that the occupants, when a severe earthquake occurs, will have enough time to get outside before the house collapses. The objective is to save lives.

The paper describes the scope of the project, the structural techniques that have been tested, identifies techniques that need to be tested, and strategies to develop the proper metodology to motivate the population to carry out by itself the recomended reconditioning, without the need of outside experts and external financial aid.

Natural disasters. Thomas Telford, London, 1993

BACKGROUND

In Peru, and throughout the Andean region, adobe has been and is one of the traditional materials for building houses. It is estimated in Peru that 65% of the rural population and 37% of the city dwellers live in mud constructions (ref. 1), predominantly adobe and a smaller number in tapial (mud compacted walls).

The reason for buiilding this type of housing is undoubtedly its low cost. In rural areas, very little money is required to acquire and prepare the necessary materials to build a home or a school, since these are available locally at minium cost and self-construction is customary. In cold climates, an additional consideration for its use is that adobe walls have good thermal insulation properties.

Nevertheless, the response of adobe houses to seismic demand has been poor, in general. Many disasters with high death counts have occured, mostly in the developing world. The worst case in Latin America this century, with the highest number of casualties and injured, is the Chimbote earthquake of May 31, 1970, north of Lima, that killed over 50,000 persons, 20,000 missing and 150,000 were injured. More than 60,000 homes were destroyed, most of them built with adobe (ref. 2).

The poor response to seismic-induced vibrations is a result of non-engineered construction, of inherent mechanical limitations of the material, massive yet fragile and low-resistant walls, configuration defects that enhance the problem, such as long walls without transversal bracing elements, excessive height from floor to ceiling, inadequate wall to wall and wall to roof joints, and foundations in soft soils (ref. 3-4).

After each important earthquake a series of brochures and manuals are prepared and distributed, with an assortment of recommenda-tions to improve the seismic resistance of adobe constructions, many of them with contradictory recommendations and, generally, without the benefit of laboratory or field tests to guarantee proper performance.

For the past twenty years, the Engineering Department of the Catholic University of Peru (PUCP), in Lima, has given special attention to research oriented to improve the seismic behavior of adobe constructions (ref. 5-9). New materials have been tested as well as different types of construction design to build new adobe housing better able to resist earthquakes. As a result, new construction tachnologies have been developed for adobe, reinforced with reeds. These have been tested with full scale models built on the table of the PUCP Structures Laboratory.

The International Development Research Center (IDRC) of Canada, funded a PUCP research project (ref 9-10) to study the response of adobe houses under simulated earthquake conditions on the shaking table. The shaking table at PUCP, the only one of its kind in Latin America, supports a maximum load of 16 tons, moves from side to side up to 15 cm in each direction. The characteristics of the shaking are matched to those of earthquake accelerograms recorded in Peru. The purpose of the IDRC-funded project was to develop improved construction techniques and better materials for adobe houses, schools and public buildings, in rural areas.

359

NATURAL DISASTERS

As a result of years of research at PUCP and many other institutions in Peru and other countries, the Peruvian E-080 ADOBE Code was adopted in november 1985 for all new adobe housing (ref. 11).

Nevertheless, the succes of learning techniques to improve the seismic response of new adobe housing will not stop future earthquakes from killing thousands of people and damaging beyond repair many hundreds of thousands of homes all over the developing world, because these new technologies are not directly applicable to existing old adobe constructions, which are of course the real problem for vulnerable communities in earthquake prone countries of the developing world.

Therefore, it is necessary to pursue projects oriented to the reconditioning of existing adobe construction, so as to mitigate damage caused by future earthquakes making use of local materials and simple do-it-yourself techniques, at a cost so modest, that the techniques can be massively applied. Although important material damage may still occur, the lifes of the inhabitants will be spared (ref. 12-13).

RESEARCH PROPOSAL

Understanding the necessity and urgency of developing a program oriented to the reconditioning of existing adobe housing, CERESIS - Centro Regional de Sismologia para America del Sur, prepared a proposal with the PUCP. It was presented at the Guatemala meeting of the Scientific And Technical Comittee for the International Decade for Natural Disaster Reduction (IDNDR), in September, 1991. The proposal was aaccepted and officially designated as an IDNDR demonstration project. It is at present in the process of being funded by GTZ of the German Government.

OBJECTIVES OF THE PROJECT

The main objective of the Project is to evaluate and adopt simple strengthening procedures, bearing in mind the effecs of site conditions and the dimensions and type of construction, to reinforce existing adobe housing, to the extent that they will resist seismic solicitations for eough time for the occupants to get out of the house before it collapses, thus saving their.

The specific objectives are the following:

a. To establish a metodology to characterize types of existing adobe housing, to determine prevalent shapes and sizes. In Peru, some of this work has been done by the Instituto Nacional de Investigacion y Normalizacion de la Vivienda (ININVI) (ref. 14) and Universidad Nacional San Antonio Abad del Cusco (UNSAAC) (ref. 15).

b. To establish a simple procedure to evaluate the seismic safety of an existing adobe house and to determine if it need be reconditioned or or not.

c. To develop simple reconditioning procedures, that make use of local materials and can be adopted without the help of professionals.

360

d. To carry out static and dynamic tests on the PUCP shaking table, to evaluate the procedure(s) most appropriate to meet the basic objective of the Project. Some of the results of past research at PUCP on properties and allowable stresses of materials will be very useful.

e. Dissemination of the developed technology, using well illustrated manuals and video cassetes, in spanish and quechua, as well as by field demonstrations. It is believed that the message to convince people to reinforce their dwellings using the new technology should adopt strategies similar to those successfully used for nation-wide vaccination campaigns. "Simple low cost measures will protect you and your family from possible death, as a result of an earthquake which is likely to occur when least expected". Pilot projects, for demonstration in selected localities, will be carried in different localities and settings.

WORK PLAN

The project will consist of three stages:

A. Planning and laboratory work.
B. Pilot demonstration projects at selected sites. Preparation of manuals and video cassetes. Regional workshop.
C. Post-earthquake evaluation, dissemination of results and application throughout the developing world.

A. The first stage, will be carried mostly in Peru at PUCP. The tasks to be performed include:

–   Revision of the existing literature. Analysis of available reports on improved adobe building techniques in Peru, the andean countries and Mexico. Characterization of adobe constructions on the coast and in the mountains (sierra). Classification of typical construction details.

–   On the basis of research results of other investigators and prior experience of PUCP, the most promising procedures for strengthening existing dwellings will be tested. The fundamental elements of the experimental program will be defined: number and characteristic of specimens, size, reinforcement details, instrumentation, intensity, displacement and acceleration and amplitude of shaking to be applied for dynamic testing.

–   Preparation of detailed plans, construction and testing of the specimens on the PUCP shaking table. All activities will be recorded on video tape.

–   Analysis and interpretation of test results and previous information, leading to practical recommendations and simple reinforcement procedures. At the same time, the results will make it possible to establish a simple procedure for the evaluation of the

361

seismic safety of an existing adobe dwelling to
determine whether or not it needs to be reconditioned.

B.   The second stage comprises demonstrations projects at
different selected sites in Peru and, if possible, in other
andean countries. The number of such projects and locations
will depend on consultation with target communities, the
size of adobe-dwelling population at risk, level of
vulnerability and hazard potential, and on the different
construction characteristics and type of soil and other
site conditions. A final step in this phase will be the
organization of a regional workshop to present and report
on the work carried out, to discussd the results obtained,
and to outline a preliminary version of the manual.

As a result of the experiences gained in the field with the
pilot projects and the conclusions reached by the workshop,
a multidisciplinary international Working Group will
prepare the final version of the manuals for massive
distribution, and involve the media in this effort. The
manual must present, in a clear and precise way, the
methodology to determine if it isnecessary to recondition
a given construction or not,and how   to go about it.

At this point, the Final Report on the Project will be prepared
and published.

C.   The third stage will take place only after an earthquake
strikes a region where a significant number of adobe houses
have been reconditioned as recommended as a result of this
Project. A detailed post-earthquake study of the effects
will provide the information needed to evaluate the
benefits of reconditioning as proposed. If the results are
as expected or even exceed expectations, many lives will
have been saved.

Perhaps even before a post-earthquake evaluation can be carried
out, it would make sense to consider similar programs in other
adobe regions of the developing world.

SCHEDULE

The first two stages of the Project will be concluded in three
years. Stage A will take two years: planning during the first
year; laboratory work, during the second half of the first year
and during the second year. Stage B will be carried out during
the second and third years: planning of pilot projects begins in
the second year and reconditioning phase finishes in the first
half of the third year. The workshop will take place at the
beginning of third year and the dissemination program will be
developed the third year.

The last stage, C, has no fixed date. It will be carried out when
a destructive earthquake strikes the region. It is expected that
post-earthquake studies will take six months, and another six
months to adjust and improved the original technology, and
disseminate the information throughout the adobe developing
world.

362

REFERENCES

1. ININVI. Estudio de la Industria de la Vivienda en el Peru. Instituto Nacional de Investigación y Normalización de la Vivienda, Lima, Perú, 1985.

2. GIESECKE A., SILGADO E. Terremotos en el Perú. Ediciones Rikchay Peru, Lima, Perú, 1981.

3. HUSID R., ESPINOSA A., DE LAS CASAS J. The Lima Earthquake of October 3, 1974: Damage Distribution. Bulletin of the Seismological Society of America. Vol. 67, No. 5, 1441-1472, October 1977.

4. REPETTO P., ZEGARRA L. Evaluación de Edificaciones Dañadas en Lima Metropolitana en el Sismo de Octubre de 1974. Publicación DI-80-03, PUCP, 1980.

5. CORAZAO M., BLONDET M. Estudio Experimental del Comportamiento Estructural de las Construcciones de Adobe Frente a Solicitaciones Sísmicas. Premio Sayhuite, Banco Peruano de los Constructores, Lima, Perú, 1973.

6. BLONDET M., VARGAS J. Investigación sobre Vivienda Rural. PUCP, Lima, Perú, 1978.

7. HERNÁNDEZ O., OTTAZZI G., MELI R., VARGAS J. Programa de Investigación Cooperativa en Construcciones de Adobe Perú-México. Pontificia Universidad Católica del Perú y Universidad Nacional Autónoma de México, 1980.

8. OTTAZZI G., BLONDET M. A Proposal for a Standard Test to Evaluate the Seismic Strength of Adobe Masonry. Proceedings of CIB 86, Advancing Building Technology, Washington D.C., 1986.

9. OTTAZZI G., YEP J., BLONDET M., VILLA GARCÍA G., GINOCCHIO J. Viviendas de Adobe Resistentes a los Sismos - Perú. Pontificia Universidad Católica del Perú y Centro Internacional de Investigaciones para el Desarrollo-Canada, Lima, Perú, 1990.

10. DIANE HARDY. A Better Adobe Home for Earthquake Regions. p. 12, UNDRO NEWS - July/August 1988.

11. ININVI. Normas Técnicas de Edificación - Norma E-080, Adobe. Lima, Perú, 1985.

12. ZEGARRA L., BARIOLA J., SAMANEZ R., MALPARTIDA C., BECERRA J. El Terremoto del 5 de Abril de 1986. CERESIS, Pontificia Universidad Católica del Perú y Universidad San Antonio Abad del Cusco, 1986.

13. ZEGARRA L. Evaluación de la Resistencia Sísmica de una Vivienda de Adobe en el Cusco, por Efectos del Sismo de 1986. Taller de Riesgo Sismico en los Andes, organizado por Multiciencias, Cusco 1990.

NATURAL DISASTERS

14. ININVI. Tipologías y Tecnologías de Vivienda de Poblaciones Menores. Trapecio Andino. Cusco, Perú, 1988.

15. VILLEGAS A. Tipología de Vivienda y Tecnología Constructiva Popular en el Cusco.
Serie:Informes y Metodologías-1. Instituto de Investigación UNSAAC - NUFFIC. Cusco, Noviembre 1990.

30. Maps in action for protecting Trinidad and Tobago from disasters

M. MATHER, National Emergency Management Agency,
Trinidad and Tobago

Introduction

1.   Mapmaking must have its origins in the earliest ages of human history, since people of preliterate as well as literate cultures possess an innate skill in map drawing. This innate capacity is further indicated by the ease with which almost anyone can sketch in the sand or on paper simple directions for showing the way. But maps may also define territory and express man's idea of the world in graphic representation.

2.   Mapmakers for more than 4,000 years have tried to find the best way to represent the shape and features of the three-dimensional Earth on two-dimensional paper, parchment and cloth.

3.   Today, the maps can be used and are being used to plot many other features apart from the topography. Maps can play a very important role not only in the knowledge of the country and its people but also for disaster management. The process comprises the collection and mapping of the hazard data and disaster response facilities. The final stage is reading of the map. Through the map user the map is transformed into an image in the mind and the effectiveness of the map depends on the reader being able to also understand it.

4.   Though the use of computers for processing maps, up-dating them and even for using disaster management is well advanced in many countries, I have in this paper compiled the use of old fashioned maps pinned on drawing boards or bound in a book for use by ordinary citizens who do not have access to computers. It is so because this technique is a low cost one, broadly applicable and adaptable to the needs of all societies.

The Necessity

5.   In recent years it has been noted that the emergency plans of most countries are either computer-oriented or bound in thickness or books. When a crisis situation develops, the computers do not work because of the absence of power, and managers hardly have time or inclination to go through the thick volumes of the plans. The result is confusion both in the minds of those who are managing disasters as well as victims which results in loss of precious time.

6.　　　　But the philosophy of disaster management should be "tackle any difficulty at first sight, for the longer you gaze at it the bigger it grows".

7.　　　　Make no mistake about it. Those responsible for providing help and aid in times of natural disasters or major man-made accidents are frequently faced with a difficult task, in conditions of great uncertainty. In such circumstances, if timely assistance and access to relevant and accurate information is not available, the process of arriving at a correct decision becomes a matter of chance. This is where Maps in Action for Disaster Management fit in.

8.　　　　Frequently, National and local authorities are faced with a crisis to tackle which they need to retrieve relevant information from a mass of files or computers under stress conditions. On the basis of this information rapid decisions have to be made which may sometimes be the difference between life and death.

9.　　　　Once a Disaster Co-ordinator has instantaneous access to the right information, he should be able to bring sufficient resources to bear on the incident to maximum effect at the right time and in the right place.

10.　　　　Disaster Response Maps provide such facilities to all those who have to deal with crisis situations. Actually, there is nothing new about this concept. Maps have been used from time immemorial to plan and fight battles. A visitor to London can still see the large maps of the world covering underground cabinet war rooms from where Churchill and his colleagues directed operations during World War II.

Benefits of Disaster Response Mapping

11.　　　　The main purpose of Disaster Response Mapping is to gather in one map the different hazard-related information for a study area to convey a composite picture of the natural hazards and the response facilities available. One area may suffer the presence of a number of natural hazards. Using individual maps to convey information on each hazard can be cumbersome and confusing for planners and decision-makers because of their number and their possible differences in area covered, scales, and detail.

12.　　　　Many natural hazards can be caused by the same natural event. The inducing or triggering mechanism which can interconnect several hazards can more easily be seen through the use of these maps. Characteristics of the natural phenomenon and its trigger mechanisms are synthesized from different sources and placed on a single map.

13.　　　　Additionally, the effects and impact of a single hazard event, as in the case of earthquakes, include different types of impacts, each having different severities and each affecting different locations.

14.　　　　The Disaster Response Mapping is an excellent tool to create an awareness in mitigating multiple hazards. It becomes a comprehensive analytical tool for assessing vulnerability and risk, especially when combined with the mapping of critical facilites.

15.　　　　The adoption of a multiple hazard mitigation strategy also has several implications in emergency preparedness planning. For example, it provides a more equitable basis for allocating disaster planning funds; stimulates the use of more efficient, integrated emergency preparedness response and recovery procedures; and promotes the creation of cooperative agreements to involve all relevant agencies and interested groups.

16.   The effective use of natural hazard information to avoid damage or to reduce loss requires a considerable effort on the part of both the producers and the users of the information.   Unless the scientific and engineering information is translated for the layman, the effective user community is limited to other scientists and engineers.

Preparing Disaster Response Maps

17.   A prerequisite to compiling individual hazards information onto one map is obtaining or creating a base map upon which to place this information.

18.   Much hazard information will be in the form of scientific investigations into the process and prediction of a potentially hazardous event and observations of the impact of past events such as earthquakes and floods. It is often in forms other than maps. This information, although a prerequisite to a Disaster Response Map, is not readily understood by the layman. It must be "translated" for plannners, decision-makers and citizens and placed on maps.

19.   Successful translation must be in a format that an average citizen can understand.   But even more important, the information must be perceived as explaining disasters that may adversely affect life, property or socioeconomic activities and the available remedies.   This can be accomplished by providing two elements - hazardous areas and location of response facilities.

20.   A planner or decision-maker evaluating a specific land use, structure, or socioeconomic activity is not usually interested in a potential event whose (1) occurrence is not expected for a very long time, (2) location is not known, or (3) size or effect is not great.   These elements vary with the phenomenon, for example:-

- Coastal areas annually exposed to winds
  and storm surges.
- Floodplains and floodways which will be
  impacted by velocities and water heights
  rainfall duration and intensity having
  a fifty-year recurrence interval.

21.   Types of information needed to assess the location of various hazards in Trinidad and Tobago is as follows:-

(a)   Hurricanes - Landfall and path.

(b)   Earthquakes, epicentres and
      geological formations.

(c)   Landslides - inventories, geological
      formations and slope.

(c)   Floods - channel, floodway, floodplain
      and elevation.

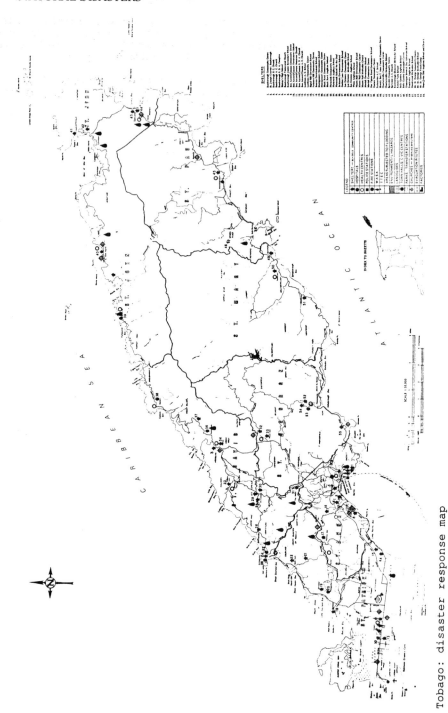

Tobago: disaster response map

22.   It is also important to distinguish between a hazard that can be defined as not present versus one whose presence cannot be properly evaluated because of limited information.   For example, a conservative approach to development because of "inadequate" hazard information can be counterproductive over time.   If the planner's or decision-maker's response to an "exaggerated" potential hazard is to avoid the area or recommend expensive resistive design, a credibility problem will occur when a "realistic" potential hazard is discovered.

23.   There is a vast array of sources of hazard information, including various public and private libraries, offices and reference centres at international, national, regional, and community levels. These entities may be concerned with infrastructure, community facilities, economic development, resource exploration, land use planning, emergency preparedness, geotechnical studies, disaster response, and many other activities.   Sometimes these sources coordinate their compiling of hazard information, but it cannot always be expected.   Many of the users of development planning information are also compilers of natural hazard information.

24.   Some hazard information can be extracted or inferred from photographic, topographic, geologic, hydrologic, climatologic, and soils information already prepared for settled regions.

25.   Compiling information from various sources includes four steps: collecting, evaluating, selecting, and combining.

Map Format

26.   The maps are based on geographical boundaries of local governments of the country and are on a scale of 1:75,000.

27.   It has been said that the usefulness of a map is in its omissions. Except for its orientation information (roads, rivers, coastlines, place names) the map is uncluttered and stripped down.   Natural hazards and response facilities are the information to be emphasized.

28.   Creating a base map from scratch is a difficult and time-consuming task; therefore, it is desirable to use an existing map as a base.   An adequate base map must be planimetric, that is, a representation of information on a plane in true geographic relationship and with measurable horizontal distances; and must have sufficient geographic reference information to orient the user to the location of the hazard and response facilities.   The top of a map is usually oriented to the north.

29.   All the four major hazards in Trinidad and Tobago shown as well as location of industries which can become sites of industrial disasters.

30.   Among disaster response facilities shown are the buildings that have been earmarked as shelters together with the recommended route to the shelters.   Also shown are hospitals, health centres, police stations, fire stations, water and electric supply installations and parks which can be used as transfer stations.   All these facilities are there for the production of people at risk.

Everything shown on a Disaster Response Map as well as the base map is a symbol representing reality.   Symbols are selected for their legibility and clarity and/or map production characteristics.

369

31.   Location can be shown through the use of basic geometric symbols - a point, a line, or an area. For example, points have been used to show landslides; lines have been used to show preferred tracks of tropical storms and areas have been used to show flooding or earthquake zones.

32.   Innumerable variations of points, lines and areas are available to the maker. Lines can be solid, long-dashed, short-dashed, or composed of points. Areas can be shaded, patterned and coloured.

33.   It must be emphasized that all the hazard information shown on the Disaster Response Map, and also the base map information, are merely symbols - some conventional, others abstract, and some innovative. Users must carefully read the explanations (sometimes called legends), all caveats, and any supplemental text accompanying a map. The Disaster Response Map maker is a key person and should leave a track (or record) for the Disaster Response Map user, for example, sources of information used, scales enlarged   or reduced, and limitations of the individual hazard information.

34.   The information shown on a Disaster Response Map is only one factor that the planner or decision-maker will be considering. The information must be clear, convenient, and not just accurate but perceived as accurate.

35.   It should be remembered that the location, design, and operation of future critical facilities and the strengthening, abandonment, and operation of existing critical facilities will be affected by a consideration of the information shown on the Disaster Response Map.

36.   Because of the geographic nature of maps, the location requirement of disasters is met, but this is not necessarily so with regard to severity and likelihood of occurrence.

37.   The likelihood, location, and severity elements of certain hazards can be easily affected by human activities. It has been noted that it is entirely possible to cause a major failure to occur in a moderate hazard zone. Likewise, it is possible to significantly disturb a site within a high or extreme zone without causing a landslide.

38.   A prerequisite for the locational accuracy of hazard information is the accuracy of the base map selected. The hazard information available and transferred to Disaster Response Maps may be accurate, but the level of precision varies greatly.   This is not necessarily because of scale or resolution, but because of the number of the field investigations, lack of information, type of experiments, and knowledge of the processes involved.

39.   The Disaster Response Map maker should assume that at some time the map will be enlarged or reduced. Map titles and explanations are usually unaffected by enlargements or reductions, but not the literal and numerical scales. Literal scales (one millimeter equals one hundred thousand meters) and numerical scales (1:000,000) remain accurate only for the original map. Therefore, a graphic scale must be placed on each map.

40.   Reality is usually difficult to perceive; this difficulty is increased when maps are used. If a map is treated as reality, it becomes easy to view the hazards in impersonal terms. The magnitude of the hazard is dwarfed, people are invisible, critical facilities and other information may look like a board game.

41.   When planners and decision-makers treat a map as mere symbols and

disregard the physical reality it represents, the results can be disastrous. Development planners or investors, for example, may be tempted to locate infrastructures needed for economic development along a line that looks the straightest and most convenient on the map. Such a route may lie within a fault-rupture zone. A dot symbol representing a town or a specific number of people conveys nothing about the town's economic base or the peoples' characteristics-age, schooling, skills, gender, or income sources. The map way is not always the best way; its limitations must be appreciated.

42.   Filling a Disaster Response Map with the symbols from several individual hazard maps may give the impression of a more thorough study, but, of course, this is not true. Simplified multiple hazard maps only create an awareness of what information exists, and (even more important) what information is missing. A Disaster Response Map cannot substitute for detailed studies and site-specific investigations.

43.   Caveats concerning the limitations of Disaster Response Maps should preferably be placed on the map but also can be included in the text accompanying the map. Methods used, assumptions made or other factors concerning the individual hazard maps used to prepare the Disaster Response Maps can also be shown.

Risk Reduction

44.   The maps help in adopting the following measures for risk reduction:-

(a)   the encouragement and support of local authorities to protect people at risk in the face of disasters;

(b)   the allocation of responsibilities for detailed planning and execution of disaster response operations in their respective regional corporations to their respective governments;

(c)   conformation of emergency planning to the normal administrative chains of command;

(d)   widespreading of mitigation and preparedness responsibilities. Once hazards are mapped on a map, mitigation measures can be taken to attempt one of the three things. Some are intended to prevent or modify the occurrence of a hazard. Building dams and levees to minimize floods are good examples of this. On the other hand, some measures seek to avoid the hazard by siting the structure out of harm's way. For instance, land use guidelines, such as those restricting growth in flood plains or on unstable slopes, can be a very effective method of avoiding hazard losses. Finally, some measures seek to strengthen a structure to reduce the damage a hazard might cause. For example, enacting and adopting construction standards are obvious ways to increase a building's resistance to

371

earthquakes or wind damage. The combination
of these techniques that will be most
effective for a community depends on its
goals and resources, as well as the precise
nature of the hazards it faces.

(e)   allocation of responsibilities to agencies
and departments so that they can contribute
to the collective purpose.

45.   In emergencies one of the first items of information required
will be the exact scene of the incident. Without scene location being
accurately pinpointed, help and assistance could be sent to wrong
locations thus leading to unnecessary suffering or casualties, perhaps
just to frustrating delays.

In order to avoid occurrences of this nature, incident location
can be pinpointed on Disaster Response Maps which are based on National
Survey. The advantages are obvious: with visual information as roads,
rivers, communities, factories, the decision maker can offer advice as to
the best route to take to the scene taking into account any last minute
diversion.

46.   It is vital that means or resources available with which to meet
an emergency situation are also readily accessible to the Disaster
Operations Officer. This is why response resources are marked prominently
on the response maps. Note that a national and county level precise tasks
will be assigned to the response agencies. Actual allocation of
equipment/vehicles will be done by the response agencies concerned who
will maintain an up-to-date inventory of their resources.

47.   Of great value will these maps be in case of chemical accidents.
With the Disaster source as a centre, a probable area can be immediately
marked on the map to show the vulnerability of population bearing in mind
the types of chemical involved and the wind speed and direction.
Evacuation options and the routes for response agencies can then be quickly
considered and decided upon to save precious lives.

48.   Permit me to utilize this opportunity to clarify roles of Incident
Commanders, County Disaster Co-ordinators and NEMA Operations Centre during
disasters.

49.   The senior fire officer at the scene of a major incident or a
major disaster becomes the Incident Commander. Should the incident involve
majority input from police or army then the command would be assumed by the
senior police or army officer as the case may be.

50.   Both the Regional Co-ordinators as well as Incident Commanders
will report to NEMA Operations Room the damages as well as requirement of
additional resources to save lives and protect property. NEMA will then
mobilize whatever national or international resources are required to bring
situation in control.

51.   The primary aim of any co-ordinator in a major disaster or major
incident is to return the situation to normality. Disaster Maps and
telecommunications can effectively enable the co-ordinator to manoeuvre
available resources, both human and technical, in order to achieve this
aim.

Putting Disaster Response Maps to Work

52.   Maps in action will facilitate in five (5) vital areas of Disaster Management. Firstly, we expect that each citizen of the country will have a Disaster Response Map of his county or borough available to him or her at his or her residence. The citizens will then be able to understand and follow warnings and instructions for their relief much better and thus minimizing adverse effects of disasters.

53.   Secondly, as soon as survey and assessment reports come, identification can be done of what the particular disaster has done to us and therefore, definition of what we need to do by way of response and recovery.

54.   Thirdly, the four stroke system of information management, information assessment, decision-making and decision out would work more efficiently in crisis situation.

55.   Fourthly, our plan already designates tasks to those organizations which have parallel responsibilities in non-disaster times, for medical area, the communication system, road clearance etc. However, some aspects would present difficulties like that of emergency feeding, shelter and evacuation. Again our response maps will be extremely valuable in making decisions on these aspects.

56.   Fifthly, effective co-ordination is a big issue for dealing with disaster situation. Our response maps will be able to point immediately to the agencies whose activities have to be co-ordinated for dealing with a particular disaster situation.

57.   The Disaster Co-ordinator will then be able to say what once Winston Churchill said from the map-pinned walls of his war time cabinet room "We must confront our perils and trials with that national unity which cannot be broken, and a national force which is inexhaustible".

References

Churchill Winston   —   History of World War II

Department of Regional   —   Primer on Natural Hazard
Development and Environment,   Management in Integrated
Organization of American   Regional Development Planning
States

Mc Nally Rand   —   The Great Geographical Atlas

NEMA   —   Developing Disaster Management
                                    in Trinidad and Tobago

NEMA   —   More on Disaster Management in
                                    Trinidad and Tobago

31. The rehabilitation of housing after natural disasters in Bangladesh

R. L. P. HODGSON, Consulting engineer, UK, and
A. WHAITES, World Vision UK

ABSTRACT

Frequent and widespread damage to housing and infrastructure in the low-lying state of Bangladesh is caused by natural disasters, including floods, cyclones, tornadoes and earthquakes.

Replacement of housing assets has, in recent years, taken the major portions of several disaster rehabilitation programmes in Bangladesh, including those which followed the 1988 floods and the 1991 cyclone. The experiences gained from differing approaches to housing asset replacement in those two programmes are reviewed and compared.

In-depth interviewing of selected beneficiaries has assisted in clarifying some of the strategic decisions made by the victims of this type of immediate impact disaster.

The difficulty of balancing cost and timeliness of response is discussed together with the problem of accurate targetting of the most needy beneficiaries. Conclusions are drawn regarding the appropriateness of housing provision within the rapid response demanded of a disaster rehabilitation.

1.0   INTRODUCTION : TWO RECENT NATURAL DISASTERS IN BANGLADESH

The low-lying, densely populated state of Bangladesh is affected frequently by natural disasters. Indeed, most of the 108 million (1991 census, Ref. 1) inhabitants are likely to experience personally at some time in their lives the effects of a tropical storm, cyclone, major flood or earthquake.

This paper examines the effects of two of the largest disasters to strike Bangladesh recently : the floods of 1988, which drove some 50 million (Ref. 2) from their homes in 55 of the state's 64 Districts, and the cyclone of 1991 in which an estimated 1.16 million (Ref. 3) lost homes and businesses and some 138,000 (Ref. 4) died. Sketches showing the areas affected by these two disasters are included in Figure 1; very few parts of Bangladesh were not affected by one or other of them.

The following notes describe relevant features of these two catastrophes. They are drawn both from published information and from analysis of the office records of World Vision of Bangladesh (WVB), a large Non-Governmental Organisation (NGO) based in Dhaka. WVB development officers in many parts of Bangladesh assisted in bringing relief to people affected by each of the disasters to be described.

Both WVB rehabilitation programmes included large components of housing replacement. Critical comparison of the different approaches adopted provides the basis for the conclusions contained in this paper.

1.1   Example 1 : the 1988 floods

Unprecedentedly widespread flooding occurred in different places at different times during the monsoon season of 1988. The areas first affected were the northern districts which, from June onwards, suffered a series of flash floods running off the Meghalaya Plateau.

More universal flooding (Figure 1(a)) came in September when a late monsoon coincided with maximum equinoctial tides. A national emergency was declared on September 1st; riverside and low-lying areas remained inundated for four to six weeks. The flood waters were, in the main, slow-moving but, none-the-less, they destroyed or damaged up to 3.7 million poorly constructed houses. Disaster relief works continued until the end of October when rehabilitation programmes supplanted them.

WVB implemented rehabilitation programmes mainly in the 106 areas affected by flooding where they had pre-existing development work. These were located in most parts of the country, including the borders north of Mymensingh, river bank areas near Sherpur and Faridpur and in the forest tracts to the west of Mymensingh. Although the floods had severely impacted on several aspects of normal life, not least the ability to generate income, housing was quickly prioritised as a relief need. Indeed, damage housing was widespread and reconstruction of homes became the principal element (54%) in the $2.2million WVB rehabilitation programme; some 4,000 new, low-cost, improved houses were built during the course of a 12 month period.

1.2   Example 2 : the 1991 cyclone

The severe cyclone which crossed the coast of Bangladesh during the night of 29th to 30th April 1991 had been first detected some four days before as it formed from a depression over the Bay of Bengal. Despite the broadcast warnings, many victims were unprepared when the storm, with maximum windspeeds of 225km/hr and accompanying 7m high tidal wave, struck close to Chittagong at about midnight.

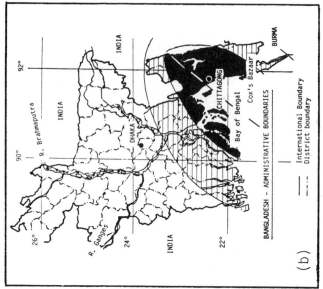

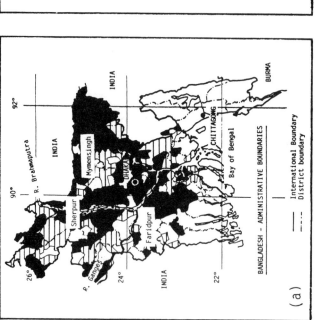

Figure 1 : The extents of two recent disasters in Bangladesh
(a) Floods of June–September 1988
(b) Cyclone of 29th April 1991.

The poor communities on the islands and lowlands bordering the Bay of Bengal took much of the impact. People sheltered wherever they could as their bamboo-framed homes were torn apart. Few coastal families did not lose one or more member as the tidal wave swept in.

WVB already had a number of community development programmes running in the Chittagong area. Their relief programme started in most of those areas on 30th April. However, as all communication with Dhaka was lost in the storm, it was some days before the majority relief programmes could start. Some victims received little or no outside assistance for two weeks.

By about a month after the cyclone the immediate devastation had been cleared and relief programmes developed into rehabilitation of the affected areas. The Government of Bangladesh (GoB) acted as a co-ordinating body in the wake of the disaster and played a key role in encouraging NGOs to provide corrugated roofing sheets to the poorest cyclone victims to help them rebuild their homes. WVB's budget for this item alone was over $1.0million which was expended by the end of November 1991. Naturally, the rationale behind this emergency asset replacement provided a main focus for the subsequent evaluation of the WVB programme (Ref. 3).

2.0   THE EVALUATION STUDIES

The two WVB rehabilitation programmes outlined above each involved an expenditure of approximately $2.25million. A substantial portion of each budget was raised through World Vision of Britain who had stipulated that the programmes should be subjected to external evaluation.

For each evaluation, the first author was included in the team to review technical aspects, particularly of housing and infrastructure elements.

2.1   Team compositions

Apart from the first author, each evaluation team included two other members. For the flood evaluation these were John Mitchell and Hugo Slim, of Rural Evaluations, while the cyclone evaluation team included Dr. Richard Palmer-Jones of University of East Anglia School of Development Studies and Stuart Rutherford, consultant to Action Aid. The reports on which this paper is based were collective productions of the relevant teams and credit is due as appropriate to all the above named team members.

2.2   Methodology

Each evaluation team spent three to four weeks in Bangladesh. As well as detailed discussion with WVB staff and examination of their records, representatives of other national and international agencies were interviewed and meetings were held with beneficiaries, both individually and in groups. In each case, schedules and itineraries were decided by the evaluation teams to achieve programme overviews as objective as possible.

Both teams placed great importance on ascertaining the perceived priorities of the disaster victims and spent at least half of the time available in affected areas, obtaining first-hand accounts of the disasters. Many interviews were unstructured and informal particularly during the flood evaluation where the victims were geographically scattered and long distances were travelled by the evaluators. Some ranking exercises were conducted to help to clarify the compositions of local communities and their relief needs.

3.0   MECHANISMS FOR COPING WITH DISASTER IN BANGLADESH

Many people in rural Bangladesh live under almost constant threat of disaster. River-side dwellers interviewed for the flood evaluation admitted that they often have to leave their homes for a month during the monsoon; the 1988 season was not an unusual hardship for them, save, perhaps, that the timing and duration of the floods were extended. What made it an emergency of national proportions was that many communities not normally affected by floods also had to leave homes and crops.

By contrast, the cyclone struck a part of Bangladesh in which disasters are rare. Being a relatively affluent, partly industrialised area, there were few aid agencies working in the worst affected area at the time. Therefore, most victims were caught unawares and, because of the disruption, had to cope by themselves during the aftermath. It was most instructive to discover the mechanisms by which they did so.

3.1   During period of warning

Few people in the cyclone affected area seem to have heeded the clear, well disseminated warnings. This was the 35th cyclone to hit Bangladesh since 1960 but there have been many more warnings (Ref. 4) and it seems that most people did not believe that the impending catastrophe would actually occur. Some thought that there might be equal risk of losing property by abandoning the home when there was no real danger and they felt it better to stay with their belongings.

Most poor interviewees were (or considered themselves to be) parts of extended family groupings which include more successful or affluent members. Once the winds came and damage was occurring, poorer victims made their ways to the more protective houses of such well-to-do neighbours. Most of the survivors interviewed had spent the night of 29-30th April in someone else's house, usually together with many others from their village.

Victims were affected in many ways. The evaluation considered principally those who had lost homes (and, usually, livelihoods) and had not the savings or income to replace them as these formed one of the worst affected groups. Less severely affected sections of the population included artisans and factory workers whose employers were able to support them; such groups did not face the harsh survival options with which the poorest communities had to contend.

3.2   Immediate aftermath

On 30th April, over a million people returned to the sites of their homes to find little remaining structure, no possessions and their food either gone or damaged beyond use. It was a confusing time and not many interviewees had clear recollections of that morning. Ref. 4 gives an overview of the devastation. The evaluation sought to identify the priorities of the victims as they replaced their losses for comparison with the activities undertaken by NGOs. Priorities were partly shaped by whether water was still standing on homestead sites (Ref. 3). Broadly, the immediate goals related to :

3.2.1   Sources of income - for many interviewees there was no income since their work places had been damaged and income opportunities from trading had been disrupted. Owners of boats, rickshaws and other similar means of livelihood made inspections to ascertain whether those were also damaged.

3.2.2   Missing family - most said that their immediate priority had been to locate any missing family members and to obtain food.

3.2.3   Shelter - it was significant that, along with locating family, this was an area where victims were often able to undertake almost immediate action. People set about collecting building debris and reconstructing shelters for themselves. Many moved into public buildings such as schools or factories until their homes could be rebuilt.

3.3   Medium term (one month plus)

The rebuilding of lives after a disaster requires access to funds. It was, therefore, the first priority area above, lack of income which restricted the rehabilitation of homes and businesses. Relief agencies set up food (and/or cash) for work schemes after both disasters but opportunities to join these and other casual employment were limited for most potential workers. Many of the poorest communities live by fishing but until boats were repaired there was little work in this sector.

Therefore, most interviewees faced an important choice in the aftermath of the cyclone : whether (1) to sit it out and trust to others' charity in the meantime or (2) to obtain a loan to get themselves going. Another option for some was to sell land or other property; those who chose this route found that, in a buyers market, prices became depressed by as much as half of normal values.

Omio Kanta Borua, pictured in Photograph 1 (Ref. 3) with his family and rebuilt home, was an example : he makes a living by transporting goods on his small boat. His thatched bamboo house was almost entirely blown away by the 1991 cyclone and everything in it destroyed in the ensuing flood. The main tidal wave did not reach his village and he, his family and nearly all his neighbours were fortunate in being

able to shelter in a well-made mud-walled house which his
wife's brother had recently built. His family stayed with
his brother-in-law until they were given materials to rebuild
their own house. In the meantime, he found that his boat was
damaged; given that both home and livelihood were lost,
after some consideration, he decided that his priority was to
repair the boat and start work again. His wife said that she
thought repairing the house to be more important to herself
and the children but agreed to let her husband take a
loan of 4,500 taka (over $100) for repairs to the boat and to
buy food. The loan was obtained from a business associate at
interest of 10% per month (interest rates in rural Bangladesh
are onerous by most European standards) and the repairs were
completed by the beginning of June. Work was not plentiful
but better than nothing so they felt this was the right
decision, especially when, subsequently, they were given
roofing sheets with a value of some $140 by the WVB
rehabilitation programme to rebuild their house. Never
having previously owned an iron roof, they were proud of
their new status and would not now (nine months later)
exchange it except in case of dire necessity. Unfortunately,
they had insufficient money to secure their roof properly;
the building frame remains crooked and, as the interviewers
stood to leave the house, one sheet was dislodged and started
to slide to the ground.

Everyone has a different story but this one sums up
the positions of many affected by the cyclone and, probably,
of victims of other sudden impact disasters in Bangladesh.
Although, by January 1992, much appeared superficially to
have returned to normal, there was a substantial undercurrent
of indebtedness which touched many of the victims interviewed
and which provided perhaps the most significant long term
impact of the disaster.

A point which came out markedly from the evaluation
was that outside assistance, while welcomed as and when it
came, was not widely significant in helping victims to cope
with a very traumatic event. Nearly all of the affected
population were on their own for nearly a week and many had
no help for a fortnight; Despite large expenditure by many
relief agencies, the outside assistance given amounted to a
small fraction of the overall economic activity in the
affected areas.

For example, if the 516 tonnes of relief grain which
were supplied during May (GoB estimates) were divided equally
among the 1.16 million most affected people then each would
have received just over one day's ration. Obviously, many
individuals received more than this and were greatly helped
by it; equally, many must have had to cope without any
assistance.

The focus of the assistance was, as has been said,
in the third priority area where much self-help was also
taking place. The rest of this paper therefore addresses the
merits of housing reinstatement in the context of a response
to disasters in Bangladesh.

4.0   REHABILITATION OF HOUSING - ALTERNATIVE APPROACHES

For roughly the same financial input, the cyclone rehabilitation programme supplied materials for nearly twice as many homes as the flood programme could build complete. However, neither approach has produced entirely satisfactory outcomes from the point of view of the beneficiaries.

The following notes compare five of the possible options available to a relief agency which wishes to assist disaster victims by replacement of housing assets.

4.1   Provide complete house

The houses supplied by WVB in 1988 were all built to a common design and measured 4.4m x 2.4m in plan area. They were constructed with braced frames made from galvanised steel tube onto which almost flat roofs of corrugated iron were bolted. Set in concrete foundation pads, this design is expected to provide considerable resistance to future flooding. Photograph 2 (Ref. 5) illustrates a typical example which has some additions by the householder.

For rapidity of construction with minimum requirement for supervision, WVB engaged regional companies to provide the houses through contracts for about 100 homes at a time. Costs per house varied slightly around a mean of about 9,200 taka ($230), depending on area and location. Many examples were examined at Faridpur, Mymensingh and Sherpur (see Figure 1 for map) and the engaging of independent contractors was judged successful in achieving uniform, high standards of construction across the country. The adoption of a single, prespecified design greatly aided the efficient supervision of contractors by the relatively few technician engineers engaged for this purpose.

Apart from some preparation of sites by the beneficiaries, the houses were supplied and erected complete by the contractors. As and when they had the funds, beneficiaries were encouraged to improve their houses by, for example, replacing woven bamboo walls with more substantial partitions or adding verandahs.

The main disadvantage of a carefully planned programme such as this was the unavoidable delay in setting it up. Construction did not start until January 1989 and some beneficiaries did not move into their new homes until a year after the floods. Some beneficiaries had already constructed new homes in the meantime. It is difficult to envisage this long time-scale in terms of rehabilitation of damage; certainly, some WVB staff considered the houses more as additions to their regular development programmes.

The costs of the houses limited the numbers that could be provided from a finite budget and, consequently, targetting of the most needy victims was difficult. Within their development programme areas, WVB were mostly aware of the most needy inhabitants but, none-the-less, some had to be excluded because of lack of funds.

Photograph 1 : Omio Kanta Borua and family beside their house near Chittagong repaired after the 1991 cyclone

Photograph 2 : Typical 1988 WVB model house, partly extended by its owner. The remains of the previous, mud-walled home are in the foreground.

4.2   Provide materials

        To improve the timeliness of housing reconstruction,
it was decided by the GoB representatives who co-ordinated
cycone relief work that housing assets lost in that disaster
would be replaced by distributing materials, principally 16
sheets of corrugated iron plus a 1,000 taka ($25) grant. The
cost per beneficiary of this approach was about half that of
providing complete 1988 model houses and materials were all
distributed within two to three months of the cyclone.

        Even so, there was at least one whole village in the
most affected area (as this was identified within two days of
arrival in the area, it was probably not the only one) where
no materials were received because, in the confusion, no NGO
established a presence there. It seemed to the evaluation
team that this degree of chance should be eliminated from the
provision of major assets such as houses. In areas where
materials were supplied, there were concerns that not all who
needed them had been able to benefit, again because needs
exceeded the quantities available.

        Certainly, this intervention was more timely than
the 1988 flood reconstruction programme. However, many of
the poorest who received these materials had neither the
skills nor the funds to construct a framework adequate to
secure the sheets. It seemed that the next strong wind would
blow away most of this programme in a lethal hail of iron.

4.3   Provide money

        It had been a thesis of the cyclone evaluation that
most of the disaster victims could have been best helped by
replacing incomes and giving immediate cash grants; a
combination of personal decision and market forces should
then come into play and encourage rapid regeneration of
economic activity. It soon became clear that in the
conditions of anarchy prevailing in some areas at that time,
this approach would have resulted in a dramatic increase in
crime. As most poor people have no bank accounts they would
have had no means for saving relatively large sums of cash
from the predations of brigands who surfaced in the wake of
the disaster.

        Organising cash for work programmes helped to
restore incomes in some localities but, as with the housing
materials, took some weeks to set up. Field staff organising
these schemes were sometimes concerned for their own personal
safety when carrying large sums for wages. However, in view
of the importance placed by the victims on this priority
area, more effective ways of replacing income should be
evolved. Making credit available through suppliers can give
financial security while avoiding the problems of
distributing cash. Replacement of income will also help to
reduce the general level of indebtedness described above.

4.4   Communal shelters

        There were not many public cyclone shelters

available in 1991 and some of those seen were in poor repair.
Since such damaging cyclones are rare, these shelters were
not often used and essential maintenance had been neglected.

The evaluation team visited private dwellings which
had survived the full force of the tidal wave, demonstrating
that good construction can provide a large measure of
protection without the need for special structures. It seems
more appropriate to construct public buildings (schools,
council offices, police stations, etc.) with sustantial walls
and upper floors; they could then serve the additional
function of sheltering the surrounding populations against
severe storms. Special shelters would be unnecessary and
there would be more incentive, through regular use, to
maintain shelter buildings in good repair. It is essential
that any initiative of this kind is allied to greater public
understanding of the well-established warning system so that
communities seek protection in good time.

4.5   Temporary shelter

As the immediate aftermath of a disaster is
widespread homelessness, there is an immediate need for
shelter. To avoid delay, temporary structures, perhaps of
plastic sheeting or canvas should be provided as soon as
possible, permitting follow-up programmes to be planned in
less haste so as to ensure that long-term rehabilitation
measures were appropriate to the affected individuals. In
some cases, regenerating income would take priority over
housing needs.

5.0   BENEFITS OF IMPROVED HOUSING

Traditional Bangladeshi houses require frequent
rethatching and replacement of rotted or insect-damaged
framework and so often represent a regular and significant
drain on household budgets. The inadequate shelter afforded
by flimsy bamboo or reed walls encourages ill health and
disease in Bangladesh's humid environment. Lastly, in the
event of flood, cyclone or similar disaster, the traditional
house affords little protection to its occupants or to their
possessions.

"Adequate shelter" is generally recognised as one of
the minimum requirements of any family (eg. Ref. 6); it seems
from the many interviews with disaster victims that most
personal effects of disaster could be ameliorated by the
widespread provision in rural Bangladesh of well made houses.
Lives could be saved by a protective structure, economic
losses greatly reduced and longer term health problems
avoided.

No doubt, providing everyone with good housing would
be costly and it is difficult to envisage such an objective
except within a broader national development strategy.   To
leave it to NGOs working in isolated areas could result in
inconsistencies and inaccurate targetting.

6.0   HOUSING IMPROVEMENTS IN THE CONTEXT OF COMMUNITY
DEVELOPMENT

It has been recognised for some time that the most
successful community developments are those in which
"participants take initiatives and action that is stimulated
by their own thinking..and over which they can exert
effective control" (Ref. 7). It has been suggested (Ref. 8)
that disaster relief operations often suffer from the lack of
such participation. Certainly, the evaluations found that
most people interviewed did have fairly clear perceptions of
where their best interests lay and would probably, given the
opportunities, be capable of evolving appropriate strategies
for individual recovery. However, victims had not often been
consulted over their immediate needs and poverty removed any
"effective control" that they might have had.

Currently, many NGO development programmes include
schemes for encouraging savings and making loans to
individuals which could be used as vehicles for channelling
funds towards improved housing. Membership of a well-
established savings and loan scheme imparts economic security
and gives a good basis for participatory development. Until
now, most such schemes in Bangladesh have concentrated on
income generation and other economic improvements to
participants' lives.

The cyclone evaluation report suggested that an
appropriate modular design for a low-cost dwelling should be
developed which would be funded by loans or grants within
savings schemes. Participants could then choose to build
their home in stages, as money permitted. In the unfortunate
event of a disaster, the homeowner would have a secure
foundation on which to reconstruct and, if desired,
rehabilitation programmes could assist by funding the next
planned phase of the construction. Sooner or later, a
substantial home tailored to the owners' needs would be
completed without the inefficiency implied in a disaster
relief programme.

To further this goal, develepment programmes which
include adult training classes (of which there are many in
Bangladesh) might include construction skills to assist
owners to build as much of their homes as possible. The
creation of mutual assistance self-build groups has been
found to help by pooling existing skills.

The above suggestions are intended to promote
discussion. Many aspects of the proposals await
clarification: suitable savings schemes would be required
throughout Bangladesh and care would be necessary to ensure
the inclusion of women-headed households and other
disadvantaged groups. The better existing schemes have much
experience of identifying disadvantaged groups and
encouraging participation by the poorest communities.

It is not likely that a single house design will
suffice to cover the needs both of areas where the
predominant hazard is flooding (in char and river-bank

districts) and those where high winds are likely. Where there is a serious threat of erosion removing the homestead plot then houses capable of being readily dismantled and re-erected have been found advantageous (Ref. 5).

Within the community development plan, participants can also be encouraged to take other measures to improve communal resistance to disaster. The planting of shelter belts of trees along exposed coasts would have taken much of the force out of the tidal wave, for example.

7.0   CONCLUSIONS

The main conclusion from two studies of multi-million dollar rehabilitation programmes is that provision of improved housing is not an appropriate response to sudden impact disasters such as those which occur in Bangladesh. The cost of an individual house precludes a fair and equal targetting and it has been found difficult to provide safe structures efficiently or in a timely manner.

Most people interviewed were able to cope to varying degrees with the immediate effects of the disaster to which they had been subjected for up to a week or more without assistance. Many were able to take rapid action to alleviate the problems of shelter whereas loss of income led to ongoing problems of debt. If NGOs are to opt for assistance aimed at the third priority of shelter, then consultation with the beneficiary is essential to ensure that his or her needs are met. This is a lesson not only for NGOs but for co-ordinating bodies such as GoB and international agencies.

It is proposed that owners could build their new homes to a modular plan, completing them in several discrete stages as money allowed. This might be allied to appropriate skill training through organised self-help associations.

In view of the long term benefits which substantial housing would provide, this is a provision too important to be left to the chance interventions of local NGO plans.

8.0   ACKNOWLEDGEMENTS

Particular thanks for their assistance during the evaluations are due to Sally Taylor and Richard Forsyth, both formerly of World Vision of Britain, who administered the respective teams. Puspah Rosario, of WVB, assisted in clarifying women's issues in each programme and Paul Das, also of WVB, was an invaluable guide to the cyclone team. The contributions of many other staff of WVB, too numerous to list, must also be acknowledged. The first author was recruited to the teams through RedR, Registered Engineers for Disaster Relief, with whom he has had many experiences of disaster relief since 1980.

9.0   REFERENCES

1.   Statistical pocket book of Bangladesh, 1991, Bangladesh Bureau of Statistics, Dhaka.

2.   Mitchell, J & Slim, H (1990) : A review of World Vision Bangladesh's Flood Rehabilitation Programme 1988-89, Unpublished report to World Vision of Britain.

3.   Palmer-Jones, R, Rutherford, S. R. & Hodgson, R. L. P. (1992) : Chittagong post-cyclone Rehabilitation Programme, World Vision Bangladesh, Unpublished report to World Vision of Britain.

4.   Haider, R., Rahman, A. A. and Huq, S. (1991) (eds.) Cyclone '91, an environmental and perceptional study, Bangladesh Centre for Advanced Studies, Dhaka.

5.   Hodgson, R. L. P. (1990) : Evaluation of technical aspects of World Vision Bangladesh Rehabilitation Programme following the 1988 floods, Unpublished report to World Vision of Britain.

6.   ILO, Employment, growth and basic needs : Report of the World Employment Conference, Geneva, 1976

7.   Acc Task Force on Rural Development, Report of third meeting of the working group on programme harmonisation, Rome, 1978

8.   Hodgson, R. L. P. (1993) : Community participation in emergency technical programmes, Proceedings of 1st International Conference on Technical Support to Refugees, ed. Reed, R. A., Loughborough, pp52-60

32. Protecting Bangladeshi communities against floods and cyclones

H. BRAMMER, International Panel of Experts, Bangladesh Flood Action Plan, and S. JONES, International Panel of Experts, Bangladesh Flood Action Plan and Centre for Development Studies, University of Wales, Swansea

Summary

Floods and tropical cyclones periodically claim many thousands of lives in Bangladesh, disrupt normal economic activities and aggravate already-severe problems of poverty, health and quality of life. Successive severe floods in 1987 and 1988 stimulated the international aid community to support a Bangladesh Flood Action Plan (FAP) aiming to identify and implement a comprehensive set of activities to protect people, settlements and economic infrastructure against recurrent flood disasters. The first phase of the FAP (1990-95) comprises 26 planning, pilot and supporting studies focussing on the identification of projects and programmes - non-structural and structural - which are technically, economically, socially and environmentally sound. The FAP incorporated a cyclone rehabilitation project to strengthen coastal embankments. Following the disastrous April 1991 cyclone, this study was amplified and project implementation accelerated, supplemented by a comprehensive cyclone-shelter construction programme (outside the FAP).

Introduction

Because of its geographical location, Bangladesh is exposed to severe flood and cyclone hazards. The vulnerability of its people to these hazards is exacerbated by high population density, widespread poverty and inadequacy of resources for investment in mitigatory measures. This paper examines the causes of Bangladesh's vulnerability to floods and tropical cyclones, and describes measures that are being taken, with international assistance, to reduce that vulnerability.

The physical setting

Floodplains of the Ganges, Brahmaputra, Meghna and many smaller rivers occupy about 80 percent of Bangladesh (Figure 1). More than 90 percent of the flow in those rivers originates outside the country, in areas receiving some of the heaviest rainfall in the world. Bangladesh itself has a tropical monsoon climate with mean annual rainfalls ranging

Natural disasters. Thomas Telford, London, 1993

from 1250 to 5000mm in different areas, falling mainly in four monsoon months; (Cherrapunji, just over the north-eastern border, averages >11,000mm).

Tropical cyclones (typhoons) originating in the Bay of Bengal are liable to affect coastal districts in the pre-monsoon and post-monsoon seasons. They often are accompanied by storm surges, which may exceed 5m in height in severe cyclones. An average of about five cyclones a year with wind speed >87km/hr occur in the Bay of Bengal. They may cross the coast anywhere between Sri Lanka and Burma (Myanmar). The frequency of occurrence in Bangladesh is highly erratic: there were 13 in the 11 years between 1960 and 1970, but only seven in the period 1971-1991 severe enough to cause human casualties.

Floods in Bangladesh are a complex phenomenon (Brammer, 1990). They include river, flash, rainwater, tidal and storm-surge floods in different, but overlapping, areas. In most inland areas, inundation is caused by a combination of rainwater and river-water flooding. High river levels caused by heavy monsoon rainfall occurring outside the country impede the drainage of water derived from local rainfall, which consequently is ponded on adjoining land.

In coastal areas, land is flooded at high tide (or at high spring tides), where embankments do not exclude such flooding. Whether land is embanked or not, flooding in the monsoon season is mainly by fresh water from rivers or rainwater, but some unembanked areas are submerged by saline water in the dry season. Storm-surge flooding (with sea-water) rarely penetrates more than a few kilometres inland from the coast or from major tidal channels.

On river floodplains, the relative extents of river-water and rain-water flooding vary from year to year according to river levels and local rainfall. In most years, rainwater flooding is most extensive, and silty river water covers only land within and immediately adjoining the main river channels, flash flood areas near hills and areas subject to tidal flooding. In high flood years, river water may cover the whole of the floodplains adjoining the main rivers. Floodwater is estimated to have covered 82,000km2 at the peak of the 1988 flood: i.e., two-thirds of the country.

Bengalis differentiate between normal flooding (barsha), to which their settlements and economic activities are well adapted, and floods (bonna) which are liable to damage crops and property, and which may endanger human lives. It is useful to maintain this distinction in English: i.e., between 'flooding' (simple inundation) and 'floods' (damaging flow or depth of water).

Bangladesh's floodplains are not absolutely flat. They comprise a succession of ridges (existing or former levees) and depressions (backswamps or old channels). Elevation differences between adjoining ridges and depressions are 2-3m on most river floodplains, but are ca 1m on tidal and estuarine floodplains and up to 5-6m in some deep basin areas (such as the Sylhet Basin in the north-east).

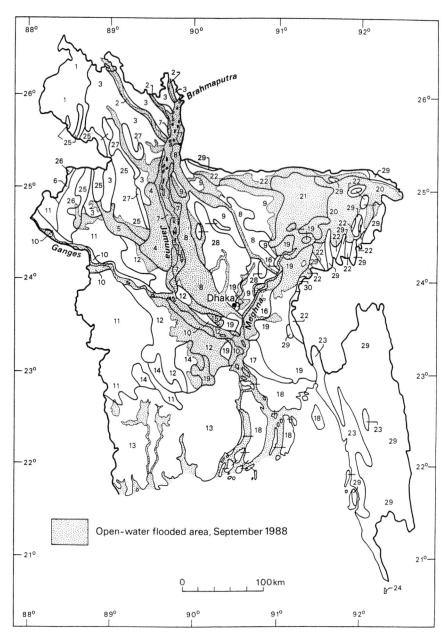

Fig. 1. Bangladesh: physiography (key on facing page)

Key to Fig. 1

1 Old Himalayan Piedmont Plain	17 Lower Meghna River Floodplain
2 Active Teesta Floodplain	18 Young Meghna Estuarine Floodplain
3 Teesta Meander Floodplain	19 Old Meghna Estuarine Floodplain
4 Karatoya-Bangali Floodplain	
5 Lower Atrai Basin	20 Eastern Surma-Kusiyara Floodplain
6 Lower Purnabhaba Floodplain	21 Sylhet Basin
7 Active Brahmaputra-Jamuna Floodplain	22 Northern and Eastern Piedmont Plains
8 Young Brahmaputra-Jamuna Floodplain	23 Chittagong Coastal Plain
9 Old Brahmaputra Floodplain	24 St Martin's Coral Island
10 Active Ganges Floodplain	25 Level Barind Tract
11 High Ganges River Floodplain	26 High Barind Tract
12 Low Ganges River Floodplain	27 North-eastern Barind Tract
13 Ganges Tidal Floodplain	28 Madhupur Tract
14 Gopalganj-Khulna Bils	29 Northern and Eastern Hills
15 Arial Bil	30 Akhaura Terrace
16 Middle Meghna River Floodplain	

These elevation differences mean that the depth and duration of seasonal flooding vary between physiographic regions and also within them. The highest ridge sites are rarely flooded; intermediate sites generally are flooded for 2-4 months; and adjoining depression centres may be flooded for up to 6-9 months; the lowest sites (bils) remain submerged for most or all of the year. Because of floodplain microrelief, such elevation differences occur within villages. As will be described later, they are highly significant for land use. Differences in depth and duration of flooding also vary from year to year because of differences in river levels and rainfall.

Coastal areas are flooded twice-daily (where not embanked), though substantial areas adjoining the Meghna estuary are tidally flooded only in the monsoon season when incoming river levels are high. As indicated above, flooding is predominantly by fresh water in the monsoon season. However, soils in many coastal areas become saline to varying degrees in the dry season due to capillary rise of moisture to the surface from a saline groundwater-table. They may also remain saline for a time in the monsoon season following a pre-monsoon storm surge, especially where this leaves breaches in coastal embankments which allow tidal flooding with salt water to occur.

The socio-economic setting

Bangladesh's socio-economic environment is characterized by high population density, prevalent poverty and predominantly rural settlement, with a majority of households dependent on agriculture or fishing.

The 1991 census gave a total population of 109.9 million, growing at an annual rate of 2.03 percent. The population is projected to double by ca 2030. The urban population is 9.3 percent, but is expected to grow to 30-40 percent of the total by 2030. Population density exceeds 1000/km2 in some interior floodplain districts, but is lower (650/km2) in coastal districts.

Some 74 percent of rural households are mainly dependent on agriculture, either as land-owners, cultivating tenants or labourers. However, many households also engage in fishing, trading or other means of subsistence, and there is considerable seasonal migration of labour for rice planting and harvesting, especially to coastal areas. For some households, remittances of money from family members working in urban areas or abroad are also important.

Land-ownership is highly skewed. In 1983-84, 4.9 percent of rural households with >3 ha owned 26 percent of the land; 24.7 percent with 1-3 ha owned 45.1 percent; while 70.3 percent with nil or <1 ha owned 29.0 percent of the total (BBS, 1992). The relative proportions of different ownership classes vary across the country. In general, there are higher proportions of small and medium farmers in the most densely settled central and south-eastern districts, and relatively more large farmers - often absentee - in cyclone-prone coastal areas, deeply-flooded interior basin areas and in drought-prone western areas. Land holdings typically are fragmented into many scattered fields averaging about 0.06ha in size. Much land is cultivated by tenants, predominantly on a 50:50 share-cropping basis.

Rural poverty is widespread, with per capita GNP, estimated in 1988 to be US$170, among the lowest in the world. Between 50 and 60 percent of housholds are landless or own less than 0.2ha of land and depend on selling their labour for survival. Underemployment in rural areas is between 30 and 40 per cent. The most recent estimates of poverty in Bangladesh indicate that 51 percent of the rural population (some 44 million people) were below the poverty line (defined as 2,122 calories/day/person) in 1986. Life expectancy at birth is 55 years, which is the lowest in Asia, and infant mortality is high. Despite indications of some marginal reduction in poverty in recent years, due mainly to the expansion of irrigation in many rural areas, rural and urban poverty remain overwhelming. About 10 percent of the rural population are both landless and homeless, and are thus especially vulnerable. Many of these people live as squatters on flood embankments and other government land.

Women perform important tasks within the household in tending livestock, homestead gardens and grain and seed stocks. About 90 per cent of the population is Muslim and the system of purdah, which restricts women to working around the homestead, is prevalent in most areas. However, increasing numbers of poor women are also becoming involved in paid labour operations outside the homestead, such as in field cultivation and rural construction activities, and in the garment industry in towns.

Traditional adaptations

Traditional settlements, economic activities and social customs are well adapted to seasonal flooding, but they are much less well adapted to the onslaught of periodic severe floods and cyclones.

Floodplain settlements are built on the highest land available: river levees or older floodplain ridges. For this reason, they often are curvilinear. Settlement tends to be more dispersed - either as individual family homesteads or small clusters of homesteads (paras) - in areas where the risk of hazardous floods is low or where flooding is shallow, as in most coastal areas.

Rural villages and small towns comprise individual homesteads on earthen mounds raised above normal flood levels. Buildings are mainly constructed on a wood or bamboo frame with matting or jute-stick walls, sometimes reinforced with a mud plaster, and with a thatch or metal-sheet roof. They are often adjoined by a small tank (pond) used for domestic water supply and often for fish production, and usually surrounded by multipurpose trees, bamboos and a small vegetable garden.

Rural roads are built on embankments to raise them above normal flood levels. However, bridges and culverts often are inadequate in size and number, (usually because of lack of funds). This can impede overland flow of water during heavy monsoon rainfall or high river floods, aggravating local flooding and leading to breaching of embankments and scouring of soil from fields adjacent to bridges. Unmetalled road surfaces often are too soft or slippery for use by motor vehicles during and after heavy rainfall - including after cyclones - and may be difficult to negotiate in the dry season because of deep ruts caused by bullock carts, pot-holes or broken bridges.

Boats are widely used for transport in the monsoon season; also in the dry season in areas with perennial river flow, including tidal areas. Small diesel engines, originally imported for use in irrigation pumps, are now widely used in boats, largely displacing sail. This has considerably speeded up rural communications.

Farmers' traditional cropping patterns are closely adapted to seasonal flooding characteristics. Rice is the principal crop, occupying about 80 percent of the cropped area. None-the-less, a wide range of dryland crops is also grown, especially in the dry season, using residual soil moisture; rice generally is grown where irrigation is available. Much land grows two or three crops a year. Farmers have selected many thousands of rice varieties adapted to local micro-environments, including differences in flooding depth and duration, and brackish water conditions; some long-stem varieties can tolerate up to ca 4m depth of water at maturity.

Figure 2 illustrates how the main seasonal rice groups (aus, aman, boro) are adapted to depth-of-flooding land types. These land types represent 'normal' flooding conditions; i.e.,

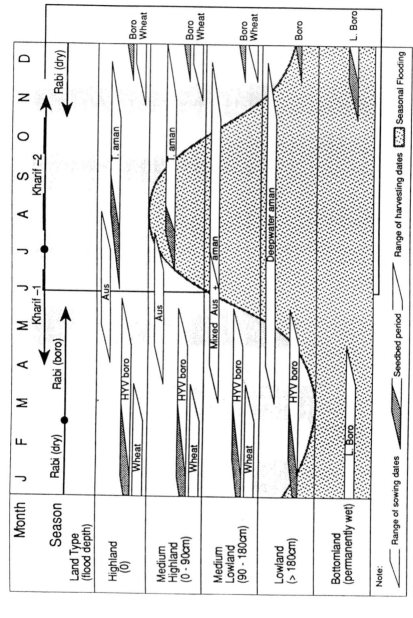

Fig. 2. Relationship of rice and wheat crops with seasonal flooding

those which farmers expect to occur approximately four years out of five. Crop damage occurs when floodwater rises earlier, higher, more rapidly or later than 'normal'. However, farmers have a wide repertoire of practices to off-set crop losses, including replanting if time and water-depth permit, and substituting an alternative crop in the following dry season; there was a big expansion of dry-season irrigation following the severe 1987 and 1988 floods. Flood and cyclone disasters, however, impoverish many farmers, inducing forced sale of land, livestock or other assets, and the incurrence of debt burdens.

Fishing is both a subsistence and a commercial activity. Most rural households engage in casual fishing for subsistence during the seasonal flooding of floodplain land; fishing of this common-property resource is particularly important for poor households. Additionally, relatively larger households catch fish from naturally or artificially stocked ponds adjoining their houses, and some lease larger tanks (ponds) or bils from Government. Professional fishermen catch fish for sale in rivers, bils and the tanks of big land-owners. Shrimp farming has expanded recently in some coastal areas, and now supports an important export industry. Marine fisheries are operated by both small artisinal groups and bigger commercial firms.

There has been a decline in capture fisheries in recent years, attributed to overfishing and interventions in the natural environment by flood protection works, use of water in bils for irrigation, and use of agro-chemicals. However, this has been compensated to some extent by an increase in culture fisheries (including shrimp farming). This trend is expected to continue as floodplain agriculture intensifies further. The change from capture to culture fisheries involves a shift in benefits from the poor, who are able to fish in open water bodies, to the rich who own most of the ponds and shrimp farms. In coastal areas, shrimp farming and salt production are both important activities.

Vulnerability

Many people in Bangladesh - possibly as many as 10 million - live in highly vulnerable areas which it is impractical to protect from floods or storm surges, and where in addition it is difficult to provide rescue and relief services. Such areas include the active floodplains (river chars) within and immediately adjoining the major rivers, estuarine char land in the Meghna estuary and low-lying tidal floodplain land adjacent to the coast.

Chars suffer the additional hazard of erosion by river or tidal currents, so that settlers periodically lose their land and have to re-build their houses in new sites, sometimes on adjacent river embankments. More than 100,000 people have now settled quasi-permanently on the Brahmaputra right embankment. Many displaced families move to Dhaka and other urban areas.

Ideally, people should not live (or be allowed to live) in such hazardous areas. It is in such areas that the majority of human casualties occur in severe floods and cyclones.

NATURAL DISASTERS

However, for many people in Bangladesh there seems little alternative, impoverished as they are by loss of family land, burdened with debts and faced with limited employment opportunities in 'mainland' areas. They surely are aware of the risks of settling on such land; and between periodic floods or cyclones, it may be possible for them to earn a more-or-less satisfactory living from farming or fishing in such areas. Although the risk of destructive floods or cyclones exists every year, the interval between such occurrences may, in practice, be 5-10 years on river chars and even longer in cyclone-prone coastal areas.

The people cannot be blamed for occupying such land; and government does not have the resources to provide employment opportunities which might attract people out of such vulnerable areas. But the existence of such populations (possibly some 4 million people altogether on river and estuarine char land) presents a serious problem for government and NGOs in providing rescue and relief services in times of emergency. Possible means of reducing vulnerability on this and other disaster-prone land are considered in a later section.

Household responses

During exceptionally high floods on river floodplains (including river chars), families may live on platforms (machas) within their houses. If flood-levels continue to rise, they may move to roofs or trees, or go by boat to any available higher ground: river or road embankments; public buldings; or the houses of more wealthy people. Livestock, especially cattle, are also moved to such higher land. However, many animals may be lost if floods are prolonged, because of the difficulty of providing grazing or fodder.

Supplies of drinking water and fuel for cooking become problematical, especially for poor households. The latter suffer additional hardships due to low food stocks and reduced employment opportunities during floods. They may, therefore, need to place themselves at the mercy of richer households or move to government or NGO relief centres. Diarrhoeal diseases often are prevalent, too, and many deaths were caused by snake-bite in the 1988 flood. Provision of medical services is difficult at the best of times in remote rural areas, and access becomes especially difficult during floods.

People living in cyclone-prone areas have little defence against strong winds and storm surges. Big land-owners generally live inland, often in urban areas; it is only the poor who reside in such vulnerable areas, together with migrant seasonal labour living in temporary shelter. The coastal embankment was not designed to prevent overtopping by storm surges; and there are wholly inadequate numbers of cyclone shelters where people could take refuge on receipt of cyclone warnings.

Even where people could escape to higher ground or shelters, they are reluctant to leave their homes until the last moment, because they fear that their livestock and other possessions may be looted. As a result, human and livestock mortality can be very high when cyclones occur, with most deaths being caused caused by drowning during storm surges. In the 1991 cyclone, children had been especially vulnerable and accounted for about 70 per cent of deaths, followed by women (20 per cent) and men (10%). More women died than men because they tended to stay at home until the last minute to look after children and livestock. In exposed coastal areas, 30 to 40 per cent of the population perished.

Government policy and strategies

It has been the policy of successive governments to protect people from the adverse effects of natural disasters to the extent possible. Several strategies have been adopted over the years: preparedness and relief; warnings and protection; and alternative kinds of development. Successive disasters have served to renew official focus on continuing needs, and strategies have continued to be refined with support from international development aid programmes.

Space does not permit more than an outline to be given of the historical development of disaster management in Bangladesh. A more detailed account is given in Brammer and Khan (1991). Two major current programmes are described in later sections: the Flood Action Plan; and a comprehensive cyclone protection programme.

Successive governments on the Indian subcontinent have had long experience with coping with natural disasters. The Bengal Famine Code, a set of administrative instructions for officials responsible for managing critical food shortages, was published over 100 years ago. It was succeeded by a Relief Code (which included instructions for 'test relief', a pre-cursor of today's Food-for-Work activities), and later, during the Pakistan period, by separate Standing Orders for Flood and Cyclone. These codes were periodically up-dated; they are again being up-dated following the 1988 flood and 1991 cyclone disasters.

Following a succession of tropical cyclone disasters in the 1960s, a Storm Warning Centre equipped with radar was set up in the Meteorological Department in the late 1960s. The Red Crescent/Red Cross Society also set up a volunteer programme for carrying warnings to villages throughout the cyclone zone. A small number of raised mounds (killas) were erected at this time, providing refuges for people and livestock against storm surge flooding. Following the 1970 cyclone, 299 concrete cyclone shelters were built, mainly funded by the World Bank, and an attempt was made to settle people living in high-risk areas in 'cluster villages' (which proved unpopular, so was discontinued).

A Flood Forecasting and Warning Centre was set up in the Bangladesh Water Development Board (BWDB) in 1972. Daily bulletins are issued during the flood season. They provide quantitative flood forecasts for the next 72 hours for the Ganges and Brahmaputra-Jamuna rivers, and for two smaller rivers adjoining Dhaka, together with more qualitative forecasts for rivers elsewhere in the country.

There is a long history of building embankments to keep out floods. Rennell, in his journal for 1767, describes embankments 12 feet high and 14 yards broad along both sides of the Ganges near Kushtia and Pabna, already breached by the river and so old that no-one could tell him when they had been built. During the 18th and 19th centuries, local zamindars (big land-lords) in coastal areas are known to have built and maintained low embankments along tidal rivers to keep out saline water.

Following severe floods in the 1950s, government embarked on a plan to provide flood protection works throughout the country. A large part of this plan has been implemented. Some 3600km of coastal embankments and over 2000km of river embankments now exist. The Ganges and Teesta rivers are fully embanked; the Brahmaputra-Jamuna is embanked along almost all its right bank and about half of its left bank; substantial sections along both banks of the Padma and Meghna rivers are embanked, as they are along many smaller rivers; and so-called coastal embankments extend along virtually the full length of tidal rivers, creating polders between them.

Sluices in coastal embankment polders provide tidal drainage, and pumps are used to drain some protected areas inland (as well as provide irrigation). Most river embankments are designed only to keep out river floods, though some have 'flushing sluices' to allow inlet or outlet of water to meet local drainage or irrigation requirements. Submersible embankments are used in the deeply-flooded, high-rainfall north-east, providing protection to the dry-season boro rice crop against early flash floods.

The primary purpose of all these embankments was to to protect agricultural production. Coastal embankments were designed to keep out saline water at high tides; they were not designed to keep out storm surges which endanger human lives. Similarly, river embankments were designed to protect cropland against flood damage; the floodplain people most vulnerable to loss of life, those occupying char land, remain unprotected (although, inadvertently, the adjoining embankments provide refuges to which these people can move during severe floods, and which large numbers continue to occupy as squatters after floods have eroded their land).

Following the severe 1974 flood (which was followed by famine), the government, while continuing to support flood control and drainage investments, turned increasingly to a strategy which encouraged intensification of crop production in the relatively safer dry season. Wheat production grew by about 1 million tons between 1975 and 1985, since when it has remained almost static at about that level. Small-scale irrigation expanded rapidly. It now covers ca 2.9M ha, and boro rice production for which it is mainly used increased by 3.7M million tons between 1975 and 1991. Boro rice now makes up one-third of total rice production. Many farmers in flood-prone areas are now much less dependent than formerly on production of monsoon-season rice crops (aus and aman).

The Flood Action Plan

Severe floods in 1987 and 1988 caused serious loss of life and damage to infrastructure (Table 1). The economic loss was

Table 1. Official estimates of losses and damage by floods in 1987 and 1988

Item	Loss/damage	
	1987	1988
Area flooded	57 000 km^2	82 000 km^2
Houses totally/partially damaged	2.5 M	7.2 M
Human lives lost	1657	2379
Livestock lost		
cattle, goats, etc	64 700	172 000
poultry	206 000	410 000
Rice production lost	3.5 M tonnes	2 Mtonnes
Roads		
trunk	1523 km	3000 km
rural	15 107 km	10 000 km
bridges, culverts	1102	898
Railways		
embankments	698 km	1300 km
bridges	166	270
Flood embankments	1279 km	1990 km
Irrigation/drainage canals	222 km	283 km
Irrigation/drainage control		
structures	541	1465
Electric power		
substations flooded	n/a	18
11 KV power lines de-energized	n/a	2000 km
Industrial units flooded	n/a	>1000
Hospitals flooded	n/a	45
Health centres flooded	1305	1400
Schools flooded	6689	13 000
Rural hand tubewells flooded	n/a	240 000

Source: mainly BWDB, 1987, and MOT, 1988. Other sources give different figures for some items.
n/a: not available.

estimated at ca US$3 million. The human distress caused to half the country's population by being marooned or evacuated, the loss of lives and property, shortage of food and water, and living in unsanitary conditions was unmeasurable. The 1988 flood in particular affected Dhaka and other urban populations as well as rural people.

These successive disasters stimulated the international aid community to support the Government of Bangladesh in seeking a permanent solution to the chronic flood problem which repeatedly undermines efforts to promote economic and social development. After a number of preliminary studies, a Flood Action Plan was prepared in 1989. This is being coordinated by the World Bank and supported by 15 aid donors (Figure 3). Further details of the background to the Flood Action Plan (FAP) are given in World Bank (1990), Brammer (1990) and Dempster and Brammer (1992).

The FAP comprises a set of 26 planning, pilot and supporting studies. These cover a wide field of interests, as is shown in Figure 3. FAP activities are numbered sequentially from FAP1 to FAP26. They include the strengthening of existing flood forecasting and disaster preparedness systems. Space does not permit a detailed description of all the various FAP components: a recent summary of progress is given in FPCO (1992). Instead, attention is focussed on five major issues which illustrate some new approaches being made under the FAP.

Flood management rather than flood protection is being aimed at. FAP14 and other studies showed that most floodplain inhabitants want protection only against moderate or severe floods (1 in >5 years frequency). They want normal flooding to continue so as to derive continuing benefits they perceive for fisheries, soil fertility and navigation.

To this end, the principle of 'controlled flooding' is being advocated. In this, river embankments would keep out unwanted high or untimely river floods which damage crops, but regulators would remain open at other times to allow normal flooding and drainage. Subsidiary embankments (mainly existing rural roads) and regulators would divide the protected floodplain into compartments, controlling the overland flow of floodwater (both river-water and rain-water).

Apart from benefits to fisheries and navigation, the reduced risk of unwanted floods is expected to encourage farmers to intensify crop production in the monsoon season. The techniques of controlled flooding are being tested by FAP20 in two pilot areas, while FAP17 is making a comprehensive study of floodplain fisheries to ascertain complementary flood management needs for fisheries.

River training is being studied under FAPs 1, 9a, 9b, 21 and 22. River-bank erosion is a serious problem along the Brahmaputra-Jamuna river and parts of the Meghna. Sirajganj, Chandpur and several other towns are exposed to this erosion, and valuable old agricultural land is being lost in places. About half the 220km length of the Brahmaputra right embankment has had to be retired - some sections several times - since it was built in the 1960s, and recurrent breaches in

Activities	Donors
Main components	
FAP1 Brahmaputra training study	IDA
FAP2 Northwest regional study	UK-Japan
FAP3 N. Central regional study	EEC-France
FAP4 Southwest regional study	ADB-UNDP
FAP5 Southeast regional study	IDA-UNDP
FAP6 Northeast regional study	Canada
FAP7 Cyclone protection project	EEC-IDA
FAP8a/b Dhaka town protection	Japan/ADB
FAP9a/b Secondary towns	ADB/IDA
FAP10 Flood forecasting	UNDP, Japan
FAP11 Disaster preparedness	UNDP
Supporting activities	
FAP12/13. Agric. review/O&M	UK-Japan
FAP14. Flood response study	USA
FAP15. Land acquisition study	Sweden
FAP16. Environmental study	USA
FAP17 Fisheries study	UK
FAP18 Topographic mapping	Finland, Swiss etc
FAP19 GIS	USA
FAP20 Compartmentalisation	NL-Germany
FAP21/22 River pilot projects	Germany-France
FAP23 Flood proofing study	USA
FAP24 River surveys & studies	EEC
FAP25 Flood modelling	Denmark etc
FAP26 Institutional programme	UNDP, France etc

Fig. 3. Bangladesh Flood Action Plan: activities and donors

the past 10 years have caused serious flooding of previously protected land.

There is a strong public demand to stop this erosion. Past attempts at bank protection by revetments and groynes have been costly and largely ineffective. FAPs 21+22 will test different methods and materials for protecting river-banks and ways of diverting channels away from important river sections. This is a formidable challenge. The Brahmaputra-Jamuna has a strongly-braided channel 10-15km wide. It has increased in width by as much as 5km in the past 30 years in some reaches, and generally shows a marked preference to erode its right bank. Test works under FAP21+22 will cost $40 million - the most costly item in the FAP portfolio.

NATURAL DISASTERS

Flood proofing includes mitigation measures other than flood
protection works. Under FAP, the term is particularly being
used for non-structural or simple structural measures to
protect lives, property, infrastructure and services against
adverse flood effects. These might include such things as:
arrangements for disseminating local flood warnings; helping
people to raise homestead mounds, shops, small factories,
etc. above highest flood level; providing flood refuges for
people and livestock; and promoting dry-season agriculture.

Such measures will be particularly relevant for the
substantial areas which cannot be protected against flooding
in the medium or longer terms. They are considered
particularly important for areas lying outside embankments,
including char areas. Base-line studies in such areas have
been carried out under FAPs 3.1 and 16 to assess needs. It is
hoped that pilot programmes for flood proofing will be taken
up by NGOs.

Public consultation and participation are being advocated
under the FAP. In the past, major water management projects
have been blue-printed over the heads of local residents.
Conflicts of interest between, e.g., farmers and fishermen,
and those living outside embankments and those living inside,
have sometimes led to the cutting of embankments during floods
(so-called 'public cuts'), making projects fail. Because of
top-down official attitudes, too, people generally have not
felt any responsibility for maintaining or operating projects,
nor to contribute to their costs. The lengthy, often
litigious, process of acquiring land for structures has also
created public opposition in places.

Efforts are being made to strengthen public involvement in the
planning, design, construction, operation and maintenance of
future projects. Guidelines on Public Participation have been
drafted for use by FAP consultants; they will be refined as
necessary after testing. FAP 20, the compartmentalization
pilot project, has led the way in consultation methodology,
but all the regional and project feasibility studies to-date
have made consultation surveys. Considerable information was
also derived from special social surveys undertaken by FAPs
12, 13, 14, 15, 16 and 23.

In addition, FPCO (the Flood Plan Coordination Organization)
has organized a round of public meetings throughout the
country involving MPs, local leaders and officials to
ascertain local perceptions of flood protection needs and to
discuss consultants' proposed technical and operational
options for flood mitigation. Apart from their value for
public relations, these meetings have provided useful ideas
and feedback to planning consultants.

Environmental aspects are receiving much more attention than
in the past. In recent years, there has been growing concern
about the possible impact of flood control interventions on
river morphology, fisheries, soil fertility, salinity, wetland
habitats, and the security and livelihoods of people living
outside embankments. Environmental impact assessments (EIAs)
are now mandatory before project approval by the Government of
Bangladesh and by many donors. FPCO with FAP16 has prepared
EIA guidelines and a manual for use by FAP consultants.

The conduct of EIAs in Bangladesh is severely handicapped by the lack of experienced ecologists and a dearth of factual information on the environment and physico-biological relationships. Experience on FAP projects to-date has been that professional input requirements for undertaking EIAs have been greatly underestimated (as they have been for public consultation). This deficiency needs to be addressed in preparing future project studies.

Overall Guidelines on Project Assessment (GPA) detailing the methods of economic, financial, social and environmental analysis to be used in project planning have also been issued. The aim of the GPA is to ensure that FAP studies are consistent in the methods they use and take into account all benefits and disbenefits.

Cyclone protection programmes

Although less frequent than floods, cyclones cause many more casualties. The 1987 and 1988 floods together killed about 3000 people. The cyclone which struck south-eastern Bangladesh on 29-30 April 1991 killed an estimated 138,000 (see Jones et al, 1993). That which struck the Meghna estuary in November 1970 killed at least 300,000.

Most of the casualties in cyclones are caused by the associated storm surge, not by the high winds. The storm surge in 1991 is estimated to have been 6m above normal high tide level (and it occurred at a time of equinoctial high spring tides). Wind speeds exceeded 200km/hr. Apart from huge human and livestock losses, substantial damage was caused to houses, trees, crops, fishing boats and shrimp farms. Long sections of the coastal embankment were destroyed, leaving cropland behind it exposed to saltwater flooding during the following monsoon season, until breaches could be repaired. Indications are that the direct impact on the balance of payments, due to export losses and additional import requirements, was of the order of 400 million and the total budgetary impact, due to lost revenues and increased expenditures, was close to 350 million, or about 25 per cent of the annual government budget.

Since the 1960s, there have been several programmes aiming to provide greater protection to people living in cyclone-prone areas: the coastal embankment project itself; improved cyclone warning system; cyclone shelters; improved roads to facilitate access for provision of relief following cyclones; and arrangements for relief distribution. Two major programmes taken up after the 1991 cyclone are described below - coastal embankment; cyclone shelters - together with a review of experience in relief distribution at that time.

The coastal embankment rehabilitation project was initiated after the 1985 cyclone, but prolonged negotiations had delayed implementation. Engineering studies - funded by EEC - were in progress at the time of the 1988 flood, and the project was incorporated into the Flood Action Plan as component FAP7. The objective of the project is to rehabiliate sections of the embankment, mainly in the south-east, which had fallen into disrepair and were exposed to coastal erosion. An additional component was the provision of feeder roads in the cyclone-prone zone.

The 1991 cyclone destroyed an estimated 200km of embankments in the south-east, necessitating an urgent revision of project plans. The revised plan is being implemented in two phases, the first of which - providing emergency works - is now in progress at a cost of about $75 million. A second phase, costing an estimated $100 million, will be taken up later.

The embankment design incorporates new features, such as 'armour-plating' of critical sections near Chittagong port and clay-coring of other sections, and providing, in places, a 1:7 seaward slope to the embankment and afforestation of the foreshore with mangroves wherever possible to break the force of storm waves. Plans to retire exposed sections of the embankment further inland were not acceptable to people who would have been left outside the embankment, and had to be modified.

It was considered impractical to raise the embankment to a height which would exclude all storm surges (which, in theory, could reach 10m in some places). However, the new design is expected to prevent or reduce the extent of breaches by future storm surges, and so considerably attenuate the volume and force of sea-water overtopping the embankment. In combination with the shelter programme described below, this should greatly reduce the risk of drowning to people living behind the embankment.

A cyclone shelter programme has been in progress, intermittently, since the 1960s. As described earlier, the first shelters (killas) were simply raised mounds: 156 of these were built up to about 1975. Following the 1970 cyclone, the World Bank funded 260 concrete shelters (of which 238 were built). Difficulties in administering the project in remote areas delayed implementation, and a subsequent programme organized by the Bangladesh Red Crescent Society (BRCS) on behalf of the Ministry of Relief and Rehabilitation provided only a further 61 shelters during the 1980s. The RCRS estimates that some 1600 shelters are needed in high-risk areas, and a further 1800 in areas of medium risk, in order to protect an estimated 3.3 million people.

Following the 1991 cyclone, there was a resurgence of government and donor interest in providing shelters. To-date, plans have been prepared to construct a further 600-700 shelters throughout the cyclone-prone zone, supported by the Saudi Fund, EEC, ODA, Germany, Japan and a number of NGOs, and implemented over the next 3 years at a cost of $70 million. Associated with the shelter programme, the RCRS volunteer warning programme will be strengthened.

New shelters will be multi-purpose, serving as schools or community shelters under normal conditions. This will overcome a problem experienced with earlier shelters, some of which were built on 'available' land remote from settlements and without provision of funds for maintenance. Under the new programme, the objective is to space shelters so that people do not have to walk more than 1.25km in order to reach a shelter during the difficult conditions which occur as a cyclone approaches.

Emergency Relief. The national relief effort following the 1991 cyclone was coordinated by the newly elected, democratic government of Prime Minister Khaleda Zia. The Government established coordination committees in Dhaka and in the devastated area. The military was operational from the outset and played an important role in assessing need, transporting relief supplies, burying corpses and carcasses, runnning health camps and maintaining law and order. Foreign donors contributed about 100 million to the relief effort, most of it through NGOs, which they considered to have a better record than Government in delivering and targeting relief supplies effectively. The US and UK also provided a military task force to provide logistical support.

Overall, the national relief effort was successful in preventing starvation and reducing suffering. Almost all survivors had received food rations within a week of the disaster and continued to receive supplies for another 4 to 6 weeks. However, some communities did face food shortages later in 1993 after the relief had ceased but before local economies had become reestablished.

Few people died after the cyclone from injuries received in the disaster or from disease. Fears that thousands would die from diarrhoea or in epidemics (e.g., due to large number of human corpses and animal caracasses which littered the area) were not realised.

NGOs are likely to continue to play a key role in supporting Government's response to disasters in the coming years, though the Government is strengthening its own preparedness and management capacity by establishing a Disaster Management Bureau, under the Ministry of Relief, with UNDP support.

References

Bangladesh Bureau of Statistics (BBS) 1992 Statistical pocket book of Bangladesh 1992. BBS, Dhaka.

Brammer, H. 1990 Floods in Bangladesh. Geographical Journal, vol.156, 12-22 and 158-165.

Brammer, H. and H.R. Khan 1991 Bangladesh case study. In Disaster mitigation in Asia and the Pacific. Asian Development Bank, Manila.

Dempster, J.I.M. and H. Brammer 1992 Flood Action Plan - Bangladesh. Outlook on Agriculture, vol. 21, No 4, 301-305. C.A.B. International, Wallingford, U.K.

Flood Plan Coordination Organization (FPCO) 1992 Proceedings of the Second Conference on the Flood Action Plan. FPCO/World Bank Resident Mission.

NATURAL DISASTERS

Jones, S. et al 1993 Evaluation/Review of the ODA Funded Relief and Rehabilitation Programmes in Bangladesh following the Cyclone of April 1991.
Overseas Development Administration, Evaluation Department (Preliminary Draft).

World Bank 1990, Bangladesh Action Plan for Flood Control, Technical Report No 40.

Keynote paper. Assessing vulnerability of low-income communities: a progress report

R. SPENCE, Martin Centre for Architectural and Urban Studies, University of Cambridge

ABSTRACT

Disaster damage scenarios have an important place in hazard protection and mitigation programmes. They can be used to raise the awareness of the local community as well as politicians and planners to the risks they face; to enable particularly vulnerable communities and structure types to be identified and targetted; and as a basis for planning upgrading programmes, building and land-use regulations. Considerable progress has been made in recent years in the methods of loss estimation and vulnerability assessment needed for such damage scenarios, particularly in relation to earthquake hazards. But their application and impact on the hazard mitigation process has so far been limited.

The paper discusses the general problems of developing useful scenarios. It reviews progress in techniques for estimating physical losses and human casualties resulting from earthquakes in low-income communities. It considers the suitability of recent loss estimation studies to the task of earthquake risk mitigation; and it identifies an agenda for research and data assembly to support further progress.

1. INTRODUCTION

A central objective of the IDNDR is to bring the benefits of growing scientific understanding of natural hazards and technical capability in disaster protection to assist (especially low-income) local communities (ref 1). On its own, of course, science and technology can achieve little; a feature of all successful disaster protection programmes is that they have involved a close three-sided collaboration - between technical specialists, local and national governments and the local community itself (ref 2). There have been many calls for a greater control by the local community in disaster protection planning (refs 3,4); it has also been suggested that the "technocratic approach" is dangerous, tending to reinforce existing divisions in society, while the real problem is the economic marginalisation of the poor, which must be addressed by political rather than technical means (ref 4).

NATURAL DISASTERS

But even within a political system which addresses principally
the need of the poorest, there will clearly be a need for the
specialist understanding of natural hazards and the means to
counter them for which scientific and technical knowledge is
required. Housner (ref 1)points to four particular ways which
the scientific community can assist:

- identification of high risk locations
- establishment and monitoring of instrument networks to
  record natural hazard data
- programmes of testing and other investigations to explore
  the relationship between hazards and their consequences
- programmes to improve public awareness of hazards and their
  consequences

All of these tasks are applicable to the whole range of natural
hazards. This paper concentrates its attention on the third of
these areas, and specifically relates to earthquakes.

It is noticeable that the vast majority of protection programmes
for vulnerable communities have in to date been implemented in
post-disaster situations (refs 5, 6, 7). There is little doubt
that the desire to avoid the devastation caused by a disaster
fresh in a community's memory is the most powerful incentive to
rebuild in a safe way. Thus construction practice in Tangshan,
China and Armenia, in Mexico City and now in Erzincan in Turkey
has been profoundly (and perhaps permanently) affected by the
experiences of recent earthquakes. But in many disaster-prone
areas, the recurrence period of "the big one" may be fifty or
one-hundred years or more. The last major event may have
occurred at a time when the shape and size of the settlement was
quite different and probably much smaller than at present; and
the present communities, and even the planning authorities, may
not be aware of the disaster potential they face. In this
respect, urban communities are arguably much more at risk than
rural communities, particularly where the new settlements have
developed rapidly, construction quality is poor, and where
siting is governed mainly by considerations of price and access,
rather than safety (ref 8). But rural communities also face
increasing risks as older, more resilient building techniques
based on increasingly scarce vegetable materials give way to
those based on poor quality and poorly understood factory-based
materials (ref 9). Several of the most catastrophic earthquake
disasters of recent years (e.g. Tangshan, Armenia) have occurred
largely because communities and governments were not aware of
the risks they faced.

As our understanding of the seismicity of the earth, and of the
recurrence of other hazards increases, one of the most valuable
contributions which the scientific community can make to
disaster protection is through studying likely future damage
scenarios. Governments rarely have the means to invest the sums
of money required to provide their citizens with adequate
protection; nor are governments always well-equipped to decide
whether investment in disaster-protection should have priority
over other desirable social expenditure (such as health,
education). But increasingly, the tools are available to inform
the community of the risks they face and of the probable
consequences of alternative options open to them.

408

Such information is the best possible stimulus to appropriate action on the part of the community, either in protecting itself, or in creating political pressure for government action, whether the protection is by means of better building standards, controlling building location, the development of insurance schemes, or the establishment of adequate relief and rescue services for use in an emergency. But for the information to be useful it must be reliable, must relate to the main risks which a community faces, and must be presented in a form which is accessible to the public at large.This paper will first review the progress which has been made in the development of the tools for future loss estimation over the last decade and then return to the question of how useful such estimations have been, and how they might be improved.

2. LOSS ASSESSMENT METHODOLOGY

Several different types of loss assessment can be used, depending on the situation. Three important types are:

a) Scenario studies   These are estimates of the likely consequences - physical losses, human casualties, economic and other effects - of a particular plausible or 'credible' earthquake on a region (which has a high probability of recurrence within the near future, say 25 to 50 years at most). Scenario studies can be used both to estimate the resources needed to handle an emergency, and also to increase public awareness of the risks (refs 10,2).

b) Catastrophe studies The probable effects of a larger earthquake which could occur but is less likely, (with an estimated recurrence period of perhaps 250 or 500 years). The purpose is to indicate the greatest risk faced, with a view to "hardening" key facilities (ref 11).

c) Annualised risk Average estimated losses from all events over some future time period may be reduced to an annualised risk - these are used for estimating insurance premiums or for cost benefit analysis of protection investment programmes (refs 12, 7).

The first two types of loss assessment require a knowledge of the faulting and the likely size and location of an event on it. The records of past earthquakes can be used both to estimate the maximum magnitude with a given time frame and the likely attenuation of effects with distance from the source. But in the absence of relevant data, alternative relationships borrowed from other areas are commonly used (refs 13,11). In some cases where there is no clear relationship between faulting and earthquake occurrence, an arbitrary location for the earthquake may need to be assumed in relation to vulnerable facilities. Annualised risk studies are more difficult to perform, because some allowance has to be made for the changes both in the earthquake potential of the faults and the nature of the building stock, which result from the occurrence of each earthquake event.

Considerable progress has been made during recent years both in defining earthquake source mechanisms and recurrence

relationships (refs 14,15) and in the development of attenuation
relationships (refs 16,17), offering the possibilities of loss
estimates of tolerable reliability. This paper will not be
concerned with these developments. But loss assessment also
requires:
- a classification of building types or other elements at risk
- a method of defining loss
- 'vulnerability' or 'fragility' curves (the former term is
  used here) relating loss to a parameter of ground motion.

3. VULNERABILITY METHODOLOGY

The appropriate vulnerability methodology differs according to
whether the elements at risk are:

- Built facilities such as buildings and infrastructure
- People
- The economy and other human activities

Of these the impacts of earthquakes on built facilities are the
easiest to assess, and some real progress has been made in
making such loss assessments. The impacts on people (death,
injury, homelessness) on human and economic activities are much
more difficult to assess, and in consequence are often
overlooked. Yet it is precisely in these areas that the most
important consequences of earthquakes are often felt. In the
1991 Erzincan earthquake for instance any protection of human
lives achieved through better building was undermined by the
collapse of all the city's major hospitals (ref 18). And in the
1991 Costa Rica earthquake, the most severe impact of the
earthquake was not the collapse of buildings, but the economic
consequences of the disruption of the country's road network
which prevented the banana crop from being brought to the export
market (ref 19).

4. PHYSICAL VULNERABILITY MODELS

Two different approaches to physical vulnerability assessment
are identifiable, which are referred to as *predicted*
vulnerability and *observed* vulnerability.

Predicted vulnerability is the assessment of the expected
performance of buildings and other facilities based on
calculated response of the building to a defined earthquake
input. Such methods have primarily been applied to reinforced
concrete frame buildings for which analytical computer models of
the response to a particular base-motion time-history are
becoming available. In one example, studies of a large number
of buildings in Mexico City showed a good correlation between
the seismic resistance coefficient of the building as a whole
and its degree of damage (ref 20).

At Skopje, Macedonia the performance of elements in laboratory
tests under cyclic loading has been combined with inelastic
frame analysis to produce damage estimates for typical
reinforced concrete framed buildings as a function of the peak
ground acceleration (ref 21) for a range of different ground
motion inputs, leading to vulnerability curves for such
buildings.

In Thessaloniki, Greece, a standard inelastic hysteretic computer model was used to predict the performance element-by-element of buildings typical of the city under base-motions which were derived from strong motion records recorded during the 20.6.78 earthquake. Damage to each element was assessed on the basis of a comparison between the resistance and the ductility demand; and from this a repair cost for the building as a whole, element by element was derived (ref 22). This was extrapolated by simple assumptions to the whole city building stock, and a reasonable fit was found beween the 'predicted' and the actual cost of repair. A similar but simplified procedure has been used to assess damage to masonry building in Colombia (ref 2).

The development of predicted vulnerability methods is vital, because it facilitates studies of the vulnerability of a building or building type for which earthquake damage statistics do not exist. But they suffer from the disadvantages that each building must be analysed individually under a particular predicted ground motion, so data collection is very extensive. Moreover the response of frame structures to different ground motions with the same peak acceleration and frequency distribution can be radically different, so much analytical work is needed to build a realistic picture even of the performance of one building. The prospects for building realistic city-wide damage scenarios from such an approach are therefore not good - their usefulness will be in extrapolating and calibrating existing vulnerability functions, and in assessing key structures.

Observed vulnerability is the assessment of the performance of buildings and facilities based on damage in past earthquakes. The systematic recording of building damage which has been carried out during the last decade has given a considerable boost to these methods. Vulnerability curves for a range of common building types have been produced by a number of authors (refs 23-26), using macrosesimic intensity as the base motion parameter. Classifications of building types vary, according to the data from which the curves were derived; the definitions of loss also vary. In studies for insurance purposes (refs 23,24) where the main purpose is to determine damage cost, the measure of vulnerability is repair cost ratio. Cochrane and Schaad (ref 24) also propose influence coefficients for age of building in three classes. In other cases (refs 25,27) separate vulnerability functions are defined for different levels of damage (moderate damage, collapse etc). The vulnerability functions produced by the Applied Technology Council (ref 26), although based on recorded damage data, were in fact defined by an expert group opinion survey to enable extrapolation to many building types or levels of groung motion for which inadequate damage data exist. Thus although widely used, they are somewhat hypothetical.

Spence et al (ref 27) have attempted to avoid the inadequacies of defining ground motion on the basis of recorded macioseismic intensity by defining a new damage-related intensity scale, pegged through a small number of local surveys to recorded strong ground motion. This work has shown that for masonry buildings, the best ground motion parameter to use for

predicting damage is mean spectral acceleration in the period
range 0.1-0.3 seconds.

5. REGIONAL AND URBAN EARTHQUAKE SCENARIO STUDIES

A number of city or regional earthquake scenarios have been
based on such vulnerability functions. Three problems which need
to be confronted in all such studies are:

- an inventory and mapping of buildings is required, in which
  buildings are classified according to their vulnerability
  type
- for each building type, an appropriate vulnerability curve
  must be chosen
- the impact of subsoil conditions on local earthquake ground
  motion has to be considered

Since inventory data is often scarce, some very coarse
assumptions are commonly made in developing the inventory, which
could have a very considerable effect on the reliability of the
output. For example, in a recent study of seismic risk in
Tehran, (ref 10) all buildings were subdivided into only three
classes, and since one of these classes constituted 80% of the
total, losses were assumed concentrated in this class. In a
study of seismic risk for Mendoza City Argentina (ref 28),
buildings were subdivided into only two classes, earthquake
resistant and non-earthquake resistant (mainly adobe houses).
In a study of losses in Sulawesi, Indonesia (ref 11), buildings
were divided into three types, permanent and semi-permanent, and
bamboo framed hut. In each of these cases, the vulnerability
curve for each class was derived from damage data from a few
recent local earthquakes and subsoil conditions were also very
crudely modelled. In the US, a number of regional damage
surveys have been carried out using inventory data from a
variety of official and insurance sources and applying the
vulnerability curves produced by the Applied Technology Council
(ref 26)). In Europe, Italy, Greece and Turkey have rich damage
data from recent earthquakes (refs 29,25)and a number of
scenario studies have been derived from them (ref 7).

In the U.K. no recent damage data exist, although there is
geologically a small probability of earthquakes up to magnitude
6, which would be large enough to cause considerable damage. In
a recent study for the DoE examining the consequences of a
hypothetical Ms=6.0 earthquake on two typical U.K. cities,
detailed inventories of both residential and non-residential
buildings and their subdivision among 5 building vulnerability
classes and between up to 60 administrative wards of the city,
were compiled from a variety of official sources, calibrated by
field surveys (ref 13). Vulnerability curves for each class
were selected by analysis of damage data for similar classes of
building in the worldwide data set held at the Martin Centre
(ref 7) related to both spectral acceleration and MSK Intensity.
Variation in local spectral acceleration was accounted for by
damage in each geographical area were derived for a scenario
earthquake using both MSK Intensity (unmodified by subsoil
conditions) and spectral acceleration, (modified by subsoil
conditions) as the ground motion parameter. This study
indicated that uncertainty in the soil amplification factor has

a much larger impact on the loss estimates than the
uncertainties in the inventory or vulnerability functions used.

Turkish damage data have been used to construct a damage
scenario for the province of Bursa in Turkey (ref 30). In this
case village census data were used to assemble an inventory of
buildings according to five types, and vulnerability histograms
for each of which were derived from damage data from previous
Turkish earthquakes, giving damage at five levels. MSK Intensity
was used as the parameter of ground motion, and some account of
the influence of subsoil conditions was made in drawing the
isioseismals for the presumed earthquake.

6. HUMAN CASUALTY ASSESSMENT

Reliable human casualty assessment has been hampered by a
serious lack of detailed data. For many earthquakes, data on
casualties have been collected on a city by city basis, and this
has made it possible to compare the numbers of fatalities and
injuries to the levels of building damage, leading to the
concept of a 'lethality ratio' - the number of people killed per
collapsed building. Various approaches for calculating
lethality ratio have been given: but a recent study shows that
the variability of the relationship between human fatalities and
building damage is very wide (ref 33).

In scenario studies, very crude assumptions are often made. In
the Mendoza City study (ref 28), for every five damaged
buildings, one fatality and five injuries were assumed; for
Tehran, one death and four injuries were assumed for each house
destroyed (ref 10). But the experience of recent earthquakes
such as Mexico City, where most of the death toll was caused by
the collapse of relatively few multiple occupancy residential
buildings, has indicated the extreme unreliability of an
approach based on such ratios. Estimating injury levels is even
more risky: fixed injury to fatality ratios are sometimes used.
But this can be misleading; in Turkey for example, the ratio of
injury to fatalities has been shown to vary (for intensity IX
locations) between 0.5 for the western part of the country to
over 4.5 for the east, primarily because of the different types
of construction used (ref 25). Indeed, for all but the most
disastrous earthquakes, most of the deaths and injuries may well
be unrelated to the failure of buildings. A study of the
injuries resulting from the 1989 Loma Prieta earthquake in
California showed that 80% were not due to structural failure -
many in fact occurred through attempts to take protective action
during the event; and the same study also showed that most
injuries - 60% - were treated outside the hospital (ref 30).

Work is in progress to develop new casualty models based on a
more realistic assessment of the causative factors involved.
Coburn et al (ref 32)for example, have proposed a model which
takes account of building occupancy patterns, the effect of
building type on numbers trapped inside and on the injury
distribution at collapse, and the effect of search and rescue
activiy on victim survivability. Some indicative figures from
recent earthquakes for each of these parameters are given.
Murakami (ref 31) proposes an event-tree model which takes most
of the above factors into account, and has been calibrated from

available data for the 1988 Armenia earthquake. It is shown
that the vast majority of deaths were caused by the collapse of
precast concrete frame buildings used either as appartment
buildings or factories.

An important conclusion of these studies is that even if the
amount of physical damage to buildings can be reasonably well
predicted, the resulting human casualties will be highly
dependent on factors such as time of day, the effectiveness of
post-earthquake rescue and emergency services and other factors
which cannot be predicted. Moreover, even for these factors
which can in principle be estimated such as the proportion of
occupants trapped at collapse and the distribution of injury
types, insufficient data has been collected in earthquakes to
date for reliable estimates to be made. Given the perishable
nature of the data involved it will clearly be necessary for
specialist epidemiological teams to be formed to study
earthquake injury during the emergency, as is now beginning to
occur in the U.S.(ref 30).

7. HOW USEFUL ARE CURRENT LOSS ESTIMATION METHODS?

It was suggested earlier that for future loss stimates to be of
value in risk reduction or earthquake protection programmes they
would need to be:

- reliable
- related to the main risks which a community faces
- presented in an accessible form

This section will briefly review the value of the presently
available loss estimates in relation to these three criteria.

Reliability
As the studies quoted show, it is now possible to make use of
seismological, soil, building inventory and past damage data to
make some estimates of future damage and human casualties in a
wide variety of situations, even in remote rural locations for
which official records are few. But is is clear from what has
been said that in many cases extremely crude 'ball-park'
assumptions have been made about building type distribution,
about the influence of soils on ground motion, and about
casualty rates. Moreover, although most vulnerability curves
used are based on past earthquake data, the number of
earthquakes from which they are drawn are often rather few, or
are events which have taken place elsewhere.

Because loss assessment is a relatively new activity, there are
very few known cases in which it has been possible to compare
losses predicted beforehand with those actually occurring. The
fit between losses predicted by proposed vulnerability
relationships and earthquakes of the past is always suspect
because the losses which occurred have inevitably been used to
create the relationships used for the estimation. Where
independent comparions have been possible the results have been
extremely poor (ref 34).

For these reasons, it is important that future loss estimates
should be stated in such a way that the real uncertainty range

414

in the estimate is made clear. In many cases, the reverse is the case, and loss estimates are presented with a spurious apparent precision (casualties to the last individual out of thousands, economic losses to the last $1, etc), without specific consideration of uncertainty.

It has been estimated that even for an earthquake of known magnitude, where good damage data from a range of earthquakes to the same building types is available, the probability of actual losses being with ± 50% of the predicted values is no greater than 40%; while human casualty estimates have only 10 to 20% probability of being within 50% of predicted values.

If 90% confidence is required, building loss estimates may range from one third to more than three times the predicted value, and casualty estimates from one tenth to about ten times the predicted value (ref 7).

If expressed in the context of such uncertainty, the loss estimates might of course be less influential on public attitudes and government action than their authors would wish, but not to acknowledge the uncertainty will ultimately lead to a loss of credibility for such studies.

Relevance
It is also by no means clear that the types of loss which are covered by available estimates are those which will actually be of greatest concern in the community. Because houses are the most numerous buildings, and there is in most areas a degree of uniformity about the methods of construction used for housing, loss estimates have frequently concentrated on housing, both in terms of physical destruction and the human casualties caused, to the exclusion of other building types.

By contrast, an international working group on building in seismic areas (ref 6) established the following order of priorities among types of building for protection:

1. lifeline buildings and infrastructure
2. schools
3. community buildings (meeting places and historic buildings)
4. productive buildings
5. houses

Of course, obtaining inventory data, locational data and loss estimates for each of these types of building creates a much more difficult task. Of the loss studies discussed above, only one (ref 13) deals quantitatively with buildings other than houses.Estimating the loss of housing is arguably of importance because the numbers of homeless can be estimated from it. But it is commonly found that those actually in need of temporary housing following an earthquake are not as numerous as such calculations would suggest.

The ATC methodology (ref 26) proposes a functional classification of buildings in addition to the physical one, and proposes coefficients for estimating degree of loss of function of the building at different periods after the earthquake. But such coefficients are based on little real data, and the actual

415

period of loss of function will depend on many factors which cannot be predicted.

Similarily loss estimates in terms of the total economic value of the buildings destroyed are of little significance if the owners will have to rebuild them themselves without assistance from insurers or government subsidy (ref 11). Nor are estimates of the total tonnage of rubble which will have to be removed after the earthquake (ref 28).

Generally, emphasis on loss estimates or those physical attributes which can easily be quantified tends to give a misleading bias to the results, and may result in serious, though much less quantifiable risks to be overlooked - such as that of a single dam failure, a toxic gas leak, or a conflagration. And they also overlook the question of how significant the earthquake risk is compared with the other 'normal' though lower risks of living.

Nevertheless, those quantitative estimates which can be made can have an important shock value - such as the statement for instance that the effects in Tehran of an earthquake with high probability of recurrence 'within the next few years' would include 400,000 deaths in the city and 1.6 million casualties (ref 10).

Accessibility
It is widely agreed that a well-informed public is one of the best ways of promoting disaster protection . However, the typical way in which loss studies are presented, through government reports heavy with statistics and academic conference papers does not help to communicate the essential message widely. There is a need for scientists to become involved with the direct communication of their results, and for government departments to present their findings in a more accessible form. California and Japan have well developed public awareness programmes - in Tokyo a metropolican disaster prevention centre is located in a highly visible way in the new City Hall with large geographical displays linking decision makers with estimated loss data.   In Colombia and Ecuador, well illustrated free leaflets have been distributed, which explain both risks and methods of protection to the public.   In Manila, a city facing multiple hazards, the urban planning authorities have produced a clear well-illustrated leaflet explaining the nature of the hazards, the expected consequences and the means of protection from them . In the U.K., the DoE will shortly publish "Earthquake hazard and risk in the U.K.", a brief well-illustrated summary of its recent study aimed at the general public (ref 13).

Since, for the most part, protection action against earthquakes must be taken by the community itself, the design and presentation of loss estimation studies needs to be increasingly tailored to using means of communication which will directly reach those who need them, rather than being commissioned and 'owned' by government departments.

8. CONCLUSION: A RESEARCH AGENDA FOR THE IDNDR

Clearly, earthquake loss-estimation studies are still in their infancy. To make them more reliable and useful there is now a need both for data-gathering and comparison of estimates with actual experience.

Much more systematic recording of earthquake damage has taken place during the 1980s than previously. But the need for physical damage recording is undiminished, because of changing understanding of the causes of vulnerability, and the continual development of new types of building and other structures. In particular, the systematic recording of the human aspects of earthquake loss - casualties, loss of income and livelihoods, homelessness - needs more emphasis than in the past. And there remains a need for better standardisation between national and international survey groups on the methods of recording damage and losses. The problems of assembling appropriately qualified teams and getting them into the disaster zone within a short time remain formidable. The work of EEFIT in the UK, EERI in USA is notable but needs continuing effort to find funding and international support.

As the number and range of loss estimation studies grows, there will be increasing opportunities to compare actual losses with those estimated. Such comparisons are essential to calibrate and improve loss estimation models - without them loss estimation will remain of low reliability and credibility. To create more opportunities for comparison, coarse loss estimation studies in a large number of high risk locations would be a better use of resources than a few highly detailed studies. And studies are needed of the ways in which loss estimation studies and other hazard and risk information can be used for greatest effectiveness in communicating with the general public.

A further research need is to find cost-effective ways to develop good building inventories and collect damage data. newly emerging techniques in information technology can be useful here. The potential for the use of both aerial photography and satellite imagery and GIS systems to develop inventory and loss data is considerable.

Finally, there is a need to consider the potential for applying loss estimation methods developed for one hazard to mitigation of others. Methods for earthquake loss estimation seem at present more advanced than those for windstorms, volcanic eruptions or landslides. But there is much in common between the methods needed in these different fields, which could be developed.

In responding to Professor Housner's 1989 Mallet Milne lecture 'Coping with Natural Hazards', Frances d'Souza (ref 1) argued that two of the most urgent problems to be tackled by the IDNDR were "how to transfer (to local communities) the belief that disaster mitigation is possible", and "how to convince governments of the cost-effectiveness of disaster prevention".This paper has indicated that there is much that can be contributed towards these important goals through developing loss estimation techniques along the lines suggested.

NATURAL DISASTERS

REFERENCES

1   HOUSNER, G.W. Coping with Natural Disasters: The
    International Decade for Natural Disaster Reduction. SECED,
    The Institution of Civil Engineers, London, 1989.

2   CARDONA, O.D. Integrated Urban Seismic Risk Mitigation
    Project: Its Coordination and Management in Cali,
    Colombia". Earthquake Spectra (to be published 1993).

3   MASKREY, A. Disaster Mitigation: A Community-based
    Approach. OXFAM, Oxford, U.K., 1989.

4   WINCHESTER, P. Vulnerability and Recovery in Hazard Prone
    Areas, Proc Conference on Earthen and Low-Strength Masonry
    Buildings in Seismic Areas, Ankara, Turkey, pp 153-166,
    1986.

5   THOMPSON, P. Report of Working Group on Implemention and
    Information Dissemination. Proc. Conference on Earthen and
    Low-Strength Masonry Buildings in Seismic Areas, Ankara,
    Turkey, pp 3-5, 1986.

6   DAVIS, I. Report of Working Group on Reduction of
    Vulnerability through Repair and Retrofit, Proc Conference
    on Earthen and Low-Strength Masonry Buildings in Seismic
    Areas, Ankara, Turkey, pp 13-14, 1986.

7   COBURN, A.W. and SPENCE, R.J.S. Earthquake Protection.
    John Wiley and Sons, 1992.

8   SPENCE, R.J.S., WELLS, E.J. and DUDLEY, E. Jobs from
    Housing. Intermediate Technology Publications, London,
    1993.

9   SPENCE, R.J.S. Materials and Construction Techniques for
    Disaster Protection, in Aysan and Davis (eds) Disasters and
    the Small Dwelling, James and James, Oxford, 1992.

10 GHAFOURY-ASHTIANY, M., HOSSEINI, M., JAFAR, M.K., SHADI,
    TALAB, J., ESHGHI, S. and QURESHI, M. Tehran Vulnerability
    Analysis, Proc 10 WCEE , Madrid, pp 533-538, Vol. 1, 1992.

11 THENHAUS, P.C., HANSON, S.L., ISMET EFFENDI, KERTAPATI,
    E.K.and ALGERMISSEN S.T. Pilot Studies of Seismic Hazard
    and Risk in North Sulawesi Province, Indonesia. Earthquake
    Spectra 9/1 (97-120), 1993.

12 EMMI, P.C. and HORTON, C.A. The Benefits of a Seismic
    Retrofit Program for Commercial Unreinforced Masonry
    Structures. Salt Lake County, Utah, Earthquake Spectra 9/1,
    (1-10), 1993.

13 ARUP. Seismic Hazard and Risk in the U.K; A Study for the
    Department of the Environment. 1991.

14 BURTON, P.W. Seismic Risk in Southern Europe through India
    Examined Using Gumbel's Third Distribution of Extreme
    Values. Geophys, J.R. Astr. Soc., 59, 249-280, 1979.

15 ROSENBLUETH, E. Public Policy and Seismic Risk. Nature and
    Resources, 27:1, 10-18, 1991.

16 ATKINSON, G.M. and BOORE, D.M. Recent Trends in Ground
    Motion and Spectral Response Relations for North America.
    Earthquake Spectra, 6.1, 15-34, 1990.

17 DAHLE, A., BUNGUM, H. and KRANNE, L.B. Attenuation
    modelling Based on Intraplate Earthquake Records.
    Proceedings of the Ninth European Conference on Earthquake
    Engineering Moscow, Vol. 4a, pp 121-129, 1990.

18 EEFIT. The Erzincan Earthquake of 13 March 1992.:A Field
    Report by EEFIT. Institution of Structural Engineers,
    London, 1993.

19 EQE. Costa Rica Report. 1991.

20 JARA, M., GUERRERO, J.J. and AUILAR, J. Seismic
    Vulnerability of Mexico City Buildings. Proc 10 WCEE,
    Madrid, pp 545-550, Vol 1, 1992.

21 PETROVSKI, J., RISTIC, D. and NEVSKI, N. Evaluation of
    Vulnerability and Potential Seismic Risk Level of Buildings.
    Proc 10WCEE, Madrid, pp 509-514, Vol. 1, 1992.

22 KAPPOS, A.J., STYLIANIDIS, K.C., MICHAILIDIS, C.N. and
    ATHANASSIADOU, C.J. Development of Earthquake Damage
    Scenarios Using a Comprehensive Analytical Method. Proc
    10WCEE, Madrid, pp 6013-6018, Vol. 10, 1992.

23 TIEDEMANN, H. Quantification of Factors Contributing to
    Earthquake Damage in Buildings. Engineering Geology 20,
    169-179, Elsevier, Amsterdam, 1984.

24 COCHRANE, S.W. and SCHAAD, W.H. Assessment of Earthquake
    Vulnerability of Buildings. Proc 10WCEE, Madrid, pp 497-
    502, Vol. 1, 1992.

25 GULKAN, P., ERGUNAY, O. and SUCUOGLU, H. Earthquake
    Vulnerability, Loss and Risk Assessment in Turkey. Proc
    10WCEE, Madrid, pp 539-544, Vol. 1, 1992.

26 ROJAHN, C. Earthquake Damage Evaluation Data for
    California. ATC-13. Applied Technology Council, Redwood
    City, California, 1985.

27 SPENCE, R.J.S., COBURN, A.W., POMONIS, A. and SAKAI, S.
    Correlation of Ground Motion with Building Damage. Proc
    10WCEE, Madrid, pp 551-556, Vol. 1, 1992.

28 CASTANO, J.C. and ZAMARBIDE, J.L. A Seismic Risk Reduction
    Programme for Mendova City, Argentina. Proc 10 WCEE, Madrid,
    pp 5953-5958, Vol. 10, 1992.

29 BRAGA, F., DOLCE, M. and LIBERATORE, D. A Statistical Study
    on Damaged Buildings and Ensuing Review of the MSK-76 Scale.
    The Southern Italy Nov 23 1980 Earthquake, Chapter 5,
    Geodynamics Project, CNR Publication 503, Rome, 1982.

30 COBURN, A.W. and KURAN (U.) (Eds). Emergency Planning and
    Earthquake Damage Reduction for Bursa Province. Earthquake
    Research Department, Ankara, 1985.

30 DURKIN, M.E. Improving Earthquake Casualty and Loss
    Assessment. Proc 10 WCEE, Madrid, pp 557-562, Vol. 1, 1992.

31 MURAKAMI, H.O. A Simulation Model to Estimate Human Loss
    for Occupants of Collapsed Buildings in an Earthquake. Proc
    10 WCEE, Madrid, pp 5969-5976, Vol. 10, 1992.

32 COBURN, A.W., POMONIS, A., SAKAI, S. and SPENCE, R.J.S.
    Reducing Human Casualties in Building Collapse: Final
    Report. The Martin Centre, University of Cambridge, U.K.,
    1992.

33 COBURN, A.W., SPENCE, R.J.S. and POMONIS, A. Factors
    Determining Human Casualty Levels in Earthquakes: Mortality
    Prediction in Building Collapse. Proc 10 WCEE, Madrid, pp
    5989-5994, Vol. 10, 1992.

34. The role of commercial insurance in alleviating natural disaster

A. F. DLUGOLECKI, General Accident Fire and Life Assurance Corporation plc, UK, on behalf of the Association of British Insurers

INTRODUCTION

A striking feature in the IPCC assessments of the impact of climate change is the absence of any allusions to insurance (refs 1, 2). In fact insurance plays a major role in alleviating natural disasters in developed economies, and has been of some assistance in less-developed countries. The purpose of this paper is to describe how insurance works, the advantages that can be provided by the free market, the circumstances in which such commercial insurance is viable and some practical problems. Finally some future issues are examined, particularly for less-developed nations. The focus is on property insurance throughout.

THE INSURANCE MECHANISM

The fundamental principle of insurance is that THE MANY PAY FOR THE FEW, by the operation of a fund collected from the many in advance, and distributed to meet the losses of the few as they happen. The intention of the insurance contract is to restore the status quo. It assumes that the proposer (the person seeking cover) will behave honestly and prudently, including taking reasonable steps to avoid or reduce losses, and revealing all the relevant facts.

The term "commercial insurance" relates to insurance where the cover or administration is provided by profit-making undertakings, not mutual funds or government. This paper will focus on property insurance as defined by the UK Department of Trade and Industry. Essentially therefore, we will consider cover relating to immobile land-based property. Clearly natural disasters affect marine property, human health and life, transport, agriculture (crops and livestock) and continuity of business activities. Sometimes natural events are compounded by human negligence, with implications for liability insurance. However, property insurance has been the class most affected by recent disasters like Hurricane Andrew.

The natural disasters we shall consider are basically weather-related (storm, sandstorm, hail, flood, frost, drought, forest fire, snow, fog) or geological (volcano, earthquake, tsunami). Other types (biological, astronomical) may be ignored for property insurance.

Main Processes

The two main processes peculiar to the insurance industry are Underwriting (accepting risks) and Claim-handling. As Figure 1 shows, underwriting risks is akin to the process of handling an agricultural commodity, starting from the crops in the field, harvesting, then storing and finally blending them. The "proposer" wishes to insure his "untreated" single risk. After risk management, this is brought to an insurable state, and placed with an insurer under the terms of an insurance contract, which is often negotiated via an agency or broker on behalf of the proposer. The insurer will have a variety of risks to administer, and may have insisted that the proposer retains some of the risk as a "deductible" so that he has a stake in avoiding loss. By further negotiation, the insurer may transfer some of the risk to a reinsurer, with an even wider spread of risks.

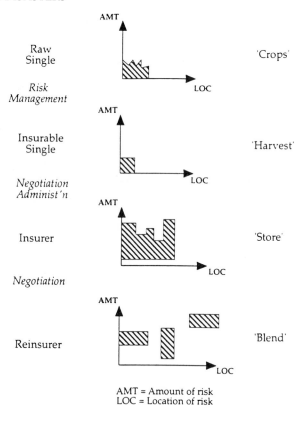

Raw
Single

AMT

'Crops'

LOC

Risk
Management

Insurable
Single

AMT

'Harvest'

LOC

Negotiation
Administ'n

Insurer

AMT

'Store'

LOC

Negotiation

Reinsurer

AMT

'Blend'

LOC

AMT = Amount of risk
LOC = Location of risk

A comparison between insuring risks (left hand of diagram)
and handling commodities (right hand).

Fig. 1. Accepting risk

Figure 2 shows the various steps in settling claims. Firstly the claim is compared with the contract of insurance to establish whether cover exists for the incident. Secondly, the site of the damage is often visited by an adjuster to quantify the loss, and thirdly the repairer(s) are intimately involved in carrying out the agreed course of action, with due controls. In the case of total loss, suitable restitution is arranged. It is not just a matter of passing money over to claimants on demand!

SYSTEMS OF INSURANCE AND NATURAL HAZARDS

As insurance is a financial mechanism, it is a feature of developed economies. Only in the twentieth century has it become a significant feature of protecting land-based property against natural hazards. The commonest early form of insurance was the mutual pool, where the contributors were also the policyholders ie. the fund was provided by those with a common risk to face. These still exist, and have the advantage that the common interest of the shareholders and policyholders can provide a clear focus on the business activity. However they'lack the ability to draw on new funds quickly and as their size increases, power tends to fall into the hands of the executive management.

Mutual insurance is not always a viable solution to financial losses (ref 3). As regards the insurance of property against natural hazards, the critical features are

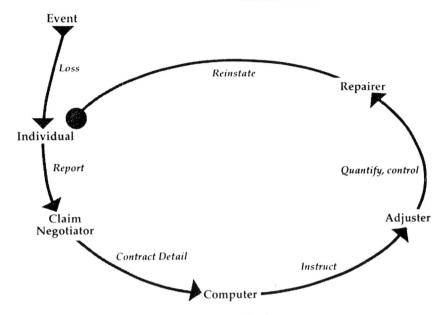

The main steps from occurrence to conclusion.

Fig. 2. Settling claims

their widespread impact, their uneven distribution over time, and their uncertain
violence. Contributions to the fund (premiums) are normally calculated on the expected
cost to the individual over a long time period with an allowance for administration
expenses. When the premiums are pooled, the intention is that they will be sufficient
in total to meet a year's claims and expenses. Any surplus belongs to the contributors
strictly, but in practice is often retained by the pool, at least in part, to meet
future claims. If a deficit occurs, it is borne by shareholders, or a further call for
premiums. In principle the pool arrangement might also cope with risks over a period
longer than a year, but there are obvious practical difficulties eg. changing
membership.

The widespread and severe impact of fundamental hazards like earthquake can destroy a
substantial proportion of Policyholders' physical capital. This means that the claims
may be many times the size of the fund, which is built up from a fraction of
Policyholders' income. Conceivably a surplus could be built up over a period to cope
with fluctuations in claims, but a major early claim will kill the fund before any
surplus can accumulate.

The alternative of making initial contributions large enough to meet any foreseeable
claim is not realistic, because the possible maximum claim is enormous. The individual
contributor would not consider it economic to commit substantial proportions of his
income and/or wealth to a common pool against contingencies which might not even occur
in his lifetime.

Commercial Insurance

Stockholder companies where the initial fund is provided by entrepreneurs,
have become more prevalent. The policyholders still contribute premiums to the fund,
but any surplus belongs to the stockholders, who also meet any deficit out of the
profit retained in the fund from prior years. This system has the advantage that it
can cope with large claims at an early point, and that losses are spread over a wider
base, since generally the stockholders are not policyholders. There is of course the
danger that the stockholders could exploit the policyholders eg. by charging exorbitant

prices for cover. In a free market with many competitors, as in say the UK or USA this is not a serious problem, but it does require government oversight of market competition. Commercial operations have relatively fast access to more funds via the capital markets, and reduce the need for public money to be diverted to disaster areas.

Commercial insurance undertakings tend to be more innovative, and this results in products which are often much wider in scope than pure disaster protection. By incorporating many perils into a single "comprehensive" policy, the overall cost of administration is significantly reduced. One possible problem is over-selling to those who do not need or cannot afford the product. Also insurance products may translate into "maintenance contracts" dealing with wear-and-tear rather than hardship.

Government Schemes

Where a risk is very great, or the government is opposed to profit making, a public scheme may be set up. This has the advantage of a wide base (the population) and very substantial funds to call upon, but it may be inefficient in operation, and slow to respond to changing circumstances. The contributions may be voluntary or compulsory, perhaps tied in with a voluntary fire policy as in France or New Zealand. Once again, the funds may not be large enough where a small country is concerned, and it may be felt that public funds should not be used to guarantee private property.

Reinsurance

All of the above systems are vulnerable to "big hits". Mutual funds and government schemes are single-country or single-district operations which means that the local economy will be damaged by the same disaster which might deplete or destroy the insurance fund. Small commercial operations will fall into the same problem, but multinational insurance companies may be able to call on resources in other territories to meet obligations.

It is possible for all of the various types of insurance scheme to gain access to more capital through REINSURANCE. This at present is only available commercially, and operates in the same way as commercial insurance. The policyholders are insurance operators, who "reinsure" part of their commitment in exchange for paying a reinsurance premium to the reinsurer. Reinsurers operate on an international scale, creating a truly global pool by accepting risks from operators in many countries. The "London Market" of companies and Lloyds is one of the biggest providers of "capacity" for such risks, supplying about 50% of international catastrophe reinsurance. As we will see, the reinsurers can also have problems with natural disasters if the actual experience turns out to be significantly worse than expected. The fact remains that reinsurance provides a very valuable service by spreading the burden of disasters further than the vulnerable communities, and by taking the immediate cost away from the public purse. By using a commercial mechanism it avoids the whims and obligations which may affect reliance on charitable relief also.

In fact well over 50% of the insured cost of most natural disasters outside USA used to be borne by the international reinsurers. However due to the recent run of man-made and natural disasters, reinsurers particularly in the London Market, have been restricting their "capacity" or volume of business and increasing their rates (price). This in turn has stimulated insurers to improve their management control and amend their own products. The total global reinsurance capacity for catastrophe weather is probably around £20 billion now.

CURRENT USE OF INSURANCE TO COPE WITH NATURAL DISASTERS

The situation differs considerably from one country to another, and of course over time. This is not the place to catalogue all the variations, but some examples will do. The insurance market in the United Kingdom is mature, and has evolved rapidly in the absence of dirigiste government policies; therefore it serves as a good example of current practice, but needs amplifications since British hazards tend to be nuisances rather than catastrophic. Also the geological hazards are not really significant here.

Up to 1960 domestic policies in the UK covered earthquake, storm and freeze (burst pipes). In 1961 government pressure added flood, and in 1971 came subsidence for domestic property, followed later by cover for "heave". Apart from these developments, there has also been a trend towards "all risks" ie. cover for all damage unless specifically excluded, towards "bedroom-rated" policies, where the property value is not specified, and towards "new-for-old", where the property is valued on its replacement price, not allowing for depreciation. These covers are almost uniformly available in the UK charged for at a rate % of the property value. The rates are starting to become differentiated to reflect the local probability of the hazards. For convenience, the rates are usually expressed in a "comprehensive" all-in figure, with the covers under one contract of insurance. The position for industrial and commercial property depends on their size. The larger enterprises tend to have cover tailored individually, while smaller ones copy the domestic property "package" approach.

In France, the government introduced a major change in 1982, by compulsorily adding "catastrophe" cover to all policies covering property or motor vehicles. The cover became active when the authorities deemed that a disaster had happened. However, it became clear that this was inequitable because people who could afford to buy the cover were receiving the benefit free. In 1990, storm cover was removed from the catastrophe regime and made a mandatory part of property insurance policies. In several European countries with a serious flood hazard, insurance for it is not generally available - Germany and the Netherlands for example.

Countries in the Commonwealth like Australia and New Zealand have followed the British pattern for most hazards. However in New Zealand, earthquake cover is in transition. It used to be financed by a government-backed pool with front-end administration provided by the commercial sector. This is now starting to pass some of the risk to the commercial insurance operation. In the United States cover for flood is government-backed, while earthquake cover is difficult to obtain in high-hazard areas, despite state intervention.

Japan is another country which is prone to hazards. It is public policy not to provide full cover for earthquake damage, forcing the individual to be actively involved in preventive measures. Many inhabitants of small island states are finding it impossible to obtain insurance against wind and flood because the main providers have withdrawn following heavy losses.

RECENT EXPERIENCE WITH WINDSTORM

Although the treatment of natural hazards for insurance varies considerably, windstorm is one peril which has generally been acceptable. It therefore gives a common base on which to examine the recent success or otherwise in dealing with an insured natural hazard. The insurance industry has been shaken by recent developments. Claims have soared in value and number, even in areas previously thought safe, like the UK. Figure 3 shows how costs have risen by an order of magnitude for storm since 1960 in the UK. At the outset a "disaster" cost less than £100 million over an entire winter, but in both 1987 and 1990 £1000 million insured damage was caused in a single day.

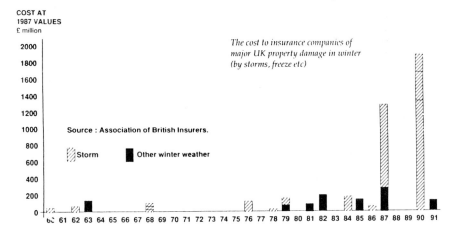

Fig. 3. Major UK winter events

NATURAL DISASTERS

TABLE 1 - MAJOR WINDSTORMS WORLDWIDE 1960 - 90

	1960'S PER YEAR	1970'S PER YEAR	1980'S PER YEAR	1990 ALONE
Number of Windstorms	0.8	1.3	2.9	4.0
Total Damage ($B)	2.0	2.9	3.4	14.1
Insured Damage ($B)	0.5	0.8	1.7	9.8

Values at 1990 prices.   Data from Munich Re.

These patterns are paralleled on a global scale, as shown in Table 1, drawn from statistics gathered by the reinsurance company Munich Re about major windstorms.   In this case the statistics include uninsured losses.   Again the total losses have risen by an order of magnitude since the 60's, and the insured costs have accelerated even faster. Since the table was prepared, data for 1991 and 1992 has become available.   It confirms the picture with several severe storms (Typhoon Mireille, Hurricane Bob, Hurricane Andrew, Cyclone Iniki).   In fact the insured damage in Andrew may reach $20 billion, thus exceeding the previous WORLDWIDE total for a single year!   Although not shown, the proportion of the cost borne by the international reinsurers is usually over 50% of the total insured cost.

Non-weather factors have influenced this trend, of course.   There has been an increase in the values exposed to damage, as economies become wealthier. Also properties have tended to become more concentrated through urbanisation, or through large-scale production plants, which increase the chance of a "big hit".   This has been compounded by property development on hazardous but scenic or convenient sites eg. flood plains, earthquake zones, and coasts.   Modern possessions are often more delicate or less repairable too, which results in more costly claims.   Marketing has raised the take-up rate of insurance, and consumerism has increased the likelihood that claims will be pursued.   Finally, insurers have created greater potential claims with measures such as index-linked values, and eliminating depreciation with new-for-old cover (refs 4, 5).   These influences are gradual, and so their effect can be seen in the ordinary progress of claims.   However, the ten-fold increase in windstorm claims is well above the "normal" claim escalation.   It reflects an increase in the frequency and severity of extreme events, perhaps an early sign of Global Warming.

Historic costs are useful to know, but the potential loss may be a multiple of the observed maximum.   For example, the cost of a repetition of the UK East Coast Flood of February 1953 could be £10 billion.   It is therefore of concern to note the problems which commercial insurance has had worldwide in coping with recent natural events.   The industry is of course dealing with other major problems - theft, fraud, unemployment, terrorism, inflation, liberalisation and pollution.   Nonetheless, it is evident that natural disasters have been one of the main causes of insurance insolvencies and withdrawals in recent years (ref 6).

Experience has shown that the relationship of weather-to-cost is exponential, not straight-line for windstorm and an increase of less than
10 kph can double the damage.   The loss rates in the worst-hit areas in England in the October 1987 "Hurricane" came to 1% of the value of the insured property, although 50% of the dwellings were affected to some extent.   In the more violent tropical hurricanes value loss rates in excess of 10% occur.   Obviously, the design and surroundings of the built environment matter - the Scottish Isles endure windspeeds over 200 kph without significant damage.   Coastal sites are particularly vulnerable due to the possible combination of tides, storm surge and wave action (ref 7).

THE ADVANTAGES OF A COMMERCIAL INSURANCE APPROACH

While no human system is perfect, a wider use of commercial insurance organisations and methods to meet the exigencies of natural disasters could have benefits in several ways.   These are preparing for the event, carrying out the physical recovery, and providing the funds for that.

Before The Event

Generally, insurers expect property owners to take good care of their property. However often before accepting a property for cover, an insurer will conduct a physical survey of the premises. Traditionally, the surveyor focused on the fire and crime hazards, and provided optional recommendations and mandatory requirements for improvements to the physical fabric (and management of operations in the building, if it were a business). This has the obvious benefit of reducing the chance of losses, and of placing some of the financial cost where it belongs, with the property-owner. Smaller properties will not be visited, but insurers often provide cheap but effective guidance through literature. Sometimes this process of risk management is carried out by the insurance intermediary.

As the seriousness of natural disasters has become apparent, the insurance industry has refined its approach by coding areas according to the degree of hazard, based on geographical data and claims history. In the USA this applies to flood, in the UK insurers have approached subsidence in this fashion, and international reinsurers have tackled earthquake through their CRESTA zones of hazard. These codes may tie in with requirements for physical construction, but they also serve as the basis for a "rating structure". The more risky the area, the higher will be the premium for the same type of building. High-hazard areas may suffer from "red-lining" ie. find it difficult to get cover. This is offset in a free market by competition between insurers for market share. Further, it can be mitigated by the voluntary practice of continuing cover for existing policyholders. The problem is then reduced to current premises with no insurance, and new premises.

For uninsured existing premises, it may be necessary to adopt some form of centrally controlled pool, or allocation system, perhaps with government backing. The difficulty of insuring new premises is in fact a major advantage. It was noted earlier that economic development has expanded into high-hazard areas. The likelihood of physical damage or financial ruin from natural disasters has been ignored, often because of the financial gain to non-involved parties eg. the real-estate owner, the construction company, and the local authority, which will see its tax base increase. As long as the financial ruin is averted by easily available insurance, unwise developments will continue. But without the promise of insurance, prospective owners and lenders will be deterred.

The price mechanism is an essential discipline of the free market, serving to prevent uneconomic use of resources. If it proves impossible to provide 100% cover for earthquakes or volcanoes in some locations this may not be unreasonable. If too many "uninsurable" risks are assigned to the insurers then the whole system may collapse. In general it is better to encourage the market to adapt its products for difficult risks in a voluntary way eg. as the UK insurance industry did for small "inner city" businesses, following the riots of the early 1980's.

The Physical Recovery

A fast return to normality is obviously required. The authorities are likely to be concerned with the restoration of public services, maintaining order, and preserving life. The insurance industry can supplement this by helping property-owners to restore their status, also with minimal public involvement. Loss adjusters can swiftly assemble skilled technicians on a global scale to assess physical damage at major sites, estimate repair costs, and recommend appropriate recovery steps. Similarly, insurers can mobilise resources on a national scale towards disaster areas, working with adjusters to appoint competent contractors to commence recovery work and prevent deterioration at major sites, and for the numerous smaller properties using the media and telephone to provide advice on recovery. With appropriate scientific forecasting, these actions can all be prepared, ready to go as soon as the event has finished. It is essential that repairs are carried out to appropriate standards; one of the recognised dangers in the recovery is that the repairs or rebuilding will be attempted by unskilled contractors. Finally, insurers may use the recovery to suggest modifications which would avert further losses.

Apart from the physical dislocation, the emotional distress caused by disasters is considerable, especially for elderly people. The prompt attention to physical requirements, and restoring of their status quo, is one of the most effective ways to reduce the human problems. Most domestic policies in the UK provide for the cost of alternative accommodation during the recovery period.

NATURAL DISASTERS

Paying For It

The insurance industry maintains liquid funds to be able to respond to the immediate need for emergency payments eg. to replace food and clothes and prevent damage to exposed interior property. Policies often extend to cover alternative accommodation while restoration is proceeding, and businesses may insure for the profit lost by interrupted operations. This process can be soured if it transpires that the policyholder has not bought sufficient protection. Some people will even try to reduce their premiums by "under declaring" their values. However, insurers and their agents do make considerable efforts to provide guidance on the matter of the appropriate values, and may be accused of overselling in fact.

The collapse of insurers from being unable to meet their obligations will of course prevent the recovery, and has occurred from time to time with tropical storms. There have also been certain recent and well publicised problems in the London Market. To some extent this can be averted by appropriate reinsurance programmes, and by government supervision to ensure that insurers have sufficient "solvency" or free capital to face unexpected demands, but this is an area which will see further development, as insurers seek to CONTROL their exposure. We will deal with this in the section on future developments. The great advantages of the commercial approach are the freeing of central resources for other tasks, and avoiding the uncertain reliance upon others' goodwill at a time of disaster.

General Aspects

The whole system of assessing risks, collecting premiums, maintaining registers of insured property, and settling claims is a huge administrative burden. The profit motive ensures that updated office technology restrains the inevitable escalation in costs. By using the same system for non-catastrophe purposes, enormous savings can be realised. Examples of this in the UK have been flood and terrorism where the cover is combined with other "perils" in a single policy of insurance. In the latter case the central government also bears some of the risk. It is a sad fact that insurance is open to abuse. Claimants may invent or exaggerate losses,and contractors may overcharge for work, particularly in emergency situations. The commercial sector is used to dealing with such problems. In particular, it is becoming common to maintain claims registers, to identify potential frauds. Insurers also appoint selected contractors whose work is regularly inspected, and who maintain high technical standards. Rapid effective communication on property damage can mitigate the effects of disasters. Whereas in 1987 UK insurers were overwhelmed by the one million claims caused by the October "hurricane", in 1990 they coped with three million claims by providing general advice at once in the media. Individual claimants had access to dedicated (often free) phonelines on a 24-hour basis, enabling repairers to be contacted and many emergencies handled without the involvement of the authorities.

FUTURE DEVELOPMENTS

The critical issue for insurers is the future pattern of natural disasters - their frequency, location and severity. Insurers tend to extrapolate from recent experience but claims data is only really of satisfactory quality from about 1980 onward. "Pure" scientific data on disasters could amplify this. However, the database on natural catastrophes is often inadequate, with insufficient length or detail on extreme events. In turn, what data is available needs to be converted into impacts in terms of today's society, particularly property assets. This would be difficult enough if the distribution of events were stable. There is evidence that storm patterns vary greatly over time on a scale of centuries (ref 8) and systematically over the El Nino cycle (ref 9). Concern is also growing about the impact which Global warming may have upon storm frequency (ref 4, 5, 6).

In the light of recent trends, we may expect to see some retrenchment in the insurance sector's willingness to cover natural disasters, or to extend into areas currently dealt with by central government. Because many property insurance contracts last for only 12 months, it is relatively easy for insurers to adapt, but the same is not true for sectors with long lead-times eg. construction, and credit institutions. Credit institutions may find that borrowers are not able to service their loans, if those borrowers cannot reinstate their losses by insurance following a catastrophe. The assets underpinning the loans may be unrealisable, if they are damaged, or may have lost considerable value, if they are in hazard-prone sites. The construction industry may expect to benefit from the demand for its services following a catastrophe. However, this demand will not be fulfilled unless finance is available, and one of the

428

efficient ways of providing funds for reconstruction is via insurance. Construction may also suffer in a more subtle way, in that new development may be constrained by fear of natural hazards, unless insurance is available to fund any reconstruction following damage. It is therefore in the public interest to promote insurability, and for reasons given above, to use the commercial insurance sector's expertise.

Clearly public policy can alleviate natural disasters by ensuring that society adopts a responsible attitude, that appropriate knowledge is acquired, and that resources are used to best effect. Some broad areas can be identified - scientific research, physical risk protection, control of acceptances, and establishment of funds. (ref 7) More knowledge is urgently required about historic and potential natural disasters. Because of its general application, such research should be publicly funded, with the results and data available for other researchers freely. In defining their areas of research, scientists should have regard to the impact on property, as well as the "purer" bio-aspects. Initiatives on practical protection can already start between insurers, planners and designers. This may initially require government sponsorship. It is well-known that without an established forum, it is often difficult to generate a healthy flow of communication between those providing the built environment and those maintaining it. Useful areas to study are already apparent - construction standards, particularly roofing; coastal defences - where the perils of storm and flood combine; and tree management - owing to the damage caused by windthrow. Other topics will doubtless emerge through debate.

Control of Acceptances

It has been customary for insurers to accept 100% of the value of a property for insurance against fire sometimes without even knowing the location of the properties for large customers or agents. Again, it has been customary for the total of all such accepted values to be greatly in excess of the financial resources of the insurer, in much the same way that a bank extends credit beyond its available funds. Of course this works as long as the insurer charges sensible premiums and only a small number of fires occur! Obviously, in a natural disaster very many claims can occur simultaneously.

One way in which insurers can cope with hazardous risks is to ration their acceptances, to perhaps a fixed amount per property, and to a total number of properties in the worst areas. Some insurers already do this for earthquake in Australia, New Zealand and USA. The most likely hazards that such "exposure limits" will apply to are flood, earthquake and volcano. Where the demand for cover is unsatisfied, the risk may have to be borne by the individual property-owner. At the same time, the premium paid will generally vary to reflect the degree of potential damage. It is a moot point whether such capping of acceptances need apply to storms. In some countries, eg. hurricanes belt islands, it undoubtedly must, while in higher latitudes the danger is less and the available funds are larger.

Catastrophe Funds

Finally, it is vital that funds are available to deal with the recovery process. Such emergency funds can be made available in several ways, as already discussed. Public funds or charity are not ideal. International reinsurance is available but may be limited in amount, and subject to competition from other countries with potential hazards. Allowing the commercial sector to build up disaster funds out of untaxed income would be attractive to insurers. It would defer the receipt of tax revenue, but that might be preferable to the other routes suggested. (There may be some debate about how such funds should be invested eg. to assist public deficit funding, but short-term political ends must not prevail.) It is significant that in the UK the government has just announced a review of this option after many requests by the insurance industry.

The problems facing less-developed countries are particularly difficult. In some cases the local economy may be insufficient to generate the necessary catastrophe funds ever, and local institutions may not be reliable enough to efficiently handle massive reconstruction. If the advanced economies use commercial insurance to tackle their own natural hazards, then public funds may flow more freely from them to other disaster-prone countries. It would be more efficient if this were done in a systematic way, and a possible programme is outlined in the next section.

NATURAL DISASTERS

A PROGRAMME FOR ACTION IN LESSER DEVELOPED COUNTRIES

Now that natural hazards have been recognised for the major problem they are, governments must consider whether their cultures and institutions can handle all the aspects, including physical devastation. Lesser developed countries are often doubly exposed with high hazard levels and low resources. The previous two sections discussed the advantages of a commercial insurance approach, and likely future trends. We now consider how those ideas might apply to lesser developed countries.

Funding

The critical issue is how to generate capital when the commercial insurance market is not willing or able to provide it. The general approach must be that certain natural hazards should be reinsured to a central pool. This pool, sponsored or controlled by the UN, would accept such 'block' catastrophe risks from national pools, which in turn would accept risks from individual national insurers.

The central pool would be funded by the premiums from the national pools, and perhaps partly by a contribution from the UN budget, possibly just to start the fund up. If the UN subsidy was substantial, this would raise questions of unfair competition with other economies also exposed to natural hazards, and might undermine the commercial reinsurance industry. However, even if external funds were not available, the pool could still start on the basis that it would pay a proportion of catastrophic losses. It might be possible to attract external capital later, and even to reinsure some of the risk commercially. There would need to be certain clear standards, which applied to all the countries participating in the pool. For example, risks would require to be physically in good condition, rates would need to reflect commercial practice in hazardous developed countries, and the local insurers would operate on generally commercial lines, even for those catastrophe risks where they bore little or none of the cost themselves. To sharpen the focus further each national pool would require to retain a substantial portion of its risk itself.

There would be many problems in setting up and running such a pooling system - which hazards should it cover, which countries, what rates and limitations, what would define a catastrophe event, how would it be managed, which currency would denominate the limiting values, how would funds be invested, what if the pool ran out of money and so on. This paper cannot possibly answer all these questions in the limited space. It would be essential to take the advice of countries where such pools already exist, in planning such a project. The loosely-based CRESTA Group of commercial reinsurers would also be able to give practical advice. A similar concept to help small island states was debated in 1992 at an IPCC International Workshop on sea level rise. (ref 10) However, the proposal was flawed in various ways - the "catastrophe" was ill-defined, non economic and speculative losses were included, there was no administrative infrastructure, and the insured parties did not contribute to the fund. In any case it is probably inevitable that any pooling system will not be able to meet all the financial consequences of natural disasters in lesser developed countries.

To underpin the national and international pools, governments should encourage a local commercial insurance market, providing products which cover as many hazards as possible voluntarily, with proper regulation. The insurers would administer "uninsurable" hazards, placing them with the national pool, although again it would be desirable for at least a part of each risk to be retained by the insurer and certainly by the property-owner. This method would assist the process of risk management and the charging of risk-related premiums. Administration of policies and claims would be efficient, since the infrastructure would already be in place to deal with non catastrophic claims and risks. Those countries not already having a commercial insurance industry could seek technical assistance in setting them up, as Poland has recently from the UK. Again there would be many questions of principle and detail to decide - what charge would be made for administering catastrophe policies and claims, how would payments be audited, what proportion of risk would be retained by each party, what premium levels would be charged and so forth.

Other Issues

As well as funding, governments should take action in other areas. Natural disasters will affect every sector of the economy, each with its own interests. The UN has launched initiatives for this type of problem in coastal zones, through Coastal Zone Management. (ref 11) The essential features are to evaluate the dangers, assess the impacts, sponsor joint planning fora where conflict can be resolved, and then develop a

430

common strategy which optimises the use of the available resources. One of the key issues is control of development of exposed sites. This collaborative approach is still evolving, but looks like the right way forward, and commercial insurers would gladly play a part if invited. It requires the political will to admit that there is a problem, and that unconventional methods may be required. At a more technical level governments can help immensely by sponsoring research into patterns of event severity and frequency, and how to avoid or alleviate damage to particularly vulnerable structures or components.

CONCLUSIONS

This paper has shown that commercial insurance is a mechanism which copes well in many situations with the property damage impact of natural disasters. Recent experience with increasingly great impacts has had some benefits in improving the operating efficiency, but this has been offset by the reduction of the available capacity, and increases in the price of insurance. For lesser developed countries, the issue of funding is a key one, but with a collaborative approach, central authorities may find that they can deploy the skills of the commercial insurance solution in an economic and efficient way, although it will probably not be able to meet all the demand for financial protection, since that it is uneconomic.

REFERENCES

1. IPCC   Impacts Assessment Of Climate Change
                 WMO/UNEP 1990.

2. IPCC   Response Strategies Assessment Of Climate Change.
                 WMO/UNEP 1990.

3. DICKSON G.   Risk and Insurance, Chapter 2.
                 Chartered Insurance Institute 1991.

4. BERZ G.   Greenhouse Effects On Natural Catastrophes and Insurance.
                 Geneva Papers on Risk and Insurance 64 July 1992. Association
                 Internationale Pour L'Etude De L'Economie De L'Assurance pp 386-392.

5. DLUGOLECKI A. Insurance Implications Of Climate Change.
                 Geneva Papers on Risk and Insurance 64 July 1992. Association
                 Internationale Pour L'Etude De L'Economie De L'Assurance pp 393-405.

6. LEGGETT J.   Climate Change and The Insurance Industry.
                 Greenpeace, London 1993.

7. CLIMATE CHANGE The Potential Effects Of Climate Change In The United Kingdom,
   IMPACTS REVIEW Chapter 13 (Financial Sector).
   GROUP   Department of the Environment, London 1991.

8. LAMB H.   Historic Storms Of The North Sea, British Isles and Northwest
                 Europe. Cambridge UP 1991.

9. GLANTZ M.H.   Telecommunications Linking Worldwide Climate Anomalies.
   ET AL   Cambridge University Press 1991.

10. WILFORD M.   Insuring Against The Consequences Of Sea Level Rise, CIEL-AOSIS
                 Background paper 4/1991, King's College London.

11. IPCC   The Seven Steps To The Assessment Of The Vulnerability Of Coastal
                 Area To Sea Level Rise - Response Strategies Working Group,
                 UNEP 1991.

35. Natural disasters and their human consequences —overcoming the vacuum between humanitarian aid and long term rehabilitation

Dr C. FERNANDEZ, Department of Agriculture, Government of the Philippines, and J. GORDON, Travers Morgan International, UK

BACKGROUND

The Philippines lies within the volcanic "Ring of Fire" and the Pacific Typhoon Belt making it prone to a variety of natural disasters which occur frequently on various scales. The "Philippine Plate" is sandwiched between the larger Eurasian and Pacific continental plates such that the major Philippine fault line runs SE-NW through the largest island Luzon giving rise to earthquakes. There are about 22 active volcanoes in the Philippines and it experiences some 20 direct hit typhoons, or tropical storms, annually giving rise to wind, rain and flood damage and coastal tidal surge. In addition over the last 10 years major droughts have occurred in the North and South of the country affecting agricultural yields in critical areas.

The majority of Philippine natural disasters do not make regional or international news, although these have a major impact on the national economy and population annually. Since mid 1990, three major national disasters have made international headlines, namely, the July 1990 earthquake in North Central Luzon, the June 1991 volcanic eruption at Mt. Pinatubo in Central Luzon and the typhoon and flooding at Ormoc in Leyte in October 1991 resulting in some 8,000 deaths (see Plate 1 for locations). This paper concerns the first two disasters and draws on the authors' experiences in the post-disaster efforts of the Department of Agriculture (DA) and Commission of the European Communities (EC). It focuses on the specific needs of those people directly affected and the longer term needs for rehabilitation and reconstruction of communities and infrastructure, as well as re-settlement.

Following both disasters, the DA played a major role with other government agencies, in the main relief and longer term rehabilitation efforts aimed particularly at the well-being of rural communities (farmers). Since 1987 the EC has had an expanding programme of support to rural communities in the Philippines, closely linked with the Department of Agriculture. Programmes include the Central Cordillera Agricultural Programme, Northern Luzon (CECAP), Aurora Integrated Agricultural Development, Eastern Luzon (AIADP) and a National Agricultural Education Project (AGRED) centred in Manila. Staff and resources from all these projects assisted in the relief operations under the auspices of the DA and EC.

Natural disasters. Thomas Telford, London, 1993

1990 EARTHQUAKE

Although the epicentre of the 1990 earthquake (7.7 on the Richter Scale), was near San Jose, damage generally followed the Philippine fault with secondary fault lines stretching north and west into the Cordillera Mountains. It affected some 7,000 sq km, approximately 40% of which covered southern part of the Cordillera (see Plate 1).

The nature of damage was diverse, extending from coastal areas through lowland plains to steep sided mountains rising to 2000m and above. The damage included: localised building collapse in Cabanatuan and San Jose: liquefaction and sinking of built-up areas in Dagupan and Aringay; extensive structural damage in Baguio; and massive landslides and road closures in the Cordillera. Many communities were devastated through loss of homes, possessions and basic social infrastructure (see Plate 2).

Landslides in the Cordillera increased by 30-40 times causing deforestation, ground instability and extensive river siltation; and the subsistence farmers lost valuable terraced agricultural land and irrigation systems. They were left without water supplies, food, medical services, schools and their livelihoods. The already limited local access network (trails and footbridges) was devastated. The only East-West road across the Cordillera was severed and all five roads to Baguio and the strategic access to the Northern Luzon rice bowl were closed, or open intermittently, for months effectively closing off acces to that part of Northern Luzon. In the Cordillera, many villages were not visited for at least a week after the main tremor and they remained completely cut off with no access, other than on foot, for many months afterwards.

The severance of access routes had much wider ramifications for Luzon as a whole because it prevented the transport of vegetables and other agricultural produce from Northern Luzon to Metro Manila, causing shortages in the capital and surpluses in the production areas. These changes to the supply pattern resulted in inflated prices in Manila and reduced prices for the producers of the north.

During the weeks after the main quake, the morale of the communities was very low due to the repeated aftershocks and secondary quakes which caused considerable further destruction. Shell shocked is the only way to describe the mood of the people, and many people were numbed for several weeks, and even months. In spite of this the Filipinos retained their humour, quickly coining the phrase "Its not God's fault it is the Philippine fault", a reference to the major fault line.

Initial humanitarian aid concentrated on urban areas because the inhabitants were able to alert the authorities to their plight most effectively but the DA came into its own in identifying which rural areas were affected and the nature of damage through their network of agricultural field technicians based in the communities.

Fortunately a pre-existing EC funded agricultural development project under the direction of the DA (CECAP) was underway which embraced many affected Cordilleran communities. Working in collaboration with other agencies, CECAP used its vehicles and

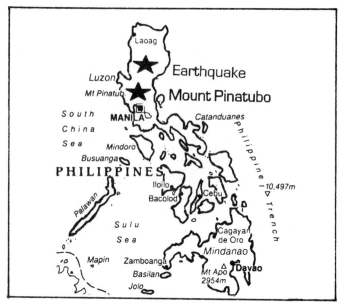

Plate 1. Disaster locations

Plate 2. Damaged buildings following the earthquake

field staff to assist in ferrying in emergency food supplies and other desperately needed aid to the communities which were cut off. Extensive use of helicopters was also required as well as transportation by foot.

Approximately 500,000 people in the Cordillera (including Baguio) were directly affected by the earthquake, of which some 80,000 lived in some form of temporary accommodation immediately after the disaster, but documentation on this is limited. Initial relief operations concentrated on providing essential food, shelter, clothing and medical aid. In the months following July 16, the stricken Cordillera communities came to rely on food aid since much of their staple standing crops of rice and sweet potato had been lost, as had commodities awaiting transport to market. This and landslide inundation of agricultural land meant the agricultural year had been lost and future years reduced in capability. The domestic animal population of the area was also almost completely killed off to meet short term food needs. Temporary shelter was extremely basic with no potable water and poor sanitary conditions giving rise to health problems. These were worsened by the damage and destruction of hospitals and other medical facilities, and the lack of access.

Throughout this period the communities showed exceptional resourcefulness and resolve in adapting to their plight which is typical of the Philippine culture (see Plate 4). This was probably born out of the strong community spirit within the indigenous communities of the Cordillera, helped by the already harsh living conditions of their subsistence environment. As the initial trauma dissipated, this strength of character and independence helped the communities to re-establish themselves, with many abandoning their temporary shelter, salvaging the remains of their homes and transferring them to safer areas. These moves merely transferring and in some cases increasing the problems, however, they had their own roof over their heads whilst others remained in temporary shelter.

Humanitarian aid is only the beginning and within days, assessments of the extent of damage and rehabilitation needs were being undertaken. The overall programme was coordinated by the Department of Highways and Works with assistance from the Asian Development Bank. At this stage the EC was eager to assist and commissioned John Gordon to help Dr Fernandez in undertaking a preliminary damage assessment in the affected areas. This work was completed within 4 weeks of the main tremor, and copies of the report were made available to the Government, to ADB and World Bank, and to EC embassies in Manila.

Based on this the EC pledged assistance in: rehabilitation of agriculture in the Southern Cordillera; re-building two hospitals; urban planning in Baguio and Dagupan; and transport planning for Northern Luzon. The underlying concept of the EC's support being to make rural and disadvantaged communities less vulnerable to the impact of future disasters. The funding for these interventions is in place and planning well advanced. The agricultural rehabilitation component commenced in August 1992 and will continue for three years. The EC intervention was part of a much wider programme to which many bilateral and multilateral agencies have pledged support and finance in order to encourage a structured and coordinated approach to the Government's rehabilitation programme.

Plate 3. Reconstruction of housing in Sante Fe Nueva Viscaya

Plate 4. Resourcefulness of Filipinos

MOUNT PINATUBO

The immediate sociological effects of the Mount Pinatubo eruption were quite different since advance warning of the impending eruption enabled inhabitants to be evacuated to safety. Consequently loss of life as a direct result of the eruption and the ash falls was minimised (lava flows being contained within the crater rim). Ash spread over a considerable distance with deposits of 1cm thick evident 100km away in Manila, closing the main international airport for a week. The volcanic eruption directly affected 1.18 million people (40% in rural areas) out of a regional population of 3.4 million. Unlike the earthquake this disaster was not over in a matter of minutes and the further on-going effects are still manifesting themselves today through: eruptions, ash falls and damage; lahar (mud flows) and siltation; flooding and gullying; sandstorms in the dry season; and so on. With some 7-9 billion cubic metres of volcanic debris from the eruption being subsequently deposited, the damage to land and the rivers and irrigation systems of Central Luzon is enormous. This lahar and consequent effects, particularly increased flooding risks due to ash falls (1 million cubic metres washed into rivers and valleys in 1991 alone), are expected to continue for at least 5 years before stabilising. Plate 5 shows the spread of ashfall following the eruption and the areas currently covered by lahar or subject to siltation and flooding damage.

To put the Mt Pinatubo eruption in an international context we believe there has been no other similar disaster in recent history where so many people have suffered such long term consequences in a populated area. The eruption had serious effects over an area within a 40km radius of the volcano. The ash deposits had dramatic impacts on shelter and agriculture (see Plate 6), and commercial fish ponds, in this very fertile and productive area of the Philippines.

Within this 40 km radius some 87,000 hectares of land were recoverable where deposits were less than 15cm and the rest has been written off for the time being. In the Pampanga River Delta 8,000 ha out of a total of 36,000 ha of commercial fish ponds were totally lost; and the livestock industry was decimated due to: the disappearance of fodder under the ash; animal death during the eruption; and collapse of rearing and production buildings.

The ash blanket destroyed trees and standing crops and rendered land infertile. Where deposits were shallow, the farmers were very quickly tilling the land, mixing the ash with the natural soil and replanting. Fortunately, the properties of the ash made this viable although soil fertility was seriously affected and hence production levels were reduced. Agricultural recovery was considerably aided by the actions of the DA in distribution of seed, fertilisers, and the provision of technical knowhow.

The effects on the fisheries will be much longer lasting as the primary problem is siltation and it is doubtful if many of these areas can be recovered. In fact further damage is likely as siltation continues; and the risks of flooding will continue as more ash is washed down into the rivers which is dramatically altering the whole hydrological flow regime of Central Luzon.

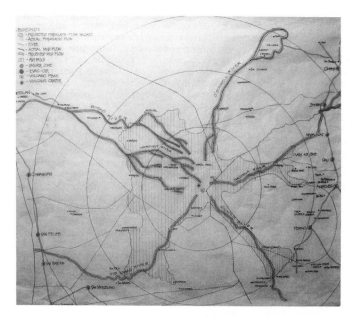

Plate 5. Extent of volcanic eruption damage

Plate 6. Digging out volcanic ash in Florida Blanca

In urban areas the initial effects were mainly building damage as well as siltation and blocking of water conduits and drains. During the rain's movement of ashfall (mud flow - lahar) into the main watercourse caused serious siltation and resulting flooding, as well as destruction of property and washing out of roads, bridges and other infrastructure. Movement of lahar towards river deltas and the sea (see Plate 7) caused further damage to in-shore and off-shore fisheries and agricultural land.

Much of the publicity focused on the effects on the American Clark Air Base and Subic Naval Base, and the eventual American pullouts from both. It is ironic to note that the eruption at Mt. Pinatubo achieved what years of insurgency, political activism and negotiation failed to do. However this pull out had a further effect on an already devastated local economy. What were the effects on the local population whilst this was all happening? Whole communities were devastated, homes and possessions were lost due to ashfall, lahar, siltation and flooding; and livelihoods were destroyed. All these resulted in a massive evacuation with over 250,000 people being moved out to temporary shelter. Although many were eventually able to return home the number of people needing to be permanently relocated is estimated to be 186,000. Twenty one sites have been identified to resettle some 50,000 families (10,000 families being from the Aetas tribes - almost the entire population of 65,000). March 1993 relief agency figures show that some 80,000 people still remain in temporary shelter.

In human terms, undoubtedly the worst affected were the Aetas tribe of Negritos whose natural homelands were on the upland fertile wooded slopes of Mount Pinatubo. The Aetas were a semi-nomadic people leading a hunter gatherer existence with little experience of agriculture and limited prior contact with lowlanders. They were driven from their homes to small towns and villages, where they were greeted by people who had also suffered badly. They were accommodated in local schools and other public buildings where they elected to camp under makeshift shelters (see Plate 8) in the grounds, feeling more at home in these than in buildings. Many died in unexplained circumstances, perhaps losing the will to live, perhaps not being able to cope with the contrasts of living in an urban environment - we will never know.

The general atmosphere in these temporary evacuation centres was one of bewilderment and listlessness. The Aetas who were used to living in groups of 5-10 families now being forced to live a gregarious existence within an urban community and perhaps most of all to conform to a regulated way of life with total dependency on others. The Aetas were extremely unhappy and the situation was potentially explosive but their resourcefulness shone through and they collected building materials from collapsed buildings to erect their own shelters. Perhaps more surprising, within four days of evacuation from their homelands we noticed that a number of women had already taken up posts as maids and domestics with people in the towns, demonstrating both the adaptability of the Negritos and the willingness of other communities to accept them.

In the immediate aftermath of the eruption of Mount Pinatubo the Government and non-government agencies coped well in providing much needed food aid and emergency assistance with external

Plate 7. Ash deposits in a river channel

Plate 8. Mount Pinatubo Refugee Reception Centre

financial help. However, since this initial stage there has been a vacuum when help with a long term rehabilitation has moved slowly. In this instance the pause was very necessary because the full impact of the disaster will not manifest itself for some years and therefore assessments of the likely longer term effects have to be completed before the Government, donor agencies and multilateral agencies are prepared to commit the necessary funding and other resources.

This is of little comfort to the people whose lives and livelihoods are affected, they are left waiting and surviving on what meagre existence they can generate in the meantime, and this inevitably leads to despair and despondency. We are now two years after the eruption and the main rehabilitation programme is still moving slowly. Government agencies have provided what assistance they can with the strong competition for their limited resources in their emerging economy but as the Mt. Pinatubo eruption develops into a series of secondary natural disasters the Philippine government cannot be expected to cope on its own.

COMMON CONSEQUENCES

Although these two disasters were very different in character, time scale and physical effects, many comparisons can be made. In both cases there were the immediate unavoidable effects including loss of life, loss of homes and possessions, infrastructure damage, and diseases associated with insanitary conditions. However, in both cases government agencies and non-government agencies were quickly on the scene with the necessary humanitarian aid. Beyond the immediate humanitarian effects there were many common consequences of both disasters including:

- the need to sustain communities with food and other basic services and necessities once the relief ceased;

- restoration of access links, communications and basic infrastructure;

- provision of temporary and long term housing and shelter;

- resettlement of permanently displaced persons;

- the need to recreate livelihoods, a particularly critical problem of the Mount Pinatubo disaster, and re-establish agricultural production quickly; and

- dealing with social consequences and post disaster trauma.

Maintenance of food supplies and basic services can be considered as an extension of the immediate post disaster relief operations, albeit at declining levels of support as communities begin to fend for themselves again. In the case of the Philippine disasters, we believe that government agencies met these needs and the donor community provided the necessary financial support. In the case of Mount Pinatubo the twin constraints of lack of alternative employment (in the region or elsewhere) and the lack of suitable resettlement land anywhere posed major problems for the Government in developing a long term rehabilitation strategy.

The Media focuses on a disaster for a short while, the coverage

441

depending on its newsworthiness. In reality, rehabilitation efforts involve considerable expenditure and take time to implement - often the causes and reasons get forgotten. Once this happens communities come to accept their situation as the "norm" and different priorities emerge. We believe that more effort needs to be devoted to prioritisation of the necessary works and the early release of funding in order that strategic repairs can be effected immediately so that the momentum of rebuilding peoples lives and livelihoods is maintained through early implementation of some advance re-building works.

DISPLACED PERSONS

Following the 1990 earthquake it was recognised that the government did not react quickly enough in addressing the temporary and long term resettlement issues. The lessons learned were addressed in the aftermath of the Mt. Pinatubo eruption. However rebuilding infrastructure is easier than rebuilding people's lives and hence a major problem following both disasters has been less than effective treatment of resettling displaced persons.

The large number of evacuees arising from the earthquake led to resettlement programmes by government and non-government organisations. Figures from the Province of Nueva Vizcaya and part of Benguet show 11 registered resettlement areas with space for over 1,300 households. To date some 1,000 spaces have been provided through government programmes but only 350 are presently occupied, and the figure is decreasing. Whereas the voluntary and NGO sponsored areas are generally fully occupied. Many evacuees were absorbed elsewhere in the community, or returned to their land shunning any offer of assistance. A case in point is the city of Baguio where it was estimated that some 15,000 people (approx 10% of the permanent population) were made homeless. No permanent resettlement areas were constructed - where did the evacuees go? It is believed that they returned to previous homes, or were absorbed by family and friends, or rented new accommodation. Some may have left Baguio, possibly returning to their original home areas.

In the case of Mt. Pinatubo, many of the Aetas who had been resettled in another part of the Philippines returned to the Mt. Pinatubo area of their own accord. In the resettlement areas permanent homes were provided in total contradiction to their semi-nomadic way of life and culture, and these are being rejected. Although tensions existed between evacuees and landowners of evacuation areas there were only a few cases of reported violence or trouble. However evacuees caused substantial damage to public buildings used as temporary shelter through cannibalisation of the interiors for firewood and building materials.

Following both disasters it has taken a great deal of time to establish permanent resettlement areas (see Plate 3) and in the case of government sites they provide inadequate housing, and many lack proper sanitation. Some 530 people have died in Mt. Pinatubo evacuation areas due to poor living conditions compared with only 300 through the direct effects of the eruption. Most people affected by Mt. Pinatubo stayed in their temporary sites since they had no alternative whereas those affected by the earthquake quickly drifted away to friends and relatives or salvage the remains of their homes.

Resettlement is costly and the Philippine economy can little afford it, hence, each relocated family has had to pay for their new home either through loan repayment or rental. However house and lot ownership remains unresolved and the families have no security of tenure for their new homes as yet. In these disaster areas, home insurance cover is virtually unknown hence the communities are paying twice for their homes, possessions and land. Additionally, a common criticism is that following both disasters available funds have been devoted to non-essential infrastructure to the detriment of providing adequate housing.

All major natural disasters have dramatic social consequences both as a result of the immediate impact of the disaster and the more protracted post disaster trauma. The immediate social consequences are the grief associated with loss of relatives, friends and possessions; and often the need to survive. Whereas the longer term social needs relate to people coping with rebuilding their lives and in many instances finding themselves with a different position in their own society. Most people cope with the immediate effects relatively well but the longer term consequences are often harder to bear and lead to despair and desperation.

All this begs the question - even if permanent resettlement is offered do the communities want it? Many will only take up this option if they have no alternative, however, most would rather have their independence and make their own arrangements, since social consequences are considerably alleviated.

THE VACUUM AND HOW IT CAN BE OVERCOME

The vacuum between the provision of immediate humanitarian aid in the aftermath of a disaster and the eventual rebuilding and rehabilitation work is a very real problem following all major disasters. Some three years after the earthquake, and two years after the volcanic eruption, many problems still exist. Some rehabilitation programmes are complete, and others just started or still being planned. The evacuation/resettlement issue needs to be resolved; and steps need to be taken to prevent reallocation of funds from one disaster relief operation to another.

As the Philippines and other countries stumble from one natural disaster to another the problems are easy to see but the practical solutions less easy to identify. From our experiences we see three distinct but related problems:

- provision of immediate and specific relief and humanitarian aid following a disaster;

- provision of longer term rehabilitation programmes and reducing the lead-in times for start up; and

- providing a definitive programme for short term evacuation and longer term resettlement of disaster victims.

All of these measures require a clear coordinated approach. Following both disasters, much work was done by NGOs as well as government organisations, however, we believe that this could have been better organised and coordinated. In the Philippines a National Disaster Coordinating Council (NDCC) has been established to deal with short term disasters, eg typhoons, but is quite unable to deal with the long term problems of the earthquake or Mt Pinatubo. The special Regional Councils (RDCCs) face similar problems; and the problems of local governments responding to such emergencies are likely to be exacerbated by the recent introduction of the Local Government Code which generally desolves power and responsibilities from Central to Local Government. These councils could be strengthened by establishing disaster preparedness strategies on a Province or Regional basis in areas prone to natural disasters. Any such programme would need to link in at a national level to address inter alia the following:

- damage assessment (physical and human) and immediate needs;

- stockpiling of appropriate temporary shelter, food and medical supplies etc;

- maintenance of communications networks;

- maintenance of emergency services; and

- identification of temporary shelter or evacuation centres.

With respect to longer term rehabilitation, following both these disasters it was apparent that the Government and the major donor agencies, particularly the EC and the ADB, endeavoured to speed up the process but understandably established procedures have to be followed before they can commit themselves to expensive rehabilitation programmes. However, if communities are to be effectively supported there must be some transitional arrangements in the meantime. One way is for agencies to maintain reserve funds on immediate call in the case of disasters as the EC do in the Philippines and which helped following the Mt. Pinatubo eruption. But these small levels of expenditure cannot maintain the social rebuilding momentum generated in the immediate post disaster period and sufficient funds need to be injected to meet this need until the main rehabilitation works commence.

We believe there is a desire by the agencies to meet this need but their systems generally make it difficult. Somehow practical steps have to be taken to shorten the typical cycle of "appraisal" followed by "putting funding in place", and then "arranging implementation" which can take 2 years or more before rehabilitation starts. Introducing a transitional stage and accepting lower levels of guarantee that the funds made available will be employed in achieving the most cost effective solutions could help. Donor agencies would need to make a committment to act quickly on the results of coordinated rapid appraisal missions, specifically targeted at transitional needs with funds being available for immediate release. Such a process of transitional aid might include:

444

Step 1: As soon as a disaster occurs selected donor agencies commit an initial traunche of funding, beyond the requirements of immediate post disaster relief. The level of funding being geared to the ability and willingness of the particular agency to support the rebuilding programme rather than accurate assessment of needs.

Step 2: Provide immediate advance Technical Assistance disaster relief managers with a specific mandate to authorise immediate funding (within certain limits) for priority actions which they judge necessary.

Step 3: Funds would then be released on a "a need-basis" by the relief managers, based on their continuous assessments, to enable implementation to proceed immediately. Clearly, they would have to work within certain guidelines but these could be fairly general and still provide the level of control required by the donor.

Step 4: Once the initial programme is underway, the relief managers can concentrate on the preparation of a longer term strategy for rehabilitation works. This might identify the need for further traunches of short term aid in order to maintain the momentum of the transitional programme, as well as a structured programme of aid and loans to achieve their full commitments to the rehabilitation work within a practical time scale.

This process might start within a month of the disaster occurring with full assessment of the needs for this transitional funding, being completed within 3-6 months. However, the transitional funds might continue to flow for two years or more until the main programme is well underway. There would of course still be the need for the donor agencies to progress mobilisation of the financial and technical support for their contribution to the main rehabilitation programme with vigour. This transitional stage must not be seen as a substitute for the main programme but as an enhancement to the support given to disaster stricken communities.

Our third concern lies in the evacuation/resettlement issues. Even under the best conditions, the history of community relocation in the Philippines has shown that it is not intended for all those who try it. If better opportunities arise then people will move on as seen in the two disasters featured here. Inadequate planning often leads displaced families to despair because they have no clear idea of what the future holds, and most resettlement programmes offer no real options.

There is a need for a more positive institutional response to any disaster and particularly towards evacuation/resettlement. Our experience indicates that the following need to be more adequately addressed in any temporary or permanent evacuation/ resettlement programme in the Philippines.

- establishment of essential water, health and sanitation facilities;

- provision of recreational and other measures to relieve boredom, particularly in short term evacuation centres;

- availability of alternative agricultural land;

445

- achieve a proper balance between housing and communal facilities;

- provision of appropriate and correctly designed shelter;

- clarification of house and land ownership; and

- provision of alternative livelihood opportunities;

- provision of alternative schooling and educational buildings.

What could be, or is being done, in the Philippines?

- The agricultural component of the EC funded Earthquake Rehabilitation Programme aims to set up a localised disaster preparedness programme in the Cordillera and assistance is being extended to resettlement areas.

- Donors could set aside contingency funds for emergency needs.

- Government calamity funds could be disbursed to disaster prone areas in anticipation of their needs.

Finally, it has to be recognised that people will tolerate very poor conditions providing they have hope and an expectation that things will improve in the future. Any advance rebuilding programme should be based on community self-help schemes with labour provided by the communities where possible. This approach serves to strengthen community spirit' as well as helping with much needed rehabilitation.

OUR FUTURE ASPIRATIONS

A number of agencies already go some way towards meeting the needs created by the vacuum between immediate humanitarian aid and the main rehabilitation programme but they must go much further if the real needs of affected communities are to be met. We firmly believe that this should be a primary aim of the support provided by the donor community.

In the Philippines we have been very encouraged by the progress made to date with the support of the EC, ADB and other agencies, and we appreciate the flexible approach which the donor community adopts in trying to continually improve systems. From our direct experience in the aftermath of the 1990 earthquake and the 1991 Pinatubo eruption we welcome the strong partnership already established between the European Community and the Government of the Philippines in alleviating the consequences of disasters. We hope to build on this partnership in the future through greater mutual understanding and commitment on both sides. Notwithstanding, in order to achieve this we are hoping for increased support in the critical period between the delivery of immediate post disaster humanitarian aid and the implementation of the main rehabilitation programmes. We fervently hope that by working together with the EC and other agencies we can deliver the necessary support to the benefit of the communities whose lives have been devastated by disasters.

36. The impact of slope movements on a rural community: lessons from Jamaica

R. AHMAD and B. E. CARBY, University of the West Indies, Jamaica, and P. H. SAUNDERS, Office of Disaster Preparedness and Emergency Relief Co-ordination, Jamaica

ABSTRACT

The slope movements of March 1986 which destroyed the village of Preston, Parish of St. Mary, Jamaica were related to the phenomenon of lateral spreading. These movements are controlled by the underlying geology and structure.

Some seven years after the disaster, the 17 dislocated families have not all been permanently relocated. The Preston experience highlights many undocumented impacts of slope movements on rural communities and is by no means a rare occurrence.

This study documents the complicated bureaucratic process of relief, recovery, and rehabilitation. The nature of the hazard is discussed and long-term mitigation strategies are proposed. The Preston experience has shown that (i) there are no specific guidelines or legislative framework within which the State may effectively assist its citizenry in the event of natural disasters, and (ii) as a society we are not prepared to deal with and manage the landslide hazard. These observations may be valid worldwide for developing countries.

The slope movements which affected Preston are likely to be repeated in other communities in St. Mary, therefore, the need for a National Landslide Management Programme is indicated. The Preston experience suggests that it is the responsibility of the local population to learn about the hazard and to prepare itself accordingly.

INTRODUCTION

Until March 12, 1986, Preston was an active farming community in the Parish of St. Mary, Jamaica (Fig. 1). Today, it is a ghost village, a victim of periodic slow slope movements which were first documented in 1946. During March to May 1986 following a period of very heavy and sustained rainfall these slope movements caused a widespread development of fissures, cracks, and fractures, as well as slumping and subsidence that affected both the regolith and the bedrock in an area of about 100 ha on the spur where Preston is located (Figs. 1 and 2;

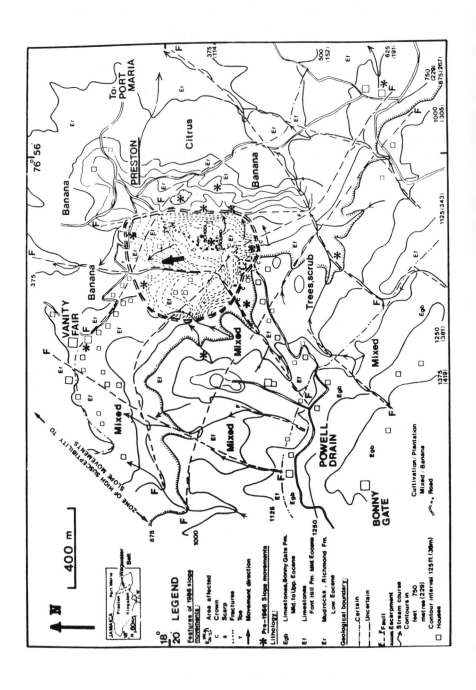

Fig. 1. Geological and geomorphic map of Preston and environs.
The location of school, road, cultivation and planation areas,
and some of the houses damaged or destroyed are shown. The
large arrow indicates the dominant sense of displacement.
Pre-movement topography is shown by dashed contour lines drawn
at 25 ft. interval. Old slope movements are also prominent.
The area north of the fault scarp is highly susceptible to
slope movements.

Map is based an aerial - photo-interpretation (1961 = I:25000;
1989 = I:1000) and limited field checks. Geology is modified
from Burke et. al (ref. 9), and the Geolgical sheet No. 21
(ref. 10). Topography is from 1:12 5000 sheets 92 C and 93 A,
old edition, Survey Department, Jamaica.

---

refs. 1-4). As a result, residential dwellings and
infrastructure in the area were damaged or destroyed beyond
repair, forcing the residents to abandon their homes and
farming lands.

The direct economic damage, based on replacement costs, was
about Jamaican $1.5M (US $273,000). This value calculated in
terms of 1991 dollars is J $4.6M (US. $307,000). Using the
culture-and-currency-independent method (ref. 5), the total
economic damage is 264 person - years or in other words, 264
person - years production are needed to repair the damage at
Preston.

The natural disaster at Preston has been the subject of
several St. Mary Parish Council meetings and resolutions,
telegrams to the political hierarchy seeking help, political
statements, news media reports, and scientific investigations.
The objective of these efforts was to provide humanitarian
relief, and assist the victims in their relocation and
rehabilitation. This exercise was perceived to be the
responsibility of the State. The scientific community had
speedily determined the nature, causes, extent, and
consequences of the slope movements, and made recommendations
for the relocation of the victims (ref. 1-4).

Slope movements are a significant geodynamic process on most
of the islands in the Greater and Lesser Antilles because of
their geographical and geological location within the
seismically active plate boundary zones of the Caribbean Plate
(ref. 3, 6). Hazards related to slope instability are an
important societal and environmental concern to Caribbean
States (ref. 3, 7). Preston provides a vivid example of the
human impact and economic losses inflicted by slope movements
on a rural community and suggests that the state must
encourage earth sciences based research and preparation of
hazard and risk maps, and the earth scientists in turn should
package this data in a language readily understood by the
populace.

This paper presents a brief scientific explanation for the
1986 slope movements at Preston, Parish of St. Mary, Jamaica,
documents the process of emergency relief, recovery and

Fig. 2. Oblique aerial photograph (looking south) of a part of
Preston. See Fig. 1 for location. The main scarp (ms) is
located within the limestones. The fault trace is marked FF.

Fresh scars are due to rock falls and topples. Sections of
road (r) have been completely destroyed. Playground (pg),
school (s), and teachers cottage (tc) are in an area showing
hummocky topography. Fracture, ff, is seen to cut through the
teacher's cottage. The slope section below school has also
slipped. Photograph by J.S. Tyndale Biscoe, 1989.

rehabilitation, and describes the human and economic impact.
The nature of the hazard is discussed and long-term mitigation
strategies are proposed.

GEOLOGICAL SETTING

Since slope movements at Preston are controlled by geology,
structure, and geomorphology, it is crucial to take these
factors into consideration in the identification and
mitigation of the hazard, and landuse planning.

The Preston area defines the northwestern extremity of
boundary between the Palaeogene Wagwater Belt of eastern
Jamaica, one of the most important structural features on the
island, and the plateau-forming Tertiary limestones (refs.
8-10). It represents an active geological environment

characterized by Neogene faulting and slope movements.

Mudrocks of the Richmond Formation constitute the basement at Preston and are capped by an approximately 100m thick slab of chalky limestones of the Font Hill Formation (Fig. 1, refs. 9-10). The mapped area is extensively faulted and displays a "staircase" topography. The main landforms from southwest to northeast, are (Figs. 1 and 2): (i) a highly dissected limestone ridge, average elevation 450m, (ii) a 38m high fault scarp within the limestones which is also highly dissected, (iii) gently sloping, fault bounded spurs oriented northeast, and underlain by chalky limestones, and (iv) a lowland area of mudrocks to the north. A number of old slope movements have been mapped and are shown on Figure 1. The geological and geomorphic framework described is characteristic of much of the Parish of St. Mary.

A number of old slope movements have been mapped and are shown on Figure 1. The geological and geomorphic framework described is characteristic of much of the Parish of St. Mary.

1986 SLOPE MOVEMENTS

Preston slope movements are a complex feature. Having evolved over a long period of time, they comprise elements that display variable morphology and geometry. The geological and geomorphological framework is ideal for gravity induced movements within the limestone slab overlying a basement of mudrocks. Most of the failures are located in the physical environment modified for agriculture, housing, and road construction.

The initial movement appears to be related to lateral spreading and was followed by slide and flow involving rock, debris and earth (refs. 1-4). The crown and main scarp are located within the fault scarp in limestones and the toe region is in mudrocks (Figs. 1 and 2). Rockfalls and topples occurred in the main scarp. The nature of movement also seems to have been variable. A vertical displacement of 2m was observed in the main scarp during April 15 to 25 (ref. 2). These movements became widespread in May to June and by September an area of 100 ha became severely affected (Fig. 1).

The slope deformation at Preston appears to have been controlled by a differential displacement of bedrock and regolith along near - vertical fractures of varying dimensions (refs. 1-4). Some of these fractures evolved into fissures. Man-made structures in the area were damaged or destroyed due to slumping, tilting, and rotation of fractured limestone blocks (Fig. 2).

In summary, we suggest that slope deformation at Preston is related to failure and movement within the tectonized mudrock basement and gravity-induced lateral spreading which resulted in the fracturing of the limestones exposed on the spur.

Based on the occurrence of slope movements, their causes, and the geologic setting at Preston, we have prepared a preliminary landslide susceptibility map for the area (Fig 3.) which should form the basis for a response.

GOVERNMENT RESPONSE

The Office of Disaster Preparedness (ODP) is the government agency in Jamaica charged with the responsibility of coordinating all national disaster management programmes including mitigation and planning. Local response is initiated by Parish Disaster Committees.

The ODP was first informed of slope movements at Preston by the Principal of the Primary School on March 12, 1986. The ODP asked the Geological Survey Division (GSD) to advise on the site conditions. The GSD report of March 27 acted as a catalyst for a combined government agency response.

On April 1, a site visit was made by a team comprising officers of the ODP, GSD, Public Works Department (PWD), Ministry of Social Security (responsible for allocating relief), St. Mary Parish Council, and the local member of the Parliament. The team recommended immediate relocation of 17 families identified as being at risk. The other recommendations were:
(i)   That the GSD, effective April 15, begin a detailed study of the area, measure the rate of movements, and predict its pattern.
(ii)   That the National Water Commission (NWC) and the Jamaica Public Service Company (JPSCo) effect preventive measures to protect water and electricity facilities.
(iii)   That the PWD and the Parish Council monitor the area on a daily basis and report to the ODP.
(iv)   That the Ministry of Education assess the problems at the school in consultation with the GSD and PWD and take appropriate action.
(v)   That the Ministry of Social Security and the Parish Council begin drafting relocation plans.

Later in April, the ODP recommended the closure of school as the fissures in the school compound had widened causing further damage to the buildings. By May 5, it became evident that movement was becoming more widespread and that all the residents of Preston would have to be relocated. The adjacent district of Oxford was warned of the possibility of being affected.

Efforts to relocate the victims continued at the Parish level, between May 1986 and January 1987 and the Ministry of Agriculture identified two potential areas, Tryall and Llangley (N.B. Both these areas are prone to slope movements). The PWD, NWC, and other government agencies were asked to provide estimates for the construction of one - bedroom units and the provision of utilities. These were submitted to the ODP in February 1987.

In the meantime some of the families had moved to stay with relatives and friends, while others opted for rented premises, with government providing a rent subsidy. One of the families refused to move and had to be persuaded to shift to a temporary location on February 26, 1987.

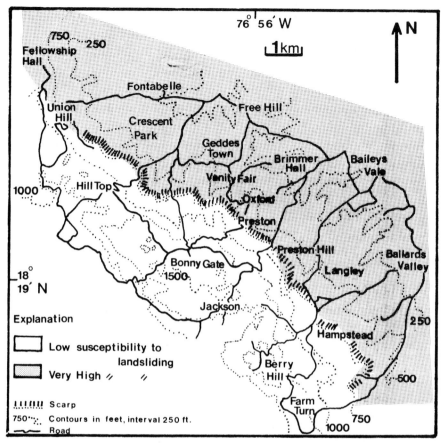

Fig. 3. Preliminary landslide susceptibility map of the
Preston area. NOTE: The map indicates the relative magnitude
of the hazard in the area for development and planning
purposes only, and should not be used to determine the
stability of the specific sites.

On April 1, 1987, the Minister of Construction announced the
formulation of "Preston Task Force" comprising all the
relevant government agencies, representatives from the
University of the West Indies, and the engineering fraternity.
Its mandate was to review and evaluate the response, and the
implications of the landslides for future developments in St.
Mary. The Task Force met on September 1, 1987 and recommended
that the 17 displaced families be relocated at Tryall and that
the affected persons be appropriately compensated by the
Government. These recommendations were submitted to the
relevant authorities by the ODP but were not acted upon.

Hurricane Gilbert of 1988 overshadowed the Preston issue. The
plight of the 17 displaced families is occasionally mentioned

in the news media, particularly when new slope movements occur, resulting in a brief rekindling of interest, but otherwise these are the forgotten refugees of Preston. The displaced victims of 1986 slope movements have not received compensation for their losses from the Government.

HUMAN AND ECONOMIC IMPACT

The 1986 slope movements at Preston completely disrupted the lives of 17 families. Their temporary relocation was to a more urban area, where the victims could not continue their farming activities. The dislocation was all the more severe because the victims were small farmers. Thus apart from the usual ties of ownership, they depended on the land for economic survival. The wider social impact was also severe. The loss of power and water mains left a wide area without electricity and water. Thus, even those houses which were outside of the landslide suffered loss of power and water. The main road into the community was severed, necessitating a detour of about 5 km. The general deterioration of the main road led to the refusal of owners of public transportation to enter the area. Farmers could not get their produce to market, and they lost income from those crops which could still have been reaped.

The primary school at Preston had to be closed. It was eventually relocated, but when it was re-opened the student population dropped from 120 to 70. Parents in neighbouring villages who had previously sent their children to school at Preston, feared for their safety and sent them to other schools.

Cost of Relocation

The geotechnical study carried out by the GSD concluded that any relocation should be regarded as permanent. The cost of relocation, including infrastructure was calculated at approximately J $1.5M (US $1.0= J $5.50 in 1986). This included building eight new houses and removing and repairing seven others. The other two families were not interested in moving to the designated area.

Perception of relocation

All but one victim eventually agreed to relocate permanently. They did voice certain reservations, however. Foremost in their minds was the loss of livelihood. The quarter-of-an-acre plot being offered was in most cases less than that previously owned. The farmers did not think they could support their families from this one plot. Also some of their income was derived from tree crops. During the three to five years needed for the re-establishment of these crops there would be a shortfall in income. So great was the concern for the loss of income that some farmers returned to the area to continue farming their plots for over a year after they had moved house, despite being warned of the danger of sudden failure of the land.

In an effort to address this concern, an alternative site was identified which would have allowed each family three acres of land for farming. This area was also determined to be landslide-prone, however and that plan was shelved.

Outcome

Seven years after the 1986 slope movements at Preston, the victims still have not all been relocated. Their fates are as follows:

i)   3 families given land nearby. One received public assistance (from the member of Parliament) to relocate.

ii)   1 moved to a neighbouring district, using personal resources.

iii) 4 moved to other parishes.

iv)   3 moved to the capital of the same parish.

v)   1 remained in Preston.

      The others could not be traced. Only one of the victims is presently receiving public assistance, in the form of a rent grant.

REVIEW OF RESPONSE

Jamaica has a well defined emergency management structure. However a major weakness exists, in that there is no legislative framework for disaster management. The ODP therefore has no legal authority and must depend on the cooperation and goodwill of other agencies to succeed in its mandate. Furthermore, its role is to coordinate. This means that it does not directly provide response or relief. These functions are variously divided among the fire department, army, police, Ministry of Labour, Ministry of Social Security, and various non-governmental organizations such as the Salvation Army, Red Cross and Church groups. Thus once the ODP has coordinated initial response and notified the various actors of the technical recommendations and response needs its function has been discharged. Any further action is purely as a monitor and a catalyst. This lack of legal authority and fragmentation of responsibility complicates and renders difficult the provision of relief, as has been witnessed in the case of the Preston disaster.

The nature of the event was an important factor in the approach to response. It seems that because the event was localized, affected only a few families and was non-catastrophic, the local authorities initially, and the government ministries eventually, did not approach the problem with any sense of urgency.

Once the affected families had been temporarily relocated, any momentum which had been gained was completely lost. Efforts by the ODP to resuscitate interest a year later with the formation of a multi-disciplinary task force focussed attention for a while. However, the funding which was needed to implement the recommendations of the task force was never provided.

It seems also, that slope movement is not viewed as a "disaster". Such events occur frequently on a smaller scale, resulting in the blocking of roads and interruption of traffic flow, loss of agricultural lands, crops, and damage to housing and infrastructure. The response is the clearing of roads by the PWD - regarded as a routine matter. The very high indirect costs associated with road blockages is not considered significant. There is therefore no mechanism for responding to the effects of slope movements on the population, and the issue is not addressed in any of the National Contingency Plans.

By contrast, the destruction of property by flooding usually elicits a quick and sympathetic response from the authorities. Indeed, damage due to slope movements is often recorded as damage due to river erosion or flooding. Several small - scale floods have occurred in Jamaica since 1986. In all cases, victims were compensated for damage. In the case of total destruction of a house, victims who qualified for public assistance were given J \$10,000. The same was done for the victims of Hurricane Gilbert in 1988. A grant of J \$10,000 would have exceeded the value of the property lost by the Preston victims in all but two cases, yet not even in the post-hurricane rebuilding process were they considered.

MITIGATION STRATEGIES

The underlying cause of the slope movements at Preston is the geologic-tectonic framework which is repeated across the island, and indeed this setting hosts some of the most spectacular slope movements in Jamaica (ref. 1). Figure 3 shows the potential for such movements in relation to the population in the southern section of St. Mary. In order to protect those vulnerable communities, several steps need to be taken. Those steps will form the basis of our recommenda-tions.

1. Legislation specific to emergency management should be enacted giving the Office of Disaster Preparedness the required legal authority for effectively discharging its mandate.

2. A landslide hazard map should be prepared for the Parish of St. Mary. This map and its simple explanation should be easily available to the public through the local Parish Council or PWD.

3. A National Landslide Management Programme should be developed. This Programme should address the matter of compensation for the victims. Options are:

   (i)   Government buys the victim's holding at market value,

   (ii) Government gives a cash grant which would allow the victim to relocate by purchasing land elsewhere, and

(iii)   Government gives a basic grant plus a low interest
        loan repayable over a long period, about 20 years.

This would allow victims to purchase land and build a house
elsewhere, and would also provide a cushion while the victim's
economic base is being rebuilt. The Programme should also
include a National Landslide Contingency Plan which would be
activated at the first report of slope movements.

4. The activation of the Landslide Plan would be triggered by
a mechanism similar to that outlined in Figure 4. Once
activated the Plan should provide a mechanism for damage
assessment. It should also prevent further development and
construction activity in the area without the permission of
the planning authorities. If the slope movements are severe
then all development activity should be banned and the area be
left as forest.

5. The National Landslide Management Programme should also
include a Public Awareness component targetted at other
communities identified as being at risk. In this programme,
the nature of the phenomenon and the probability of the
community being affected should be clearly explained and the
community should be encouraged to institute its own monitoring
programmes and contingency plans. Simplified hazard zonation
maps such as the one shown in Figure 3 should be prepared for
each community and should provide the basis for community
action.

6. Each community, in consultation with the ODP, Parish
Council, PWD, managers of public utilities, and principals of
schools, should draft plans for the protection and maintenance
of lifeline facilities and relocation of schools if necessary.

7. The local Parish Disaster Committee must be sensitized by
the ODP to the need for immediate response to slope movements.

CONCLUSIONS

The geological and geomorphic framework controls the slope
movements which destroyed Preston in 1986. Anthropogenic
factors and January to May 1986 rainfall have played a
significant role in the resurgence of these slope movements.
The conditions leading to the slope instability have been
identified for an area of about 50 km around Preston (Fig. 3).

Although recurring slope movements continue to cause
significant losses in Jamaica and the Caribbean, it is
unfortunate that the indexing of natural disasters on the
basis of low frequency, dramatic events, such as hurricanes
and earthquakes has led to an underestimation of the extent
and economic significance of slope failures. Recent advances
in the understanding of slope instability suggest that slope
movements are perhaps the most amenable to measures directed
towards avoidance, prevention or correction
(ref. 11). However, our response to natural hazards is
providing relief rather than mitigation.

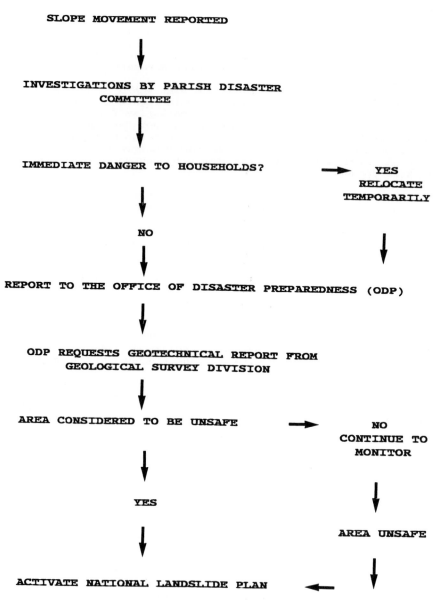

Fig. 4. Proposed trigger mechanism for the National Landslide Contingency Plan.

The Preston experience has shown the urgent need for a National Landslide Management Programme to be instituted by the Office of Disaster Preparedness for the protection of vulnerable communities.

It is important that the landslide hazard and risk maps be prepared for rural communities. These maps should form the basis for public education programmes, community based action and monitoring, and landuse planning.

ACKNOWLEDGEMENTS

We are grateful to the Director of the Office of Disaster Preparedness, Kingston for providing us information on their response to the Preston slope movements. Ahmad would like to express his gratitude to Jerry DeGraff and U.S. Geological Survey for providing literature on geohazards. Miss Beverley Reynolds of the ODP kindly typed the manuscript.

REFERENCES

1.   Ahmad Rafi Recent earth movements at Preston, St. Mary, ODIPERC News. The Office of Disaster Preparedness, Kingston, 1986, vol. 1., No. 2, April, 1 and 4-5.

2.   Bryce R., Harris N., and Rammelaere M. Preston Lands - a geological phenomenon. Biennial Report of Geological Survey Division, April 1985 - March 1987, Kingston, Jamaica, 20-30.

3.   De Graff J. V., Bryce R., Jibson R. W., Mora S., and Rogers C. T. Landslides: their extent and significance in the Caribbean. In: Brabb E. E. and Harrod B. L. (eds.), Landslides: Extent and Economic significance, 51-80, Balkema, Rotterdam, 1989.

4.   Williams F. A. The socio-economic and environmental impact of land failures in Preston - St. Mary. B.A.(special) thesis, unpublished, Dept. of Geography, University of the West Indies, Kingston, Jamaica, 1987.

5.   Working Party on World Landslide Inventory, D. M. Cruden, Chairman A suggested method for a landslide summary, Bulletin International Association of Engineering Geology, 1991, No. 43, April, 101 - 110.

6.   Ahmad Rafi, Scatena F. N. and Gupta A. Morphology and sedimentation in Caribbean montane streams: examples from Jamaica and Puerto Rico. Sedimentary Geology, 1993, in press.

7.   Manning P.A.S., McCain T., and Ahmad Rafi Landslides triggered by 1988 hurricane Gilbert along roads in the Above Rocks area, Jamaica. In: Ahmad Rafi, (ed.), Natural Hazards in the Caribbean, 1992, Special Issue No. 12, Journal Geological Society of Jamaica, 34-53.

8.   Mann P., and Burke K. Transverse intra-arc rifting: Palaeogene Wagwater Belt, Jamaica. Marine and Petroleum Geology, 1990, vol. 7, November, 410-427.

NATURAL DISASTERS

9.   Burke K., Coates A. G., and Robinson E. Geology of the Benbow Inlier and surrounding areas, Jamaica. Transactions Fourth Caribbean Geological Conference, Port of Spain, Trinidad, 1965, 209-307.

10.   Geological Sheet No. 21, Port Maria, Scale 1:50000, Geological Survey Department, Kingston, Jamaica, 1978.

11.   Varnes D. J. Landslide hazard zonation; A review of principles and practice, 63p., UNESCO, Paris, 1984.

37. Vulnerability accumulation in peripheral regions in Latin America: the challenge for disaster prevention and management

A. MASKREY, Intermediate Technology Development Group, Peru

The Argument

A recent study (MASKREY, LAVELL, 1993) has shown that small and medium sized disasters in peripheral regions are a new and up-to-now unrecognized problem in Latin America. While national and international disaster prevention and management organizations are still concentrating their attention on major catastrophes affecting large metropolitan areas or with a national impact[1] disasters are now occurring with growing frequency and magnitude in regions without a previous history of disastrous events.

The central argument of this paper is that the increasing frequency and magnitude of disasters in peripheral regions in Latin America is due to the changing spatial distribution and the increasing velocity of vulnerability accumulation.

Vulnerability is clearly related to the ability of households or communities to cope with and recover from outside events and particularly to shocks and sudden change. Most researchers now consider that vulnerability tends to concentrate in disadvantaged groups in certain regions due to the dynamics of political-economic processes. The changes in the political economy in Latin America over the last twenty years have led to a process of rapid accumulation of vulnerability in peripheral regions placing enormous strain on community and household decision-making and making it increasingly difficult to adapt to and cope with natural hazards, in the face of rapidly changing economic and territorial conditions.

In this context, if vulnerable communities are to be protected, existing disaster research, management and prevention models in Latin America need to be revised and redesigned during IDNDR. It is vital to promote research and information systems which can lead to training programs and the adoption of new models appropriate to peripheral regions. This task should be a central responsibility of those national, bilateral and multilateral agencies with an interest in protecting vulnerable communities in the Latin America region

---

[1] - Mexico earthquake, 1985, Ruiz volcano, Colombia, 1985 etc.

NATURAL DISASTERS

Introduction: Disasters in Peripheral Regions

In May 1990 and in April 1991, the Alto Mayo region in the Peruvian Amazon was devastated by two large earthquakes. In April 1991, only two weeks after the second Alto Mayo event, an equally severe earthquake affected the province of Limón on the Atlantic coast of Costa Rica. In 1991 and 1992, disasters with similar characteristics affected the Choco and Uraba regions respectively in north-west Colombia[2]. Given the occurrence of a number of earthquake disasters within a very short period of time, in regions without a history of disastrous events, it is vital to examine whether these events can simply be dismissed as consequences of fate or coincidence or whether they are due to new casual factors, which have not yet been adequately identified and understood.

None of the disasters mentioned were of enormous or catastrophic proportions. The numbers of dead and injured were not particularly significant (105 deaths in the two Perú earthquakes and 48 in the case of Costa Rica) and none of the disasters attracted widespread international attention, aid [3] or the interest of disaster researchers. Both the Perú and the Costa Rica disasters took by surprise the national authorities as well as the population of the respective regions.

In general terms, the regions where the disasters occurred can be considered as peripheral in their respective countries. Both are, in ecological terms, areas of humid tropical forest, with a low population density and few large urban centers. While, they are typical of those regions in many Latin American countries, which are perceived from the capital city as "large empty green spaces" on maps, both have been radically transformed over the last twenty years by development plans implemented by governments and international agencies[4]. Over this period, both regions experienced a series of cataclysmic changes following the construction of new highways linking them to the economic and political centers of their respective countries. In fact. the similarities between what happened in the Alto Mayo following the building of the *Carreterra Marginal* (MASKREY et al., 1991) and what happened in Limón following the building of the Limón-San José highway , (both coincidentally implemented between 1974 and 1978) are highly revealing and perhaps only two visible examples of the kind of development policies implemented in tropical peripheral areas, in many parts of Latin America, since the 1960's. Apart from road building , these policies emphasized the provision of infrastructure, credit programmes for monocropping or for cattle raising and the colonization of new areas through directed migration. The results of these policies unfortunately were not foreseen. The destruction of forests, soils and hydrological resources and a process of territorial occupation that overflowed the capacity of the available infrastructure soon began to characterize development in these regions. While in Peru these factors are additionally complicated by subversion and drug trafficking, it is better to think of these problems as only underlining the peripheral character of the regions in question. This

[2] - At the time of writing we do not have accurate information on the Colombia disasters. For that reason the analysis which follows refers exclusively to Perú and Costa Rica. A study of the Colombia disasters is currently underway (coordinated by DNPAD in association with OSSO) and we shall be integrating the results of these studies together with those of Costa Rica and Peru in the coming months.

[3] - It is a rather perverse fact that the amount of international aid provided for disaster relief and reconstruction tends to be proportional to the number of deaths and inversely proportional to the number of survivors.

[4] - A full description of this process in the Perú case can be found in MASKREY, ROJAS, PINEDO, Raices y Bosques: San Martin, Modelo para Armar, ITDG, 1991.

462

"development" induced from outside, led to what we will call a process of extremely rapid and violent vulnerability accumulation, configuring a new and high risk to disaster over the last couple of decades.

The predominance of monocropping for different markets creates dependence on external economic factors and reduces food security. In the Alto Mayo, local food production actually fell by 60% between 1970 and 1987, compared to the size of the urban population due to the introduction of rice and maize monocropping for the Peruvian urban market. The rate of migration into peripheral regions leads to the uncontrolled creation of precarious settlements in hazard prone areas and an increase in the destruction of natural resources. Again in the Alto Mayo the population is estimated to have doubled from 74,210 to 150,000 inhabitants between 1981 and 1991. In 1987, studies showed that 35% of the land area was under cultivation despite the fact that only 7% can be considered as suitable for annual cropping. All these factors, and others, combine to make peripheral regions and their population increasingly vulnerable to the effects of hazards.

The explosion of spatial horizons and an acceleration of economic time has transformed regions which for centuries were little more than historical and geographical backwaters and where time was all but standing still. Natural hazards such as earthquakes in all the regions mentioned have occurred in the past, without causing disaster, and we have no reason to suspect geological change as being responsible for the events of the last three years. Rather, it is the accumulation of vulnerability in these peripheral regions over the last two decades which has been responsible for the sudden occurrence of disasters. The sheer velocity of change and the consequent shortening of people's time horizons has meant that vulnerability has accumulated so quickly that it has not been incorporated into the consciousness of either the regional population or national authorities. The fact that these disasters were unexpected is not, therefore, hardly surprising.

A recent research project on the Alto Mayo and Limón disasters (MASKREY, LAVELL, 1993) has shown that existing disaster management models and training programs in Latin America are still based on the assumption that future disasters in the region will be major catastrophes affecting large metropolitan areas and are totally inadequate for dealing with the very different characteristics of disasters in peripheral regions. However, if vulnerability is indeed accumulating in peripheral regions, then disasters of the kind experienced in the Alto Mayo and Limón are only premonitory events of larger and even more unexpected catastrophes which will occur with increasing frequency in regions of this kind in the future. If this is so, then this new spatial distribution of vulnerability and its increasingly rapid and violent accumulation need to be carefully analyzed, researched and incorporated into the design of new disaster management and prevention strategies in Latin America during the International Decade for Natural Disaster Reduction.

This paper will firstly review existing conceptual models of vulnerability to disaster in order to show that vulnerability is more a characteristic of determined political economic models than of given hazard types. It will then go on to relate changes in the Latin American political economy over the last twenty years with the changing spatial and temporal characteristics of vulnerability. Finally it will look at the implications of these changes for disaster management and research in Latin America during the IDNDR.

NATURAL DISASTERS

Conceptual Models of Vulnerability

It is impossible, in the context of a paper such as this, to provide any sort of rigorous overview of the vast literature which has developed on vulnerability over the last decade or so. However, there is sufficient consensus in the work of recent authors to establish that a clear relationship does exist between vulnerability accumulation and economic and political change.

Until the late 1970's, the dominant conceptual model of vulnerability, as expressed in documents produced by UNDRO (UNDRO, 1979)and others, was that vulnerability was a convenient way of measuring the degree of exposure to a given natural hazard. In other words, vulnerability was considered as the direct relationship between risk to disaster and the hazardous event. The characteristics of vulnerability were described in relation to the hazardous event. Little attempt was made to relate vulnerability to underlying economic, social and political processes. This approach to vulnerability was typically expressed through phrases like *"people are vulnerable to strong earthquakes because they live in non-engineered earth houses"*. In this model, hazard was seen as the active factor in the disaster risk equation and vulnerability as the passive factor.

Over the last decade, the work of a number of researchers (HEWITT, 1983; WILCHEZ-CHAUX, 1989; WINCHESTER, 1992; CANNON, 1991; MASKREY, 1984 and 1989 just to name a few) has developed a different conceptual model of vulnerability. In this model, which seeks to explain why people and structures become vulnerable to hazards through analyzing causal economic, social and political processes, vulnerability, as a characteristic of a given political-economy, becomes the active factor in the disaster risk equation, shifting the emphasis away from hazard.

A good summary of this conceptual model of vulnerability is provided by Cannon (CANNON, 1991):

" ....there are particular characteristics of different groups of people, determined by economic and social processes, which mean that with the impact of a particular type of hazard of a given intensity, some avoid disaster and others do not. The processes which make people more or less vulnerable are largely the same as those which generate differences in wealth, control over resources and power, both nationally and internationally. The vulnerability concept is a means of translating known every day processes of the economic and political separation of people into a more specific identification of those who may be at risk in hazardous environments"

The incapacity of people to absorb shock or sudden change and recover from it may stem from a number of different vulnerable conditions such as: insecure housing; settlement location in hazard prone areas; low income which does not cover household expenditure; asset depletion and lack of reserves; reduction of biodiversity and an absence of social protection measures at community and wider society level. These vulnerable conditions emerge through the operation of different social, economic and political mechanisms such as: the existence of regional, class, ethnic and gender inequalities in decision making and the way income is distributed and land markets operate. These mechanisms in turn characterize the operation of wider processes such as: urbanization; massive demographic movements and displacements; the expansion of markets; external and civil wars and international debt problems.

464

If vulnerability suddenly accumulates in peripheral regions in Latin America and disasters start to occur with growing frequency in those regions, then the cause of these changes, therefore, must lie in the dynamics of the political economy, rather than in changing geological or hydrometoerological processes per se[5]. How the political economy in Latin America has changed over the last twenty years is crucial to a clear understanding A look at the changing dynamics of the political economy over the last twenty years is the topic of the next section of the paper.

Stability and Change in the Political Economy: from Fordism-Keynesianism to Flexible Accumulation

Harvey (HARVEY, 1991), uses the concept of accumulation regimes and modes of regulation as a tool to identify periods of stability in social, economic and territorial processes and at the same time periods of change and rupture and these terms will be used for the purposes of this paper.

Many economists now use the term Fordism-Keynesianism to characterize the long period of social and economic stability experienced in most industrialized countries between the Second World War and the 1970's. This period of economic "boom" consolidated an accumulation regime, characterized by what is now generally described as "Fordism" and a mode of regulation of this regime now generally described as "Keynesianism". Accepting the risk of excessive generalization, this period in the world economy could perhaps be described as a period of *mass production for mass markets.* This phrase embodies concepts such as: standardization; uniform value systems and forms of social conduct; specialized structures of technological innovation; the development of large, vertical and hierarchical organizational structures and a rigid social and territorial division of labor. This is the period when modernism was the dominant ideology and economies of scale were the dominant economic doctrine both in the capitalist as well as in the then socialist world.

The crisis of Fordism-Keynesianism, sparked off by the energy crisis of 1973, moved the world out of the retarded stability of the post-war epoch into a period of economic, social, political, cultural and territorial turbulence, which is still being processed (as the recent crisis of a number of Fordist survivors such as General Motors and IBM shows). Fordism-Keynesianism was already showing signs of stress in the 1960's, but it was only after the energy crisis of the 1970s that a series of problems became really evident: the rigidity of long-term large-scale investments in fixed capital, which took for granted a steady growth in unchanging markets; the rigidity of the labor market; a general incapacity to underwrite the costs of an equally rigid social reproduction system and the exhaustion of the modernist ideology which sustained it.

Generally it is accepted that with the crisis of Fordism-Keynesianism, a new accumulation regime baptized by recent authors as flexible accumulation has emerged on the basis of a number of strategies which were adopted to successfully survive the recession of the 1970s.

---

[5] - It is important to recognize that changing climatic patterns and flood and drought occurrence are related to economic and social change, through mechanisms such as deforestation and global warming, thus creating a feedback relationship between vulnerability accumulation and hazard occurrence However, there is no evidence to relate earthquake occurrence or geophysical processes in general to changes in the political economy.

One was to accelerate time: reducing the turnover of capital , which in turn meant increasing the ephemerality of the products and services to be produced. Time acceleration was in turn dependent on technological innovation - however, not the sort of innovation associated with Fordist production but a much more incremental, rapid and incestuous sort of innovation; producing slight modifications in products and services for market niches which come and go in a "twinkle of the eye". Another strategy consisted in extending markets into new spaces. From the 1970's onwards a process starts to emerge, described by Harvey (HARVEY, 1991) as the "annihilation of space through time". The development and decreasing cost of transport and communications at all levels conspires to reduce spatial barriers and friction, creating the conditions for a real world market, which at the same time, however, becomes increasingly fragmented and diversified. Patterns of consumption come and go at an increasing velocity. Production becomes increasingly diverse and flexible so as to permit rapid transformations in order to compete in increasingly ephemeral markets. Spatial decentralization and mobility becomes the order of the day in order to be able to take advantage of the comparative advantages of different spaces. Labor relations become increasingly characterized by sub-contracting and temporary contracts and by increasingly flexible and horizontal organizational models.

The transition from the stability of Fordism-Keynesianism to the turbulence of flexible accumulation obviously produced an impact in Latin America, which, at the same time, was radically different to that experienced in the advanced industrial countries. In the scope of this paper it is impossible to develop a rigorous empirical verification of either the change itself or its economic, social, political and spatial implications. However, an analysis of the Peruvian case does give quite a clear indication of the essential character of the change which is occurring.

The economic and social development models promoted in Latin America between the Second World War and the 1970's could, perhaps, be best described as peripheral Fordism-Keynesianism. Most countries adopted an industrialization process in this period based on import-substitution and on an increased role for the state both in promoting economic development as well as in making direct investments in productive and social infrastructure. This is the period characterized by very rapid growth of Latin American capital cities due to migration from rural areas and the desarticulation of traditional social and economic structures.

In the Peruvian case, in the period 1940 to 1981, Lima grew from representing 9.7% 0f the national population and 27.7% of the national urban population to represent 27% of the total national population and 41.5% of the total urban population of Peru. At the same time by 1972 Lima concentrated 73% of the industrial establishments in the country and in 1981 represented 51% of the gross domestic product of Perú. After Lima, the second department (Junin) had only 4.6% of the gross domestic product in 1981, which illustrates the degree of economic and territorial centralization achieved.

Perhaps the key difference with the advanced industrial world is that Fordism-Keynesianism never managed to establish itself as a viable and above all stable alternative in Latin America, either in terms of a regime of accumulation which manages to articulate the economy as a whole or as a social and political mode of regulation. The accumulation regime only managed to take root in a small number of modernized and industrialized enclaves, while the mode of regulation proved to be highly unstable, leading to perpetual and endemic conflict in both the social and political sphere.

466

In parallel with the crisis of Fordism-Keynesianism at world level, the Latin American political economy also experienced quite dramatic changes since the 1970s. The growth of micro and small scale enterprises in the "informal" sector of the economy of the region has now been quite widely studied and recognized (DE SOTO, 1985; VILLARAN, 1992) as well as the relative dynamism of the economies of peripheral regions in the different countries (VERGARA, 1988; MASKREY et.al.1991).

In the Peruvian case, while between 1961 and 1972, the urban population of Lima grew at a rhythm of 5.75% a year, between 1972 and 1981 this had slowed down to 3.8% a year. In comparison, the tendency was completely different in medium sized cities in peripheral regions of the country. The urban population of Rioja, one of the principal urban centers in the Alto Mayo, was growing at a rhythm of only 2.9% a year between 1961 and 1972 but accelerated to 11.16% a year between 1972 and 1981. Juliaca in southern Perú increased its rhythm of growth from 5.73% to 7.77% in the same census periods and Huancayo in the central sierra from 2.96% to 5.77%, to give examples of cities in regions with completely different geographical characteristics.

A look at tendencies in industrial production only confirms the above pattern. During the period 1971-1987, while the gross industrial product was growing by 2.4% a year in Lima, in the region of San Martin (where the Alto Mayo is located) it was growing at 15.7% a year . Other regions, such as Huancavelica in the central sierra, were enjoying growth in their gross industrial product at the staggering rate of 22.6% a year (VILLARAN, 1992)

At the same time while small scale industry was providing 19% of industrial employment and 10.5% of Peru's gross industrial product in 1971, by 1987 it was providing 31.74% of industrial employment and 22.64% of the gross industrial product (VILLARAN, 1992).

In other words, the political economy in Peru, and probably in many other Latin American countries as well, has gone through a dramatic change over the last twenty years. Given the relationship between change in the political economy and the generation of vulnerability, it is hardly surprising that the spatial and temporal parameters which govern vulnerability in Latin America have changed quite dramatically in the last two decades.

The Spatial Distribution of Vulnerability

The different regimes of accumulation and their respective modes of regulation are characterized by different patterns of spatial organization. The changes in the regime of accumulation in Latin America over the last two decades imply changes in where and how people live and hence in where and how vulnerability is accumulated. Different regimes of accumulation and modes of regulation are characterized, therefore, by quite differing spatial distributions of vulnerability.

The implantation of peripheral Fordism-Keynesianism in Latin America, as we have observed, was not accompanied, as in the advanced industrial countries, by a long period of economic and social stability and growth and a relatively stable spatial organization of production, on the basis of long term investments in fairly rigid fixed capital. In Latin America, stability was only achieved for far shorter periods and only in certain modern enclaves. Fordism-Keynesianism, in Latin America, led to the explosive growth of large cities and the transformation of traditional rural economies. All this led to a spatial accumulation of vulnerability in cities and particularly in major metropolitan areas. The rapid growth of

467

marginal settlements in all Latin American cities (often with unsafe building on hazard prone sites)and the inability of import-substitution to provide a sustainable basis for economic growth and for meeting social needs, are key factors which led to this concentration of vulnerability in major urban areas. By the 1970's quite a large percentage of the population of cities such as Lima had become extremely vulnerable, with a low capacity to absorb the impact of hazards or to recover from them (MASKREY, ROMERO, 1985). The impact of disasters in Latin American cities, in the 70s and 80s, was unsurprisingly far greater than in the 1940s or 1950s, and this is directly attributable to the concentration of urban vulnerability during that period.

At the same time, the radical changes in the political economy of the region since the 1970s has led to a very different spatial accumulation of vulnerability - in peripheral regions. The growth of secondary cities, the incorporation of new regions into national and international markets and the growth of small scale often informal sector industries in these regions, accompanied by new patterns of population growth and displacement, are only some of the mechanisms and processes which have led to this accumulation of vulnerability. The occurrence of disasters, such as those of 1990 and 1991 in Peru and Costa Rica, provide new empirical evidence of this process of change. While the overall process at the Latin American level has not been clearly analyzed and defined, it is now clear that in peripheral regions there is an increasing concentration of population with a decreasing capacity to absorb the effects of natural hazards and to recover from disaster.

On the basis of a more rigorous examination of the kind of macroeconomic, demographic and spatial indicators mentioned above, it ought to be possible to show how much and what kinds of vulnerability are being concentrated in which peripheral regions in Latin America and to predict the occurrence of new disasters in the coming decades. The disasters, now occurring are not "surprising" in any real sense. They are quite predictable consequences of empirically measurable changes in the spatial political economy and in the spatial distribution of vulnerability.

Temporality and Vulnerability Accumulation

A principal difference between peripheral Fordism-Keynesianism and flexible accumulation, as they have manifested themselves in the Latin American context, is the sheer velocity of economic, territorial and social change. Due to the increasing speed and turbulence of change in the political economy the rate of vulnerability accumulation also accelerates. Vulnerable conditions, in fact, thrive in periods of economic and territorial instability and rapid change. This has not, perhaps, been sufficiently emphasized in existing work on vulnerability analysis, which still tends to interpret sudden change and shock in terms of hazard occurrence rather than as an inherent condition of the political economy per se. Apart from the spatial accumulation of vulnerability in peripheral regions discussed above, the temporal characteristics of vulnerability are also changing.

The reasons why the accumulation of vulnerability accelerates in periods of turbulence in the political economy are not hard to identify. Many natural hazards, such as earthquakes occur over quite long time cycles and the ability of social and economic decision making at all levels to incorporate hazard as a variable depends on the time horizons being used. When decisions on investment and location are made on a thirty or forty year time horizon, in a context of market stability, it is likely that, providing reliable information on hazards is available that this will be taken into account in the decision making process. When decisions are being made in conditions of rapid flux and change, when time horizons are shrinking to their minimum expression and in regions where accurate information on hazards is not available, then it is far more unlikely that hazard will and can be taken into account. If vulnerability refers to the incapacity to absorb shocks and to recover from them, then the acceleration of increasingly violent social, economic and territorial changes will almost certainly lead to an increase in vulnerability, with or without the impact of hazards.

It is worth exploring in a little more detail how perceptions of time affect community and household level decision making and lead to an acceleration in vulnerability accumulation. Under current economic conditions in peripheral regions, decision making horizons may be reduced to a year-by-year or even in extreme cases to a day-by-day basis. Marginal farmers in tropical regions such as Alto Mayo are forced to continue deforesting in order to cope with increasingly short term economic horizons: to plant coca for new external markets, for example. Their objective is immediate economic gain for survival purposes. The medium term ecological effects of deforestation: which can be measured in terms of increased vulnerability to both drought and flood, due to a modification of the hydrological regime, are on a different time scale - far longer than that being employed by the marginal farmer. The tendency towards increasing ephemerality in markets and products and shortening turn-over time, therefore, conspires against the consolidation of a longer term decision making process, which could take into account either gradually evolving 'slow-onset' hazards such as erosion or those rapid-onset hazards such as earthquakes which may occur only every twenty or thirty years. Paradoxically, the situation is similar in many ways in the decisions made by high-income investors, although obviously their ability to absorb and recover from disaster is far greater. Investments in tourism infrastructure in coastal areas of Latin America, often in areas with high flood or cyclone risk, may be based on a recuperation of the investment over a five to ten year period. On this basis it is difficult for the investor to take into account hazard risk on a twenty, thirty or fifty year basis.

As a historical analogy, it is interesting to look back to Engel's work on living conditions in mid-19th century Britain, to see the sort of vulnerability which was emerging in the rapidly growing industrial cities, due to an extreme acceleration of economic time with the move over from craft to industrial production. This is in contrast to the virtual elimination of vulnerability in the advanced industrial countries during the retarded stability of the Fordist-Keynesian period, in which one could argue time was artificially slowed down.

Migration patterns, deforestation, the formation of new settlements and a dependency on "boom and bust" markets are the factors which are leading to the acceleration of vulnerability accumulation in peripheral regions in Latin America The sheer velocity of change makes it very difficult for hazards to be taken into account in decision making. The principal difference to vulnerability accumulation in large metropolitan areas, between the 1940's and 1970s, lies in the ephemeral nature of vulnerability itself. The kind of vulnerability which now characterizes the political economy is much less subject to rigid spatial, social and economic boundaries and hence is far more unpredictable. As will be discussed in the next section of the paper, this challenges our ability to protect vulnerable communities in peripheral, using existing disaster management and prevention models.

Vulnerability in Peripheral Regions and the Challenges for Disaster Prevention and Management in the IDNDR

When change becomes too rapid, it defies our capacity to understand it, process it and act by it. Possibilities for incorporating disaster preparedness, mitigation or prevention into local decision making processes, depends on moving decision making onto the same time scale as hazard occurrence. Authors such as Maskrey (MASKREY, 1984, 1989) emphasized the process through which increased vulnerability can lead to increased levels of consciousness, which in turn can lead to the incorporation of disaster mitigation within the agenda of community organizations. However, recent experiences of disaster mitigation in peripheral regions (MASKREY, LAVELL, 1993) shows that even the consciousness of risk itself can run aground due to the sheer velocity of change. When production and living patterns change as quickly as market and economic conditions, vulnerability accumulates so fast that it overtakes the ability of decision-making structures deal with it. In these conditions, disasters will always be unexpected. Migrants in new areas are unaware of the levels of risk; government official are forced to take decisions with obsolete data and maps; while people adapt to one kind of risk a new kind is already emerging to take its place. Local and indigenous knowledge developed over centuries becomes obsolescent overnight, due to rapid change in contextual conditions.

At the same time, while experiences such as the reconstruction program in the Alto Mayo MASKREY, 1992), which introduced a new seismic resistant building technology, show that it is possible to develop locally appropriate mitigation strategies with large scale results, it is questionable how long even programmes like these can be maintained. The introduction of new technologies may be in the end as ephemeral as the social, economic and territorial conditions in which they are inserted and there is no guarantee that any long-term reduction of vulnerability will occur. Migration, radically changing economic conditions and social and institutional instability conspire against any long-term "accumulation" of vulnerability reduction.

These issues pose a number of quite serious problems both for disaster research as well as for the development of disaster prevention and management strategies in the Latin America region.

In the first place, how can research itself make sense and above all be applied in contexts of such rapid change? Much research on vulnerability, particularly in rural areas, has emerged from the anthropological tradition and is readily applicable in contexts of limited space horizons and very slow time. When space explodes and time accelerates such research becomes increasingly difficult to undertake and its relevance increasingly ephemeral.

Secondly, disaster prevention and management models In Latin America also require change. In general terms, these models were designed for large disasters in major metropolitan areas and rely on centralized decision-making and the existence of formal organizational and governmental structures. Their application in disasters in peripheral regions has not been successful, to say the very least (MASKREY, LAVELL, 1993).

If the hypothesis presented in this paper are correct, and disasters such as those which occurred in the Alto Mayo and Limón are only the initial expressions of a new disaster scenario in the region, then the challenges for disaster management and prevention strategies, during IDNDR in Latin America are quite serious. This paper offers no instant recipes to reduce vulnerability but rather recommends a strategic approach for building up appropriate disaster prevention and management capacity in the region, with a focus on four main tasks:

- Apart from the ideas expressed in this paper there is still a lack of rigorous empirical evidence on the relationship between development models and vulnerability accumulation in Latin America. It is vital to develop research to monitor change in the social, economic, demographic and ecological indicators which can be used to measure the accumulation of vulnerability in peripheral regions. With the recent availability of GIS technology it is now feasible to develop information systems on vulnerability accumulation in the region. At present the orientation of disaster research is still on hazard monitoring. A principle conclusion and recommendation of this paper is that vulnerability monitoring is at least as important and must be included in any research agenda for IDNDR. Without accurate and up-to date information on vulnerability levels in peripheral regions it is difficult to foresee future improvements in disaster prevention and management capability in the region.

- Apart from the recent study on the management of the Alto Mayo and Limón disasters (MASKREY, LAVELL 1993), there have been few systematic studies on the effectiveness of existing disaster prevention and management models in peripheral regions, which can provide evidence and recommendations for change. There is an urgent need for systematic, comparative research on these disasters, which can inform the development of new models. At present, the recently formed Network for Social Studies on Disaster Prevention in Latin America (LA RED, 1993), is trying to develop a research program which should provide the knowledge base needed to develop new models. Research initiatives such as this are vital if future models are to be really appropriate to the specific conditions of Latin America.

- The training of disaster prevention and management specialists in Latin America is still carried out on the basis of inappropriate models. There is also therefore an urgent need to develop a regional training capacity built up on the basis of research into disaster management and prevention issues in Latin America. The research mentioned above is the necessary pre-condition for setting up such a training programme.

- There is a need to combine information, research and training strategies together in the context of pilot disaster prevention and management projects which should be implemented in a number of peripheral regions in Latin America. Only in this way will it be possible to validate different management and prevention instruments in practice and develop new programme models which can be more widely applied.

Instead of emphasizing increased post-disaster emergency assistance as the solution to vulnerable communities in peripheral regions, it is the responsibility of national, bilateral and multilateral agencies, with an interest in disaster prevention and management in Latin America, to invest at least a proportion of their scarce resources in the kind of strategic approach mentioned above. This is the only way to avoid a large and perhaps unexpected increase in disaster impact in the region over the coming decades.

Bibliography

CANNON, Terry, 1991, A Hazard Need Not a Disaster Make: Rural Vulnerability and the Causes of Natural Disaster, manuscript presented to the conference "Disasters: Vulnerability and Response", DARG/IBG/RGS, London, 1991.

DE SOTO, Hernando, 1985, El Otro Sendero, ILD, Lima, Perú.

HARVEY, David, 1992, The Condition of Postmodernity, Basil Blackwell, Oxford.

HEWITT, K. (Ed), 1983, Interpretations of Calamity, Allen and Unwin, New York.

LA RED (Network for Social Studies on Disaster Prevention in Latin America), 1993, Research Agenda and Constitution, Lima, Perú.

471

NATURAL DISASTERS

MASKREY, Andrew, 1984, Community Based Hazard Mitigation, in Disaster Mitigation Program Implementation, Virginia Polytechnic Institute.

MASKREY, Andrew, ROMERO, Gilberto, 1985, Urbanización y Vulnerabilidad Sísmica en Lima Metropolitana, PREDES, Lima, Perú.

MASKREY, Andrew, 1989, Disaster Mitigation: A Community Based Approach, OXFAM, Oxford.

MASKREY, Andrew, ROJAS, Josefa, PINEDO, Teocrito, 1991, Raices y Bosques: San Martin: Modelo para Armar, ITDG, Lima, Perú.

MASKREY, Andrew, 1992, Introducing Disaster Mitigation in a Political Vacuum: Experiences of the Reconstruction Plan Following the Alto Mayo Earthquake, Peru 1990, in Disasters and the Small Dwelling, (Yasemin Aysan and Ian Davis Eds.), James and James, London.

MASKREY, Andrew, LAVELL, Allan, 1993, Manejo de Desastres y Mecanismos de Respuesta: Un Análisis Comparativo del Alto Mayo, Perú Limón, Costa Rica, (unpublished manuscript), ITDG / FLACSO.

UNDRO, 1979, Disaster Prevention and Mitigation: a Compendium of Current Knowledge, UNDRO, New York.

VERGARA, Ricardo, 1988, El Proceso de Urbanización en el Trapecio Andino, Fundación Fridrich Ebbert, Lima, Perú..

VILLARAN, Fernando, 1992, El Nuevo Desarollo: la Pequeña Industria en el Perú, ONUDI / PEMTEC, Lima.

WILCHEZ-CHAUX, Gustavo, 1989, Desastres, Ecologismo y Formación Profesional, SENA, Popayan, Colombia.

WINCHESTER, Peter, 1992, Power, Choice and Vulnerability: a Case Study in Disaster Mismanagement in South India, James and James, London.

38. A bridge rehabilitation project in Bangladesh funded by the ODA

I. A. KHAN, Rendel Palmer and Tritton, UK, and F. KARIM, Roads and Highways Department, Bangladesh

BACKGROUND TO THE PROJECT

Major damage to Bangladesh's existing highway network by flooding is inevitable as many roads and bridges are in a poor state of repair. During and just after serious monsoon flooding or following a cyclone it is crucial that help can reach those left homeless and short of food. If road links are severed at this time then vulnerable communities are threatened with further suffering and loss of life. Furthermore, the brittleness of the highway infrastructure is recognised by many as an important obstacle to the country's economic development.

Bridges have proved to be the weakest link in the land transport system in Bangladesh. Once destroyed by the swollen waterway over which they ought to provide a safe crossing, they are difficult and expensive to rebuild. First a temporary bridge has to be constructed speedily to get traffic moving again (especially important when rapid distribution of emergency relief supplies may save lives in areas of devastation cut off by the collapse). Even when Bailey bridge components are available to form the deck, there remains the problem of supporting the temporary spans safely. Later, once the flood has subsided, a new bridge has to be constructed.

Hence the Government of Bangladesh (Roads and Highways Department, RHD) finds itself in a vicious circle. Each flood season, scarce funds earmarked for new works or for routine maintenance have to be spent on stop-gap bridge repairs, and very limited progress can be made towards the essential long-term objective of constructing durable replacement bridges.

It was against this background that in 1985 the UK's Overseas Development Administration (ODA) agreed with RHD to set up and finance the Bridging and Institutional Development Project with the following two initial components:

1. **Priority A Bridges:** 5 major bridges to meet the immediate needs of the country (1986 to 1991).

2. **Priority B Bridges (Phase I):** 25 (subsequently reduced to 24) short to medium length bridges with training and institutional development to meet the long-term objective

NATURAL DISASTERS

Table 1   Official Estimates of Losses and
           Damage by Floods in 1987 and
           1988.

Loss/Damage	1987	1988
Area flooded	57 000 km^2	82 000 km^2
Houses totally/partially damaged	2.5 M	7.2 M
Human lives lost	1657	2379
Livestock lost:		
cattle, goats, etc.	64 700	172 000
poultry	206 000	410 000
Rice production lost	3.5M t	2M t
Roads: trunk	1523 km	3 000 km
rural	15 107 km	10 000 km
bridges, culverts	1 102	898
Railways: embankments	698 km	1300 km
bridges	166	270
Flood embankments	1279 km	1990 km
Irrigationed/drainage canals	222 km	283 km
Irrigation/drainage control structures	541	1465
Electric Power:		
sub-stations flooded	n/a	18
11 KV power line de-energised	n/a	2 000 km
Industrial units flooded	n/a	> 1 000
Hospitals flooded	n/a	45
Health centres flooded	1305	1400
Schools flooded	6689	19 000
Rural hand tubewells flooded	n/a	240 000

Sources: mainly BWDB, 1987 and MOI 1988.

of providing a durable road transport network throughout Bangladesh (1987 to 1993).

This paper focuses on the second of these.

The loss or damage to a total of 2000 bridges and culverts (see Table 1 extracted from Ref 1) during the exceptional floods of 1987 and 1988 highlighted the need for early effective action.

PROJECT OBJECTIVES

This project, together with the earlier Priority A Bridges project, is aimed at making a prompt, effective and sustainable contribution to improving the reliability of Bangladesh's land transport system. Specifically, the Priority B Project aims to:

a.   select 25 bridges on the National Highway system for rehabilitation.
b.   design and construct 25 (later reduced to 24) bridges which are robust enough to withstand modern traffic loads, and severe floods and earthquakes.

474

b.   train RHD staff to use certain modern design technology and to supervise construction to ensure an adequate standard.
c.   train local contractors' staff: to plan and manage their projects more effectively, to apply basic technical principles which will ensure durability (while adding little to initial cost), and to use modern plant and techniques.
d.   add to the pool of useful construction plant in the country.
e.   develop, in conjunction with RHD, a computer based bridge management program to assist RHD log inspection information and plan maintenance and replacement of their existing bridges.
f.   train RHD staff to carry out bridge inspections and to use the bridge management program.

PROJECT DESCRIPTION

General

To achieve these aims ODA's support to the project has included provision from the UK of:

*   management, bridge engineering, and institutional development expertise through consultants Rendel Palmer and Tritton (RPT);

*   galvanised steel superstructures, bridge bearings, and some items of major plant and other equipment, all procured through the Crown Agents.

Of the 25 bridges, 4 near Dhaka were designated "training bridges" with the intention that they should form a practical training ground for RHD supervisory staff and contractors' personnel. ODA also funded the local costs for construction of the approach embankments and the piers and abutments for these training bridges. RPT was designated Engineer for the construction of the 4 training bridges, while RHD was Engineer for the remainder with RPT acting in an advisory and support role.

Selection of the Bridges to be Rehabilitated

From 1161 bridges on Bangladesh's national highways (trunk roads) 92 were short-listed for detailed economic assessment on the basis of a preliminary view of the seriousness of their condition. Subsequent study showed that reconstruction of 62 of these would be economically viable, with an internal rate of return greater than 15%; and the final list of 25 bridges was drawn up on the basis of their rate of return ranking, together with geographic and bridge length considerations.

The location of the selected bridges is shown on Figure 1, and further information on the bridges is given in Table 2.

Reasons for Bridge Collapses

The great majority of bridge collapses in Bangladesh are caused by scour undermining foundations. Valuable lessons for design and reconstruction were learned from examining the evidence from

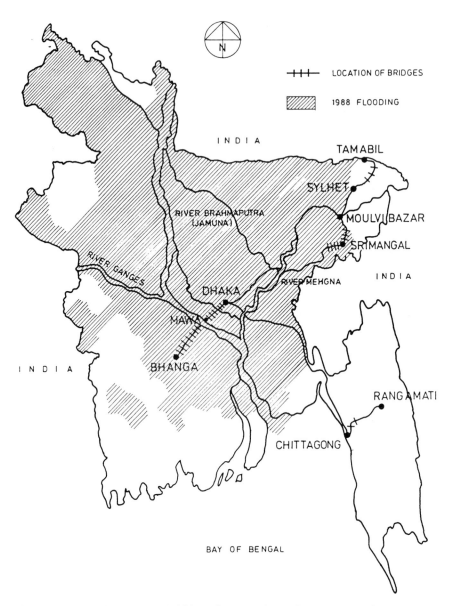

Fig. 1. ODA bridges rehabilitation project in Bangladesh: location of bridges

Table 2 ODA Priority B Bridges – Locations, Lengths and Costs

CON-TRACT NO.	NAME OF BRIDGE	LOCATION	TYPE	LENGTH (m)	TOTAL LENGTH (m)	LOCAL COSTS (Tk)	OFFSHORE COSTS (£)	TOTAL COSTS (£)
1	Abdullapur	Dhaka-Mawa Road	Beam	52.5	52.5	26,485,662	61,620	439,987
2	Binagown	Shaistagani-Srimangal Road	Beam	20.0	147.5	12,690,750	28,133	209,429
	Layercol 2	Shaistaganj-Srimangal Road	Beam	30.0		14,666,566	30,400	239,922
	Belashi	Shaistaganj-Srimangal Road	Beam	45.0		14,800,153	70,148	281,579
	Srimangal Basti	Srimangal	Beam	12.5		9,520,881	13,079	149,092
	Nowgawn	Srimangal-Moulvi Bazar Road	Beam	15.0		11,061,024	16,187	174,202
	Bahamura (*)	Srimangal-Moulvi Bazar Road	Beam	12.5		9,818,587	12,694	152,960
	Shadupati	Srimangal-Moulvi Bazar Road	Beam	12.5		8,669,371	12,694	136,542
3	Kuchia Mora 2	Dhaka-Mawa Road	Truss	36.6	81.6	23,229,224	94,598	426,444
	Hashara	Dhaka-Mawa Road	Beam	45.0		22,816,027	71,150	397,093
4	Korisor	Sylhet-Tamabil Road	Truss	82.2	191.3	50,960,683	206,400	934,410
	Zontapur 2	Sylhet-Tamabil Road	Beam	20.0		11,416,459	28,369	191,461
	Lokipur 2	Sylhet-Tamabil Road	Beam	17.5		13,997,548	20,798	220,763
	Khalespur	Moulvi Bazar-Sylhet Road	Beam	22.5		15,885,533	34,617	261,553
	Mandanhat	Chittagong-Rangamati Road	Beam	12.5		10,751,909	12,547	166,146
	Santirdip	Chittagong-Rangamati Road	Truss	36.6		22,869,146	94,710	421,412
5	Umpara	Dhaka-Mawa Road	Truss	45.7	45.7	32,003,575	139,500	596,694
6	Bakorgandi	Bhanga-Mawa Road	Truss	41.1	128.5	23,806,361	120,427	460,518
	Bangla Bazar	Bhanga-Mawa Road	Truss	27.4		26,343,580	77,818	454,155
	Baghoir	Dhaka-Mawa Road	Truss	60.0		31,220,308	227,707	673,711
7	Bhanga	Bhanga-Mawa Road	Truss	27.4	204.9	31,392,862	78,242	526,711
	Bogail	Bhanga-Mawa Road	Truss	78.0		43,875,221	312,913	939,702
	Bamonkanda	Bhanga-Mawa Road	Truss	32.0		25,933,200	93,078	463,552
	Soriida	Bhanga-Mawa Road	Beam	22.5		16,098,221	61,182	291,157
	Pamchar	Bhanga-Mawa Road	Beam	45.0		20,953,678	123,227	422,390

(*) This bridge was not included in the final project

failed bridges, including during and following the 1987 and 1988 floods. Investigation into the 1987 flood damage (Ref 2) found little or no evidence of failure due to hydrodynamic loading on the structures themselves; instead, the report states ".... the major cause of failure was the scour of abutment and pier foundations during a lengthy period of discharge at scouring velocities through the bridge and culvert openings." Photos 1 and 2 show typical examples of failures on the Dhaka to Sylhet road due to the 1987 flood.

This pattern was repeated during the 1988 flood. Indeed, 7 out of the 12 existing bridges to be rehabilitated under this project were washed away during the 1988 flood.

Scour at bridges during flood results from a combination of the following factors:

* incorrect siting of the structure
* inadequate waterway opening
* weak erodible bed material
* changes in patterns of overland flood flows due to construction of other embankments or flood bunds.

While good compaction of the approaches (Photo 3) is required principally to provide a stable base for the road pavement, it provides the added benefit of making the embankment more scour resistant. Safiullah, in his study of flood embankment damage (Ref 3), suggests that lack of proper compaction was one of the main reasons for their failure.

Improvements in Bridge Designs

The design of the 24 bridges was carried out in Dhaka by an RPT team of bridge engineers with support from local engineering consultants Bangladesh Consultants Limited, and with the close involvement of RHD. This close coordination with RHD was considered important not only to ensure that local concerns, such as width of footways and adequate clearance for country boats, were properly addressed, but also as a first step in transferring technology to enhance RHD's capability to undertake similar work in the future themselves.

Weaknesses and deficiencies in earlier designs were addressed by incorporating the following features:

* piled foundations
* scour protection
* detailed hydraulic studies
* design against earthquake effects

These features, and the reasons for their adoption, are discussed in more detail below.

An underlying principle behind design and construction decisions was to employ traditional labour intensive methods wherever possible, e.g. excavation, carrying fill or concrete (Photo 4), stone breaking for concrete aggregates, etc; and only to use heavy plant where it is indispensable for robust and durable construction. In this case the mechanical energy of heavy plant was imperative for pile driving and for compaction of approach embankments.

Photo 1. Bridge collapse on Dhaka-Sylhet road: October 1988

Photo 2. Culvert failure on Dhaka-Sylhet road: October 1988

Photo 3. Compaction of embankment material

479

Photo 4. Carrying concrete in head pans

Photo 5. Erection of galvanised steel beams

The main load-bearing steel girders are light and relatively easy to lift into place (Photo 5). Apart from making erection easier they also keep the overall superstructure load down, while the concrete deck slab provides a low maintenance surface. For short spans I-sections were used (Fig 2), but for longer spans truss girders were required (Fig 3). Being galvanised, the steel should not need painting for at least 15 years.

Piled Foundations

Geotechnical investigations (deep boreholes, cone penetrometer testing and laboratory testing) were carried out at all bridge sites ahead of detailed design of the bridges. The soils encountered generally consisted of loose alluvial deposits with extremely poor bearing capacity. From the soil characteristics and the forecast flood discharges scour depths were estimated at between 3 and 5 metres. As anticipated from observed bridge failures it was clear that deep foundations would be required at all sites.

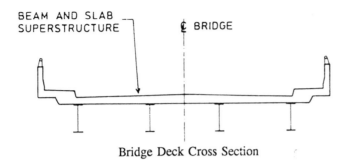

Bridge Deck Cross Section

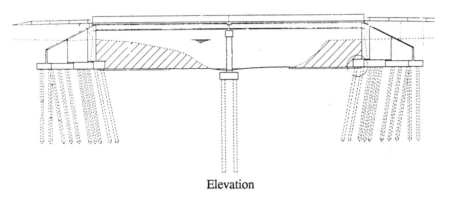

Elevation

Fig. 2. Typical beam and slab bridge

Traditionally, deep foundations in Bangladesh have been constructed using open-well brick caissons. These are constructed by hand by building up the well above ground level and excavating the soil inside the well so that the whole well sinks under its own weight (sometimes supplemented with kentledge) to the required founding level. This form of construction has certain drawbacks, including the length of time taken for construction, lack of tensile strength, practical limits on the depth to which they can be sunk, and relatively high cost.

The alternative method of constructing deep foundations is to use piles. The technique has been used more and more commonly in Bangladesh in recent years. Piles can be installed quickly, can be easily reinforced against tension or bending, and can be driven or drilled to safe depths. Therefore piled foundations were adopted for the Priority B Bridges project. These largely consisted of driven reinforced concrete piles varying in length from 9 metres to 27 metres connected at their heads by a reinforced concrete cap. A limited number of driven cast-in-situ piles were also employed where it was impractical to use the precast concrete piles.

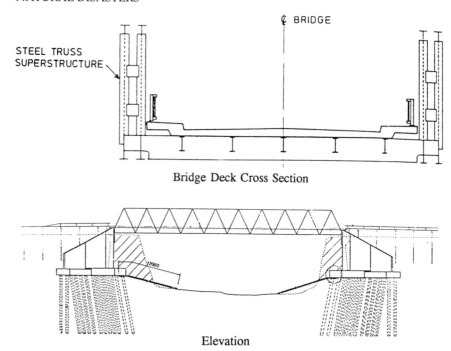

Bridge Deck Cross Section

Elevation

Fig. 3. Typical truss girder bridge

Increasing use of piled foundations has led to a high demand for piling pant within the country, and as part of the project ODA supplied a BSP hydraulic piling rig with a hammer adjustable up to 7 tonnes and a 60 tonne RB600SC crawler crane for operating the rig, handling piles and for other general lifting work (Photo 6). This equipment was capable of driving raked (inclined) piles, which are more efficient in resisting the horizontal loads from abutments than vertical piles. Prior to this project raked piles had hardly been used in Bangladesh, but once contractors saw the capability of the new rig they ingeniously developed their own inclined rigs for use with their diesel hammers (Photo 7).

Scour Protection

It would have been uneconomic to design pile groups to withstand large horizontal forces under the maximum scour condition, and so protection works were designed around abutments similar to the example shown in Figure 4. The fine loose bed material is kept in place by a synthetic filter fabric which in turn is kept in place and protected by stone filled wire baskets known as reno mattresses (Photo 8).

The synthetic filter fabric has high durability and allows water to pass through to relieve any pressure build-up while soil particles are retained in place. This technology has been widely adopted in countries with similar scour-prone silty sand soil

Photo 6. Lifting pile into BSP rig prior to driving

Photo 7. Driving concrete piles with local rig

Fig. 4 (below and facing page). Typical scour protection

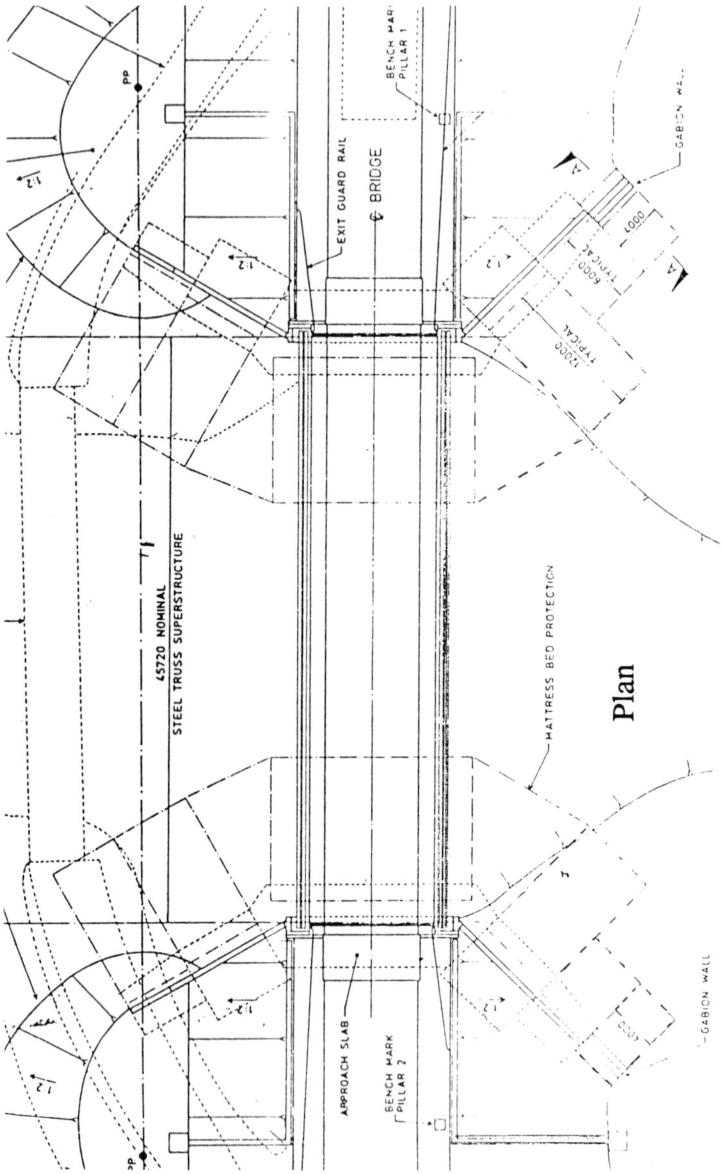

Plan

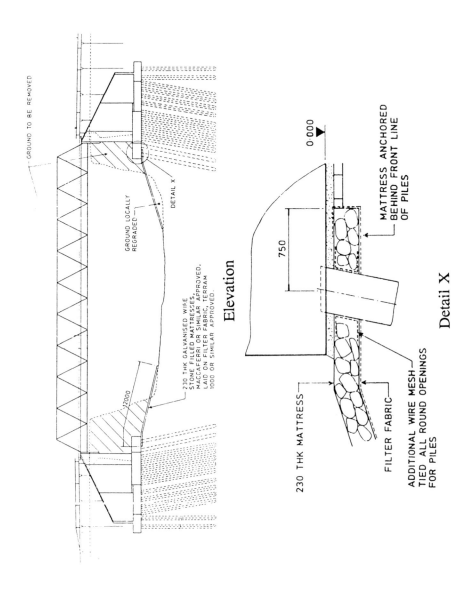

GROUND TO BE REMOVED

GROUND LOCALLY REGRADED

DETAIL X

230 THK GALVANISED WIRE STONE FILLED MATTRESSES, MACCAFERRI OR SIMILAR APPROVED, LAID ON FILTER FABRIC, TERRAM 1000 OR SIMILAR APPROVED.

2000

Elevation

0.000

750

MATTRESS ANCHORED BEHIND FRONT LINE OF PILES

230 THK MATTRESS

FILTER FABRIC

ADDITIONAL WIRE MESH TIED ALL ROUND OPENINGS FOR PILES

Detail X

Photo 8. Reno mattress protection in front of abutment

such as Holland, and there are huge potential benefits for its
further application in Bangladesh. The cost of the provision of
this scour protection for the bridge in Photo 8 was only 2.3% of
the contract value.

Hydraulic Engineering

The embankment for the Dhaka-Mawa-Bhanga highway on which 12 of
the project bridges are located forms a dam across the floodplain
of the River Padma. During the 1988 flood this highway was
entirely submerged, with up to half a metre of water over-topping
the road.

Although bridge spans on this route had been substantially
increased during initial design, Professor McDowell estimated
that bridge openings would have to be increased as much as
threefold to keep flow velocities low enough to avoid deep scour
(Ref 4). Apart from unacceptable cost implications this would
have imposed an undesirable concentration of flow at just a few
locations. Instead it was recommended that the required extra
waterway should be provided by additional culverts distributed
through the embankment at regular intervals along the road. On
the Dhaka-Mawa section of the route the Asian Development Bank
has provided the necessary culverts under a separate project.

Earthquake Effects

Bangladesh is in an active earthquake zone, being affected by the
tectonic movements which have created the Himalayas. Active
faults such as the Dauki fault and the western part of the
Shillong plateau have generated high magnitude earthquakes in
historic times. The Bangladesh earthquake resistant design code
(Ref 5) divides the country into zones with basic seismic
coefficients of 0.08 x gravity in the north-eastern zone, 0.05
x gravity in the central zone and 0.04 x gravity in the southwestern zone. This code was adopted for guidance in the design
of the project bridges.

Earthquake shaking imposes high horizontal loads which structures must be able to resist in a ductile way. Also, the differential movement between supports must not lead to collapse of any span. A further important risk in Bangladesh is liquefaction of the loose alluvial founding soil, causing failure of foundations if they are not deep enough, or buckling of piles if the piles are not stiff enough. All these risks were considered in design.

Human Resource Development

Training of RHD and contractors' engineers was undertaken in two stages (pre-construction and construction), and in two ways (classroom lectures/seminars by experts during the monsoon seasons, and practical on-site technology transfer by the project team). The extensive syllabus included the following areas:

* construction planning and management
* site supervision
* bridge foundation design and construction
* hydraulic design for bridges and culverts
* scour protection of bridges
* formwork and reinforcement
* erection of steel superstructures
* all aspects of concrete design and construction
* embankment placement and compaction
* inspection and maintenance of existing bridges

At the end of each series of lectures the participants were asked to complete course assessment forms which invited comment on the content, presentation, audio-visual aids, etc. The information from these forms and from a questionnaire, together with interviews, formed the basis for a formal mid-term appraisal. The feedback was for the most part very positive, and it was clear that most of the technical and management principles had been effectively communicated.

It was also clear to the project team that the classroom and on-site training of contractors' engineering staff resulted in the adoption of improved construction techniques and better quality workmanship.

Computerised Bridge Inventory

The initial framework for the computerised bridge inventory system was an early derivative from the consultants' bridge management program HiSMIS, which in turn incorporated the principles in Ref. 6; but was specially adapted to suit the types of highway structures found in Bangladesh. Once complete, the system will store information on all structures on the national highways throughout Bangladesh. It will be used to prioritise rehabilitation and preventive maintenance of bridges and culverts, and should allow RHD to move away from crisis management towards more efficient planned use of funds.

Impact of the Project on Vulnerable Communities

Some fifty million people were affected by the 1988 flooding (Ref. 7). The extensive and prolonged suffering caused to so many people is without parallel in the history of Bangladesh. People who sheltered on the Dhaka-Mawa road told the project staff that the first relief supplies reached them two weeks after flooding isolated them. The project bridges now nearing completion will provide reliable links in the road, and will allow the prompt delivery of humanitarian assistance following any future disaster, whether flood, cyclone or earthquake.

The knowledge gained and shared by all those who have participated in the project should help towards further appropriate engineering intervention, and the goal of a robust and maintainable road network.

REFERENCES

1. ASIAN DEVELOPMENT BANK, Disaster Mitigation in Asia and the Pacific, p. 90, Manila, 1991.
2. SMEC/BCL Damage Assessment - 1988 Flood - Final Report, Dhaka, November, 1988.
3. SAFIULLAH A.M.M., Embankment for Flood Protection: Success and Failure. paper presented at the Institution of Engineers, Dhaka, 1988.
4. McDOWELL PROF D.M., Hydraulic design of Bridges on Mawa-Bhanga Road, Dhaka, 1988.
5. GEOLOGICAL SURVEY OF BANGLADESH, Seismic Zoning Map of Bangladesh and Outline of a Code for Earthquake Resistant Design of Structures, Dhaka, 1979.
6. TRANSPORT RESEARCH LABORATORY, Overseas Road Note 7 (Volume 1): A Guide to Bridge Inspection and Data Systems for District Engineers, and (Volume 2): Bridge Inspector's Handbook, Crowthorne, U.K., 1988.
7. CHOUDHRY C.F., Natural Disasters in Bangladesh and their Mitigation, student essay, Dhaka, 1989.

Keynote paper. Worldwide technology transfer for natural disaster reduction

W. W. HAYS, US Geological Survey, and B. M. ROUHBAN,
UN Educational Cultural and Scientific Organization, France

ABSTRACT

Although transfer of technology for reducing community
vulnerability to natural hazards is taking place every
day throughout the world, many of these activities may
fail unless a new concerted worldwide effort is
initiated to accelerate and improve the process. Past
experience has exposed several problems and shown that
transfer of technology succeeds when the following
elements are present: 1) a goal, which requires
researchers practitioners, and decisionmakers to work
together to change the social, technical,
administrative, political, legal, and economic forces
which shape the policy environment; 2) strategies to
transfer ownership of information, knowledge,
experience, and know how from researchers to
practitioners and decisionmakers; 3) a national mandate
assigning institutional responsibility, accountability
and funding for adopting and enforcing risk management
policies and practices; 4) internal advocates and
external champions who are empowered to leverage their
efforts and resources through networks of cooperating
organizations; and 5) "windows of opportunity" provided
by political forces or natural disasters to deepen
understanding and to effect changes in policies and
practices concerning the hazard-, built-, and policy
environments.

THE NEED

This paper presents a strategic plan to accelerate and improve
worldwide transfer of technology for natural disaster reduction
during the 1990's. The goal is to reduce community vulnerability
to natural hazards (i.e., eliminate flaws in planning and
development). These flaws make communities throughout the world
susceptible to socioeconomic impacts from: floods, landslides,
wildfires, severe storms, earthquakes, tsunamis, droughts, and
volcanic eruptions.

The potential for disaster is greatest when communities are
located:

--in or adjacent to seismogenic zones capable of generating
damaging earthquakes,

NATURAL DISASTERS

--along coasts where hurricanes, cyclones, typhoons, storm surges, or tsunami flood waves strike,
--in flood plains subject to inundation from riverine floods or flash floods,
--in regions prone to tornadoes,
--near active volcanoes,
--on unstable slopes susceptible to landslides triggered either by meteorological or seismological sources,
--along wilderness/urban interfaces susceptible to wildfires, and
--in regions prone to drought episodes.

Reduction of community vulnerability to natural hazards requires a long-term process to change the hazard-, the built-, and the policy-environments of the community (fig. 1). These changes take time because the process depends on actual experiences with natural disasters and on current and ongoing research to deepen understanding of the six forces (called STAPLE forces in this paper): social, technical, administrative, political, legal, and economic. The STAPLE forces shape the policy environment and are the key to reduction of community vulnerability. They vary with time, place, and circumstances (fig. 2). The hazard environment produces or generates the physical effects (hazards) which can adversely impact the community and its built environment. The built environment (i.e., buildings and lifeline systems) is at risk (i.e., faces potential loss from these hazards), depending on location, value, exposure, and vulnerability. The community decisionmakers determine the mix of risk management policies and practices that are needed to protect the people and the built environment.

A strategic plan for accelerating and improving worldwide technology transfer is urgently needed to effect changes in the STAPLE forces and, ultimately, the hazard-, built-, and policy-environments. At present, many nations do not have either a mandate for causing such changes or a strategic plan to reduce their risks from natural hazards. As a result, flaws in planning, siting, design, and construction occur, are repeated, and are often perpetuated, even after a disaster strikes. These flaws cause the people and built environment to be at unacceptable levels of risk (i.e., to face unacceptable economic loss, loss of function, deaths, and injuries) and, even worse, to remain at these unacceptable levels even after a disaster strikes. At present, the direct economic losses worldwide from natural hazards not only reach nearly $50 billion annually (ref. 1) but they also are increasing with time. Socioeconomic impacts from natural hazards are causing redirection of scarce resources needed for urgent societal needs, a slow down and modification of community development plans, unnecessary personal hardship, and, in some cases, adverse environmental impacts.

THE PROBLEM

Many experts believe that the world's current technology base (i.e., information, knowledge, experience, and know how) is adequate to reduce any community's vulnerability to natural hazards (ref. 2). However, even though adequate technologies are available, they are not being transferred to end users and implemented at a rapid enough rate in both developed and developing countries to change the policy environment and reduce the risk. Too few communities have adopted policies that: 1) stop increasing the risk for new development, 2) start decreasing the risk for existing development, and 3) continue improving preparedness plans for the inevitable damaging event.

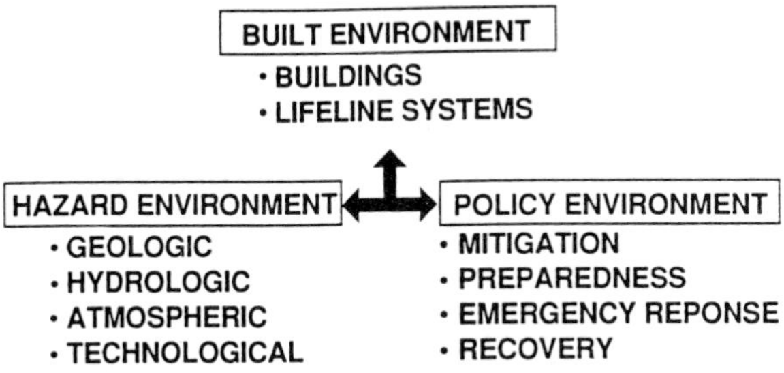

BUILT ENVIRONMENT
· BUILDINGS
· LIFELINE SYSTEMS

HAZARD ENVIRONMENT ⟷ POLICY ENVIRONMENT
· GEOLOGIC   · MITIGATION
· HYDROLOGIC   · PREPAREDNESS
· ATMOSPHERIC   · EMERGENCY REPONSE
· TECHNOLOGICAL   · RECOVERY

Figure 1.--Schematic illustration of the hazard-, built-, and policy environments which control community vulnerability to natural hazards.

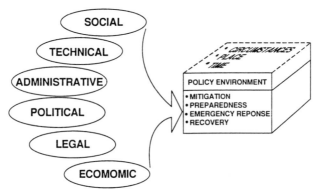

Figure 2.--The forces shaping the community policy environment that must be changed by technology transfer.

Three problems continue to hinder transfer of technology for natural hazard reduction throughout the world (ref. 3). They are: 1) resistance to change; 2) coordination and communication, especially at disciplinary interfaces, between researchers, practitioners, and decisionmakers; and 3) failure of end users to take "ownership" of new technologies (fig. 3).

Past experience (refs. 3-5) has shown that:

1. The status quo for natural disaster reduction will be maintained until external forces (e.g., those associated with political decisions or a natural disaster) compel changes in the hazard-, built-, and policy environments that will make the community's people, buildings, and lifelines less vulnerable to natural hazards.

2. Coordination and communication, especially at disciplinary interfaces between researchers, practitioners, and decisionmakers are not likely to change much until external forces compel them to work together at the margins of their disciplines to change the STAPLE forces.

491

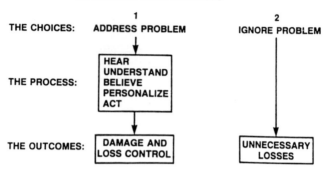

Figure 3.--Schematic illustration of the process required to transfer "ownership" of technology from researchers to practitioners.

3. Inability or reluctance of practitioners to take ownership of new technologies is often a result of lack of understanding of the technology, the inability to change the STAPLE forces, or not being part of the process(ref. 2).

THE SOLUTION

To be successful, the technology transfer program should seek to change the STAPLE forces. An accelerated worldwide technology transfer program should institutionalize a long-term process that will enable researchers, practitioners, and decisionmakers in a community to work through the problems of apathy, communication, and understanding, thereby transferring the "ownership" of available technologies (i.e., information, knowledge, experience, and know how developed within and outside their country). The researcher is seeking answers to the questions: where, how big, or how bad and why; the practitioner to the questions: when, how big, how bad, and where; the decisionmaker to the questions: what should I do to save lives, reduce damage and economic loss that is feasible technically, socially, and economically. Once answered to everyone's satisfaction the new technologies are owned; they can then be adapted for use in local risk management policies and practices.

An ideal end result for communities throughout the world is as follows:

1. Social--increased public awareness and understanding by all sectors of the public of the potential socioeconomic impacts of natural hazards (i.e., casualties, damage to community lifelines, homelessness, joblessness, financial repercussions, insurance demand, and cost of recovery).

2. Technical--increased understanding of the hazard-, built-, and policy-environments and the options for risk management (i.e., prevention, mitigation, preparedness, prediction and warning,

492

intervention, emergency response, and recovery and reconstruction).

3. Administrative--increased responsibility and accountability of existing organizations for reducing community vulnerability.

4. Political--increased political leadership for legislative mandates to reduce community vulnerability.

5. Legal--increased responsibility and accountability for actions to reduce community vulnerability.

6. Economic--increased investment in cost effective risk management policies and practices.

STRATEGIC PLAN FOR TECHNOLOGY TRANSFER

The essential elements of a strategic plan are described below. They are:

1. Strategic Direction (i.e., the goal).

Goal: The goal is to establish the planning, research, educational, and policy framework needed to accelerate and improve technology transfer that will lead over time to a significant reduction in vulnerability to natural hazards for every community throughout the world during the 1990's. This effort should seek to build every community's capacity for attaining sustainable development of the built environment. This goal is a realistic extension of that adopted for the International Decade for Natural Disaster Reduction (IDNDR), on December 22, 1989 by 155 member states of the United Nations (ref. 2). The IDNDR's goal is to prevent or mitigate natural disasters through a concerted cooperative worldwide effort during the 1990's. Through expanded and enhanced coordination, communication, post disaster evaluation, research, and public policy options, the STAPLE forces and, therefore, the policy environments of every local community throughout the world can be changed. Continuing government-academia-industry linkages can deepen understanding of the social, technical, administrative, political, legal, and economic forces that shape the policy environments in each local community.

Reduction of community vulnerability to natural hazards will also contribute to the realization of broader urgent national goals, such as:

--economic growth,
--hazard-resilient infrastructure,
--reduced environmental impact,
--enhanced science education,
--stronger international relations.

The basic premise is that the existing knowledge base from research and post disaster studies is adequate for reducing community vulnerability and that every community throughout the world can have access to the experience of others.

The kinds of community changes that are envisioned include:

--efficient transfer of technology among and between national researchers, practitioners, and decisionmakers as well as with counterparts worldwide.
--new and improved preventive mechanisms and techniques.

493

--interdisciplinary approaches to mitigation, which integrate all available knowledge and benefit from the continuous flow of new knowledge from ongoing research and interaction of researchers, practitioners, and decisionmakers.
--new cost effective remedial measures.
--expanded and improved educational and training programs

One immediate outcome of effective technology transfer is an increase in both the number and competencies of professionals in a country.

2. Strategic Paths (i.e., choosing the best ways to get from where we are now to where we want to be--the goal)

Any community that wants to reduce its vulnerability to natural hazards has to choose realistic, cost effective strategies that will change the STAPLE forces and ultimately its hazard-, built-, and policy environments. The choice of strategies is facilitated when there is a national mandate that assigns one or more institutions responsibility and accountably for coping with: a) apathy, b) differences in perspectives of researchers, practitioners, and decisionmakers, and c) the need for abandoning or improving ineffective technology transfer activities. It is well known (refs. 3-7) that every community can reduce its vulnerability by taking incremental actions that either prevent or minimize the physical and social demands of natural hazards and/or increase the community's capabilities to cope with them. The community's options for risk management include the following choices:

1.   Prevention--actions that prevent the occurrence of physical and/or social demands or actions that prevent loss of community capability.

2.   Mitigation--actions that reduce the physical and/or social demands or actions that protect community capability.

3.   Preparedness--actions that anticipate and reduce the physical and/or social demands or actions that enhance and protect community capability.

4.   Prediction and Warning--actions to predict and warn the populace about the occurrence and consequences (where, how big, when, and probability) of physical and/or social demands or actions to protect community capability from eminent events.
5.   Intervention--actions taken while the physical effects of the natural hazard are still developing in order to lessen the expected physical and/or social demands or actions that lessen the expected impacts on community capability.

6.   Emergency Response--actions that define the expected physical and/or social demands or actions that manage and reallocate community resources to protect community capability.

7.   Recovery--actions that stabilize the physical and/or social demands for actions that restore and improve community capability.

The Scientific and Technical Committee (STC) of the IDNDR provided a mandate for technology transfer for each participating nation when it set three targets for each nation to reach by the year

494

2000 (ref. 6). These are minimum targets which any nation should be able to meet with existing technologies. The targets are:

1.   National assessments of risks from natural hazards with these risks being taken into account in development plans;

2.   Mitigation plans at national and/or local levels that involve long-term prevention, preparedness, and community awareness; and

3.   Ready access to global, regional, national, and local warning systems and broad dissemination of warnings.

3.   Resources (i.e., leadership and human/financial resources needed to reach the goal).

In response to the STC's recommendation to establish national committees, more than 100 nations have established committees. Hence, the required leadership and institutional resources are now available throughout the world to accelerate and improve technology transfer.

Every country has internal advocates for reduction of community vulnerability who are (or could be) active participants in an existing network of cooperating organizations that can provide a comprehensive, balanced, and integrated program of technology transfer (fig. 4). These networks are not only cost effective but their products are also politically acceptable. Each country's individual members of the network can also serve as external champions to provide training and technical assistance, upon request, to other nations.

4.   Implementation of Strategic Plan (i.e., incremental execution of the strategies).

Communication and coordination between researchers, practitioners, and decisionmakers is the key to effective implementation (fig. 4). Coordination is the most effective way to increase the capacity of professionals and to leverage scarce resources.

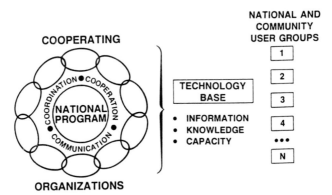

Figure 4.--Schematic illustration of how a network of cooperating organizations can accelerate technology transfer during the 1990's.

NATURAL DISASTERS

Interactive communication of the interdisciplinary professionals who are working at the margins of the state-of-the-art and state-of-practice is essential for success. Urban planners, emergency managers, health and medical care specialists, architects, engineers, and scientists have important ongoing roles in reducing the vulnerability to natural hazards in their community. Urban planners plan the way groups of engineered and non-engineered buildings are combined to form streets and ultimately an environmentally compatible and hazard-resistant urban center that meets the diverse needs of the populace. Health and medical care specialists and emergency managers organize the human and material resources of the community for emergency response and recovery. Architects design individual buildings, focusing mainly on the building configuration, non-structural elements, and occupant safety. Engineers, architects, and scientists work together to ensure that new or retrofitted existing buildings will meet the legal requirements of the local building and land use regulations and preserve life and property values by withstanding the physical effects of natural hazards (i.e., such as wind velocity, flood waves, ground shaking, and ground failure).

5. Evaluation (i.e., documenting progress, keeping the goal realistic, and making adjustments to optimize the strategies). The worldwide occurrence of each natural hazard provides a scientific laboratory which should be used as a basis for learning and for evaluating progress toward the goal of reducing community vulnerability to natural hazards. These occurrences provide new data and experiences on the continuum of natural laboratories provided by mother nature. Research and post-disaster studies should be widely disseminated; those that are unknown, ignored, unused, or misused are worthless for reducing community vulnerability to natural hazards.

Post-disaster studies of damage patterns and failure modes in the built environment have shown that several planning and development flaws occur repeatedly in communities throughout the world (ref. 5.). They have provided important lessons which should be incorporated in a worldwide technology transfer program to eliminate or correct specific flaws in community planning and development. Some of the basic principles distilled from these lessons are summarized below as a type of checklist:

 1. Natural Disasters--A natural disaster occurs when a natural hazard such as an earthquake, hurricane, etc., causes increased physical (e.g., ground shaking, ground failure, etc.) and social (e.g., deaths, injuries, fire fighting requirements, law enforcement requirements, loss of tax base, etc.) demands on the community and/or decreases the capabilities of the community (e.g., loss of medical facilities, loss of schools, loss of function, etc.)..

 Natural hazards (i.e., disaster agents) act only as triggering events; natural disasters are the result of human and societal actions, in response to the physical phenomena. Different disaster agents create different physical and social demands on the community and reduce its capabilities to cope, especially when not anticipated.

 A community should stress a mix of realistic physical and social solutions instead of just physical solutions in its disaster reduction planning cycle.

 2. Disaster Reduction Planning--the disaster reduction planning cycle consists of four interrelated elements: 1)

mitigation, 2) preparedness, 3) emergency response, and 4) recovery.
Planning must deal with the potential conditions of increased demand and decreased capacity in the community following the occurrence and socioeconomic impacts of a catastrophic event.

3.   Risk Assessment--a community should have a current risk assessment(i.e., determination of the chance of loss to the buildings, lifeline systems, and community services). The main factors in risk assessments are: (a) the location of buildings, facilities, and lifeline systems within a community; (b) their exposure to the physical effects of a natural hazard; and (c) their vulnerability (that is, potential loss in value or function) when subjected to these physical effects. It is essential that the community understands itself--its capacity (i.e., capabilities as well as deficiencies) for coping with the potential disaster agents and their likely physical and socioeconomic impacts.

4.   Mitigation--mitigation requires a community to undertake long-term actions a step at a time to protect community capabilities from the demands of natural hazards. Mitigation measures encompass those actions, taken before the event, that prevent or reduce the physical (e.g., ground shaking, ground failure, flood waters, high wind velocity, etc.) or social (e.g., deaths, injuries, etc.) demands of a natural hazard and/or protect essential community capabilities (e.g., emergency command center, schools, hospitals, fire fighting capacity, etc.). Typical mitigation measures include: building regulations and land-use zoning ordinances, retrofit of structures, remediation of soils, base isolation of essential buildings, facilities, or lifelines, etc.

Every community can increase its capacity for adopting and enforcing mitigation measures through technology transfer.

5.   Preparedness--preparedness measures can be short-or long-term. They include emergency response planning, prediction and warning, short-term strengthening of structures, training, response exercises based on scenario events, etc. Preparedness measures encompass those actions that a community can take before the event that either anticipates and reduces the physical and social demands of natural hazards and/or enhances and protects community capabilities.

Before the potential disaster agent strikes, a community should have:

--   an analysis of potential physical (i.e., damage) and social vulnerabilities (i.e., deaths, injuries, loss of homes, loss of jobs) within the community.
--   knowledge of important community systems and their organization of, structure and responsibilities.
--   baseline data on existing community resources.
--   a comprehensive reviewed and exercised emergency response plan. A plan that is out of date may be worse than no plan at all because it can give the illusion of being prepared.
--   a system for collecting damage information.
--   a process by which damage information can be analyzed and acted on.

"Disaster vulnerable" structures and high risk groups of people should be identified. Social vulnerability is greatest among: a) the elderly, b) the poor, c) children, d) those without a motor vehicle, e) newcomers to the community, and f) those lacking language skills of the host society.

6. Prediction and Warning--prediction and warning, an important component of community preparedness, requires modern technologies and ongoing scientific research. A prediction is based on science and depends on continuos monitoring in space and time of the causative mechanisms that are capable of generating a potentially damaging event. A warning is an interpretation of a prediction that takes public policy and public needs into account.

Prediction and warning is a process involving three activities: 1) assessment (at present the strongest part), 2) public dissemination (the weakest part), and 3) response of people (the most important part).

Weather forecasting is well advanced (e.g., hurricane), but at present, earthquake prediction (i.e., location, magnitude, and time of an eminent earthquake) is still in the research mode.

7. Emergency Response--The technology for comprehensive multihazard emergency response exists; therefore, every community can increase its capacity to respond after an event strikes and to manage and reallocate community capabilities to meet urgent needs, such as urban search and rescue, and a variety of emergency assistance requirements.

No disaster agent destroys everything in the community; therefore, an urgent task during the emergency response is to determine what has been lost and what still remains as a resource for use in either emergency response or in recovery, or in both.

8. Search and Rescue--the first 48 hours are critically important for saving victims trapped in the rubble of collapsed buildings, bridges, or other structures.

A urgent problem encountered repeatedly during emergency response is how to distinguish between real and urgent problems and the imagined or "mythical" problems. Common myths are:

-- human beings will panic or break down in a disaster.
-- disaster victims will be passive and totally dependent on organizations outside the community for help.

Community search and rescue operations are affected by:

-- the type of disaster agent.
-- the location intensity, and duration of the disaster agent.
-- the occurrence of secondary, consequent, or resultant natural or technological hazards .
-- the social organization and "mitigation ethic" of the community.

9. Recovery--Every community can increase its capacity for recovery. Recovery measures encompass those actions a

community takes after the disaster to stabilize physical and social demands and/or to restore and improve community capabilities. Recovery involves restoring and improving community capabilities for productivity to at least their pre-earthquake or pre-disaster level. Full restoration can not always be achieved. In an optional recovery process, the community will try to take advantage of the opportunity a disaster provides by improving its capabilities for coping with future natural hazards. Such improvements may not always be realized because of political and economic factors, especially if socioeconomic impacts of the disaster were large.

In a disaster, interaction increases markedly and, for a time, a notable lack of conflict and disagreement results. Communities shift toward what is called "emergency consensus"--agreement on a common set of priorities for community action. This process can lead to efficient and cost-effective restoration of community services.

At present, the strategy of many communities throughout the world is to minimize or ignore mitigation and preparedness, emphasize emergency response, and rely on outside assistance (relief) to restore community capabilities during recovery. This strategy is costly and ineffective for reducing community vulnerability because the flaws in planning and development that existed before the disaster will not been eliminated or corrected. In the long run, it is much more expensive to recover from a disaster than to invest in mitigation strategies which will reduce or prevent future losses.

CASE HISTORY--SEISMIC ZONATION IN ALGERIA

The seismic zonation study in Algeria (ref. 3) following the magnitude 7.2 El Asnam earthquake on October 10, 1980, is an excellent example of technology transfer. This earthquake accelerated transfer of technology in Algeria more than any other past Algerian earthquake, even though other recent earthquakes such as the 1954 Orleansville event were also devastating. The El Asnam earthquake killed 2,700 people, injured several thousand, left 300,000 homeless, destroyed buildings and lifeline systems, and slowed economic development in a rapidly growing region for 10 years. Recognizing the long-term risk from future earthquakes, Algerian authorities froze construction in the stricken area and took specific steps after the El Asnam earthquake to change their national and local building and land use regulations as a part of the long-term recovery and reconstruction program. With the assistance of UNESCO, an international tender was prepared to obtain a skilled consultant to produce the required technical products (e.g., seismic zonation maps) and to develop a process to transfer the technology on seismic zonation to Algerian scientists, engineers, and urban planners. A contract having these requirements was awarded to Woodward Clyde Consultants in 1983. Immediately thereafter, Controle Technique de la Construction (CTC), the Algerian organization empowered to lead the program, took additional steps to ensure transfer of technology by asking UNESCO to create a Control Board to act as their technical advisor, to monitor the study by Woodward Clyde Consultants, and to facilitate technology transfer. A Control Board, consisting of a chairman from the U.S. Geological Survey and 15 international experts having knowledge and experience in all aspects of seismic zonation, was established in 1983 to perform three tasks on behalf of CTC and UNESCO:

1. identification of technical issues associated with the seismic zonation study of the stricken area and 10 rapidly growing urban centers in the region,

2. evaluation of the quality and usefulness of the final products (i.e., the regional- and urban-scale seismic zonation maps) and process used to transfer technology to the Algerians, and

3. technology transfer activities to compliment those of the contractors.

Technology transfer was accelerated by convening five multidisciplinary training workshops on topical problems in seismic zonation. Each one was convened 1 or 2 days before each of the scheduled project meetings between Woodward Clyde Consultants, CTC, and their Algerian partners. The training workshops were designed to introduce Algerian professionals (e.g., scientists, engineers, urban planners, and code officials) to the wide variety of issues inherent in seismic zonation and to help them gain self confidence as well as know how. Algerian scientists learned how to conduct paleoseismicity studies, for example. Technical aids such as maps, exercises to illustrate professional judgment, and a glossary of technical terms (both in French and English) were provided to each of the approximately 50 Algerian participants in each workshop. Algerian professionals were also assigned roles in each workshop; they lectured, coached Algerian colleagues in the exercises, and helped to evaluate the workshops. Awards were given to all participants who completed each training workshop.

More than a decade after the El Asnam earthquake, all indications are that transfer technology of seismic zonation to Algerian professionals was successful. Algeria now has a modern building code and updated, realistic urban master plans that incorporate the earthquake hazard in the planning. Algerian scientists have applied their new know how to excavate new trenches and to perform a seismic zonation study of Ouled Fares, a small urban area near El Asnam, and recently they started work on Algiers, the capital, which was destroyed by a large earthquake in the 18th century. They convened international conferences on Seismic Zonation in 1984 and 1993 to transfer technology on seismic zonation to professionals from neighboring countries. A new institution, the Institute of Earthquake Engineering and Applied Seismology (CGS), was established in 1984 with about 10 professionals. It now has 46 professionals. Two hundred strong motion accelerographs have been purchased since 1980 and deployed throughout Algeria to complement the modern seismicity network installed earlier. At present, Algerian professionals are contributing to SEISMED, a cooperative regional project involving 18 nations to reduce earthquake risk in the Mediterranean region (ref. 4).

SUMMARY

The IDNDR provides an unprecedented opportunity to improve and accelerate technology transfer for natural disaster reduction during the 1990's. An opportunity like this to accelerate and improve worldwide technology transfer for natural disaster reduction may never occur again. It must be seized!

REFERENCES

1. Merani, Neelan S., 1991, The Reduction of Natural Disasters, in Aaron, John M and Hays, Walter W. (eds.), The Challenge of IDNDR, Episodes, v. 14, no. 1, pp 1-6.

2. United Nations, 1989, International Decade for Natural Disaster Reduction, 44th Session of the General Assembly, Resolution 44/256, 6p/.

3. Hays, Walter W. and Rouhban, Badaoui M., 1991, Technology Transfer, Episodes, v. 14, no. 1, pp. 66-72.

4. Hays, Walter W., van Essche, Ludovic, and Maranzana, Franco, 1991, SEISMED and IDNDR: Opportunities to Reduce the Risk From Earthquakes and Other Natural Hazards, Episodes, v. 14, no. 1, pp. 13-18.

5. United Nations Centre for Regional Development, 1987, Challenges of the IDNDR, Nagoya, Japan, 129 p.

6. STOP Disasters, 1991, First Session of the Scientific and Technical Committee, no. 1,/May-June, pp. 4-7.

7. Kreimer, Alcira and Munasinghe, Mohan, (eds.), 1992, Environmental Management and Urban Vulnerability, Report 168, The World Bank, Washington, DC.

501

39. Towards an improved understanding of the performance of low-rise buildings in wind storms

R. P. HOXEY, A. P. ROBERTSON and G. M. RICHARDSON, Silsoe Research Institute, UK

ABSTRACT

Wind storms have caused considerable damage in the United Kingdom in recent years, and as elsewhere in the world, low-cost structures have been the principal victims. Agricultural structures have been particularly affected, and, for this reason, work at Silsoe Research Institute has been directed at improving the understanding of wind loading on agricultural structures in order to improve their design whilst retaining their cost-effectiveness. This work now lends itself to a much wider field of application.

Full-scale measurements have been conducted on a wide range of buildings to define the pressure distributions generated and to identify the geometric parameters that are important in the design process. This work provides valuable insights into the performance of low-cost structures and helps to explain the instances of wind damage suffered by some of the structures on which measurements have been made during this project.

The fundamental research being conducted at Silsoe Research Institute develops scientific methods which can be utilised to improve the performance of buildings subjected to wind storms. This technology has applications to the design of low-rise buildings throughout the world and a simplified method of assessing wind loads is proposed to cover single and two-storey buildings.

INTRODUCTION

Throughout the world, wind storms cause extensive damage to low-rise structures, particularly domestic housing and commercial units which can often be categorised as 'non engineered' or 'low engineering input' structures. This damage is widespread, caused in the tropics by tropical storms or hurricanes such as 'Andrew', and in northern and southern latitudes by cyclonic storms. These storms have dramatic impacts in both the developing and the developed world.

The International Decade for Natural Disaster Reduction encourages the wind engineer to focus attention on mitigating

Natural disasters. Thomas Telford, London, 1993

damage caused by wind storms. It is accepted that a compromise must be found between robustness of the structure and the cost of construction. It is only through careful experimentation and the acquisition of good quality data that a satisfactory compromise can be made.

The estimation of wind loads on a structure is a complex problem: the wind speed at the structure is influenced by the severity of the storm, the upstream conditions (the presence of other structures, trees and vegetation), undulations in the land (speeds increase near the crest of a hill), and building geometry. These factors are covered in national and international standards on wind loading (see for example refs. 1-5) but these documents are intended for the design of all buildings which generally leads to a more complex procedure than can be justified for low-cost domestic housing. Also, as a consequence of a more general application, codes fail to represent accurately the pressure distributions generated over small low-rise buildings, often underestimating both the uplifts generated in separated flow regions and the extents of these regions.

If the design of low-rise buildings is to be improved, appropriate simplifications need to be introduced into existing standards, and more realistic pressure coefficients for a limited range of building geometries need to be incorporated. This will enable the design to be carried out at a lower technological level which will encourage the use of the information, leading to more efficient and safer housing. In this presentation some simplification is proposed in assessing the design wind loads:-

1. The building should be designed as if unsheltered since the presence of surrounding structures which provide beneficial shelter may not persist throughout the design life of the building. Generally, the fully exposed building will be subjected to greater loads than will the partially sheltered building. (It is known that local cladding loads may increase for partially sheltered buildings, but this is a relatively small effect which may be ignored here).

2. The fetch should be considered to be open country since vegetation and trees can be destroyed in strong wind storms. This condition gives a sensible worst case for design but is not unduly conservative.

3. Low-rise buildings are not likely to be designed on an individual basis and therefore the orientation of the building with respect to the prevailing wind direction will not be pre-determined. Hence the maximum wind speeds should be assumed to arise from the direction which has the greatest effect on the building according to its geometry (see 4. below).

4. The building geometry parameters of height, span, length, and roof pitch, including such details as variable eaves overhang, have a profound effect on the wind loads experienced by the structure. These parameters need to be

503

rationalised to a limited set which appropriately accounts for building geometry effects. This is the main subject of this paper.

The assessment of wind load is only one aspect of structural design. Other loadings (such as that due to snow), the response of the structure, the types of construction materials, the cladding used, the fixings and the foundations all need to be considered in the overall structural design. The way the wind load is transferred from the cladding through the fixings and the intermediate structure to the frame and foundations is all part of the wind loading design process, and needs to be considered further. New information has been obtained from analyses of the Silsoe Structures Building and this will be described further in this paper.

FULL-SCALE EXPERIMENTAL WORK ON THE SILSOE SITE

Background

An extensive range of full-scale measurements have been made on over 30 agricultural buildings selected for their geometry and suitable exposure. These measurements, made under natural wind conditions, have defined the external pressure distribution and the internal pressure, thus establishing the net wind loads on each building. Portal-framed buildings have been investigated together with glasshouses of traditional shape (including multi-span structures), greenhouses of curved arch construction clad in film-plastics, and open-sided buildings used for storing agricultural products. These measurements provide the basis for assessing the effects of geometry in the prediction of wind loads. Results have been analysed and extensive pressure coefficient data have been derived. Simplified design pressure coefficients are proposed in the next section where the objectives are to adequately account for the effect of building geometry whilst retaining appropriate simplicity. To obtain further information on the structural performance of low-rise buildings in wind storm conditions, a portal-framed building was erected at Silsoe (Fig.1) for assessment of both the wind loads on the structure and the structure's performance when subjected to dynamic wind loads.

Wind structure

Reliable interpretation of measurements of wind loads on a structure requires information on the atmospheric boundary layer conditions at the site. The basic data necessary in the case of a neutrally stable boundary layer (i.e. where there is no thermal mixing) is a measure of the surface roughness parameter and the turbulence intensity. These parameters can be determined from measurements of the vertical profile of horizontal velocity obtained by setting anemometers at different heights. An example of the velocity profile for the Silsoe site is presented in Fig.2. where the surface roughness parameter z_o was found to have a value of 0.01 m. The same anemometers were used to measure the turbulence levels in the horizontal plane. The turbulence intensities measured in the streamwise (u) direction and transverse (v) direction are presented in Fig.3, where the intensity (I) is the ratio of the rms value of velocity to the streamwise mean velocity. An

Fig.1. Silsoe Structures Building - a portal framed building of 13 m span, 24 m long, 4.1 eaves and 10° roof pitch. The plates on the building house pressure tapping points

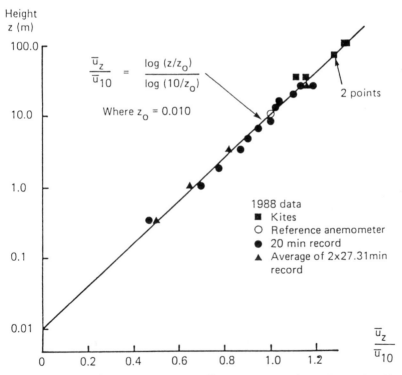

Fig.2. The streamwise velocity $\bar{u}_z$ compared with the velocity $\bar{u}_{10}$ at the standard meteorological height of 10 m in the atmospheric boundary layer at the Silsoe site

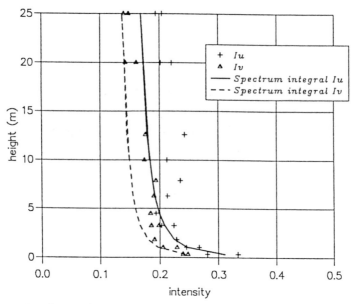

Fig.3. The intensity of turbulence in the atmospheric boundary
layer for the streamwise (u) and lateral (v) components. The
spectrum integral represents a lower bound which applies to a
stationary process.

increase in turbulence intensity close to the ground is
apparent in both components.

Pressure measurements

A large number of static pressure taps were installed on the
surface of the Silsoe Structures Building to sense the
pressures generated by the wind (ref. 6). Plastic tubing of
6 mm internal diameter transmitted the pressures at the tapping
points to pressure transducers located centrally within the
building. This tubing restricted the high frequency response
to 3 Hz (3 dB down). Pressures were measured over an extensive
period when wind speeds exceeded 8 m/s. This condition ensured
adequate instrumentation response and also ensured that the
flow patterns over and around the building were similar to
those that develop at the design wind speed. During pressure
recordings, simultaneous measurements were made of the
windspeed and direction at the ridge height of the building.
This enabled non-dimensional pressure coefficients to be
derived which are suitable for use in design. An example of
the mean pressure coefficients obtained for the Silsoe
Structures Building is shown in Fig.4, where isobars are
plotted over the surface of the building.

Structural response

The central portal frame of the Silsoe Structures Building was

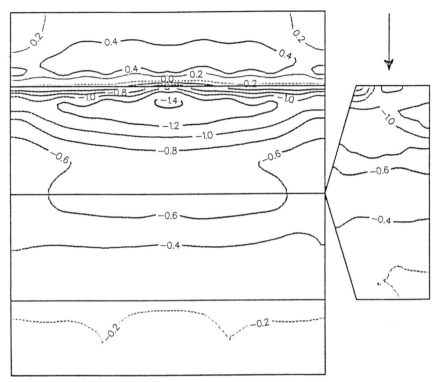

Fig.4. Mean pressure coefficient contours for the Silsoe Structures Building obtained from full-scale experiments

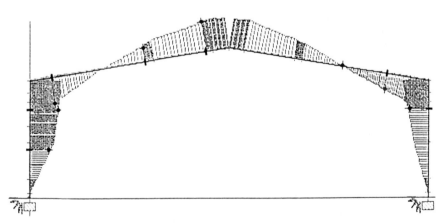

Fig.5. Bending moments for the central portal frame computed from the distribution of surface pressure with an appropriate foundation rotational restraint compared with measured values (+) at 8 positions

instrumented with strain gauges to sense bending moments. Two
side rails and two purlins were also instrumented. These
strains were monitored continuously during periods of strong
winds and the measurements analysed to indicate how the
building responded. This experiment was conducted with each of
three different connection arrangements between the frames and
their foundations: a pinned foundation connection; a 2-bolt
connection giving partial rotational fixity; or a 4-bolt
connection giving greater rotational fixity to the column
bases. These measurements have been analysed and the
performance of the building assessed. The bending moment
distribution computed from the pressure distribution is
compared in Fig.5 with measured bending moments and good
agreement is demonstrated. The results show that when the
behaviour of the structure is known, the application of the
measured pressure distribution gives a good prediction of true
bending moments as would be expected, but that there is
considerable sensitivity to details such as the fixity at the
foundations (refs 7-8).

Alternative approaches - wind tunnel and computational fluid
dynamic modelling

Full-scale experiments provide the only realistic method of
measuring loads at close to the design Reynolds number in a
correctly simulated boundary layer flow. The disadvantage of
the full-scale approach is the lack of control of the wind and
the limited availability of suitable buildings on which to make
measurements. Controllable experiments can be conducted at
lower cost in boundary layer wind tunnels, where the
atmospheric boundary layer is commonly scaled by a factor in
the range of 100 - 300. This gives 2 - 3 orders of magnitude
difference in the Reynolds number. This is generally
considered to be unimportant in the case of bluff body
aerodynamics (ref.9) where there are distinct flow separations
triggered by sharp building corners. However, there is
emerging evidence that the curvature of the streamlines
associated with separated flow regions remains sensitive to
Reynolds number and that, as a consequence, significant errors
remain in the simulation of separated flows at small scales.

For low-rise buildings there also remains a difficulty in
simulating the atmospheric boundary layer close to the ground.
The normal technique in boundary layer wind tunnels (ref.9) is
to provide an extensive fetch of roughness elements to thicken
the boundary layer. This will generate a mean velocity profile
similar to that shown in Fig.2 for the atmospheric boundary
layer. However it is usual practice to discontinue the
roughness elements some distance upstream of the model, to
encourage homogeneity of the flow at the model position. This
is evident in Fig.6 where the velocities close to the ground
are greater than those expected for a linear log law as found
in Fig.2. It is important to simulate the wind structure
correctly over this region in low-rise building studies:
failure to do so will lead to errors in the prediction of wall
pressures and possibly to fundamentally erroneous flows over
the entire building. Roughness can be extended close to the
model to overcome this problem, but this must be done with
carefully chosen roughness sizes, to ensure that the turbulence

intensity and the spectral characteristics of the turbulence are similar to those of the full-scale boundary layer.

The differences in velocity gradient (Fig.6) result from a boundary layer grown over a surface which was initially too rough, followed by a transition region of correct roughness and finally an excessively smooth surface on which the model was mounted (ref.10). The increased mean velocities associated with the development of the inner boundary layer over the final smooth surface may account for the reduction in turbulence intensities compared with the full-scale values (Fig.7).

When the atmospheric boundary layer is correctly simulated, the wind tunnel provides controllable conditions for the simulation of wind loads and is an essential part of any experimental programme to determine the influence of building geometry on wind loads. The mean pressure distribution for a 1:100 scale model of the Silsoe Structures Building is shown in Fig.8 and can be compared with the full-scale measurements presented in Fig.4. A difference can be seen between the full-scale and wind-tunnel measurements in the separated flow region on the windward roof slope where there are significantly greater suction loads indicated by the full-scale results. Further measurements (ref.10) have shown that this difference is unlikely to be associated with any deficiency in the simulated boundary layer and at the present time it is tentatively concluded that the separated flow curvature is Reynolds number dependent.

Recent developments in the field of computational fluid dynamics (CFD) make numerical modelling a possible alternative to wind tunnel experiments. The computational approach is currently limited by suitable models of turbulence. The commonly adopted approach is to represent the total turbulent kinetic energy as a scalar (k) together with a dissipation rate (ϵ) and this technique has been used to predict pressure distributions around buildings in a simulated atmospheric boundary layer (ref.11). The method has been refined and alternatives attempted using Reynolds stress models and large eddy simulations (ref.12). This is a rapidly developing area but some encouraging results have been obtained which make CFD a useful tool to the wind engineer (ref.13). The method has particular advantage in assessing the effect of changes of geometry in a single geometrical parameter such as roof angle or height/width ratio. Such a single-parameter study would be difficult to conduct at full-scale.

Neither wind tunnel modelling nor numerical modelling approaches can simultaneously embrace studies of the structural response of low-rise buildings under wind because of the complexity of modelling structural characteristics and details. Structural behaviour studies thus necessitate full-scale testing of the type conducted on the Silsoe Structures Building.

Both modelling approaches offer significant help to the wind engineer in designing structures and should be used in conjunction with full-scale experiments. The results of combining these approaches is described in the next section where an attempt is made to define the wind loads on low-rise

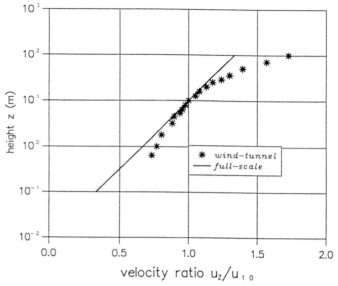

Fig.6. The streamwise velocity ratio developed in a boundary layer wind tunnel using roughness elements (height scaled by x 100)

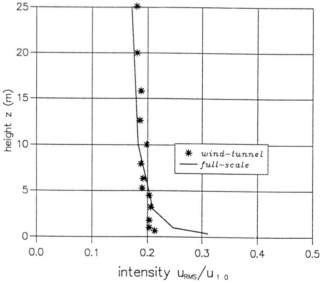

Fig.7. The streamwise intensity of turbulence for the boundary layer wind tunnel (height scaled by x 100)

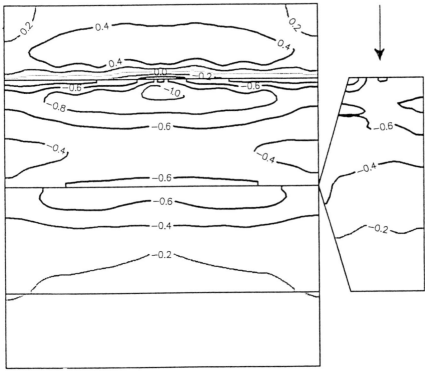

Fig.8   Mean pressure coefficient contours for a 1:100 scale
model of the Silsoe Structures Building obtained in a boundary
layer wind tunnel.   Comparison with full-scale measurements
show differences in the pressures generated by the separated
flow region at the leading edge of the windward roof slope
which extend over most of the roof

buildings according to the height, span, and roof pitch of the
building.

DESIGNING BUILDINGS TO RESIST WIND

There are two distinct steps in the procedure for assessing the
wind load which should be used in the design of a building.
These are:-

(i)   The assessment of a design wind speed, which will take
      into account statistical factors associated with risk.
      For example, this may be the wind speed for a particular
      site that has a known probability of being exceeded in a
      given period, e.g. a probability of 0.02 of being exceeded
      in a one year period.

(ii) The conversion of the design wind speed into loads on the
      building.   The wind speed is converted to a dynamic
      pressure which is combined with deterministic pressure

Fig. 9 (below and facing page). Proposed design pressure coefficients

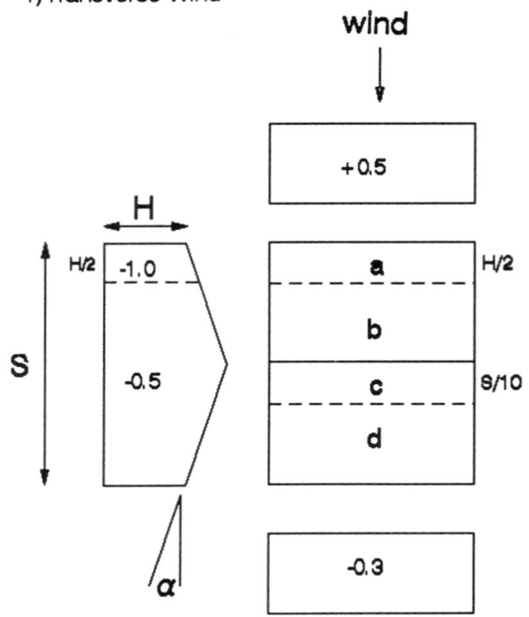

H/S ≈ 0.3 (single-storey buildings)

α	a	b	c	d
10°	-0.9	-0.5	-0.9	-0.6
15°	-0.8	-0.4	-1.1	-0.6
20°	-0.4	-0.2	-0.7	-0.6
25°	±0.2	+0.1	-0.6	-0.6
30°	+0.3	+0.3	-0.6	-0.6

H/S ≈ 0.7 (two-storey buildings)

α	a	b	c	d
10°	-1.7	-1.1	-0.9	-0.8
15°	-1.5	-0.9	-1.1	-0.8
20°	-0.9	-0.6	-0.9	-0.8
25°	-0.7	-0.4	-0.8	-0.8
30°	-0.4	-0.2	-0.8	-0.8

1) Transverse Wind

Wind →

+0.5

H/2

S/10

a
b
c
d

-0.3

H

-1.0

H/2

-0.5

S

α

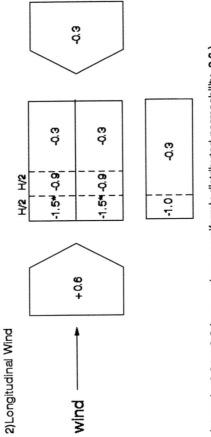

2)Longitudinal Wind

wind

H/2 H/2

-0.3

-0.3

-0.3

-1.5* -0.9

-1.5* -0.9

-1.0 -0.3

+0.6

Internal +0.6 to -0.6 (no openings or uniformly distributed permeability -0.3)

* These local coefficients are likely to occur for glancing wind direction and not the direction shown

513

coefficients to obtain the pressures acting on the surfaces of the building. To be usable by the designer in structural analyses, the pressure coefficients need to be presented in a simplified form, e.g. as shown in Fig.9. However, to promote efficient designs, the data need to reflect the dependence of pressures on building geometry.

The assessment of design wind pressure is set out in national codes and standards. The values can usually be modified to give risk factors acceptable to the building manufacturers, the customer, or local authorities who check procedures. Care should be taken in assessing risk as structural design introduces safety or uncertainty factors to reduce the risk of failure. These factors are often introduced in material standards (e.g. ref.14). For agricultural buildings, where the human occupancy may be low, these factors are reduced (ref.15) which gives some reduction in cost. Since there are very few failures of engineered agricultural buildings, it can be deduced that this relaxation is acceptable. However, safety or uncertainty factors should only be reduced when the quality of design information is enhanced. This should be taken into account in relation to the pressure coefficients presented here. The coefficients in some cases give greater loads than are given by some national standards but the uncertainty is reduced and hence lower safety factors would be justified.

For practical application, the complex patterns presented in Fig.4 need to be simplified and account taken of the different building geometries which represent low-rise buildings in practice. The experiments conducted on agricultural buildings have been used to provide simplified data for buildings with roof pitches of 10 - 30°, spans of 5 - 30 m, and eaves heights of 2 - 6 m. Although the building length has a significant effect on the pressure coefficients, it can be assumed that the length of the building will generally be greater than its span, which reduces considerably the significance of length on pressure distribution.

Simplified pressure coefficient information is presented in Fig.9 for buildings which can be broadly classified as single-storey (height/span approx. 0.3) and two-storey (height/span approx. 0.7) buildings . This simplification gives realistic values which can be applied easily, thus assisting efficient design. Some interpolation of the coefficients is permitted between the given height/span and roof pitch values, but this should be done with care. The existing information from full-scale measurements does not cover roof slopes above 30°, which are not uncommon in domestic housing. There is experimental evidence to support the use of higher roof pitches as a means of reducing the wind uplift on roofs, but this is at the expense of using more materials and increased lateral forces.

The pressure coefficients given in Fig.9 consist of overall values for structural design, and local coefficients for cladding design. The local coefficients around the perimeter of most building surfaces indicate the regions where cladding will be subjected to the greatest loads. These should be used to assess the requirement for additional cladding fixings. Where the eaves overhang the side of the building, it is essential that these local coefficients are used in combination with the pressure coefficients on the adjacent side face of the building to predict the peak net loads on the cladding. It is in these regions that the cladding is most susceptible to damage.

To obtain the net loading on the face, it is necessary to define the internal pressure within the building. This is dependent upon the permeability of the surfaces, particularly of the walls. For example, if a building has uniform typical porosity on all surfaces, the internal pressure coefficient can then be assumed to take the value of -0.3. However, this may not cover all aspects of the building's function and in general internal pressure should be assessed on the basis of flow through dominant openings and the external pressure at those points. The internal pressure can be assessed from an analysis of permeability and may take coefficient values within the extremes of $+0.6$ to -0.6 given in Fig.9. This is a potentially complex part of the design exercise, as internal pressure will change with wind direction and several cases may need to be considered.

The pressure coefficients presented in Fig.9 are intentionally simplified and are restricted to a limited range of common building geometries. It is considered that such simplifications will lead to more efficient design, reduce the design time and have a cost benefit to the designer, constructor and user of the buildings, particularly in developing nations.

Concluding remarks

Basic research conducted in the UK on wind effect on buildings has broad application in the developing world. The information presented will enable buildings to be constructed which are more efficient, more resistant to wind storms, and so will reduce the risk of disasters. To implement this work, close contacts are sought with countries at risk where it will be necessary to conduct field work to take account of local conditions and construction methods. International collaboration and support would be welcomed in order to promote this objective.

Acknowledgements

The work reported here has been supported by The Ministry of Agriculture, Fisheries and Food and by the Building Research Establishment. The wind tunnel results were obtained from studies conducted in The Boundary Layer Wind Tunnel Laboratory at the University of Western Ontario, Canada.

References

1. American National Standard. Minimum design loads for buildings and other structures. ANSI A581 - 1982, USA.
2. Australian Standard. Minimum design loads on structures. AS 1170.2 - 1989 Part 2 : Wind loads.
3. British Standard. Code of basic data for the design of buildings: CP3: Chapter V: Loading: Part 2: Wind loads, British Standards Institution, 1972.

4.	Draft British Standard. Draft BS 6399: Loading for buildings: Part 2: Code of practice for wind loading. BSI Document 91/16625, British Standards Institution, 1991.

5.	Draft European Standard. Draft Eurocode 1: Basis of design and actions on structures: Part 2.7: Wind loads. Document CEN/TC250/SC1/1992/N93, CEN, 1992.

6.	Robertson, A.P.; Glass, A.G. The Silsoe Structures Building - its design, instrumentation and research facilities. Divisional Note, DN 1482, Silsoe Research Institute, October 1988.

7.	Robertson, A.P. A study of base fixity effects on portal frame behaviour. The Structural Engineer, Vol. 69, No.2, January 1991, 17-24.

8.	Hoxey, R.P. Structural response of a portal framed building under wind load. Journal of Wind Engineering and Industrial Aerodynamics, 38, pp 347-356, 1991.

9.	Cook, N.J. The designer's guide to wind loading of building structures, Part 1 (1985) and Part 2 (1990), Butterworths.

10.	Richardson, G.M.; Surrey, D. The Silsoe Building: A comparison of pressure coefficients and spectra at model and full-scale. Progress in Wind Engineering. Proceedings of the 8th International Conference on Wind Engineering, pp 1653-1664, Editor A G Davenport, London, Ontario, Canada, 1991.

11.	Laurence, D.; Mattei, J.D. The current state of computational bluff body aerodynamics. Bluff Body Aerodynamics and Applications Conference, Melbourne Australia 7-10 Dec. 1992.

12.	Murakami, S.; Mochida, A.; Hayashi, Y.; Sakamoto, S. Numerical study on velocity-pressure field and wind forces for bluff bodies by k-ϵ, ASM and LES. Progress in Wind Engineering, Proceedings of the 8th International Conference on Wind Engineering, pp 2841-2852, Editor A G Davenport, London, Ontario, Canada, 1991.

13.	Hoxey, R.P.; Robertson, A.P., Basara, B.; Younis, B.A. Geometric parameters that affect wind loads on low-rise buildings; full-scale and CFD experiments. Bluff Body Aerodynamics and Applications Conference, Melbourne Australia 7-10 Dec. 1992.

14.	British Standard. BS 5950: Structural use of steelwork in building: Part 1: Code of practice for design in simple and continuous construction: hot rolled sections. British Standards Institution, 1990.

15.	British Standard. BS 5502: Buildings and structures for agriculture: Part 22: Code of practice for design, construction and loading. British Standards Institution, 1987.

40. Windstorm hazard in Northwest Europe

R. MUIR WOOD, EQE, UK

ABSTRACT

Windstorms present by far the most significant natural hazard in northwest Europe. Damage is not only a direct consequence of wind-loading as some of the largest windstorms have also generated major storm-surges, which have historically given rise to the greatest material and human losses of all natural disasters in northern Europe. The ability to make informed societal decisions concerning hazard and loss mitigation requires knowledge about the potential sizes and recurrence intervals of events. However while the location-specific hazards of wind-speed and sea-level exceedance are widely studied, in order to explore the complete impact of a storm, a more holistic approach is required. A century of research on earthquake effects has generated a whole range of principles and techniques, such as multifactorial intensity scales, and microzonation, that can be readily adapted for the study of windstorms. Using such methods it becomes possible to exploit the many centuries of historical information on past windstorms in sufficient detail to be able to develop regional event-type and event-size recurrence relationships.

INTRODUCTION

Mid-latitude windstorms are caused by the interactions between the cold polar and warm equatorial air-masses. Unlike true hurricanes (fuelled by evaporation of surface sea-water at temperatures in excess of 27°C), these cyclones are powered by the thermal contrast of the two air masses. Extreme differences in temperature produce the most turbulent cyclonic disturbances with the highest accompanying wind-speeds. These windstorms are commonly far larger than hurricanes with diameters of up to 3000km.

Temperature differences along the polar front are most profound in early Autumn, although can be sufficient to generate severe storms at any period from October to April. An influx of new hot or cold air can continue to power the storm for several days. When such cyclones become swept along by the jetstream, at speeds sometimes in excess of 100km/hr, there are very significant variations in windspeeds on their northern and southern flanks. The jet stream maintains an easterly flow in the northern hemisphere but also sustains enormous ripples that generally wander between a north-east to south-east orientation, and hence the most severe storms have a relatively restricted range of tracks. While there is an overall simplicity to a cyclonic disturbance such systems may also be multiple, interactive or otherwise complex.

While hurricanes can sometimes sustain mean windspeeds in excess of 70 m/s, even the most extreme peak windspeeds in these mid-latitude storms are rarely in excess of 60m/s (1m/s = 2.24 miles/hr, 3.60 km/hr and 1.94 knots/hr). Friction over the land-surface slows the accompanying windfield, and by creating low-level wind-shear increases turbulence.

Historical research on Northwest European windstorms has been pursued for more than 35 years by Professor Hubert Lamb, founder of the Climatic Resarch Unit at the University of East Anglia, culminating in the compilation of reconstructions of the meteorology of the most important and interesting Northwest European storms (ref. 1). However before 1900 only scattered observations are available of atmospheric pressure, temperature, wind direction and estimates of wind strength, and as a small variation in the pressure gradient can have a significant impact on windspeeds, it would not be appropriate to predict windspeeds on the basis of these reconstructions alone (ref. 1). However there are very large amounts of primary historical documentation on extreme wind-storm events throughout the past 900 years and in exploring the hazard of windstorms it is possible to pursue a 'phenomenological' approach, mapping reported effects, not reconstructed causes. This approach can be considered identical to the exploration of historical earthquakes through the assessment of the spatial distribution of intensities.

The most significant windstorms are transnational events, that cannot be properly comprehended without exploring their full course. By searching for primary sources on windstorms across all affected countries in Northwest Europe it becomes possible to reconstruct complete individual events and to explore windstorm hazard in terms of peak windspeeds and storm-track geometries.

In any holistic treatment of windstorms it becomes important to include accompanying storm surges. It is often forgotten, for example, that the great flood of February 1st 1953, that drowned 2100 people in southern Holland and eastern England, was on the previous night a disastrous windstorm in north-east Scotland, which felled 1.8 million m³ of forest timber. A particular storm track will cause a storm surge that tends to be concentrated on a specific section of coastline. Hence it becomes all important to consider each windstorm, and all its consequences, as a single phenomenon.

Detailed research on historical storm surges has been undertaken for the Netherlands (ref. 2), for northern Germany (ref. 3) and for Denmark (ref. 4), although no research of comparable historical quality exists for Britain. Such research, assisted by tide-gauge records of storm surges, provides the basis for defining the annual probability of a storm surge exceeding some level at a particular location. However this same data needs revisiting when considering the probability that several locations along a coastline will be affected by the same event, or when exploring the totality of both wind and surge related damage associated with a single windstorm event.

THE WINDSTORM FOOTPRINT

In order to begin a holistic treatment of windstorms it is necessary to explore the spatial structure of the cumulative windfield (the windstorm footprint) encountered in the passage of a major windstorm. Detailed studies of windfields recorded at closely spaced recording instruments (refs. 5 & 6) have revealed considerable variations in peak wind-speeds over small distances and confirmed a general model for windstorms: that violent fluctuations of wind velocity of shorter time-scale (strong gusts) result from the descent of relatively large masses of eddies carrying with them a wind-speed from upper levels.

However there is a 2-3 order of magnitude disparity between the spacing of instruments when employed by wind-engineers, and the typical spacing of meteorological wind-speed recorders, even in densely populated areas such as southern England or northern France. It seems highly likely that the spatial variability encountered in the windfield footprint is on a far smaller scale than the typical separation of recording stations. For example, at the time of the 1990 January 25th storm in southern England two wind-speed recorders were in operation at Gatwick Airport, both in unobstructed locations, separated by about 1500m (ref. 7). The eastern instrument recorded a peak gust speed of 39m/s, the western station of 34m/s: a 15% variation.

The large number of continuously recording windspeed instruments now available in a number of countries in western Europe makes it possible for the first time to explore the degree of spatial variability in peak wind-speeds from the same windstorm. It is instructive to compare the windfields of the January 25th 1990 and October 16th 1987 windstorms. In Fig 1 the peak wind-speed data for these two storms has been sampled, along a 100km wide corridor of the most severe winds (the storm track). For the 1987 storm the range of variability of peak windspeeds in Britanny was quite large (at least 15 m/s) but by the time the storm had reached Sussex and Kent this variability appears to have declined (chiefly through a reduction in the peak gust speeds) such that all peak wind-speeds lie within a range of 5m/s. Along the course of the 1990 storm the range of variability of peak windspeeds in Cornwall was also around 5 m/s, but in passing towards the east this had increased to more than 10m/s in south-east England. It appears that the texture of the storm had become less dense, a smaller proportion of the area affected being subject to the most severe gusts.

This difference can be seen just as clearly in the composition of extreme gusts observed in continuous wind-speed records of the two storms. The record from Shoeburyness, Essex for the 1987 storm showed a peak gust speed of 45 m/s while that from Bristol for the 1990 storm showed a peak gust of 41m/s. (In both cases anemometer recordings have been employed that showed peak gusts of around 95% of the highest wind-speed recorded within 100km of the site.) For both records the number of gusts that reached to within >95%, >90%, >85% and >80% of the peak gust has been plotted in Fig 2. It will be seen that there are around three times as many gusts for all categories in the 1987 storm (ie. a higher fractal dimension) relative to the 1990 storm. (The reason that the 1987 storm was 'dense' was because there were many gusts close to the maximum. In contrast if one or two extreme gusts had not intercepted the recording station in 1990, as evidently happened at many stations along the path of the storm, then the peak gust recorded could have been > 5m/s slower.)

The distinction between these storms can be seen even more markedly by comparing the distribution of peak windspeeds in a 100km wide transect at right angles to the storm's path (Fig. 3). The 1987 storm shows a very

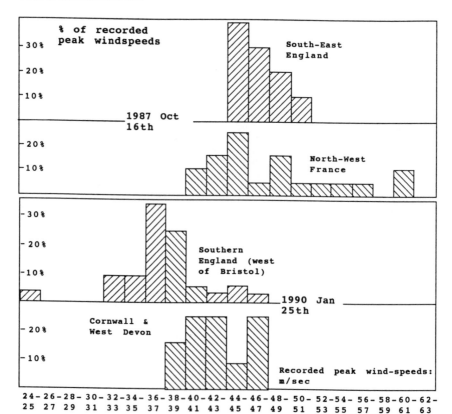

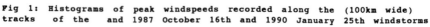

Fig 1: Histograms of peak windspeeds recorded along the (100km wide) tracks of the and 1987 October 16th and 1990 January 25th windstorms

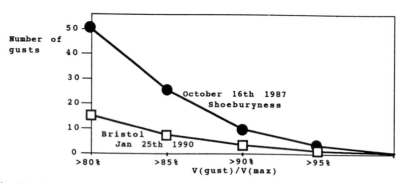

Fig 2: Number of gusts approaching the peak gust speed in windspeed records of the 1987 Oct 16th and 1990 Jan. 25th windstorms

520

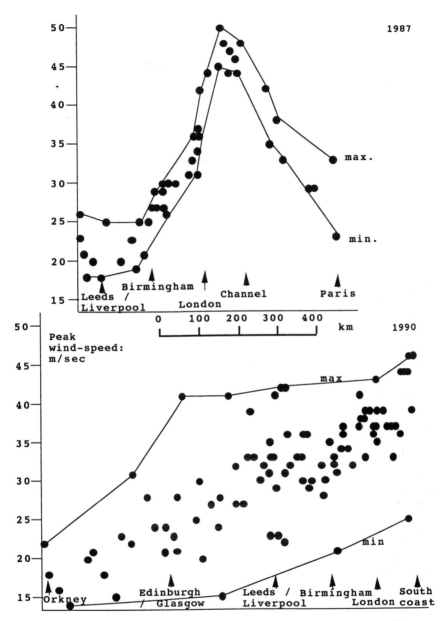

Fig 3: Cross-sections of recorded peak wind-speeds orthogonal to the paths of the Jan 25th 1990 and Oct 16th 1987 windstorms

steep peak wind-speed gradient on its north-west flank consistent with the location of the centre of the depression. Across the whole storm there is very little variability (generally less than 5 m/s) in recorded peak gust speeds. In contrast while the transect across the 1990 storm shows a general increase in peak windspeeds, in passing towards southern England the variability of even this general trend is everywhere around 10 m/s. However amidst this trend there are a small number of recorders, even in northern England, that experienced peak gust speeds comparable with those of southern England. Clearly this was not a simple depression. From the path of a weather balloon launched in the midst of the storm in south-west England two separate high velocity zones were detected in the atmosphere (ref. 8), implying a compound cyclonic disturbance. It is evident that one cannot simply contour the 1990 windfield, except in terms of the relative proportion of different areas of the overall windfield that appear to have been affected by peak gusts of different speeds. As the work done by the wind (and hence the consequential damage) is proportional to the third power of the windspeed (dynamic pressure multiplied by the run of the wind), in terms of damage potential the mean of the peak-windspeed in any region may best be considered as the root mean cubed of the recorded peak windspeeds.

The windfield footprint of extreme winds is accumulated during the passage of a storm like brush strokes painting a wall. Some windstorms contain a relatively sparse distribution of severe gusts from the upper air masses, and hence the footprint of severe wind-speeds remains very patchy. In other storms the number of these extreme eddies is so great that in effect almost every area of ground is covered with one or more severe gusts. This variability gives the windfield footprint a 'texture'. Within this texture there may be some kind of characteristic scale (as determined by the typical individual size of an extreme gust). Such scale effects, best seen in the spatial distribution of damage among some widely distributed uniform 'proxy' wind-speed indicator, such as foresttrees or house roofs, typically reveal gust dimensions of hundreds of metres. Such scale effects are important to insurers who may need to avoid potential concentrations of loss. Once it was assumed that variations in damage probably accorded with some influencing factor such as topography. The behaviour of low-level airmasses within a windstorm is now recognised as a chaotic, and hence largely unpredictable, phenomenon. Following the 1968 gale in central Scotland an aerial surveyor of the tree-fall reflected that 'it would be untrue to say that the logic of the damage pattern was wholly clear from a bird's eye view' (ref. 9).

In the absence of any direct instrumental evidence of internal structure the range of peak wind speeds in a windstorm footprint is most readily handled as a gust density function. The 1987 windstorm was high density; the 1990 storm was low density. Published attempts to contour peak windspeeds have traditionally and mistakenly assumed that the wavelength of variation is greater than the separation of the instruments. For a low density windstorm contouring nearest neighbour peak windspeeds is both highly subjective, and also nonsensical, as can be seen from two contrasting attempts to map the 1990 Jan 25th windstorm over southern England from the same data-set (refs., 10 & 11).

AN INTENSITY SCALE FOR WIND

The most important resource from which to explore the hazard of windstorms is detailed accounts of past storms. However in order to make use of this resource it is necessary to translate damage information into peak wind-speeds.

In the late 19th Century earthquake intensity scales were established in Italy loosely based on the twelve point Beaufort scale for wind. These earthquake intensity scales continued to evolve through the 20th Century, becoming more and more detailed and multifactorial. In contrast the Beaufort scale remained almost unchanged. This reflects a contrast in the development of rival instrumentation in the two sciences. Windspeed recorders first became employed around 1900, but the equivalent instrument for earthquakes is the strong motion recorder, which did not become generally established until the 1960s, and was not widespread until the 1980s. Instrumental data effectively stunted the evolution of the Beaufort scale, while intensity for earthquakes has remained a fundamental concept, gaining new vitality through the potential it offered for reconstructing pre-instrumental earthquakes.

In attempting to determine a correlation between windspeed and damage it is important to ensure that the wind-speed recorder and the damage affected area have experienced the same windfield. Hence wherever possible the calibration of wind-speed and damage data should be based only on high density windfields in which recorded wind-speeds give an accurate picture of the prevailing peak gust speeds. From empirical observations it appears impossible to calibrate damageability data with peak wind-speeds with a resolution much better than about 5m/s and in the construction of a wind intensity damage scale, this has been taken to be the size of individual intensity increments.

Every class of structure, moveable or immoveable, fabricated or organic has its own vulnerability function that determines the degree to which there is disruption or damage as a function of wind-speed.Since 1970 there have been a series of severe windstorms in Northwest Europe for which there exists a very detailed coverage of windspeed information, with peak gust speeds up to, and in excess of, 50 m/s. These windstorms provide numerous examples of different classes and degrees of damage, some of which have been studied statistically (refs. 12, 13, 14, 15). Out of all this experience data a multifactorial Wind Intensity Damage Scale ('WINDS') has been constructed with 5m/s increments, designated with Roman numerals: (beginning at a peak windspeed of 25m/s). The full documentation of the scale is to be discussed elsewhere. As an illustration the definition of Intensity IV (40-45m/s) is given as:

Intensity IV (Peak windspeed 40-45m/s)

Large isolated areas of high tree-fall in woodlands, although overall tree fall is only around 5%. Widespread (up to 40%) minor damage to domestic roofs and chimneys. Some gable ends of houses damaged. Significant proportion of greenhouses, light sheds and traditional (unbaled) haystacks blown away. Small proportion of barns severely damaged. Isolated minor damage to churches, and public buildings: roof lead occasionally rolled. Small proportion of untethered caravans overturned, as well as some light lorries. Small proportion of signal posts, road signs etc, blown over. Occasional well built brick factory chimneys blown down. Sea-salt blown many kilometres inland.

Historical descriptions of a storm rarely contain all the detail that is necessary to apply the full range of factors in the scale. However this is no different to the problems encountered in applying intensity scales to historical descriptions of earthquake effects. The key to intensity assignment is to identify which factor is of greatest significance. This is generally not an individual account of damage but rather some estimate

of the relative proportion of properties, trees etc. affected. Sometimes
the descriptive detail is so meagre and the uncertainty of intensity
assignment so great that it is necessary to assign more than one
potential intensity grade. However the purpose of assigning intensities
is to be able to map the overall windfield footprint and the degree of
variability that exists in the peak gust speeds across this footprint.

For well documented storms numerous accounts of damage can help define
the regional intensity field, with as much variance as exists in a modern
windfield defined from instrumentally determined wind-speed data.

WINDSTORM HAZARD

Having collected primary documentation on a large number of major
historical windstorms and mapped the damage information using WINDS
intensity it has proved possible to identify some key features of
windstorms that relate to the overall understanding of hazard. The
historical record suggests that most damaging windstorm events can be
characterised in a small number of classes. Principal among these are the
'pseudo-hurricane' and the 'broad-track' windstorms.

The 1987 narrow track (with peak windspeeds restricted to a zone
typically 80-150km wide), high density, high wind-speed event is the most
distinctive and through the combination of high winds speeds (typically
up to, or in excess of, 50m/s) and high gust density causes the greatest
concentration of losses. These features give it something of a
'pseudo-hurricane' character, although of course neither the physics of
the disturbance nor the severity of windspeeds are comparable. Similar
'pseudo-hurricane' events include storms in 1968 and 1739 in central
Scotland, 1756 around the Scotland-England border, 1661 across central
England, 1800 along the southern Channel, and 1581 in northern France.

The second class of severe storms is typically broad (peak windspeeds
distributed over a band 200-400km wide) with a relatively low gust
density windfield, but with windspeeds reaching up to 45m/s. A good
example of a storm of this character is the 1976 January 2nd-3rd storm
through northern England and the south North Sea.

Some storms are more complex. The 1990 January 25th could be considered
as a combination of these two storm classes, and probably consisted of
two interacting cyclonic disturbances. This storm also illustrates the
propensity for a storm to change its windfield character along its path,
in particular when passing over land. At landfall this
event was a high density storm but after about 200km of rough terrain
hadbecome converted to a low density storm.

As the most severe and damaging events across north-west Europe gain some
of their momentum from the jet stream, tracks of damaging storms tend to
trend between north-east and south-east with the most dominant
orientation being almost due east. There is a clear latitudinal variation
in storm frequency, with a concentration of storm tracks along the
north-west continental margin of Scotland and Norway. The severe storms
of 1987 and 1990 January 25th suggest a concentration of storm paths in
southern England, and taking just 20th Century (ie instrumental) data it
would appear that the southern Midlands of England are free from such
events. However this impression is contradicted by the last twenty years
of the 19th Century when there were three severe storms through this
region (see Fig. 4). This is a powerful demonstration of the importance

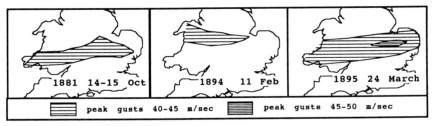

Fig. 4: Storm tracks of three late 19th Century storms through the English Midlands

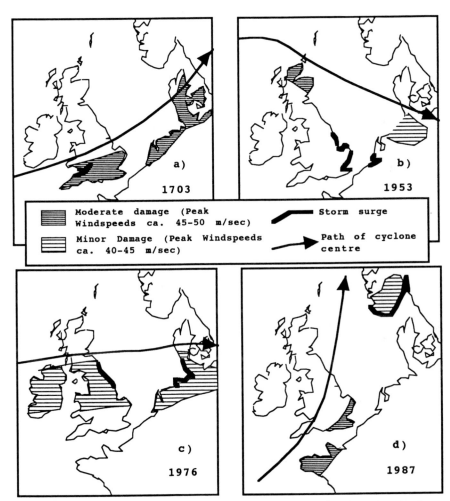

Fig. 5: The relationship between storm-surge and storm-track for four characteristic NW European windstorms

of exploring hazard over suitably long time-periods. The historical record of severe windstorms suggests that the recurrence of extreme windstorms is more uniform across England than is suggested from a simple extrapolation of the short-term record of instrumental wind-speeds (ie. by analogy with earthquakes, that there is a regional variation in b value).

A number of events in the historical record can be shown to have had larger areas of extreme (45-50 m/s) windspeeds than the 1987 storm, and some also indicate higher windspeeds. In particular the 1839 January 6th-7th windstorm through Ireland and northern England stands out as the most damaging event of the past two centuries in Britain with windspeeds locally in excess of 50m/s (refs. 16 & 17).

The reconstruction of the windfields of past windstorms can assist in microzonation: the identification of particular localities where windspeeds are consistently lower or higher than the surrounding regions, chiefly as a result of the windward topography. The highest surface friction is created by the irregularity presented by numerous buildings, so that cities have a pacifying effect on near-surface winds, although increasing low-level turbulence. Major atmospheric waves in the lee of mountains can have the effect of raising surface wind-speeds. Such an effect is notable at the city of Sheffield, where very widespread damage can be found to have been concentrated in a number of westerly gales, most famously in 1962 February 16th-17th when 110,000 houses were damaged and 100 destroyed (ref. 18). Although largely forgotten a similar concentration of damage was encountered in a windstorm on December 16th 1873 when around ten people were killed in the city and, as in 1962, a disaster committee was instituted to organise relief (ref.19).

STORM SURGES

Storm surges are generated by a combination of wind stress on the sea-surface and by barometric pressure differentials. The first effect is generally the dominant one, as pressure differentials on their own can only make a difference in sea-elevation of a few tens of centimetres, although this can become amplified where a storm passes from deep to shallow water or where there is a natural funnel in a coastline. The largest surges are produced by the most intense windstorms. A particular storm track defines the movement of the low pressure centre and the orientation of prevailing winds, and hence generates a surge in a specific area. The distribution of shallow seas in Northwest Europe is relatively complex and this in turn makes for a wide range of possible storm surge events. The impact of any surge event is however ultimately determined by the fortuitous conjunction with the astronomical tides. Hence there is no simple correlation between storm severity and the ultimate elevation of a sea-flood. Four 'typical' storm surge events accompanying four different tracks of severe historical windstorms are illustrated in Fig 5.

a) The December 7th - 8th 1703 windstorm was one of the most severe ever known across southern Britain (ref. 20). From intensity mapping of the very widespread destruction, windspeeds up to 50m/sec, but with a moderate gust density, are indicated over a wide track passing ENE from western Britain through the Netherlands into northern Germany and Denmark. A storm surge was generated in the Bristol Channel, that became amplified in the outer Severn estuary where towns on both coasts were flooded to a depth of more than 1m. In the river Avon, the surge reached more than 2.5m inundating the Bristol docks, causing considerable losses to cargo. This surge occurred five tides before springs, an even higher storm surge flood accompanied a storm in January 1606.

b) The 31st January 1953 storm involved severe windspeeds in north-east Scotland with peak gust speeds in excess of 45m/sec. An unusual storm track passing first to the east and then southeast around northern Scotland, accompanied by severe northerly winds, generated a significant storm surge in the early hours of February 1st. This surge was 2.2-2.5m high around East Anglia and the outer Thames estuary, causing major flooding, although the surge generally arrived after high water. On the southern Netherlands coasts in Zeeland and Zuid-Holland the maximum surge of 4m arrived ahead of high water, but still had an amplitude of almost 3m through high tide (ref. 21). In combination with the wave action more than 50 dykes were overwhelmed, flooding around 2,000km^2, destroying 1000 farms, and drowning around 1800 people.

c) In the 2nd - 3rd January 1976 storm highest windspeeds were observed on the Frisian islands (45m/sec), although windspeeds of over 40m were recorded at a number of locations in central England causing the destruction of almost 1 million m^3 of timber. A storm surge was recorded all along the coast of England on January 3rd advancing from the northern North Sea, with water levels in the north higher than those of 1953 although lower to the south. The only town to suffer flooding on this coast was Cleethorpes at the mouth of the Humber. However the storm surge was far more severe on the north German coast rising to levels never previously recorded, reaching 6.45m above mean sea level at Hamburg (4.65m above mean high water). Fortunately dykes had been raised after the 1962 (0.85m lower) storm surge although the Hamburg port area was flooded causing insured lossses of DM500 million. This event is typical of easterly tracking storms that pass across central Britain and the southern North Sea, and is perhaps the most common of all the major storm-surge events in the region. The Grote Mandreke drowning of January 15th 1362, when many parishes vanished completely along the coast of Schleswig Holstein, with an estimated 11,000-30,000 deaths, accompanied one of the most damaging windstorms known from the historical record of southern central Britain, with a ENE trending storm track.

d) The October 16th 1987 storm was a narrow-track high density storm system that passed to the north-east across Britanny and south-east England. 7.2 million m^3 of timber was lost in France, 3.9 million m^3 in England. The channel crossing was too short to generate a significant surge, but in passing across the North Sea a surge reaching 1-1.9m above expected levels developed around southern Norway (ref. 1), causing greatest damage in the sheltered Oslo Fjord, where a large shipment of recently unloaded Japanese cars was inundated.

These four storm surge events are illustrative of the combination of windstorm tracks and surges. However there are many other storm - surge combinations that can be found in the historical record, affecting different sections of coastline. For example the western coast of Sweden, including the port of Gothenburg, is prone to storm surges, as in the great Christmas Day 1717 windstorm, the same event that caused catastrophic flooding along the south-east coast of the North Sea from northern Holland to Schleswig Holstein (southern Denmark) taking 11,000 lives. Storm surges also affect the eastern coast of the Irish Sea and are particularly damaging in the low-lying coastal plains around

NATURAL DISASTERS

Lancashire and north-eastern Wales. On February 26th 1990 a windstorm generated surge of around 2.5m broke sea defences at Towyn, on the North Wales coast, flowing 2km inland and flooding 750 properties, most of them single storey with up to 1.5m of water, some of which ponded for several weeks. The south coast of England is also prone to storm surges, the port of Plymouth was flooded in the 1990 January 25th storm. On January 1st 1877 a storm surge flooded many channel ports, including Southampton, Weymouth and Dover.

The landfall for windstorms can be anywhere along the Atlantic coast of Europe. The Irish ports of the south and west coasts suffer occasional inundation (as in surges in 1974), and the coasts of Belgium, and the Pas de Calais region have also been affected. One very intense storm passed through southern Portugal on February 15th 1941, creating a storm surge accompanied by waves up to 18m high that flooded the main square in Lisbon. The storm destroyed 600 boats in one Portuguese port, and caused damage equivalent to half the country's annual budget (ref 22).

DISCUSSION

An appropriate response to windstorm hazards has traditionally been left to engineers who base their decisions on the probability of exceedance of windspeeds or sea-levels at a single location. However society needs to have a holistic view of total windstorm effects and impacts, to determine the economic cost of protection relative to the potential benefits to human life and property. In particular it is necessary to explore the overall economic and human consequences of low probability events. Traditionally the only time a society takes effective action in disaster mitigation is following a major catastrophe, or if it is fortunate, a major near-catastrophe. As a result losses tend to be highest in those areas that have been fortuitously free of events for a long period. The 1987 and 1990 windstorms were far more damaging in the calm wind-climate of southern England than they would have been in wind-buffeted western Scotland.

For critical installations, such as nuclear power stations, low-probability extreme wind-hazard should be considered not simply in terms of conventional wind engineering definitions of loading, but with regard to the spatial and temporal context of the whole storm event. Extreme storms will disrupt national electricity supply and telecommunications, and for coastal locations extreme winds can generate extreme storm surges. The most severe storms (such as 1703) are commonly accompanied by tornadoes and thunderstorms. As in hurricanes, a major contributor to damage, in particular to cladding, comes from aerial missiles of debris.

Windstorm hazard also cannot be considered time-independent. A particular conjunction of warm and cold air-masses in the North Atlantic can act as a breeding ground for highly energetic cyclones, producing a sequence of damaging storms tracking along the jet-stream. Such a sequence was observed through late January and February 1990, involving at least four systems that caused significant losses, over varying areas of Britain, France, Germany and the Netherlands. Similar sequences are known from earlier periods: as for example through December 1792 across Britain and the southern North Sea (ref. 1).

Storm surges are sufficiently common around the south-eastern North Sea to have been the chief concern of regional governments in all the affected countries for several centuries. Major campaigns of sea-dyke construction around the southern North Sea occurred in northern Germany following the disastrous 1717 December 25th surge (in which 11,000 lives were lost), and again following the 1795 December 11th surge that rose 0.4m higher. Although dykes were raised another metre, the storm surge of 3-4 February 1825 still took 800 lives. After the 1962 storm surge when 16% of Hamburg was flooded and 315 people died, DM 1.7billion was spent on bringing sea defences up to +9m a.s.l. Following the 1976 storm surge, dykes were also raised along the western coast of Jutland sufficient to contain much of the storm surge of 24th November 1981 when water-levels at Esbjerg and Ribe reached up to 5m higher than predicted.

Following the 1953 storm in the Netherlands dyke-heights were calculated on an annual probability of exceedance of 10^{-4} (based on a combination of tidal elevations, predicted storm surges and wave exposure). As the very existence of the nation depends on storm surge defence the topic has a fundamental national priority. In the preparation for the construction of the Thames barrier attempts were also made to calculate the 10^{-3} and 10^{-4} annual probability storm surge elevations. However in most regions there is no simple uniform concept of risk level, and where events are uncommon, or recording is inadequate, the 10^{-4} event may itself be very imperfectly predicted. Elevations of sea-defence are generally based on some political balance determined by the cost of raising defences relative to the value of assets at risk. This produces a relatively ad hoc approach to storm defence. The annual probability of flooding as a result of overtopping or breaching of sea defences for low lying communities along the eastern coast of England passes from 10^{-4} up to higher than 10^{-2}. The rise in global eustatic sea-levels, at least since the end of the little Ice Age, combined with continued sinking around the southern North Sea (chiefly from forebulge subsidence associated with the Fennoscandian postglacial rebound dome) means that all sea-defences are subject to an increasing risk of breaching or overtopping.

The response to storm surges is particularly critical because traditional forms of sea-dyke protection create a 'cliff-edge (or more appropriately dyke-crest) effect' whereby communities expand in a false sense of security and the casualties caused when an overtopping or breaching event occurs are much greater than if the 'protection' had never been established. Sea-dykes began to be constructed from the 12th Century AD in the Netherlands, as a means of reclaiming highly fertile farmland. Before that time, in the area potentially flooded by storm-surges, settlements were only established on dwelling mounds. Major losses of life in storm surges in the 13th and 14th Centuries may reflect more an inadequate and over-complacent response to the hazard that followed the initial stages of protection, than a genuine increase in event magnitude.

In well protected countries, along the southeastern North Sea the 'cliff-edge effect' means that one passes rapidly beyond the 10^{-3} -10^{-4} annual probability of exceedance from no casualties to casualties on a Medieval scale (>10,000?). Storm surge protection should also consider the longer term perspective: that as the land continues to sink and compact, and sea-levels continue to rise, the potential disasters that will be associated with a breach of the defences become increasingly catastrophic. In contrast low levels of protection and occasional flooding along parts of the British coast discourages accumulations of concentrated value, and offers a realistic reminder of the hazard. It can also encourage sedimentation to proceed, the only absolute way of protecting the land. However, as in the Third World, this casual approach reduces property prices, creating concentrations of the most vulnerable (such as the elderly), as at Towyn, flooded in 1990.

In historic storms (in the absence of a storm-surge) the large proportion of loss of life was at sea. Several thousand sailors were lost in the 1703 storm, and several hundred in each major windstorm in the early 19th Century. Weather warnings to sailors were started around 1860 (soon assisted by the introduction of the telegraph) and harbours prevented ships leaving when storms were forecast. Also throughout the 19th Century regulations were introduced concerning seaworthiness. These two practices had a dramatic effect on reducing marine casualties in storms by almost two orders of magnitude.

The most significant onland casualties from the effects of wind in this region are known from northern France: in the 1581 Easter Day windstorm at the village of Bresles, near Beauvais, the stone belltower fell through the church in the middle of Mass causing 23 deaths and 54 wounded (ref 23). In a windstorm in 1757 the collapse of a theatre in a windstorm at Havre de Grace killed an estimated one hundred playgoers (ref. 24). Despite the introduction of wind-loading requirements in domestic building regulations, onland losses of life in windstorms have shown no significant fall since the 19th Century, any gains in structural stability being more than offset by the human desire to share the suburban environment with highly hazardous trees.

As a result there are significant reductions in windstorm fatalities at night. In England the indoor casualties (from failures of chimney stacks, roofs, walls and trees on buildings) were five in 1987 (peak winds 2-6 a.m.) and six in 1990 (peak winds 11a.m. - 2 p.m.), but the outdoor direct casualties in 1990 (42) were six times higher than in 1987, 29 involving tree fall, 21 of these in vehicles. For comparison, in the night-time storm of 1703 (peak windspeeds probably touching 45m/s) there were 21 indoor deaths in London alone (population less than 10% of that of today), almost all from falling chimney stacks (ref. 20).

The only community at present taking a holistic approach to windstorm hazard is that of insurers and reinsurers. The January - February 1990 winter storms occasioned insured losses greater than $7 billion. Annualised windstorm losses in north-west Europe can be expected to be significantly in excess of $1 billion/year. New computer aided underwriting tools employing the latest understanding of the windstorm hazard, (such as EQE's WindCap ref. 25), can assist in defining levels of premium appropriate to risk, and can help balance a reinsurance portfolio to guard against concentrations of value along a particular storm-track. As indicated by the $200 million losses (largely uninsured) accompanying the recent Ms5.2 Roermond earthquake (a decadal event in the populated regions of North-West Europe) windstorm losses in this region are around two orders of magnitude larger than those accompanying earthquakes.

The move towards an improved understanding of risk by the insurance industry will probably prove to be the factor that finally makes storm-surge hazard a political issue. Insurers will soon be armed with sufficient knowledge of hazard and vulnerability to encourage them to increase premiums or refuse cover (and consequently obstruct mortgages) in highly vulnerable coastal communities. The political outcry that follows should for the first time promote discussion as to the whole problem of windstorm hazard, and the difficult decisions that society must take in offering present protection without inviting future catastrophes.

REFERENCES

1. LAMB H. Historic storms of the North Sea, British Isles and Northwest Europe, p204 C.U.P., Cambridge, 1991

2. GOTTSCHALK M.K.E. Stormvloeden en rivieroverstromingen in Nederland: Deel I – De Periode voor 1400, Deel II – De Periode 1400-1600, Deel III De Period 1600-1700, publ. van Gorcum, Amsterdam 1971, 1975, 1977.

3. ROHDE H. Sturmfluthohen und sakularer Wasseransteig an der deutschen Nordseekuste, Die Kuste 1977 vol. 30, pp52-143, Heide i H. (Westholsteinsche Verlag Boyens & Co).

4. GRAM-JENSEN I. Sea floods – contributions to the climatic history of Denmark, p76 1985 Danish Meteorological Institute Climatological Papers No. 13, Copenhagen

5. MAEDA J. and ADACHI K. On the spatial structure of longitudinal wind velocities near the ground in strong winds, J. Wind Eng. & Industrial Aerodynamics, 1983 vol 15, 197-207.

6. MACKEY S. and KO PIUS K.L. Spatial configuration of gusts, pp41-52 in K.J. Eaton ed., Wind Effects on Buildings and Structures Proc 4th Internat. Conference, Heathrow 1973.

7. MARKLOW A.B. and LUNNON R.W.The comparison of winds at two sites at Gatwick Airport during early 1990, Meteorological Office Bracknell, Report 1990/54.

8. PINE W.S. A further note on the severe storm of 25 January 1990, J. Met 1991 vol. 16, 7-14.

9. NEUSTEIN S.A. Damage to forests in relation to topography, soils and crops, Forestry Commission Bulletin, 1971 vol. 45, 42-48.

10. HAMMOND J.M. The strong winds experienced during the late winter of 1989/90 over the United Kingdom: historical perspectives, Met. Mag., 1990 vol. 119, 211-5.

11. MCCALLUM E. The Burns' Day Storm, 25 January 1990, Weather, 1990 vol. 45, pp166-173.

12. BULLER P.S.J. Gale damage to buildings and structures in the United Kingdom, 2 January 1976, Building Research Establishment, Current Paper CP42/77.

13. BULLER P.S.J. Damage to buildings and structures caused by the gale of 16 October 1987, Building Research Establishment Note, 1988.

14. BULLER P.S.J. Damage to buildings and structures caused by the gale of 25 January 1990, Building Research Establishment Note 136/90.

15. SURREY WILDLIFE TRUST, After the Storm, Woking 1989.

16. SHIELDS L. and FITZGERALD D. The 'Night of the Big Wind' in Ireland, 6-7 January 1839, Irish Geography, 1989, vol. 22, 31-43.

17. MANCHESTER GUARDIAN Jan 9th, & 12th 1839.

18. THE TIMES Feb 19th, 1962.

19. THE TIMES Dec. 17th & 23rd 1873.

20. DEFOE D. The Storm: or, a Collection of the most remarkable casualties and disasters which happen'd in the late dreadful Tempest, both by Sea and Land, London, 1704.

21. QUARLES v. UFFORD H.A. The disastrous storm surge of 1 February, Weather, 1953 vol. 8, 116-121.

22. THE TIMES 1941 Feb. 17th, 18th, 19th.

23. LEBLOND V. Recueil Memorable d'aulcuns cas advenus depuis l'an 1573 tant a Beauvais qu'ailleurs, 1909 Publications de la Societe Academique de l'Oise, p7.

24. GENTLEMEN'S MAGAZINE, April 1757, p6.

25. MUIR WOOD R., NUNEZ I. & SCAWTHORNE C. New tools for estimating windstorm portfolio losses, EQE Review, Spring 1993, 1-5.

41. Promoting principles for better typhoon resistance in buildings—a case study in Vietnam

J. NORTON, Development Workshop, France, and
G. CHANTRY, GRET, France

Summary

There is no one solution to safe housing, but there are strong basic rules one can follow for making one's building safer. Making people aware of how they can achieve this - more easily and more cheaply than many think - takes time, and motivation is as much a factor as money. But the process is slow, and projects need time to achieve results that can be sustained and repeated.

1. BACKGROUND

1.1. The problem and context

Almost without fail each year typhoons sweep across the coastal plains of the central and northern areas of Vietnam, leaving behind them a trail of loss of life, massive destruction to property and infrastructure, and wastage of crops. In the aftermath of each typhoon, the population and the authorities mobilize to rehabilitate their region. Scarce resources of materials and money are consumed in the effort of reconstruction and relief: the same resources that could be far better used for the development of the region, where at present many subsist on rice and fishing. In effect the rehabilitation effort acts as a major break on the region's development efforts and capacities. Reducing the damage to buildings would thus make a major contribution to an overall improvement and development of living conditions, as well as allowing people to return as quickly as possible to normal living conditions. Damage prevention is thus an essential part of development action.

In the case of houses and public buildings of these coastal regions, much of the damage could be reduced, and in the case of minor typhoons even avoided, if only preventive steps were taken to make the buildings stronger and less at risk from typhoon damage. To do so, far less effort and money is required than gets used up in the annual reconstruction effort. Sadly, action to safeguard the home is often only done at the very last minute, or once the storm is already there.

In October 1985 two very strong typhoons struck Binh Tri Thien

Zone, (which was divided into the three provinces of Quang Binh, Quang Tri and Thua Thien-Hué in July 1989), in central Vietnam. Local authorities reported quite severe damage: 875 persons dead, 49,000 houses destroyed, 230,000 houses damaged, 2,600 classrooms destroyed or damaged, 6 hospitals and 250 health centres damaged. A UNCHS mission in March 1986 highlighted the fact that the most affected buildings - in terms of damage, loss of materials and difficulty in reconstruction - were the 'transition' houses - those neither traditional nor totally modern, but using a mixture of whatever materials and techniques people can afford - and small communal buildings. The mission also noted that what engineering know-how existed at national and provincial levels was not available to the builders most directly concerned with all types of building.

A UNDP proposal was made to provide funds for a three-project 'package' of assistance, with the Vietnamese Government, aimed at reducing damage in the future: improvement of flood/typhoon warning in Binh Tri Thien Zone; telecommunication facilities for flood forecasting and warning in the Zone; and demonstration of storm resistant building techniques the Zone. It is the third of these which this case-study describes (ref. 1).

1.2. Initial objectives

The overall objectives of the 'demonstration of storm-resistant building techniques' project were defined as attempting to address the situation identified in the UNCHS mission, through the organization of housing and small building vulnerability workshops. These workshops were to initiate activities to inform the local authorities and the public about measures that can be taken to reduce the impact of natural disaster on physical structures. A parallel objective was to assess the feasibility of replication of the programme and the techniques proposed at provincial and national level.

The outputs originally called for a series of training workshops for builders on how to build more disaster resistant houses and small buildings, linked to the construction of several demonstration prototypes. Simplified, illustrated building manuals for the use of local builders were to be produced. Results were to include local builders better trained in typhoon resistant building techniques, greater awareness amongst government institutions and departments on housing disaster preparedness, and provincial and national action plans for the establishment of a permanent capacity to implement a housing and small building vulnerability reduction programme.

In the event, considerably more was achieved, with a perspective to a more long-term sustainable programme.

2. TYPHOON-RESISTANCE OF EXISTING BUILDINGS

2.1. Overview

The majority of buildings in Binh Tri Thien Zone are small

534

Development Workshopellings with adjoining buildings for
kitchens, selling, workshops and animal sheds. Apart from a
few contemporary major public buildings (notably in Hué) many
of the public buildings use forms and methods similar to those
used in the smaller domestic building, and, from the point of
view of storm resistance, present similar strengths and
weakness. Most buildings, whether modern or old, can be
considered primarily in terms of a supporting framework
holding up the roof. The walls are in most cases light-weight,
and often contribute little to the structure. From the
viewpoint of typhoon resistance one can identify three main
"families" of construction: the traditional buildings;
buildings with a mixture of materials and techniques - the
'transition' house evolving towards the 'modern' dwelling; and
the local public buildings in the districts of each province.
The latter two are today jointly characterized by poor
detailing and frequent poor quality, and since they
increasingly represent the contemporary building stock of the
areas, they are a major preoccupation for typhoon resistant
construction.

Traditional buildings typically survive typhoons much better,
and some contemporary larger public facilities survive well
too. The frail thatched houses of the poor are rapidly
destroyed, and although these are the people it is hardest to
help with protection, their homes are nevertheless in general
quite quickly repaired.

2.2. Traditional buildings

Traditional buildings, whether on the scale of the palace and
the tombs and temples in the area or that of the house,
exhibit quite consistent characteristics: a framed structure
formed by many substantial heavy wooden posts and short span
beams, the whole held together by finely executed mortise and
tenon joints. The roof, often with hipped ends, is an integral
part of this vertical and horizontal framing. Between the
structural elements the walls are filled in with a variety of
materials, ranging from wattle and daub through to fired brick
or timber shutters. On older tiled roof buildings it is common
to see exposed masonry ribs which help hold down the roof
covering.

The combination of good jointing, small structural units and
large timber sections give the traditional building structural
integrity and stiffness, and these make traditional buildings
very able to resist typhoons.

Today increasing scarcity of timber has pushed costs up,
making the construction of a traditional house very expensive:
nevertheless, one still finds the traditional beautifully
executed timber frame used in new houses, where it is regarded
as a fine status symbol. Sadly, the quality of wall cladding
and roof covering are not always of similar standard, and this
is but one example of the second category of houses and public
building in the area: the transition building.

2.3. Contemporary habitat: the 'transition' building

Today, a much wider variety of materials and techniques of

building are employed than in the past, some of which are the hybrid forms of traditional building, others attempts to apply new techniques or to use new materials such as reinforced concrete, often without the necessary skill to do it well or the money to get things right. Others depend on using locally available grasses and bamboos. The construction of most houses is an ongoing process: with the difficulties of acquiring materials the various parts and elements that make up the building are often linked together in a haphazard manner, more influenced by what is available at the time than by what might best protect and secure the investment that is being made. These buildings are characterized by the weakness of the joints between elements, which thus easily fail; and by the increasing lightness and lack of rigidity in the structure and cladding, offering less resistance to high wind pressures. One sees 10cm thick masonry walls held by lime mortar with nothing to give them stability; or tiled roofs supported on flimsy structures where there is little to inhibit the tiles being blown off the roof. Everyone would like to achieve a local version of the 'modern house', epitomized by the use of a reinforced concrete frame and a flat concrete terraced roof: but in the meantime the step by step investment that is made in materials such as tiles, bricks and cement is at high risk from the frequent typhoons. Moreover, the execution of buildings even with good quality materials is becoming so bad that little resistance is provided against the effect of high winds. This is just as much a problem with small and medium sized public buildings as with domestic 'modern' construction.

2.4. Public buildings

Public buildings, although designed by technicians, are just as much at risk to storms. The weakness in detailing and execution are compounded by the design of the buildings: a trend towards high unframed structures, the use of gable end walls with little rigidity, large verandahs where the roof is greatly exposed to uplift. The effect of Typhoon Irving in 1989 typified this problem, with the major collapse of hospitals and schools in the Thanh Hoa province.

3. COSTS AND PRIORITIES

3.1. Costs

Even buildings little able to resist the effect of cyclones, are far from cheap. At 1989 prices, a thatch and bamboo frame structure cost 50,000 Dong/m2; a bricks and tile roof structure 200,000 Dong/m2, and a reinforced concrete structure with a concrete flat roof some 300,000 Dong/m2. Put these prices against the monthly wage of a local engineer, in the order of 45,000 Dong/month, and one has an idea of the magnitude of the investment. The affordability of housing appears even worse for village farmers and fishermen. When one considers that this investment is scarcely protected against the damage caused by a typhoon, it is easier to understand the impact of the cost of recovery after a typhoon to families and the state alike; and to understand the necessity of investing a bit more to make buildings and materials more secure.

3.2. Prevention or recovery?

Typhoons of varying intensity hit the Vietnam coast: small intensity 'yearly' typhoons, where damage should be small; medium '10 year' typhoons causing far more major damage: lighter buildings, notably those of thatch and bamboo walls, resist badly, and more solid buildings should resist better but invariably do not; and massive '100 year' typhoons which cause major devastation. The effect of typhoon winds for all but the frailest structures is progressive: in a medium typhoon, bamboo and thatch shelters frequently collapse rapidly under the initial buffeting of the wind. Damage to more substantial buildings comes in a sequences of events, where elements are weakened or loosened by pressure and suction: the tiles begin to lift on the eaves and ridges, the complete roof blows away, followed by the collapse of the roof frame. Walls are either flattened or carried off, depending on the structure. Rapidly, 70 or 80% of the building can be razed to the ground or blown away and 40 to 50% of the materials lost beyond recovery.

Against this cost and loss, comprehensive surveys carried out by project participants during 1989 and 1990 showed that an extra construction investment of 10% (on more solid buildings) to 30% (on thatch and bamboo shelters) would make most buildings able to resist small and medium scale typhoons. A major task of the programme was therefore to persuade people to spend time and money on preventive action in order to secure their investment.

3.3. Who builds and how?

Houses in the Binh Tri Thien Zone are built for the most part by local semi-skilled builders, employed in some capacity even in the simplest construction. The family invariably helps with the work too. Local materials are used for the most part. Little or no attention is paid to typhoon resistant construction details, and there are no applied regulations. When a typhoon arrives, last minute measures are taken to stop the tiles blowing off, or the walls collapsing, by which time it is often too late. Public buildings, designed by local technicians at provincial and district level, who carefully follow the rules for reinforced concrete design, have had habitually little attention paid to typhoon resistant detailing and form. The local building brigades and contractors who do the construction have often little contact with the designer, and pay even less attention to quality control: this sad state of affairs has become too often the accepted norm.

After a typhoon, the population and the province mobilizes in a major effort to reconstruct, but the quality of work that contributed to the collapse of the building beforehand is repeated: at the next typhoon the building will be just as much at risk. Thus the cost of recovery is compounded by its repetitive nature.

4. DEVELOPMENT WORKSHOP/GRET'S APPROACH AND OUTPUTS

4.1 Overall approach

NATURAL DISASTERS

As well as workshops for local builders, Development Workshop and GRET chose to implement a programme which also integrated workshops and seminars for provincial decision-makers and construction technicians and those involved in information dissemination. All of these are concerned with improving the understanding about cyclone resistant construction methods, with their dissemination to the general public, and their application in public and domestic building and have a part to play in an Action Plan for promoting typhoon resistant construction.

As such, the aim of the programme was not to build houses for people, or (in the main) to train builders, but rather to promote the building of safer houses and public buildings by families and the local authorities alike, and bearing in mind the considerable diversity in the ways in which people actually build and can afford to build. (See sections 2 and 3 above.) The programme had to reflect this diversity, and propose ideas which would enable the widest range of the population to have access to them.

In practice, the programme developed around three main seminar/workshop sessions, culminating in an Action Plan in each of Binh Tri Thien Zone's three newly-formed provinces.

4.2 Demonstration buildings

In response to the call for demonstration buildings, each workshop was accompanied by the design and construction of a modest public building (a primary school, a health centre and library). Builders were trained both through the practical work on these and through their participation in workshops. (In total 42 technicians and 36 builders were trained.)

But in practice, although the demonstration buildings provided good ground for showing ideas and for raising the profile of the programme, they were far from considered to be the central element of the programme.

4.3 Learning through surveys and participatory work

The programme focused in a sense much more on developing amongst the participants an appreciation of that which exists already in local building practice, and going on to establish a link for the participants between the theory of engineered design and standards - rarely applied in local practice - and the realities of building construction in Binh Tri Thien Zone. Thus, each set of workshop participants themselves surveyed the local building characteristics to identify weakness and potential strengths. These surveys were based on ten key points of typhoon resistant construction (see Illustration 1) put forward by Development Workshop/GRET and refined during the workshops. The surveys confirmed there were ample examples of good typhoon resistant design and construction techniques within existing building practices, on which to base recommendations for each individual province for domestic and small public building.

4.4 Technical dossiers

From these surveys in each workshop session for each province

Illustration 1: Ten Key Points of Typhoon Resistant Building

the participants produced illustrated dossiers serving as reference guides. Interestingly, the participants in the workshops rejected the idea of a technical building manual for wide dissemination, on the grounds that it would need to be very varied and complex unless it related to the specifics of a particular district or sub region, and thus difficult to use. Instaed they produced a short, clear document explaining the ten key points of typhoon-resistant construction, i.e. design principles rather than detailed building practices (ref. 2).

It should be noted here that once practical work on the sub-contract started, it became clear that technical knowledge about the realities of typhoon resistant building techniques was, at least at provincial level, much lower amongst technicians, with a few exceptions, than had perhaps been perceived at the time of the UNCHS mission, and that what knowledge there was had been highly theoretical, with little application on the ground. One important aspect was to draw attention to the cost of construction, for the average thatched house, for a transition building, and for local modern construction, and to estimate the extra cost incurred in making each type of building typhoon resistant. (See Illustration 2.) There had been little notion of what it would cost to make buildings safer.

4.5 Communication materials

The project was increasingly concerned with the exchange of information between technicians and builders, and the communication of techniques to the people in the province most directly involved with domestic building. Many locally applicable ways to communicate information about typhoon resistant construction techniques were explored, including using existing popular mobile video shows, and a variety of media were used aimed at various target groups: posters, videos, games, radio announcements, and a film, 'Our house resists the storm', starring a famous Vietnamese actress.

4.6 Public education campaigns

These materials were then used in two public education campaigns, which proved even more dynamic than might have been hoped, and which undoubtedly helped to raise the awareness both of the general public, and of decision-makers and technicians amongst government departments and institutions.

In the first prototype campaign, held in a District (i.e. at sub-provincial level), local institutions mobilized included the People's Committee, the Technical Services, the school 'Red Cross' brigades; the Disaster Preparedness Committee, District mobile videos and the local radio service were also used. In two weeks over 5000 people saw the video, numerous posters were distributed and commented on - and the programme participants gained ideas about how to improve on this already encouraging first campaign.

In the second campaign - a full-scale Provincial Public Education Programme - activities were multiple and rich. In Hué, the newspapers ran full page articles and press releases.

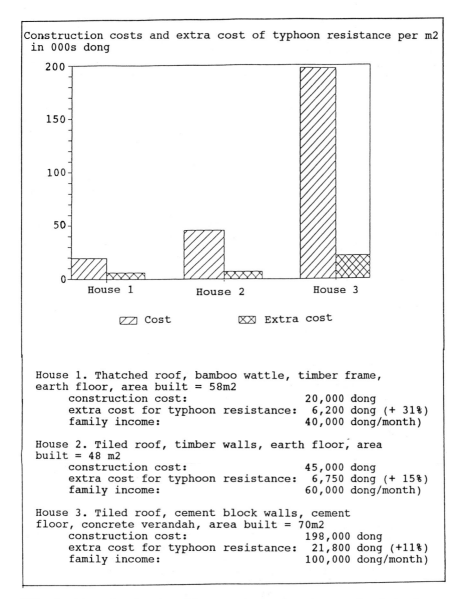

Construction costs and extra cost of typhoon resistance per m2 in 000s dong

House 1. Thatched roof, bamboo wattle, timber frame, earth floor, area built = 58m2
    construction cost: 20,000 dong
    extra cost for typhoon resistance: 6,200 dong (+ 31%)
    family income: 40,000 dong/month)

House 2. Tiled roof, timber walls, earth floor, area built = 48 m2
    construction cost: 45,000 dong
    extra cost for typhoon resistance: 6,750 dong (+ 15%)
    family income: 60,000 dong/month)

House 3. Tiled roof, cement block walls, cement floor, concrete verandah, area built = 70m2
    construction cost: 198,000 dong
    extra cost for typhoon resistance: 21,800 dong (+11%)
    family income: 100,000 dong/month)

Illustration 2: Construction costs and extra cost of typhoon resistant measures for various building types.

NATURAL DISASTERS

The project team toured the province and appeared on local TV with provincial leaders to carry the message further. Provincial and district radio announced the programme and the time of showings for the film 'Our house resists the Storm', watched each time by several hundreds of people before the showing of main feature films. Photo and drawing exhibitions showing activities against natural calamities were organized, and in schools competitions were held for poetry and drawing about the Campaign for Typhoon Resistance Building. Finally, throughout the province the Women's Union, The Youth Union and the Farmer's Union organized public gatherings on the same theme. All over the province over 2,500 large posters were shown in the main places of gathering, the markets, bus stations and cafés. On an officially-declared 'Provincial Day of Disaster Preparedness', youth brigades paraded in the streets of each District with special banners, and radio and TV ran special programmes. This campaign met with great enthusiasm and several Districts prolonged activities into a second month.

4.7 Implementing a provincial Action Plan

Overall, the framework for such activities has been the application of a provincial Action Plan which in the future will draw for its implementation in part on existing provincial funds but also on external funds as and when the latter are available for training new support teams. The Action Plan was defined to create the structure, expertise and supporting material necessary for providing practical assistance in cyclone resistant construction to the people of the region. It was based on the use of existing local technicians and local builders, the former to train and provide advice, the latter to provide practical advice through their involvement with most building activities on the private and public market. The Action Plan was developed collectively during the first seminar held for decision-makers and in their subsequent participation in the technicians' and builders' workshop which followed on directly from the seminar.

4.8. The 'Cyclone Resistant Construction' unit: a local capacity to operate the programme

Central to the Action Plan has been the development of a core team - the 'Cyclone Resistant Construction Unit' - first within the Institute of Building Design in Hué, and progressively in other provinces. The role of the core team was to provide in the future the coordination of the provincial programme for typhoon resistant construction, and to assure the design and production of documents and graphic materials needed to do so. They also undertake the training of provincial and district staff, and that of local builders. The core team has an ongoing role of programme evaluation and improvement of products and processes.

The constitution of the IBD core team, all of whose members participated in the workshops and seminars, has strongly influenced the ongoing activities of the project. Development Workshop and GRET staff felt that it was important that this team, who played a leading role in the project, should go through the experience of running training programmes in two

of the three provinces, and running the prototype Public
Education Campaign, on their own without the presence of
foreign experts. To facilitate this, materials and guide-lines
for running both activities were supplied by DEVELOPMENT
WORKSHOP/GRET, and they also had the communication and
technical dossiers that the participants themselves had
prepared in the first of the three provinces. After a joint
review, these were then translated into Vietnamese and
prepared as individual handouts to participants. The core team
rose admirably to the challenge and successfully ran both
types of activity, with evaluation and review jointly
undertaken between the second and third provinces.

One measure of the success over a relatively short period - 14
months in all - of such activities, was the public
announcement by the President of the 'third' Province (Thua
Thien-Hué) that he was pledging not only material but also
financial support to the campaign, a gesture of support and
confidence of considerable significance. At the start of the
project such public official recognition would have been hard
to envisage.

5. THE ACHIEVEMENT OF DEVELOPMENT OBJECTIVES

5.1 Impact

The impact of the project and the achievement of genuine
development objectives can in the long run only be assessed in
terms of less damage occurring in future typhoons. It is still
premature to make a real assessment of this sort, although in
areas where the programme has been run, damage levels are down
in subsequent typhoons which have hit the region in 1992,
albeit neighbouring areas still suffer.

The programme can realistically be seen to have achieved its
immediate objectives: a provincial institutional capacity,
embodied in the Core Team, has been developed with a working
methodology and Action Plan, to enable information to be
communicated to local authorities, local builders and the
general public about measures that can be taken to reduce the
impact of natural disaster on physical structures. At the same
time, the feasibility of replication of this approach on a
provincial and a national basis has not only been assessed but
also tested: the Core team from IBD have run programmes in the
Provinces of Quang Binh and Quang Tri. There is wider interest
at national level to see the spread of such programmes in this
decade of Disaster Preparedness.

On the ground, a large number of technicians and builders were
trained and several demonstration buildings were completed,
including some independently of the project itself using a
small surplus budget. There was a much greater level of
awareness of what can be done amongst the authorities of the
three provinces, thanks to the seminars and Public Education
Campaigns.

In terms of overall impact the project can be seen as
positive: the constitution of specially trained teams, a
process of training technicians and builders which has been
tried and tested, and the development of an excellent local

knowledge of 'what is possible'. Linked to the experience of
the public information campaigns, this represents a real
capacity to identify applicable techniques, evaluate them, and
undertake their diffusion. There have also been specific
achievements, such as the re-introduction in one demonstration
building of small holes on the underside of roofing tiles to
allow one to tie them down with wire to the battens - this
once common practice had disappeared.

5.2. Limitations

Nevertheless, after almost two years of sustained action, the
programme (as distinct from the project) must still confront
some major issues. It is clear that for the many families who
live in the thatch, branch and bamboo structures, there is
still very little chance that their home will resist more than
a strong storm: a major typhoon will cause damage and loss.
The extra cost of strengthening these buildings, small though
it is, is still very high to families whose income is
negligible. What money there is goes towards more immediate
day to day needs. It is realistic on the other hand to
envisage the improvement of transition buildings, to resist at
least a medium 'ten year' typhoon; but still there is
insufficient protection against the massive '100' year
typhoons, in reality much more frequent in recent years along
this coast, which destroy essential public infrastructure as
much as private homes. The economic situation of the country
and the people imposes severe limitations on what can in
reality be achieved.

For the individual family, the notion of spending extra scarce
resources on protection against a typhoon that may not hit
your home remains hard to accept: child vaccination has taken
time to become accepted; 'vaccinating' your home against
typhoon damage has much further to go before the idea of such
investment is popularized. There still needs much more
promotion and active demonstration in each commune and village
of the benefits that such strengthening brings. These remain
tasks for the years ahead.

6. TOWARDS SOME CONCLUSIONS

6.1. Long-term contacts

Efforts have been made to continue informal ongoing contacts
between the Vietnamese counterparts and the project
contractors. Development Workshop and GRET staff have
continued whenever possible to visit the Binh Tri Thien Zone,
and to have meetings in Hanoi with the local project staff.
This has been important. Nevertheless, for the long term
insertion of the programme into the annual round of activities
in typhoon effected regions, ongoing support inputs are
necessary. In short, a programme of 14 months would seem to us
to be too short to have a sustainable impact, despite local
commitment and skills.

6.2. Local level support

In the Action Plan's application, the experience of 1990
showed the very important role that the local institutions for

information dissemination, for education, and for political decision have to play in mobilizing resources - of people and money - and in complementing the skills of the more centralized institutions. In effect, it is important that future actions concentrate on mobilizing organizations and people at the village level, which represents the real local social unit, as well as developing the provincial institutional support and organizational capacity.

6.3. Meeting the 'on-cost'

It is also clear that, although the extra cost of strengthening buildings against typhoons is proportionately not great, it is still an extra cost, whether public or domestic, which is difficult or even impossible to afford. A programme of demonstration of typhoon resistant building techniques would have much greater impact if it could at the same time address the economic issue of how people can afford to make this short term investment in order to obtain the benefits of having much less to repair or replace after the next typhoon. Whilst ideas such as housing credits to the rural poor were almost impossible to consider in early 1989 in the region, much has changed since then, and lessons should be drawn from the examples of housing loan programmes linked successfully to disaster mitigation, as in Bangladesh. (Ref. 3).

6.4. The role of demonstration buildings

The project originally required demonstration buildings - new structures which show a variety of techniques, and give opportunities for training. Such buildings can play a significant symbolic role, provided that the purpose of the demonstration remains highly visible: that people can see the techniques - rather than have them, for example, covered with plaster. Demonstration should be an ongoing action. However, there is a much greater potential impact to be achieved through demonstrating how to 'retrofit' or rehabilitate existing domestic buildings so that people can see how their own existing buildings can be made stronger. This approach is both cheaper and closer to the reality of needs in many villages and communes. The lower cost of working with existing structures offers the opportunity of working in far more villages than is possible with a programme involving three or four new buildings.

6.5 The need for core-funding

The financial implication for Vietnamese counterparts of operating the programme with, in reality, very scarce resources, has posed a major potential threat to the efficient functioning of the programme. Each government institution has, since 1989, needed to progressively assure its own income and financial autonomy. This means that there are great pressures on an institute to sign contracts which are income generating, and which thus potentially conflict with a development project. Core funding both for ongoing operation of the information programme and to develop a suitable and accessible housing loan programme are necessities for the future, and show some signs of being achieved.

NATURAL DISASTERS

REFERENCES

1. The UNCHS/UNDP "demonstration of storm-resistant building" sub-project was implemented by a consortium of non-profit organisations, Development Workshop and GRET (B.P. 13, 82110 Lauzerte, France), in collaboration with two Vietnamese counterpart organizations: the Institute of Public Building (IPB), Hué - the principle partner - and the Institute for Housing and Public Building Design (IHPBD), Hanoi.

2. INSTITUTE OF PUBLIC BUILDING, Ghiai thich va huong dan 10 xay dung chong bao (Manual on the ten key principles of typhoon resistant construction), IBD with Development Workshop/GRET, Hué, 1990.

3. The examples of the Grameen Bank and of BRAC in providing housing loan assistance to the very poor amongst the landless rural population of Bangladesh provide models of action directed at resolving specific problems encountered by floods and typhoons. With extremely high repayment rates, the success of such programmes in terms of the scale of their impact and 'spin-off' socio-cultural benefits has been notable.

42. Data management for disaster planning

I. R. DAVIS, International Development and Emergency Relief
Consultants Ltd, UK, and D. BICKMORE, formerly NERC
Experimental Cartography Unit, UK

INTRODUCTION

The succession of disaster events in recent years has obliged
many governments, sections of the UN system and certain Non-
Governmental Organisations to overhaul their disaster
management information systems. This is to cope much more
effectively with increasing demands that flow from expanding
risks facing populations from various hazards.

This paper will look at the range of data that are required at
what stage in the planning process, certain problems in data
management and finally, assuming that some of the necessary
data are actually available, the development of a Geographic
Information System [GIS]. (ref.1)

PREREQUISITES FOR EFFECTIVE DISASTER PLANNING

Any major disaster affects a wide range of sectors of a
society which can include political, social, cultural,
environmental, physical, technological and economic aspects.
They also can strain the full resources of a given country.
Therefore attempts to reduce risks through effective disaster
preparedness, mitigation measures and efficient emergency
management are dependent on the mobilisation of all sections
of an affected community or even country. There are a number
of requirements for effective response:

1. Political commitment that is maintained at all levels of
   national and local government;

2. A governmental structure with clearly defined authority
   and an appropriate budgetary commitment to maintain
   effective disaster planning;

3. A realistic, up-to-date, well rehearsed preparedness plan
   that is comprehensive in scope, operational at all
   levels: [central, provincial and community] as well as
   being understood and accepted by the relevant authorities
   and the affected population;

4. An emergency management system, ideally the
   responsibility of the National Disaster Coordinating

Council [NDCC] under the chairmanship of the National Disaster Coordinator [NDC]. This system will need to be linked to designated responsibilities within line ministries.

5. A mitigation plan, leading to its application with a wide diversity of structural and non-structural measures.

6. The gradual 'normalisation' of disaster planning and implementation. This will require public education, the development of enabling legislation, emergency management, institution building and the application of resources. With such measures the safety of persons and the protection of property can ultimately be integrated into the culture of a society.

THE BROAD SCOPE OF DATA REQUIREMENTS

To serve such plans, systems and procedures for protection and emergency management a comprehensive disaster information system is required. This is a complex undertaking that can take many years to construct since it involves a wide spectrum of data requirements, but the essence of such a system is the efficient collection and processing of data. This can be broken down into a chain of requirements:
   - identification, selection, acquisition, verification, quality control to maintain uniform standards, storage, retrieval, maintenance, synthesis, analysis and finally the application of data.

All of these tasks are needed at some stage in the planning process, and our paper is concerned with the management and priorities for such information.

The identification and selection of data for Disaster Planning has to be based on the availability of reliable information on the range of topics. Some concern the normal functioning of government, linked with emergency planning procedures as well as good up to date topographic maps plus information on hazard, vulnerability and available resources. Some data is likely to be well defined, and logically organised whilst other information may not exist, or where available may be both fragmentary and of dubious quality. Uniformity of data is likely to be a persistent problem. These are the typical difficulties and discrepancies in a disaster planning system for a industrialised society, so within a developing country even wider gaps can easily be imagined in view of their limited professional resources to process and apply data. However, before dwelling further on the implicit difficulties it is necessary to review the data requirements in the stages of disaster planning and implementation.

DATA NEEDS IN THE VARIOUS STAGES OF DISASTER PLANNING

Thirteen categories of data are suggested in this paper to support preparedness and mitigation planning. This information is required within six stages of disaster planning, which are best conceptualised as a cyclical rather than linear process. This is because disaster planning is a continuous process that once started has to be continually developed to relate to a moving target with ever changing patterns of hazards, vulnerability and resources.

All the data noted below has to be related to the broad cycle of disaster management which is indicated on Fig.1. 'The Cycle of Disaster Planning in Six Stages'. This diagram indicates a logical sequence of actions for disaster planning, both in a pre-disaster context as well as management during and after an emergency. These progressive steps embrace pre-disaster actions that concern the initiation of disaster planning, the diagnosis of risk, deciding on levels of protection leading to detailed preparedness and mitigation planning [Stages 1, 2, 3 and 4] The diagram also indicates how post-disaster information on damage, casualties, recovery assistance etc can be usefully incorporated into the management system. [Stages 5 and 6]

Having established the sequence in the stages of disaster planning, it is possible to superimpose the data needs at each stage in the sequence. They are indicated on Fig. 2 'The Cycle of Disaster Planning in Six Stages: Data Needs'. Further detailed lists of data requirements that integrate information needed in all the stages of disaster planning are indicated in Appendix 1.

Stage 1   INCEPTION OF DISASTER PLANNING,
[to initiate a National Disaster Management System]

Whilst it is obviously desirable for responsible governments to establish disaster planning in stable conditions, with methodically planned action to protect their citizens, the normal process is for disaster planning to begin as a 'knee-jerk reaction'. Typically, there is a hasty response to political pressure, or public outcry after the failure of a given government to plan adequately for the disaster that is the focus of attention. Is also clear that once disaster planning has been started, further disasters, which may be in another country can act as a powerful stimulus to remind officials to maintain preparedness plans in a state of readiness.

The initiation process is often undertaken with minimal awareness of what plans have to be made, and what information is needed to inform the decision makers. Ultimately data has to be available on the full scope and detailed nature of the system of disaster planning, including the legal framework of the system. This information provides the basis for the entire planning process for preparedness and mitigation. However, it is not uncommon for public officials in one of the key line ministries of a government to be unaware of the scope of disaster planning that relates to their own ministry.

Stage 1 Data Requirements:

1.1 Disaster Planning System Data:
Data is needed on the Disaster Planning System, who is designated to do what, where, when, how, with whom and under whose authority.

549

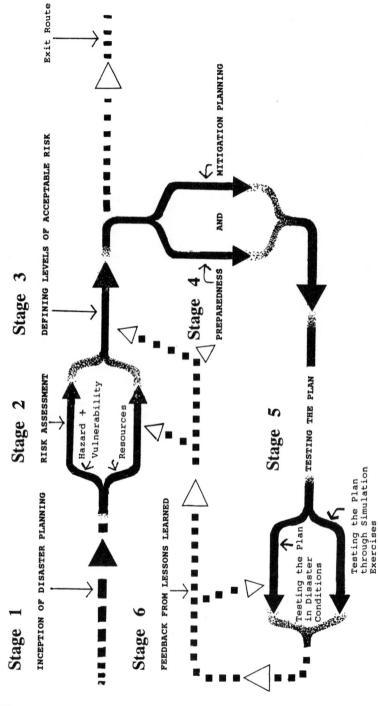

Fig. 1. The cycle of disaster planning in six stages

Stage 1 — INCEPTION OF DISASTER PLANNING

Stage 2 — RISK ASSESSMENT
Hazard + Vulnerability
Resources

Stage 3 — DEFINING LEVELS OF ACCEPTABLE RISK

Stage 4 — PREPAREDNESS AND MITIGATION PLANNING

Stage 5 — TESTING THE PLAN
Testing the Plan in Disaster Conditions
Testing the Plan through Simulation Exercises

Stage 6 — FEEDBACK FROM LESSONS LEARNED

Exit Route

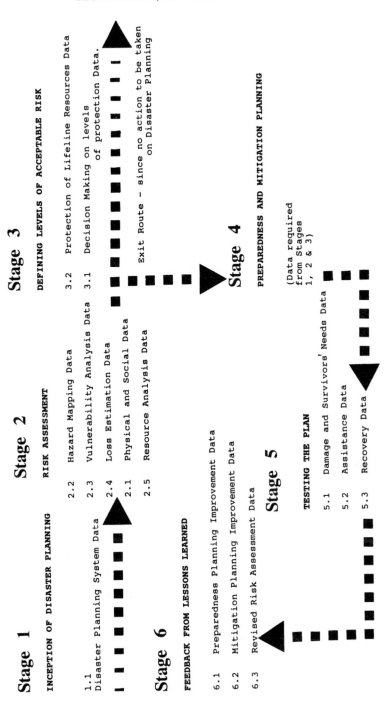

Fig. 2. The cycle of disaster planning in six stages: data needs

NATURAL DISASTERS

Stage 2   RISK ASSESSMENT

The aim of this diagnostic process is to balance known Risks against available Resources. Whilst measures to reduce risks logically must begin with this assessment process, nevertheless this vital diagnostic process is often omitted, or tackled half-heartedly. This results in authorities planning their economy or infrastructure to resist threats that may not be serious, or conversely that may well exceed expectations.

Risk assessment can be regarded as a five part process that takes place in a logical sequence:
First, there is the need for Physical and Social Data, followed by the assessment of potential Disaster Risks through a combination of Hazard Mapping , Vulnerability Analysis and Loss Estimation. Having measured the likely problem the final step is the Analysis of Resources.

2.1 Physical and Social Data

'Base-line data' are needed to provide a solid 'chess board' on which all subsequent hazard, vulnerability and resource data have to stand.

A key requirement is the need for topographical mapping.
The tradition in most western countries is to make topographic maps at a range of scales often from 1/25k to 1/250k, whilst attempting to maintain some consistency between scales. The nature of the topography and the nature of the risk will both determine what can be legibly displayed on a standard map sheet. One of the merits of holding information in a database is that only selections of the data need be instantly displayed for a user at any one time. This permits much greater data quantities to be held in the database and rapidly and coherently accessed. But up to date, topographic mapping, even at 1/50k or 1/100k, is still far from being universally available.

A further requirement is to know the population density and distribution in the areas at risk. Census data, if accurate, can provide such information, and may also reveal vital additional details on such matters as population age profiles, the mobility of communities over time and occupational patterns. Such data can be invaluable tools as a basis for risk assessment.

Stage 2 Data Requirements

[See Appendix 1 for a Summary of Locational Datasets that could be supported by a GIS Database, if reliable data and trained staff are available.]

2.1 Physical and Social Data:
These have to include topographical maps at appropriate scales, and census data etc.

2.2 Hazard Mapping

Hazard mapping reveals the areas which are particularly

susceptible to seismic, volcanic, flood, drought, avalanche and high wind forces. Hazard information is needed in spatial and temporal terms on such matters as location, frequency, duration and severity [ie wind speeds, water flow data etc]. The data is obtained through local scientific analysis as well as historical investigation of past hazard incidence. With this information it may be possible, in certain situations where data is available, to suggest contours that predict the severity of risk, [ie a map that indicates a 200, 100, 50, 20 and 10 year return period for a flood event]

Many forms of Hazard Mapping need to be undertaken at an international level. Examples include major projects to map the seismicity of the Balkan Region and hurricane risk facing the Caribbean, has been studied at a regional level. For such threats, which can affect a number of neighbouring countries, there will be value in a regional approach to hazard mapping.

However, whilst data is needed at this macro-scale, hazard information is also needed at the micro scale particularly when mapping hazards in urban areas. For example it will be vital to know which soils are subject to seismic liquefaction and which are not as essential information in developing land-use planning controls.

Stage 2 Data Requirements

2.2 Hazard Mapping Data:
Identification of areas prone to natural hazards. Spatial and temporal information is needed on the location, frequency, duration, severity and hazard characteristics.

2.3 Vulnerability Assessment

The next stage is to assess the vulnerability of persons or property to the hazard which has been mapped. This is another complex data collection process to determine elements 'at risk'. These include social, economic, cultural, political and physical/ environmental factors. Thus, for example, data on vulnerability will include information on such elements as: social groups- including age, gender and ethnic factors, patterns of land ownership, specific buildings, or parts of them, economic assets, agriculture and livelihoods. Whilst aspects of Hazard Mapping are required at a macro, regional scale, vulnerability analysis is always a 'site-specific' process with a concern for the unique characteristics of a local situation.

Stage 2 Data Requirements

2.3 Vulnerability Analysis:
These have to include data that identifies who and what is exposed to the hazard which has been mapped.

2.4 Loss Estimation Data

With detailed knowledge of hazards and vulnerability it may be possible to construct models that predict the impact of a given event in a specific time/place. Scenarios can be developed at various levels of sophistication that foresee casualty patterns, scales of damage and the secondary economic impact of the disaster in relation to varying scales of hazard impact. Such predictions have a wide variety of applications, in for example hospital planning and emergency management. Thus loss estimation provides a sharp focus for the introduction of risk reduction measures.

Stage 2 Data Requirements

2.4 Loss Estimation Data:
These have to include data on the anticipated consequences, in terms of deaths, injuries and damage patterns of various scales and types of hazards in diverse locations.

2.5 Resource Analysis

Assessment of hazards and vulnerabilities will reveal a range of critical problems which precede the final analysis, that of available resources, often termed an 'assessment of capacities'. In addition effective hazard and vulnerability assessment will provide a series of pointers that indicate the type and location of resources that are needed. For example, if the risk assessment in a cyclone prone area has revealed that a community of fishermen live in makeshift dwellings on an exposed beach, then a wise resource assessor would already be primed to know what to look for:

* community leaders to disseminate cyclone warnings;
* available safe land, or a community facility for an evacuation;
* a school teacher who could assist in developing a public awareness programme that addresses the risks that face this community.

Therefore the same team that conduct the vulnerability assessment may very usefully also be looking for the solution to the problems they have identified.

Local strengths or capacities can cover a wide diversity of elements: community coping mechanisms that help them to survive under adverse conditions, an inventory of local leaders and institutions that can fulfil a vital role in times of acute need, locally available skills, community facilities, such as a school that can provide temporary shelter, cash, credit, the location and quantity of goods that may be needed in an emergency, a local evacuation plan etc.

To summarise, risks need to be balanced by resources, including funds, with the ultimate aim of a safe, stable equilibrium. Therefore the diagnosis of risk is best regarded as a joint analysis of profit and loss, a positive and negative process.

Stage 2 Data Requirements

2.5 Resource Analysis Data:
These have to include an inventory of community coping mechanisms, local leadership and institutions, skills, labour, community facilities, cash, credit, emergency goods and vehicles, local preparedness plans etc.

Stage 3   DEFINING LEVELS OF ACCEPTABLE RISK

3.1 Decision Making on Levels of Protection:

Information gathered through the various processes in Stage 2 is then passed to political leaders in a suitable format to enable them to decide on a responsible course of action. Typical questions include:

* Should they initiate risk reduction measures to protect their citizens or are there other more pressing risks to address such as road safety or AIDS public information programmes?

* If they decide to proceed with risk reduction against natural hazards what level of protection is required? For example, should infrastructure be planned or upgraded to resist a flood that recurs every 20, 100 or 200 years?

* Should certain critical elements such as schools and hospitals be given extra levels of protection?

* What is the 'perception of risk' of the affected community?

Decisions on such matters are always difficult judgements concerning what is essential, sensible- in the light of other threats to the society that require urgent action, acceptable, affordable or politically expedient.

Stage 3 Data Requirements

3.1 Decision Making on Levels of Protection Data:
These have to include the summary of the data that supports the technical advice emerging from the risk assessment process. Data is needed to define who in which ministry is to make decisions in which sectors, [ie building standards, river controls, coastal protection, economic assets, lifeline facilities etc.]

3.2 Protection of Lifeline Resources:
Enhanced protection is needed to ensure that vital resources will survive hazard impact. The criteria to establish these targets for enhanced protection includes the following considerations:

- density of occupation;

- the age of the occupants, for example, one reason why schools tend to get higher protection than other public buildings is because children have a very long life ahead of them, and they are the future of any community. This poses an ethical issue as to whether on such grounds, a school should merit more protection than, say, a home for the elderly?

- cultural/ historical importance;

- emergency, life saving functions;

- the economic importance of the facility. For

example, a factory that is destroyed can adversely affect the entire economy of a region.

3.2 Protection of Lifeline Resources Data:
Which facilities: agriculture or economic asset require what level of protection? Therefore data on the type and location of such facilities is needed, such as medical facilities, schools, police stations, key governmental buildings, TV stations, public utilities, airports, bridges, key economic assets, livestock and crops etc.

In Fig.1 an exit route has been inserted between stages 3 and 4. This is to recognise that the elected leaders of some countries may decide in the light of the diagnostic data on potential risks presented through Stage 3, as well as other pressing demands on the public purse that it will not be realistic to undertake protective planning. But if it is decided to proceed, then the planning process is the next stage.

Stage 4. PREPAREDNESS AND MITIGATION PLANNING

The data needed for the planning process will have been collected in Stages 1,2 and 3 as noted above. This aims to provide the essential raw material to enable accurate protective planning to take place.

Stage 4 Data Requirements

4.1 Preparedness and Mitigation Planning:
These have to include the full data sets that are identified above in Stages 1, 2, 3 and 4.

Stage 5   TESTING THE PLAN
[in actual Disaster Situations and through Simulations]
In the representation of Stage 5, two ways are indicated to test the plans that are developed in Stage 4. One way is through simulation exercises and public drills. This approach is obviously a rather inadequate method to determine whether a preparedness plan will work or not and such plans do not begin to address the effectiveness of structural mitigation measures. But, short of testing under actual conditions simulation exercises and drills are the only substitute.

However, the acid test will be an actual disaster situation. Following such events there is a requirement for accurate information on the impact of the event in terms of deaths, injuries and damage to property as well as the specific needs of the surviving population. Such impact data must include knowledge of the developing disaster event, including any new threats that may be emerging as a secondary impact such as earthquake aftershocks.

Data are also needed on the character, scale, location, timing and impact of assistance. Such information has to be given in precise spatial terms as well as severity of impact [ie scale of injury, level of building damage etc]. In the past there has been much confusion concerning the value in using such vague classifications as 'injured', 'affected', 'homeless' etc and a valuable attempt has recently been made by the Federation of Red Cross Societies and the Centre for Research in the Epidemiology of Disasters [CRED] to provide a set of much more precise definitions that replace such vague terms.

Stage 5 Data Requirements

Testing the Plan
5.1 Damage and Survivors' Needs Data:
Following a disaster, impact data is needed on casualties, deaths, damage to property, secondary impact on the economy as well as the detailed and continually needs of the surviving population.

5.2 Assistance Data:
Data is needed concerning the on-going inventory of requests for external help, pledges of forthcoming support as well as the receipt of assistance.

5.3 Recovery Data:
As the recovery operation proceeds the sequence of needs assessment, requests for assistance and the actions taken to aid recovery can be logged into the management system.

Stage 6   FEEDBACK FROM LESSONS LEARNED

Information on changes needed in preparedness and mitigation planning as well as on risk assessment will need to be passed back to an appropriate stage in the cyclical planning process.

Stage 6 Data Requirements

Feedback from Lessons Learned:
6.1 Damage and Survivors' Needs Data:

6.2 Preparedness Planning Improvement Data:
As the preparedness plan is followed in a disaster operation or rehearsal conditions data is needed on any area where it was found to be ineffective with the reasons stated.

6.2 Mitigation Planning Improvement Data:
The disaster may have exposed the inadequacy of mitigation measures. These need to be noted through expert analysis of damage survey data to enable improvements to be introduced.

6.3 Revised Risk Assessment Data:
Following a major disaster it is essential to review Risk Assessment Data on hazards and vulnerability since the event may have significantly changed the hazard map: such as earthquake occurrence in an unanticipated location, unexpected patterns of vulnerability, wind speeds beyond predicted velocity and changes in the course of river.

In the remainder of this paper two questions will be addressed:
    * What are the main problems associated with the management of Data in Disaster Planning?

    * What are the role of information systems, such as a GIS in the reduction of disaster risks to people and property?

NATURAL DISASTERS

TYPICAL PROBLEMS CONCERNING DATA MANAGEMENT

1. Lack of political commitment to undertake risk assessment

One reasons why disaster planning, or more specifically risk assessment is seriously neglected or haphazardly undertaken is a direct consequence of the extensive scope of information needs. There is also the task of data processing and its application which many countries find daunting. Their caution relates to the high financial and human cost in maintaining an information system to cover the range of subjects noted above. Therefore it is not surprising that few industrialized countries, let alone developing countries have managed to establish a comprehensive information system to support disaster management.

2. Lack of available personnel with appropriate skills.

There is an acute shortage of skilled personnel in many developing countries to identify information needs, train the collectors of data and process it from analysis to the point when it can provide policy advice.

3. Lack of Base-Line Data

As already stated the process of Risk Assessment described in Stage 2 starts with the need to anchor all hazard, vulnerability and resource data to a map base. Therefore census data is needed that broadly identifies who lives and works where. If this information is unavailable or fragmentary it is doubtful whether effective risk assessment can take place. In a workshop on the IDNDR held at the Royal Society in 1992, Hugh Cholmondley, Director of the Caribbean Division of the UNDP and the Resident Representative of the UN in Jamaica during Hurricane Gilbert, stated that at that time the Government of Jamaica had no inventory of capital stock in any sector or in any location:

> " The Government had no idea what it owned, where it was, what its replacement cost was, where were farmers and what were they planting in what particular area,....before you talk about assessments of damage you have to know how many schools you have got and where they are" (ref.2)

4. Lack of Topographical Mapping

This arises from such causes as shortage of funds to furnish surveying on a consistent basis and, especially, to update surveys completed a decade or more ago. It should also be observed that within some countries, mapping is only available to limited numbers of authorised users - e.g., the military - and remains unhappily inaccessible to scientists, planners, etc.

Appendix 1, para 3(d), indicates some 'faux de mieux' measures that may be necessary for the disaster planner in extremis. But some of these measures do assume a level of technical competence and access to modern high-tech equipments or resources. The same situation is also liable to be truer still so far as the list of supplementary features identified in para 3(e) (i- xiv) of Appendix 1 is concerned.

A current poignant example reveals the lack of access to mapping, which may be typical of many countries. Following severe flash flooding in Lushoto, Tanzania in February 1993, local officials are severely handicapped in managing a complex relief/ recovery operation without the support of ANY maps. There are several reasons for this omission. The only map in the Office of the District Commissioner is at a scale of 1:250,000, far too small to be of any use in this context of a localised disaster and the Government's National Mapping Survey Office in Dar-es-Salaam does not have any mandate, or resources, to supply maps to District Offices. Furthermore District Officials in Lushoto are totally unaware that there are excellent maps of their area to a scale of 1:50,000, updated by British Ordnance Survey as recently as 1988.

A senior government official, familiar with the structure and staffing of District Offices commented that even if local officials did know of the existence of these maps, or were trained in their use, they would still not have sufficient funds available within local budgets to purchase them. If they were to be provided free by the Ministry to District Offices then he confidently assumed that they would be sold by a local official on the day of their arrival to supplement a meagre Local Government salary, [the map referred to above costs US $3.00, approximately 10% of a senior local officials monthly salary]

5. LACK OF HISTORICAL RECORDS FOR HAZARD MAPPING

In many developing countries the lack of reliable historical records of past disaster events makes hazard mapping difficult to undertake with any degree of confidence. This problem was intensified in certain countries that became independent of their colonial powers, where historical records may have been lost in the change in power, or in certain contexts were even deliberately destroyed, in the euphoria of Independence, to be 'rid of the past'.

6. LACK OF SOCIAL AND ECONOMIC DATA ON PATTERNS OF VULNERABILITY

Whilst the techniques of hazard mapping for seismic, volcanological, hydrological and meterological factors are well established, progress in developing an agreed methodology for many of the social and economic elements of vulnerability analysis are still rudimentary. (ref.3)

7. LACK OF DATA THAT IS RELIABLE, OF UNIFORM QUALITY AND IN A USABLE FORMAT

All of these data sets needed for effective disaster management. Yet all three can be elusive again due to a lack of money, education or political will. One important development which is needed will be to establish 'categories of reliability' in order to define what margin of error is tolerable for what type of information to be used for what purpose.

Pragmatism would indicate the need to recognise that whilst these are good standards to aim for, it will be exceedingly rare for there to be uniform, reliable and usable data available given the resource limitations of most developing countries. Therefore wise officials have no option other than to 'make-do' with the best data they can get secure, whilst doing all they can to promote the collection of data to fill important gaps.

8. LACK OF COMMUNICATION TO TAKE THE INFORMATION GATHERED IN DAMAGE AND NEEDS SURVEY AND FEED THIS BACK INTO IMPROVEMENTS IN RISK ASSESSMENT, AND PROTECTIVE PLANNING.

The officials who collect vital post disaster information tend to have a restricted time frame. Their concern is naturally to put the data they collect to immediate humanitarian use. Many of them work within the 'emergency planning culture' which shares these values. However the data they collect is also the bread and butter of improvements in the overall planning system. Without the 'Feedback From Lessons Learned' Stage 6 in Fig. 1 there is a serious loss of vital knowledge.

Finally we will turn to the use of computer technology to support the data needs defined in this paper.

THE ROLE OF INFORMATION SYSTEMS

"The requirements for establishing an effective disaster management information system involve assessing user needs, determining functional requirements of the system, developing alternative conceptual design models, developing a data base design, selecting appropriate hardware and software and testing the design in a pilot system before full implementation of the system begins"
Glenn O. Johnson (ref.4)

Integration of Disaster Planning into Environmental Management

GIS offers an important opportunity to assist in the vital process to 'normalize' disaster planning within the much broader process of resource management and development planning. This opportunity is presented since it is likely that risk assessment will gain when it not regarded as a discrete process, purely concerned with disasters. Rather it should be considered as one of many essential elements of environmental management. Thus a water catchment system can be mapped and modelled using computer technology with a concern for rainfall patterns, land drainage, general river and flood plain management, water supply, sewage disposal, land irrigation and water transportation. In addition there could be added three disaster risks: drought, flood and river pollution. In each of these cases appropriate warning systems can be developed as a part of regional and local preparedness planning.

Current Experience

Already certain developing countries: Colombia, Peru, Indonesia, Philippines, China (ref.4) Jamaica and India, for example, are actively developing GIS tools for disaster planning. In Sub-Saharan Africa a number of academic and voluntary organisations including Save the Children Fund [SCF] have been developing a GIS to assist in the Early Warning of

Impending Famine. (ref.5) Within the industrialised world GIS is being extensively used in disaster/ recovery management. The city of Los Angeles may be a world leader in this field having spent the past decade constructing a GIS. Officials have digitised urban maps at a scale of 1:24,000 to indicate block level data with the superimposition of layers of data on hazard, vulnerability, damage, administrative and utility boundaries and disaster preparedness which includes evacuation routes, emergency shelter sites, lifeline resources etc. GIS has also been used as a management tool throughout the earthquake reconstruction of the city of Kalamata in Greece.

One key development for developing countries with resource limitations is the rapid expansion in the technology of GIS. It is now possible to use relatively inexpensive software on computer hardware [PC's, digitisers, scanners and laser printers], which are currently available at a fraction of the cost of 5 years ago.

As a first step it is to be hoped that the IDNDR conference in Yokohama in 1994 will review and compare progress with GIS as a disaster planning tool in developing and industrialised countries. There is an obvious need to share the experiences, and ideas of various countries in this rapidly expanding field. It is also necessary to review whether there has been any progress in tackling some of the chronic problems of data management, some of which are noted above. One very encouraging recent development has been the readiness of the UN system, and bilateral donors to provide technical assistance to developing countries wishing to develop Management Information Systems for improved disaster planning.

The Synthesis of Data

In the pre-GIS era Disaster Planning was [and for most contexts this situation still prevails] a rigidly divided set of discrete processes. Damage survey was one activity, the vulnerability assessment of buildings was another. Post-disaster assessment of survivor's needs had no connection with an assessment of social vulnerability in the same area and post disaster damage and economic losses was not used as a tool to develop loss estimation scenarios. Similarly the detailed review of post disaster impact was not built into the data for hazard mapping, etc.

Reasons for this failure to link processes that are potentially vital for each other, which bridge the artificial division of the subject with its emergency and preventive functions have already been discussed. However a further explanation for this failure has been the sheer difficulty in synthesising differing sets of data, collected by different branches of government.

CONCLUSION

This paper has emphasised that one of the foundation blocks of effective action to reduce risks, and to manage assistance more effectively is a reliable information system. Current computer technology is providing a valuable tool to assist in this process. Geographic Information Systems [GIS], where database information is integrated with digitised maps are now enabling officials to analyze, query and explore data in a manner that was previously impossible. As noted above, this technology is already being used for disaster planning in a number of developing countries. However, computer based management information systems have no magical properties that replace the need for planned human action to process accurate information. Furthermore, any data processing system remains totally dependent on a flow of reliable, uniform data, and this requirement remains at the heart of any useful system. The hackneyed saying: 'garbage-in, garbage-out' is as appropriate in the disaster planning field as in any other sector.

GIS offers an important opportunity to reduce the vulnerability of communities to disaster. It's contribution to risk reduction, that may ultimately revolutionise disaster planning and implementation, will be for ALL six stages of the planning process, [indicated on Fig.1], to be fused into an integrated management information system. Once established, with all the safeguards noted in this paper to maintain the quality of data, such an information system could be continually updated and adapted in response to changing needs and circumstances.

APPENDIX 1

Summary of locational datasets that could be supported by a GIS Database, if reliable data and trained staff are available.

1.   Define area at risk within country (e.g. by lat/long)

2.   Define hazards
      (earthquake, flood, high winds, volcanic etc.) (ref.6)

3.   Form an inventory of locational items :

      a.   Topographical mapping - Scales of coverage - larger
            scales than 1/1m (1 km to 1 mm) of existing paper
            maps - dates of survey - contours/relief, interval
            and accuracy - romanised or local lettering -
            indications of graticule or grid.

      b.   Digital mapping - Data converted, e.g., from (a)
            above plus format and data structure employed -
            method of digitising (vector or raster) - size of
            dataset and availability e.g., on disk and/or
            broadly available format (e.g. Arc-Info) - is
            dataset fully topological? - samples available for
            experiment?

      c.   Remote sensed date - Details (e.g. Spot Image,
            Landsat, AVHRR) - coverage of area at risk - dates -
            cloud cover %age - local registration detail -
            special derivatives, if any (e.g. vegetation or land
            use interpretation?)

      d.   If no mapping available at appropriate scale :

i. Attempt to establish point positions of conspicuous objects by GPS fixing.

ii. Obtain remote sensing or air cover and cobble up mosaic or similar.

iii. Derive sketch maps (roads, rivers, coastlines and names of conspicuous towns and features, embellish subsequently with locations/details of lifelines- bridges, critical buildings, etc).

e. Supplementary locational features - (N.B. This list can be endless depending on elements relevant to risk location. The following selection are items of particular interest which tend to be omitted from topographic maps - and of course from remote sensed data):

i   Geological surveys - data relevant to seismic activity - land slip records and perilous angles of slope - structural geology especially fault lines - geochemistry, particular aspects [seek also local specialist advice]

ii   Soil survey mapping - local point and aerial analyses - angles of slope [seek local specialist advice]

iii Hydrological data - river flow records with dates and gauging station details historically - extreme flood limits - lake level mean depth - ensure digitised river patterns record down stream network within catchment boundaries and e.g. through lakes.

iv   Climatic data (e.g. Met stations) - locations and altitudes (fitting topography) - continuity of records.

v   Wind speed records - if available.

vi   Marine coastal data - charts with scales and dates as available and correspondence with topographic coastlines - coastal geomorphology - tidal and surge records.

vii Census datasets - agricultural census data with dates - boundaries of census statistics (do they correspond with other local census boundaries?) -categories of statistical information - supplementary land use patterns (possibly derived from remote sensing data) - forestry zones.

viii Population census date - precise boundaries for statistics hopefully corresponding with topographic details - dates - categories of information - names of boundaries related to polygons and names and locations of capitals.

ix   Epidemiological datasets - Where available these are sometimes related to population census data but they often record only location of place of death.

x   Roads - On assumption that road pattern is provided from topographical maps, identify relevant details such as road carrying capacities, bridge engineering details or tunnels or cuttings.

xi   Railway Networks - stations etc as above

xii   Airports - technical details as above.

xiii   Docks - technical transportation loading details as above.

xiv   Buildings - housing types often evident generally from topography but additional need to identify construction categories (e.g. anticipating earthquakes) - also to pinpoint lifeline facilities, ie administrative HQ's - hospitals - schools - broadcasting stations as locally relevant.

Local resources may or may not provide the above locational data in consistent and plottable form; furthermore some of the above may be locally irrelevant or unsustainable. Limitations of time or resources may also make assembly of such data impossible on a consistent basis. So far as items in 3(e) i-xiv are concerned, local advice from specialists about sources of information and access to recorded facts is essential.

REFERENCES

1. HAGERTY D. GIS: Origins, Application and Potential. The Macedon Digest, The Australian Journal of Disaster Management, 1991, vol.6, No.2 June, 1-3

2. DAVIS I. (ed.) Report of the Workshop: Opportunities for British Involvement in the International Decade for Natural Disaster Reduction [IDNDR], p.15 Published on behalf of the Science, Technology and Engineering Committee for IDNDR, Royal Society 27 March 1992

3. ROGGE J.R. A Research Agenda for Disaster and Emergency Management, chapter 4: Vulnerability and Risk Assessment' pp 15-18,. Prepared for the United Nations Development Programme and the United Nations Disaster Relief Coordinator, Disaster Research Unit, University of Manitoba, Winnipeg, Canada May 1992

4. JOHNSON G. Anhui Mission Report, CPR/91/712 Rehabilitation Assistance to Anhui Province following the Flood Disaster , May- July 1991 Report on Management Information Systems, p. 3/11 Unpublished report to the Government of Anhui Province PR China and the UNDP Beijing May 1992

5. INTERNATIONAL CARTOGRAPHIC ASSOCIATION, Pan-European Environmental Policy: Some relevant GIS applications, Section 5: Anticipation of Disasters, Speakers: I.Davis, J.Seaman and C.Toomer, pp. 27-28 EUROCARTO X Conference, Trinity College, Oxford, 16-18 September 1992

6. NATURAL ENVIRONMENT RESEARCH COUNCIL, Report of the NERC Unit for Thematic Information Systems 1989/91. Hazard Modelling p.15 Natural Environment Research Council , Unit for Thematic Information, Dept. of Geography, University of Reading, 1991

43. Procedures for repair and retrofitting of earthquake-damaged RC structures based on selective assessment and intervention

A. S. ELNASHAI, Imperial College of Science, Technology and Medicine

1. INTRODUCTION

Earthquake-resistant design of structures may be undertaken using either *direct design* or *capacity design* principles. In the former case, members are designed to resist forces calculated from the code-imposed storey shears, distributed according to relative stiffness of members. In capacity design, the structure is viewed as comprising two types of zone; dissipative and non-dissipative. The dissipative zones are those responsible for the mobilisation of the desired failure mode, chosen to maximise overall energy absorption capacity and avoid collapse. All other zones are considered non-dissipative. The dissipative zones are dimensioned first, then their likely overstrength is estimated. The sources of overstrength in structures include:

- Higher concrete compressive strength.
- Confinement.
- Larger area of steel due to availability of bar diameters.
- Higher yield strength of steel.
- Strain-hardening.

The non-dissipative parts of the structure are then designed to withstand forces consistent with the strength of dissipative parts, including overstrength. In this way, the structure is rendered much less sensitive to the characteristics of the input motion, since it can only respond in the ductile mode which was envisaged in the design phase. Hence, capacity design leads to safer structures.

2. Significance of Selective Assessment and Intervention

Whereas application of capacity design principles to new structures is relatively straightforward, existing structures pose a different set of questions. Hence, assessment of existing structures in seismic regions has to consider the need for conversion from direct to capacity principles in repair and strengthening. In its most general form, response of RC structures is viewed as comprising flexural stiffness and strength as well as ductility. This is depicted in Table 1 below.

Table 1. Response Characteristics of RC Members

	K_f	K_s	C_f	C_s	μ_d
Re-instatement	√	√	√	√	√
Enhancement	√	√	√	√	√
Reduction	X	X	√	X	X

K_f	Flexural stiffness	μ_d	Ductility ratio
K_s	Shear stiffness	√	May be required
C_f	Flexural capacity	X	Not normally required
C_s	Shear capacity		

Natural disasters. Thomas Telford, London, 1993

In Table 1, 're-instatement' is the recovery of a response parameter to its original level, 'enhancement' and 'reduction' imply effecting an increase or a decrease in the response parameter, respectively. In rare cases, a reduction in a response parameter may be required. As shown in Table 1, to change the failure mode from shear to flexure, a reduction in the flexural capacity may be the most effective solution for a structure that has not been 'capacity' designed.

The above argument has implications on future investigations of structural behaviour of RC members subjected to earthquake loading. From the structural response investigation standpoint, methods of assessment, such as experimental testing, have to make a clear distinction between the response in flexure and that in shear. There are several examples of research efforts that have recognised the significance of separating flexural and shear deformation contributions (Lefas, 1988, Lefas and Kotsovos, 1987), but had shortcomings with regard to (i) application of realistic boundary conditions, and to (ii) use of accurate methods for separating the two deformational components. Both issues, namely boundary conditions and shear/flexure separation methods, were studied by Pilakoutas (1990) and Elnashai and Pilakoutas (1991), as discussed in subsequent sections.

In recognition of the role played by the degree of regularity in the nonlinear dynamic response of structures subjected to earthquake loading, codes give guidance on the acceptable level of irregularity that would not impair the development of ductile failure modes. Adherence to the code regularity clauses would warrant the use of simplified analysis and the recommended values of behaviour factors. The various codes therefore attempt to encourage the use of regular structure by prescribing one or more of the following measures.

-   Regularity classification and restrictions on design methods.
-   Configuration regularity (plan and elevation).
-   Stiffness regularity.
-   Mass regularity.
-   Strength regularity.
-   Penalty on irregular buildings.

The problem of selective intervention, for repair or strengthening, may arise when a structure was deemed regular according to the code in force at the time of construction, but more strict regulations were introduced at a later stage. Moreover, the process of repair or strengthening may cause regularity violation. Hence, another aspect of seismic response of RC structures which is affected by the concept of individual member response characteristics is re-assessment of existing buildings, where newly-defined regularity criteria of stiffness and strength are imposed on structures that were designed and constructed prior to code enforcement. This imposition of new limits of acceptability dictates re-assessment based on separate consideration of stiffness, strength as well as ductility.

Finally, the repair and retrofitting process of damaged RC structures should be directed towards not only repair of the individual member, but also the effect of this repair on the overall structural response. This would be of significance where a direct design code is replaced by a code based on capacity design principles.

In the light of modern code development, (where the evaluation of a 'behaviour factor' is central to the seismic design-assessment-repair process) the above three aspects of response characterisation require techniques to test, design and repair structural systems, bearing in mind the individual response parameter of the members. The modification of these parameters, namely stiffness, strength, ductility, would ideally lead to a higher behaviour factor. This has direct bearing on the safety of the ensuing structure, hence on the vulnerability of the community as a whole. Figure 1 depicts the hierarchical relationship between local and global seismic response characteristics. It provides a framework for vulnerability reduction by selective repair and strengthening by identifying the effect of local intervention on the global seismic response.

In most cases covered by Table 1 above, it is essential to assess and affect, for design and repair, respectively, the member response parameter under consideration, with little or no effect on other parameters. Adoption of this approach is in harmony with the capacity design philosophy. It enables tight control of the behaviour and failure mode of RC structures, leading to rational

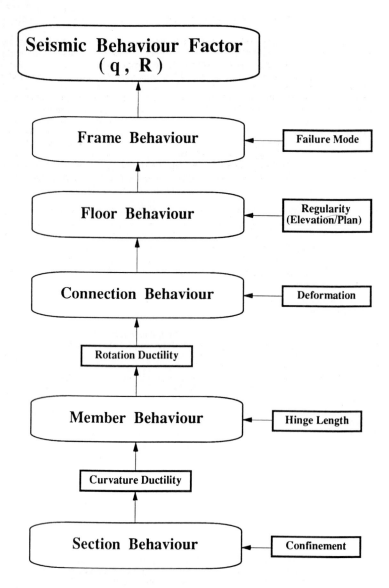

Figure 1: Conceptual relationship between local and global seismic response characteristics

design, assessment and repair solutions, as discussed in subsequent sections of this paper. This approach may therefore be termed 'capacity redesign'.

3. Uncertainties Associated with Conventional Repair Schemes

The most widely-used techniques used for seismic repair and strengthening, observed during post-earthquake reconnaissance work, are in-situ jacketing, shotcreting and epoxy resin injection. Several problems arise that cast doubt over the effectiveness and controllability of these techniques. In the case of epoxy resin injection, it is very difficult to ascertain the degree of penetration of the resin into the complex crack configurations resulting from cyclic loading. Therefore, the level of reinstatement of stiffness is uncertain. Moreover, the displacement at which the repaired parts of the structural member starts picking-up load is also uncertain.

With regard to jacketing, the increase in stiffness and strength is usually quite substantial. For example, a 300x300 mm member with a 50 mm jacket will have more than 200% increase in elastic stiffness. The strength enhancement, on the other hand, will be a function of the ratio of reinforcement. If this 200%+ increase in stiffness is to be avoided, a jacket of thickness less than 50 mm would be required. However, this will be impractical for construction purposes.

4. Selective Assessment of Shear and Flexural Response

Reinforced concrete members respond in a mixed flexural/shear mode, dependent on their geometry, design, loading and boundary conditions. Whilst the behaviour of members such as shallow beams and beam-columns is mainly governed by flexure, RC walls respond in the above-mentioned mixed mode. Therefore, it is crucial that testing arrangements can reproduce both aspects of the behaviour, if the observations are to be suitable for development of design criteria. Two testing programmes were completed at Imperial College (Pilakoutas, 1990 and Lopes, 1991), where the flexural- and shear-dominated behaviour was investigated. As shown in Figure 2, the testing arrangement 'a' leads to testing of a geometric aspect ratio of about 2.0, which is the approximate limit between flexure and shear prominence. Testing arrangement 'b' is that used by several researchers to investigate the response of squat walls (Lefas, 1988). In the latter case, in addition to problems due to direct load-transfer from the loading beam to the foundation, the loading beam applies a confining stress condition which is not present in the bottom portion of RC walls in a building. Observations from such testing arrangement should be treated with caution. Rig 'c', on the other hand, applies the load through an arrangement that leads to a 'natural' transfer of load to a low aspect ratio wall, hence the results obtained will reflect the true behaviour more closely.

5. Design Scenarios Requiring Selective Intervention

Above, a general statement is made regarding the necessity of developing techniques to assess and affect individual member characteristics. Below, some typical situations dictating the application of selective repair and strengthening techniques are presented.

5.1 Strength-Only Scenarios

5.1.1 Capacity Redesign

Within the context of the 'capacity design' concept, failure mode control is essential for the realisation of the predicted behaviour and sequence of plastic hinge formation. This concept has been formulated recently, hence existing structures would only fortuitously conform to a desirable failure mode. The first proposed scenario, in support of the case for selective assessment and intervention is the re-assessment of a structure designed according to conventional 'direct design' concepts. It is required to alter the sequence of plastic hinge formation to satisfy the new 'capacity design' failure mode. However, the stiffness distribution in the structure is in accordance with the code procedure, hence no increase in stiffness is required. Indeed, an increase in stiffness would cause violation of the regularity conditions specified by the code. In this case selective intervention is required, to effect an increase in strength without an increase in stiffness.

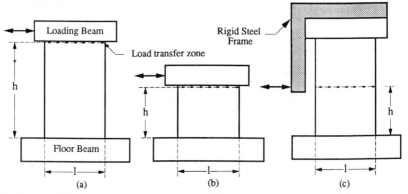

Figure 2: (a) Flexure-dominated loading test arrangement. The artificial confinement provided by the loading beam affects a small distance relative to the height of the wall, (b) shear-dominated loading leading to aspect ratio less than the intended value due to direct transfer of load from the stiff loading beam to the foundation, (c) shear-dominated loading avoiding the problems of direct load transfer in (b).

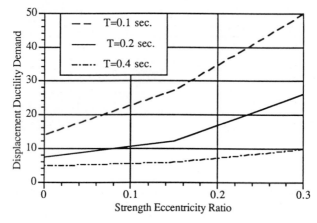

Figure 3: Effect of strength eccentricity on displacement ductility demand under El Centro earthquake for three periods of vibrations of a three-element model (adapted from Xian, 1992).

5.1.2 Strength Eccentricity

Seismic design codes impose conditions to reduce the effect of torsional vibrations on the shear forces at column heads. This is defined in terms of limitations on the eccentricity, defined as the distance between the centre of mass (where the inertial load is applied) and the centre of rigidity (where the elastic reaction to the inertial forces is applied). However, no provisions exist for strength eccentricity. This effect was shown (Xian, 1992) to increase ductility demand, as the structure starts to respond in the inelastic domain (Figure 3).

It is conceivable that a structure may be stiffness-symmetric but strength-asymmetric. This can be demonstrated by considering the relationship between strength and stiffness of moment resisting frames and RC walls. The latter may be used to balance the frames stiffness distribution, thus almost certainly creating a strength eccentricity. This scenario leads to the conclusion that a selective assessment and intervention scheme is required to increase the strength of parts of the structure without a consequential increase in the stiffness.

5.1.3 *Variability in Materials*

The effect of variability in steel yield stress on seismic response and design has been studied for steel frames (Kuwamura and Kato, 1989, Elnashai and Chryssanthopoulos, 1990 and others). The effect of yield stress variations on the behaviour factors and energy absorption of RC frames was studied by Alexandrou (1991). For a mean steel yield of 400 N/mm^2 and a standard deviation of 25 N/mm^2, a frame (Figure 4) was analysed using the FE package ADAPTIC (Izzuddin and Elnashai, 1989).

The above analysis highlighted the effect of local member strength on the overall seismic performance; the frames for which the results vary by up to 293% are nominally identical. It is hence concluded that in such cases, a strength-only intervention would be required, and no stiffness change should be allowed, thus emphasising the importance of the concept of selective assessment/intervention.

5.2 *Stiffness-Only Scenarios*

There are several applications where an increase in stiffness without an increase in strength would be required. The most common of such scenarios is the case of damage to a reinforced concrete structure due to small magnitude earthquakes, which will reduce the stiffness of the structure due to cracking. However, for flexural members in particular, a commensurate reduction in strength does not necessarily occur. Therefore, in repair of such a structure, reinstatement of stiffness, with no effect on strength, should be the objective of the intervention scheme.

The second scenario of stiffness-only intervention is the case of a stiffness-irregular structure that violates newly-imposed code design criteria. Application of a conventional intervention scheme, such as jacketing, which has a simultaneous effect on both stiffness and strength, would require a complete re-design to ensure that the ductility of the structure is unaffected. It follows that application of a selective assessment and intervention, under stiffness-only conditions, is an appropriate solution, leading to the satisfaction of code requirements without a complete re-design.

5.3 *Ductility-Only Scenarios*

Here, inadequate detailing of the existing structure requires intervention to increase the ductility of the member, without significantly affecting its strength and stiffness. This is a commonly-encountered problem, and its solution is considerably more straightforward than the stiffness- or strength-only intervention, as discussed in subsequent sections of this paper.

6. Feasibility Study of Selective Repair and Strengthening

In the above sections, the consequences of local member behaviour on the overall structure were exemplified by focusing attention on a number of cases where the global assessment and design criteria dictate the specific objective of the local intervention scheme. Here, some novel ideas aiming at selectively affecting a single response parameter with little or no effect on other structural characteristics are presented. Preliminary results from stiffness-only selective intervention are given.

6.1 *Strength-only Intervention*

Two schemes were designed and tested at Imperial College, where additional steel bars or plates are used, in conjunction with a delay mechanism, to increase the strength without affecting the stiffness. In scheme (a), shown in Figure 5, steel bars are added and a mechanical coupler is used

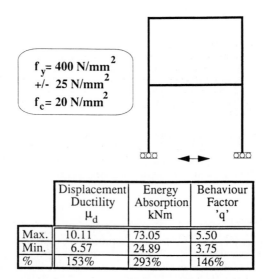

	Displacement Ductility μ_d	Energy Absorption kNm	Behaviour Factor 'q'
Max.	10.11	73.05	5.50
Min.	6.57	24.89	3.75
%	153%	293%	146%

Figure 4: Variability of response parameters of an RC frame with material variability as shown in the box. The frames analysed are nominally-identical since their strength variations are within practically-observed limits.

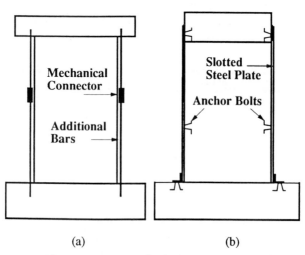

(a)   (b)

Figure 5: Strength-only intervention (a) use of additional bars and mechanical couplers. The couplers have a tolerance within which the bars do not carry load, (b) use of slotted steel plates. The slots are designed to allow for the displacement beyond which strength is increased due to the presence of the steel plates.

to adjust the tolerance in displacement beyond which the bars take part in the load-carrying process. In the second case (b), steel plates are bolted to the wall sides, where the bolts can travel within a groove before bearing on the steel plate, thus contributing to the flexural capacity of the member.

Early results from this repair/strengthening scheme are shown in Figure 6. In the former figure, the target strength of 80 kN was achieved without a change in stiffness using externally-applied slotted steel plates, as shown in Figure 5 (b). The drop in strength at a deflection of about 24 mm is due to the intentional disengagement of the intervention system. The plots clearly indicate that the objective of the intervention scheme has been fulfilled. However, problems arise in proposing a definition of ductility for this shown response pattern, due to the two levels of yield force. Such issues need further examination.

In a practical situation, several other alternatives exist, such as the insertion of steel bars within a plastic duct, with a bar length longer than the distance between the top and bottom slabs. The above schemes are indeed practical, since they are at worst as cumbersome as existing jacketing techniques.

6.2 Stiffness-Only Intervention

According to the sample scenarios given above, the situation may arise where an increase in stiffness without an increase in strength is required. This can be effected by one of the two techniques shown in Figure 7 below, amongst others. The scheme in Figure 7 (a) comprises the addition of closed hoops in the vertical plane spanning the heavily cracked zone (flexural plastic hinge). The hoops are not attached to the foundation beam, hence they do not contribute to the strength of the critical section. The number and location of the vertical hoops dictates the level of stiffness increase.

In the second proposed scheme, shown in Figure 7 (b), a steel plate is glued to the area affected by flexural cracks, using epoxy mortars. This plate is again attached to neither the loading nor to the foundation beams, hence provides no continuous load-transfer mechanism. The location and width of the steel plate dictates the level of stiffness increase imposed on the RC member, hence control over the response parameter can be exercised. Preliminary results from tests at Imperial College (Elnashai and Salama, 1992) indicate that this technique is more effective in stiffness re-instatement than epoxy resin injection. Moreover, it is not possible to control accurately the extent of epoxy mortar penetration, hence little or no control can be exercised on the level of stiffness increase.

In Figure 8, the stiffness of a wall model subjected to severe cyclic loading is plotted vs. maximum cyclic displacement. The figure shows that using steel plate adhesion, of a width and location dictated by the target stiffness increase, results in fully-predictable response; in the case shown, the objective was to reinstate the intact performance. It is also clear that the strength was unaffected, hence no effect on strength distribution would have been inadvertently introduced. Comparison with the effect of epoxy resin injection of cracks (Elnashai and Salama, 1992) showed that the new proposed system is much more controllable.

6.3 Ductility-Only Intervention

This is the simplest application of selective assessment and intervention, where the structural member is deemed satisfactory for both stiffness and strength criteria, but is required to demonstrate extra ductility in order to increase the global behaviour factor. Here, additional stirrups may be added by drilling through the member. Alternatively, steel U-shaped plates may be bolted to the area where additional ductility is required, as shown in Figure 9. In either situation, the number of bars (or plates), their diameter (or thickness) and their spacing dictates the level of ductility enhancement.

The application of such techniques will have no effect on the stiffness and strength of the member, since it is only affecting the confined compressive strength of the concrete. (It is established that the effect of concrete confinement on flexural strength is minimal, especially for low levels of axial load). This is demonstrated in Figure 10, where the load-displacement plot of a wall tested at

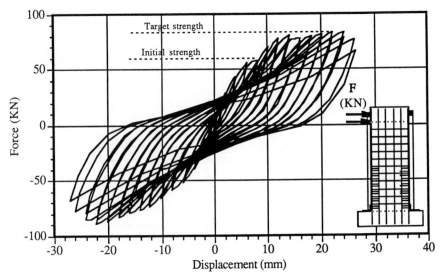

Figure 6: Test results for strength-only intervention by use of slotted steel plates. The initial stiffness is identical to the bare model stiffness. This is confirmed by the zero strain gauge reading on the steel plates up to about 8 mm displacement.

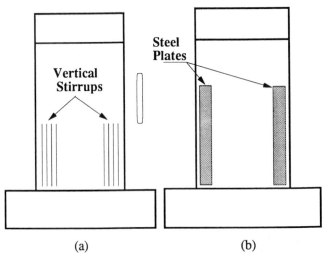

Figure 7: Stiffness-only intervention (a) use of closed vertical hoops, (b) use of unanchored bonded steel plates. The two devices do not provide a load path hence have no effect on strength. The location, width and height of the device may be selected to provide the required stiffness reinstatement, with due regard to the required plastic hinge length (by slitting the plates horizontally to allow for yielding at various sections).

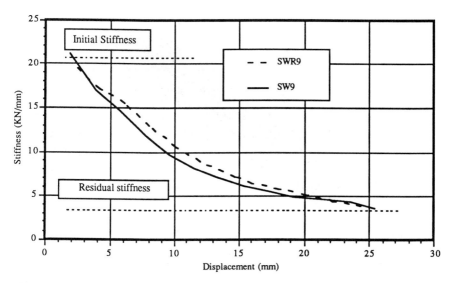

Figure 8: Test results of stiffness-only intervention. The solid line is the displacement vs. stiffness plot from cyclic loading of the intact wall. The dashed line is for the wall after repair by bounded steel plates. Other tests results (Elnashai and Salama, 1992) showed that the regain in stiffness by epoxy injection cannot be controlled.

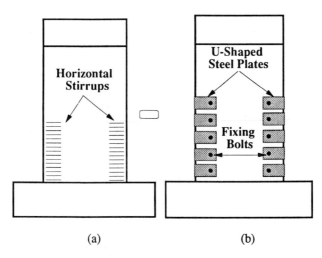

Figure 9: Ductility-only intervention (a) use of closed stirrups, (b) use of U-shaped steel plates and fixing bolts. Several narrow plates are used to avoid affecting the stiffness of the models.

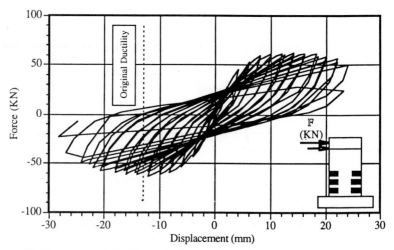

Figure 10: Test results of ductility-only intervention using U-shaped steel plates. 'Original Ductility' is that of an identical test specimen subjected to an identical loading regime but without the intervention scheme.

Imperial College and incorporating the the ductility-only scheme shown in Figure 9 (b) is given. The wall had reinforcement similar to other control models, but with no internal stirrups. The addition of the new selective repair scheme had no effect on neither the stiffness nor the strength. The ductility was substantially increased.

Figure 10. Ductility-only Results. Load-Displacement for a wall with U-shaped steel profiles. The original limit of displacement (Original Ductility) was reached under the same cyclic loading regime as all other walls, where a reduction in capacity signified the attainment of the ultimate displacement.

7. Conclusions

Advanced seismic design philosophies render full control on the behavioural pattern and failure mode of structural members and systems necessary. Therefore, individual contributing mechanisms should be identified and controlled. The former requirement, identification of individual load-resistance mechanisms, requires careful consideration in load application, history and boundary conditions used in the laboratory and in analysis, as well as accurate techniques to separate the two contributing mechanisms of shear and flexure.

The requirement of control poses new challenges to the designer, whereby means of affecting one response characteristic without the others have to be developed. It is shown above that realistic design, repair and retrofitting scenarios lead to the conclusion that stiffness, strength and ductility should be treated selectively so as to maximise the structural behaviour factor. This in turn will allow a reduction in design forces and increased confidence in earthquake response.

Methods of affecting individual response parameters are suggested, based on tests and analysis conducted at Imperial College, and preliminary results are given. It is demonstrated that the approach of selective assessment/intervention is the answer to the above-mentioned identification and control requirements. The general approach used in this paper provides a framework within which tighter control on the seismic response of RC structures can be exercised. This would naturally lead to more effective repair and strengthening techniques, thus increasing levels of safety.

8. Acknowledgement

The work described in this paper is part of an ongoing research programme on the seismic performance of reinforced concrete structures. The experimental work on RC walls referred to was funded by the UK Science and Engineering Research Council. The SERC also funded the testing of repaired walls. The tests were expertly undertaken by Mr.A.I.Salama, Doctoral Candidate at Imperial College, who also prepared several of the figures presented.

9. References

Alexandrou, E., 1991. Seismic Response of RC Frames with Material Variability. MSc Dissertation. Engineering Seismology and Earthquake Engineering Section, Imperial College, London.

Elnashai, A.S. and Chryssanthopoulos, M., 1991. Effect of random material variability on seismic design parameters of steel frames. *Earthquake Engineering and Structural Dynamics.* 20(4): 101-114.

Elnashai, A.S. and Pilakoutas, K., 1991. Interpretation of Testing Results for RC Panels. *ACI Journal*, under review.

Elnashai, A.S., Pilakoutas, K. and Ambraseys, N.N., 1990. Experimental behaviour of RC walls under earthquake loading. *Earthquake Engineering and Structural Dynamics* 19 (3): 389-407.

Elnashai, A.S. and Salama, A.I., 1992. *Selective Repair and Retrofitting Techniques for RC Structures in Seismic Regions.* Engineering Seismology and Earthquake Engineering, Report ESEE/92-2.

Eurocode 8, 1988. *Structures in Seismic Regions.* EUR 12266 EN, CEC, May.

Izzuddin, B.A. and Elnashai, A.S., 1989. *ADAPTIC, A Program for Static and Dynamic Analysis of Structures by Adaptive Mesh Refinement; User Manual.* Engineering Seismology and Earthquake Engineering Report ESEE/89-7.

Kuwamura, H. and Kato, B., 1989. Effect of randomness in structural members yield strength on the structural systems ductility. *Journal of Constructional Steel Research* 13: 79-93.

Lefas, I.D., 1988. Behaviour of RC Structural Walls, PhD Thesis, Imperial College, London.

Lefas, I.D. and Kotsovos, M.D., 1987. Behaviour of RC structural walls: a new interpretation. *IABSE Colloquium on Computational Mechanics of Concrete Structures*, Advances and Applications, Delft.

Lopes, M.S., 1991. Seismic Behaviour of RC Walls with Low Shear Ratio, PhD Thesis, Engineering Seismology and Earthquake Engineering Section, Imperial College, London.

Lopes, M.S. and Elnashai, A.S., 1990. Behaviour of RC walls subjected to high cyclic shear. *9th European Conference on Earthquake Engineering*, Moscow, September.

Pilakoutas, K., 1990. Earthquake-Resistant Design of RC Walls, PhD Thesis, Engineering Seismology and Earthquake Engineering Section, Imperial College, London.

Xian, D., 1992. Inelastic Response and Effective Design of Asymmetric Buildings under Strong Earthquake Loading, PhD Thesis, University College, London.

45. Earthquake resistant design and construction of buildings for the self-help school construction programme in Northern Pakistan

T. S. PAUL, Ove Arup & Partners International, Singapore,
J. W. PAPPIN, Ove Arup & Partners Hong Kong Ltd,
and R. E. HUGHES, International Heritage Conservation and
Management, UK

INTRODUCTION

During the past five years the Aga Khan Housing Board, Pakistan (AKHBP)
have been implementing a self-help school construction programme (SHSCP)
for schools in the Northern Areas and Chitral regions of northern Pakistan.
During the late 1980's the AKHBP commissioned a research and development
programme to further develop a range of construction materials and
technologies appropriate for the school buildings (Ref.1). Richard Hughes
was employed by the AKHBP to review this work with a specific brief to
examine four experimental schools constructed using different building
materials (Ref.2). As a result of this review, Ove Arup & Partners were
appointed in January 1991 to carry a seismic hazard assessment of the
region and to provide engineering design advice for the developing school
programme(Ref.3). This paper describes the school construction, derivation
of the seismic design criteria, methodology for site selection and the
structural design of the school buildings. The primary objective of the
engineering design was to reduce as far as possible the vulnerability of
the school buildings to earthquakes, taking account of the available
construction materials and existing construction practice.

The architectural scheme for a typical school consists of two single storey
rectangular buildings with flat roofs. Figure 1 shows typical plan layouts
for the school buildings. Based on the SHSCP research and development
programme the AKHBP concluded that the hollow concrete block wall
construction was the most appropriate for the school buildings.

SCHOOL CONSTRUCTION

At present the school buildings are being constructed at a number of sites
in Northern Pakistan under the guidance of AKHBP technical staff. Each
village donates the land for the building and provides the labour during
the construction period. The AKHBP provides the technical assistance,
moulds for the blocks and roof beams, cement and reinforcement steel.
Plate 1 shows a typical reinforced hollow concrete block school building
nearing completion. In particular it worth noting the very high quality of
the construction achieved on site.

A major feature of the buildings is that they consist of only two main
modular components, the hollow block and the roof beam. The channel blocks
used as permanent precast formwork for the intermediate reinforced concrete
ring beams are made by splitting a hollow block in two. These modular
components are precast locally on site using the purpose built moulds.

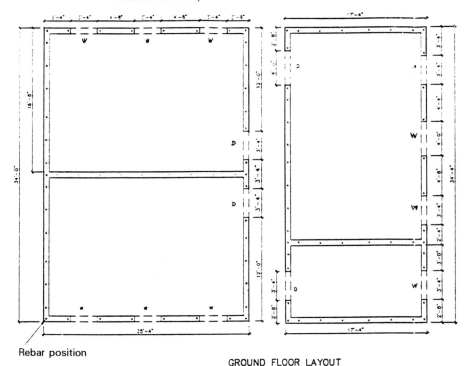

Rebar position

GROUND FLOOR LAYOUT

Figure 1: Typical School Plan Layout

Plate 2 shows the typical hollow blocks and the relatively portable
equipment used in their construction. Typical beams are illustrated in
Plate 3. The roof detail composed of the inverted T beams and the hollow
blocks is shown in Plate 4.

The primary contributions from the project team were to design and
recommend two key modifications to the buildings in order to increase their
earthquake resistance. These modifications consisted of using:

- intermediate continuous ring beams within the hollow concrete block
  walls at window sill and lintel levels. These combined with the
  vertical reinforcement bars provide a confined masonry wall system
  and replaced the wire mesh used in the research and development
  school.

- a cast insitu roof beam to provide structural connectivity between
  the walls and the roof.

Both of these modifications are discussed in greater detail in the
following sections.

The cost of the basic primary school unit consisting of two rooms and a
toilet block is approximately £10,000. This includes building material
costs, skilled and unskilled labour, and AKHBP technical assistance.

Plate 1: Typical Hollow Concrete Block School Construction

Plate 2: Precast Hollow Concrete Blocks
(Insert: Portable equipment for constructing blocks)

Plate 3: Precast Concrete Roof T-Beams

Plate 4: Typical School Roof Construction

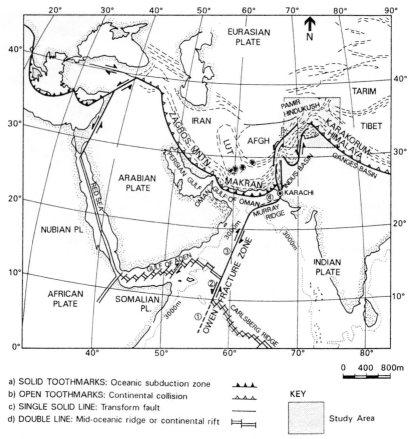

a) SOLID TOOTHMARKS: Oceanic subduction zone
b) OPEN TOOTHMARKS: Continental collision
c) SINGLE SOLID LINE: Transform fault
d) DOUBLE LINE: Mid-oceanic ridge or continental rift

KEY

Study Area

Figure 2: Regional Tectonics

SEISMIC DESIGN CRITERIA FOR BUILDINGS IN NORTHERN PAKISTAN

The northern region of Pakistan is located in one of the more seismically
active areas of the world, at the tectonic plate boundary between the
Indian subcontinent and the Eurasian land mass. This section describes
briefly the available tectonic, geological and seismological data for the
region, the seismic hazard assessment methodology and the recommended
seismic design criteria for the school buildings.

Regional Tectonics and Geology

Figure 2 shows the main tectonic features of the region. The tectonic
environment is dominated by the continental collision between the Indian
and Eurasian Plates resulting in the formation of the Hindu Kush, Karakoram
and Himalayan mountain ranges. Satellite imagery, aerial photographs,
geological maps and seismological data have been used by a number of
authors to identify "active" fault zones in Pakistan (for example Ref.4)
and these indicate that several major fault systems exist within the study
region.

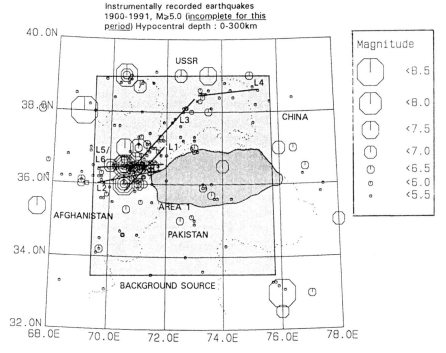

Figure 3: Instrumental Earthquake Data and Seismic Source Model

Regional Seismological Data

The seismicity of Northern Pakistan has been the subject of several studies during the past twenty years (Ref.5). The instrumental earthquake data for the period 1900 to 1990 is shown in Figure 3.

Seismic Hazard Assessment

For engineering design purposes the seismic hazard may be defined as the level of ground motion due to seismic activity at any particular location which can be exceeded within a given time period or which may arise due to a specified earthquake.

The probabilistic seismic hazard methodology developed by Cornell (Refs.6,7) was used to determine the level of ground motion hazard. This methodology is considered more appropriate than deterministic methods as it takes account of earthquakes occurring in a number of postulated seismic source zones at various distances from the site.

Based on the regional tectonic and seismological data the seismic source model superimposed on Figure 3 has been adopted. The seismic activity is assumed to be uniform within each source zone. The seismic source parameters describing the nature of the earthquake activity (e.g. earthquake recurrence, maximum and minimum magnitude, and focal depth) are summarised in Table 1.

583

NATURAL DISASTERS

Table 1: Seismic Source Parameters (Refer to Figure 3)

SEISMIC SOURCE ZONE	ACTIVITY RATE (No Events M>4/year)	FOCAL DEPTH (km)	
Background	7	15	
Area 1	24	50	
Line 1	13	85	M_{min} = 4.0
Line 2	14	125	M_{max} = 8.5
Line 3	5	125	b-value = 0.9
Line 4	3	125	
Line 5	9	175	
Line 6	15	225	

During the literature review carried for the project no attenuation relationships for Pakistan were obtained. As a result the relationships developed by Crouse (Ref.8) for subduction zone environments have been used. These relationships are based on accelerogram data recorded at soil sites from subduction zones around the Pacific Ocean.

The probabilistic seismic hazard analyses have been carried out using the SISMIC program developed by Ove Arup & Partners. The 5Hz spectral acceleration values corresponding to a 500 year return period (annual frequency of 2×10^{-3}) were calculated. The 500 year return period effective peak acceleration (EPA_{500}) was determined by dividing the 5Hz spectral acceleration by 2.5 (Ref.9). This EPA_{500} value was then used to define a seismic zone factor compatible with the US Uniform Building Code (UBC:1988), (Ref.10). The SEAOC "Recommended Lateral Force Requirements & Tentative Commentary" (Ref.11) used in California and on whose philosophy the UBC:1988 code is based recommends that the ground motion hazard level for which a building is designed should have a 90% probability of not being exceeded during a 50 year period (equivalent to a return period of approximately 500 years). This philosophy is considered appropriate for essential community buildings in Northern Pakistan.

For Northern Pakistan the calculated 500 year return period EPA_{500} values range from 4.0 to 6.0 m/s^2 within the region. UBC:1988 assigns areas with EPA_{500} > 4.0 m/s^2 as Zone 4, the highest zone.

Recommended Seismic Design Criteria

In order to determine the lateral force requirements for the school buildings in Northern Pakistan it was recommended that the UBC:1988 guidelines for design and construction be adopted using a seismic zone factor, Z = 0.4.

SITE SELECTION PROCEDURES

The northern region of Pakistan is one of the world's most actively

584

changing landscapes. As the mountains are being created by tectonic movements discussed in the previous section geomorphological processes are continuously eroding the landscape (Ref.12). In particular the various types of slope instability (e.g. rockfall, debris flows and landslides) are a major hazard to the people and buildings. The objective of the school site selection is to determine "safe" locations for each building.

As discussed in the previous section earthquakes are a major hazard in the region and the engineering design of the school buildings aims to reduce their vulnerability to earthquake ground motions. However, earthquakes are not the only natural hazard to be considered; slope instability although generally more localised in its effect can result in a similar destructive impact. Unlike earthquakes it is often possible to influence the consequences of geomorphological hazards by:

- site assessment

- site protection measures

- modifying the potential hazard (e.g. slope stabilisation)

In general the latter two options are usually very expensive and therefore site assessment provides the most effective method of reducing the vulnerability of people and buildings to landslide hazards.

To address the site assessment issue the project team developed the methodology shown in Figure 4. This methodology incorporates both local and expert knowledge as the basis of the assessment and consolidates the process currently undertaken informally.

STRUCTURAL DESIGN PHILOSOPHY

The structural design philosophy adopted was based on two main criteria:

- The safe performance of the structure under earthquake loading

- The durability requirements to meet the proposed design life of 50 years.

Lateral Strength Requirements

Lateral strength is only one contributor to the performance of a building under earthquake loading. Other factors include quality of construction and materials, regularity in plan and elevation, ductility and maintenance of the structural system in a good condition. However it is essential to ensure that there is sufficient lateral strength to resist the forces induced by earthquake ground motions. This is particularly important for masonry buildings such as the SHSCP schools where the available ductility is limited.

At the time of the project Pakistan did not have any seismic regulations for buildings, Ref.13, and therefore it was not possible to derive lateral strength requirements directly from local practice. Reference was therefore made to the Indian Code IS:1893 (Ref.14) and to UBC:1988. The former was considered potentially relevant because it is used in regions similar to the SHSCP study area. UBC:1988 was chosen because it is a well respected code commonly adopted outside the United States, including Pakistan.

The ultimate lateral strength requirement from UBC:1988 was estimated to 25% of the building dead weight. This is based on a zone factor, $Z = 0.4$,

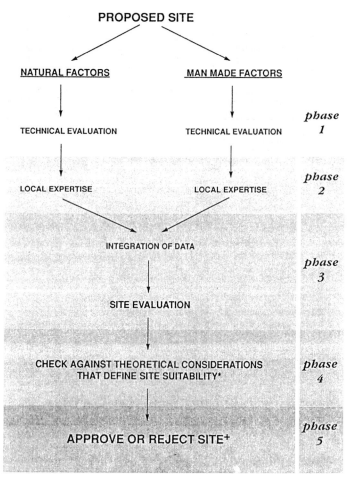

PROPOSED SITE

NATURAL FACTORS   MAN MADE FACTORS

TECHNICAL EVALUATION   TECHNICAL EVALUATION   *phase 1*

LOCAL EXPERTISE   LOCAL EXPERTISE   *phase 2*

INTEGRATION OF DATA   *phase 3*

SITE EVALUATION

CHECK AGAINST THEORETICAL CONSIDERATIONS THAT DEFINE SITE SUITABILITY*   *phase 4*

APPROVE OR REJECT SITE+   *phase 5*

Figure 4: School Site Assessment Methodology

a short period masonry structure with a structural Rw factor of 6 (appropriate for "reinforced" masonry) and an importance factor, I = 1.0.

Comparison of the UBC:1988 and IS:1893 guidelines result in broadly similar lateral strength requirements. UBC:1988 requirements have been adopted as these are consistent with the assessment of seismic hazard described above. It should be noted that the quantity of construction materials required are not very sensitive to the lateral strength requirement which is primarily governed by detailing and connectivity of the structural elements.

The structural analysis adopted a simple model which considered the worst possible cases of force distribution ignoring any beneficial interaction between the different structural elements and load sharing. A robust approach was adopted in the detailing of the junctions between structural elements. This structural continuity maximises the redundancies in the system thereby enhancing the ultimate performance of the structure under earthquake loading.

Table 2: Eurocode 8 (Draft) - Confined Masonry Requirements

This type of masonry shall be confined by horizontal and vertical structural reinforced concrete tie-beams adequately bonded together and anchored to the elements of the main structural system.
In order to obtain an effective bond between tie-beams and masonry, casting of the concrete shall follow the construction of the masonry wall.
The cross-section of both horizontal and vertical tie beams shall not be less than 150 x 150mm.
Vertical confining elements shall be placed at both sides of any wall opening with an area of more than __m^2, (N.B. the current draft of EC8 does not specify the minimum area of opening confinement) at every intersection between walls, and within the wall if necessary in order not to exceed the spacing of 5m.
In each vertical or horizontal tie-beam the reinforcement shall be not less than 2.5cm^2 of cross-section. If more than one steel bar is adopted in the tie beams, the reinforcement shall be put together by regularly spaced stirrups.
Continuity of the reinforcement shall be achieved by 60 diameters overlap.
Wall thickness shall not be less than 240mm.
The ratio between the storey height and the wall thickness shall not be greater than 15.

SCHOOL BUILDING ELEMENTS

For the masonry structures under consideration conformance with the requirements of the draft Eurocode 8 (Ref.15) was considered appropriate, based on the experience and practice in the high seismicity regions of Southern Europe.

Part 1.3, Section 6 of Eurocode 8 "Specific Rules for Masonry Structures" proposes three classes of masonry buildings: unconfined masonry, confined masonry and reinforced masonry. Each class is considered applicable to single storey buildings in high seismicity regions, with reinforced masonry recommended for taller structures.

Reinforced masonry buildings are required to have horizontal reinforcement at 600mm vertical spacing within the walls. This was judged unnecessarily stringent and complex for a single storey building in a rural area. Unreinforced masonry walls are required to have a minimum thickness of 300mm, which is significantly greater than the 200mm adopted for the SHSCP schools. As a result the school buildings have therefore been designed to comply with the requirements for confined masonry structures. The requirements of Eurocode 8 for confined masonry are given in Table 2. The principal features are horizontal and vertical tie beams at the top and bottom of walls, at the ends of walls or major intersections and around major openings such as windows. Figure 5 shows a typical wall cross section of the school building.

Ground Beams

The ground beam provides the structural continuity of the loading path to

587

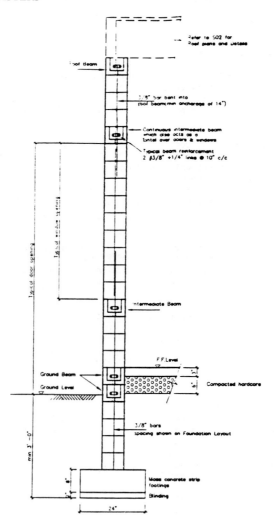

Figure 5: Wall Cross-Section

the foundations by bridging across the door openings. The effects of local concentrations of load such as uplift forces are re-distributed by the ground beam into the wall diaphragms.

Intermediate Ground Beams

The intermediate ground beams are positioned at window sill level and at the top of window/door level. These beams, together with the ground and roof beams, and vertical reinforcement divide the wall into a robust two-way grillage (confined masonry system) providing high resistance to the potential earthquake forces. In addition these intermediate beams assist control of thermal cracking in the walls thereby improving the durability of the structure.

Hollow Concrete Block Walls

The uplift, bending and shear forces imposed on the wall elements have been estimated by applying the earthquake load at the centre of mass of the structure in two orthogonal directions. The distribution of forces into these elements will be in proportion to their relative combined stiffnesses.

The walls consist of hollow concrete blocks partially filled with reinforced concrete. (Vertical steel bars are placed in approximately every fourth void along the wall and these are filled with concrete to form vertical reinforced concrete elements). The remaining voids aid the thermal performance of the school building. The vertical steel bars resist out-of-plane bending of the wall and possible uplift forces.

Roof Beams

The roof beam serves as a horizontal frame restraining the perimeter of the roof and ensuring the roof's performance as a diaphragm, capable of distributing effectively the horizontal forces to the walls. It provides an insitu connection between the walls and the roof.

In order to construct the roof beam connecting the walls and the roof the project team developed a parapet block to act as both the facing element and the insitu formwork, Figure 6. This has the advantage that it is self-supporting and does not require falsework to maintain it in position while the insitu concrete is placed. It also has an external appearance significantly larger than the hollow concrete blocks highlighting the importance of the wall-roof connection to earthquake resistant design.

Roof Structure

The roof of the building is one of the most important elements of the building both from structural and durability considerations. It consists of precast T-beams, hollow concrete blocks and an insitu reinforced concrete screed as shown in Plate 5. Two systems were considered for reinforcing the surface roof screed, reinforcing bars and wire mesh. The main issues regarding the screed are:

- structural integrity of the roof is essential to the structural integrity of the building.

- structural integrity of the roof requires the contribution of the screed.

- for the screed to be effective it must be protected against the weather by ensuring that it contains sufficient cement and reinforcing to resist cracking and deterioration from the weather.

The reinforcing bar system provides the best technical solution as the mesh is relatively fine and therefore acts as a sieve preventing coarse aggregate from passing through it and bonding effectively to the blocks and beams below. However, this problem can be overcome by using a larger mesh which has the same effective reinforcing area in both directions as the bars. The wire mesh is a cheaper option.

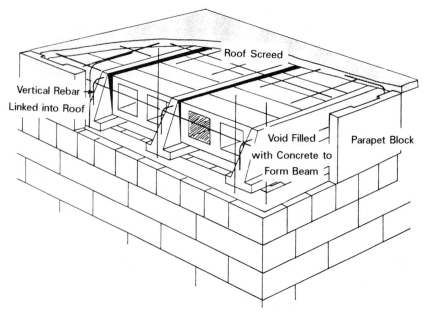

Figure 6: Roof Beam Detail

CONCLUSIONS

This paper has illustrated how engineering design can be practically be incorporated into the construction of school buildings in Northern Pakistan - a region of high seismicity. The primary objective of reducing the vulnerability of the buildings (and therefore the inhabitants) to earthquake and landslide hazards has been achieved by:

- determining quantitatively the seismic hazard for northern Pakistan and accounting for this in the structural design of the buildings.

- developing a formal methodology for site selection incorporating both local and expert knowledge. This aims to reduce as far as possible the vulnerability of the school buildings to geomorphological hazards, for example landslides.

- ensuring the building geometry is regular to reduce potential torsional forces induced by earthquakes.

- designing the structural details such as the hollow concrete block wall, the wall-roof connection and the roof itself to be robust and to maintain structural connectivity during an earthquake.

The school construction uses local skilled and unskilled labour, local materials, and imported cement and steel reinforcement. The AKHBP provides the technical assistance and project management. This cooperation has proved successful as shown by the high quality of construction achieved on site. It is the wide vision of the AKHBP that has been the impetus behind this project to reduce the vulnerability of these communities to the natural hazards of the region.

TECHNOLOGY, KNOWLEDGE TRANSFER AND THE FUTURE

ACKNOWLEDGEMENTS

During the project we held valuable discussions with Mr.D.Lefort (AKHBP Architect), Mr.Mushtaq (AKHBP Engineering Consultant), Mr. J.Norton (Development Workshop), Drs. R.Spence and A.Coburn (Cambridge Architectural Research). (Shaikh Rashid Mohammad (AKHBP Executive Officer) provided useful information on the school research and development programme). The contribution of these individuals is gratefully acknowledged.

REFERENCES

1. MUNTAZ,B.K.;NORTON,J. and HASAN,A. Self Help School Construction Programme Northern Areas and Chitral - Second stage of research and development. Report to the Aga Khan Housing Board Pakistan, April 1990.

2. HUGHES, R.E. Self Help Schools Northern Areas Pakistan - Consultants Field Report to the Aga Khan Housing Board Pakistan, November 1990.

3. OVE ARUP & PARTNERS. Self Help Schools Northern Areas/Chitral - Engineering Design. Report to the Aga Khan Housing Board Pakistan, October 1991.

4. KAZMI,A.H. Active fault systems in Pakistan. Geodynamics of Pakistan, Ed.Farah and De Jong. Geological Survey of Pakistan, 1979.

5. QUITTMEYER,R.C. and Jacob,K.H. Historical and modern seismicity of Pakistan, Afghanistan, northwestern India and southeastern Iran. Bulletin Seismological Society of America, 1979, vol.69, no.3, 773-823.

6. CORNELL,C.A. Engineering Seismic Risk Analysis. Bulletin Seismological Society of America, 1968, vol.58, 1583-1606.

7. NATIONAL RESEARCH COUNCIL. Probabilistic Seismic Hazard Assessment. National Academy Press, Washington D.C., USA. 1988.

8. CROUSE,C.B.; VYAS,Y.K. and SCHELL,B.A. Ground motions from subduction zone earthquakes. Bulletin Seismological Society of America, 1988, vol.78. no.1.

9. NATIONAL EARTHQUAKE HAZARD REDUCTION PROGRAMS (NEHRP). Recommended provisions for the development of seismic regulations for new buildings, 1988. Building Seismic Safety Council, Washington D.C, USA.

10. UNIFORM BUILDING CODE (UBC). 1988, International conference of building officials. Whittier, California, USA.

11. STRUCTURAL ENGINEERS ASSOCIATION OF CALIFORNIA (SEAOC). Recommended lateral force requirements and commentary, 1988.

12.HUGHES,R.E. Yasin Valley - The analysis of geomorphology and building types. Proc. Conference on the International Karakoram Project, vol.2, 253-289. 1981.

13. INTERNATIONAL ASSOCIATION OF EARTHQUAKE ENGINEERING (IAEE). Earthquake resistant regulations - a world list, 1988.

14.INDIAN STANDARDS INSTITUTION. Criteria for earthquake resistant design of structures - IS:1893, 1984. New Delhi, India.

15.COMMISSION OF EUROPEAN COMMUNITIES. Draft Eurocode 8 - Structures in seismic regions. 1989, Luxembourg.